Pg NG - FERTILIZATION

Developmental Anatomy

A Textbook and Laboratory Manual
of Embryology

By

LESLIE BRAINERD AREY, Ph.D., Sc.D., LL.D.

Robert Laughlin Rea Professor of Anatomy, Northwestern University

FIFTH EDITION

With 590 Illustrations, Many in Color

W. B. SAUNDERS COMPANY

PHILADELPHIA AND LONDON

To

WEBSTER CHESTER

PROFESSOR OF BIOLOGY, COLBY COLLEGE

An inspiring teacher, scholarly scientist and true friend of youth
who laid my biological foundations, tendered encouragement
and help in mastering early difficulties and
pointed the way to greater
opportunities

THIS VOLUME

is inscribed with a deep sense of admiration
and gratitude

PREFACE TO THE FIFTH EDITION

The main objective that dominated the preparation of the present edition was to replan and improve the presentation of the topics comprising general development. To this end Part I has been reorganized along new lines, the text wholly rewritten and many new illustrations introduced. Among the more drastic changes are those in subjects such as growth and histogenesis in Chapter I, maturation in Chapter II, cleavage and gastrulation (Chapter IV), human embryos and their membranes (Chapter VI), and placentation (Chapter VII). Consideration of the fetal membranes of vertebrates in general has been segregated and unified (Chapter V). Completely new chapters treat of reproductive cycles and their hormonal control (Chapter VIII) and of the fundamental concepts and problems of experimental embryology (Chapter IX).

The changes in Parts II and III are chiefly corrective, so as to make the descriptions consonant with the new information that has been established in the six-year period since the publication of the previous edition. Although far less extensive than the changes in Part I, these alterations have resulted in the whole book being reset in fresh type. Some new illustrations, and improved cuts for most of the others, strengthen these chapters. In the book as a whole there are now 1361 drawings, of which 186 are new. In spite of the presence of 23 chapters instead of the previous 19, the book nets one less printed page than before.

A diligent attempt has been made to review the world literature in embryology since 1940, and particularly as it affects human development. As in earlier editions, superscripts interspersed throughout the text agree with numbered entries in a bibliography at the end of each chapter. These citations direct attention to newer or controversial interpretations, and no attempt has been made to provide such extensive bibliographies as would be necessary if traditional views were to be documented. In some instances recent contributions with comprehensive literature reviews have been given preference in citation over more weighty, but older, researches. Unless the context clearly implies the contrary, the reader may assume that the unfolding of the developmental story in this book is an account of his own formative course.

Acknowledgment is extended to the publisher for liberal collaboration, to Dr. George W. Corner who generously supplied illustrative material from the Carnegie Institution, to Miss Lucille Cassell whose facile brush continues to enrich the illustrations, and to Dr. Victor Hamburger who offered constructive suggestions regarding the reorganization of Part I.

L. B. AREY

CHICAGO, ILLINOIS

CONTENTS

PART I. GENERAL DEVELOPMENT

PART II. SPECIAL DEVELOPMENT

PART III.   A LABORATORY MANUAL OF EMBRYOLOGY

PART I. GENERAL DEVELOPMENT

CHAPTER I

INTRODUCTION

THE NATURE AND SCOPE OF EMBRYOLOGY

Embryology is the science that treats of the origin and development of the individual organism. But what is the meaning of 'development' when used in this sense? It is a gradual bringing to completion, both in structure and in function. Its chief characteristic is cumulative progressiveness, in which each component act and result loses significance unless viewed against what precedes and what follows. Although the vital processes employed in the development of an individual may not differ specifically from those exhibited in the activities of the final organism, their results tend to be permanent rather than transitory. That is, they establish patterns of form and of function rather than merely maintaining what has already been perfected.

The Developmental Period.—The development of many animals is divided by the incident of birth or hatching into prenatal and postnatal periods. For a long time attention was focused on the events taking place before birth, when the most striking advances occur in these animals as a whole. Only gradually was it realized that important changes, beyond mere growth, continue to occur even to the adult state. This broader concept of embryology brings into its range all the developmental events resulting from sexual reproduction.

Many animals, including such vertebrates as fishes and amphibians, are capable of an independent existence at relatively immature stages; these free-living forms, with much or most of their development still before them, are called *larvæ*. It is quite otherwise with reptiles, birds and mammals. The human newborn, for example, is fairly complete anatomically, yet utterly dependent on its elders for food and care. Throughout infancy, childhood and adolescence come the completion of some organs and a gradual remolding of body shape. Only at about the age of twenty-five are the last of these progressive changes finished and the body stabilized in the adult condition.

It is instructive to list the divisions of the life span in man and thus to re-emphasize how many of these entries belong to the developmental period:

Prenatal life
- *Ovum.* Fertilization to end of first week.
- *Embryo.* Second to eighth week, inclusive.
- *Fetus.* Third to tenth month, inclusive.

Birth

Postnatal life
- *Newborn.* Neonatal period; birth to end of second week.
- *Infancy.* Third week until assumption of erect posture at end of first year.
- *Childhood.*
  - *Early.* Milk-tooth period; second to sixth year, inclusive.
  - *Middle.* Permanent-tooth period; 7 to 9 or 10 years, inclusive.
  - *Later.* Prepubertal period; from 9 or 10 years to 12–15 years in females and to 13–16 years in males.

Puberty

- *Adolescence.* The six years following puberty.
- *Adult.*
  - *Prime and transition.* Between 20 and 60 years.
  - *Old age and senescence.* From 60 years on.

Death

The Fields of Embryology.—The general topic of development sub-divides conveniently into morphological and functional categories. The morphological division deals with form, structure and relations, and is purely descriptive and comparative in treatment. It traces the formative history of animals from the germ cell of each parent to the adult, resulting offspring. Its objective is to paint the progressive panorama of change that cells, tissues, organs, and the body as a whole undergo in attaining their final states. These unified descriptions of advancing form, structure and relations can be designated by the term *developmental anatomy*. The other division of embryology is functional and attempts to explain, on the basis of experiment and analysis, the ways in which development works. How seemingly mysterious happenings can be resolved into familiar physical and chemical phenomena; how parts interact in determining and co-ordinating the evolving embryo; how fetal physiology makes its beginnings and then operates—all these, and more, constitute *developmental physiology*. Most of the effort in this field has centered about an attempt to discover the forces, factors and mechanisms that govern development. This experimental attack on dynamic causation has come to be known as *experimental embryology*.

All multicellular animals have certain similarities in their ways of development. It is, however, only in the very earliest stages that all the different kinds of embryos have much in common structurally. Within closely related groups the correspondence in the form and method of development is greatest and lasts longest. Thus all vertebrate (*i.e.,* back-boned) animals are built about a common anatomical plan and have the same fundamental style of development. Naturally some variant methods are utilized and some type peculiarities exist, while in the end 'higher' vertebrates achieve certain greater complexities than do 'lower' ones. Although *comparative embryology* is indispensable for gaining a broad understanding of development, its former importance in supplying missing pages of the human story has diminished greatly. In the experimental field alone is there a high degree of dependence on lower forms.

The Value of Embryology.—A general conception of how man, like other animals, develops from a single cell should share in the cultural background of every educated mind. From the philosophical side, embryology is a key that helps unlock such secrets as heredity, the determination of sex and organic evolution. To the medical student, embryology is of primary importance because it supplies a comprehensive and rational explanation of the intricate arrangements of human anatomy. The body does not just happen to be arranged as it is. Each end-result is preceded by a definite course of developmental events, and anomalies can be explained on the basis of departures from the usual pattern. Embryology is also able to interpret vestigial structures, to explain growth, differentiation and repair, and to throw light on some pathological conditions. For all these reasons it is essential to sound training in anatomy, pathology and surgery. Furthermore, obstetrics is to a certain degree applied embryology, while pediatrics and other specialties find it directly useful.

THE HISTORICAL BACKGROUND

Several centuries before our era, Aristotle (384–322 B.C.) wrote the first treatise on embryology. It was a mighty compendium of observation and argument, so far in advance of his age that for nearly two thousand years almost nothing of significance was added. Aristotle was the first to formulate the alternative that an embryo must be either preformed and only enlarging during its development or it must be actually differentiating from a formless beginning. He decided in favor of the latter interpretation and thereby set off a controversy which extended through the centuries. Although Aristotle discovered many astonishing facts in comparative embryology and followed the general progress of the developing chick, he naturally fell into error on things about which he had to speculate. Thus he credited the popular belief that slime and decaying matter are capable of producing living animals, and he described the human embryo as organizing out of the mother's activated menstrual blood. Such origins were disproved by Redi (1668), although the death blow to the persistent belief of the spontaneous generation of microscopic animalcules and bacteria was dealt only in 1864 by Pasteur. That every living organism comes from a pre-existing, living organism (*omne vivum ex vivo*) and that every cell arises from the subdivision of a pre-existing cell (*omnis cellula e cellula*)

are fundamental concepts, so commonplace today that their long struggle
for recognition is often overlooked.

Until about the year 1800 it was generally believed either that a fully
formed animal exists in miniature in the egg, needing only the stimulus of
the sperm to initiate growth and unfolding, or that similarly preformed
organisms, male and female, constitute the sperms and these merely enlarge
when they get inside the eggs (Fig. 1). To be consistent this doctrine of
preformation had to admit that all future generations were likewise encased,
one inside the sex cells of the other, like so many Chinese boxes. Simple
mathematical considerations made such a concept difficult to defend. In
recent years certain features of the preformational point of view have been
reintroduced into biology, but in a far more subtle form than the original
doctrine taught. Due largely to the influence of Morgan since 1910, it is
now conceded that the chromosomes of the fertilized egg
contain in their genes definite determinative powers over
development.

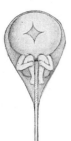

The preformation theory was virtually destroyed by
Wolff (1759–69) who, like Harvey in the preceding century,
saw the parts of the early chick embryo take shape as new
formations. But Wolff was able to go further and show
that the germinal region first consists of 'globules' (*i.e.,*
cells) lacking in any arrangement that can be related
directly to the form or structure of the future embryo.
Only gradually did these globules organize into rudiments
which could be traced into the several organs of the embryo.
This method of progressive development from the simpler
to the more complex, through the utilization of building
units known as cells, is *epigenesis*. Many years, never-

Fig. 1.—Human
sperm cell, con-
taining a minia-
ture organism, ac-
cording to Hart-
soeker (1694).

theless, elapsed before Wolff's views gained proper recognition. The final
chapter in the obituary of the original doctrine of preformation was written by Driesch (1900) who proved that in many forms the daughter cells
of a fertilized egg (*i.e.,* half- or quarter-eggs), when separated, will develop
into complete embryos. The present view on these matters is that development is strictly preformational as regards the genes and their hereditary
influences, but rigorously epigenetic in actual constructional activities.

With the overthrow of preformation, scientists sought afresh what it
could be that the egg transmits to the next generation. Darwin and others
thought that each part of the body might contribute something to the sex
cells of an individual, and that these representative tokens could make the
operation of heredity physically possible. Weismann (1883) argued convincingly that the facts are quite otherwise, a child in no way inheriting
its characters from the bodies of the parents but only from their sex cells.

These germ cells, in turn, acquired their characters directly from preexisting germ cells of the same kind. The germ plasm is a self-perpetuating, cellular legacy which has existed as an unbroken stream through the ages. At each new generation a temporary body is built up around it, to serve as a carrier of the germ cells and to hold them in trust for the forthcoming offspring (Fig. 2). The reason, therefore, why offspring resembles parent is because each develops from portions of the same immortal stuff. Modern investigation has shown that the self-perpetuating elements are really the genes, and that these occur identically in the body cells as in the sex cells. Weismann's belief in a fundamental difference between sex and somatic cells has lost much of its original force, but his concept of germinal continuity threw a great light on the nature of the hereditary process.

Harvey (1651) and Malpighi (1672) contributed fundamental descriptions of the stages of the developing chick, as seen with simple lenses. How these observations were refined by Wolff (1759–69) has already been told. In 1817 Pander demonstrated the three primary germ layers from which the chick embryo and its constituent parts develop. Von Baer

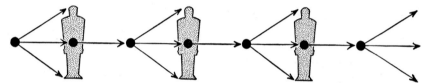

Fig. 2.—Diagram showing the concept of the continuity of germ plasma.

(1829–37) soon afterward broadened this concept to a generalization for all animals, determined the origins of the principal organs and made the science of embryology comparative. Exactly 150 years after Leeuwenhoek (1677) reported the discovery of the sperms of man and other mammals, von Baer (1827) identified the mammalian egg. For these far-reaching contributions, which influenced all subsequent growth of embryology, he has justly been honored as the 'father of modern embryology.' Cleavage, or subdivision of the egg into the building units of the embryo, was first definitely described by Prévost and Dumas in 1824, but its true meaning had to wait for the recognition of the cell as the structural unit of the organism. This biological landmark was set by Schwann in 1839, and about twenty years later the egg and sperm were recognized as true cells. Hertwig, in 1875, was the first to observe and appreciate the main events involved in the fertilization of an egg by a sperm, while Van Beneden (1883) soon proved that the male and female sex cells contribute the same number of chromosomes to the fertilized egg. The present epoch was made possible when Balfour (1880) reviewed, digested and made accessible the earlier, scattered facts.

2

Like biology in general, embryology has passed through three stages. The first was pure description and fact-gathering. At present it continues chiefly in the program of obtaining a well-rounded account of human development; His and Keibel in Europe and Minot and Mall in America were the original leaders in this endeavor. The second stage was comparison, in which the observations on various animal types were classified and compared, and common trends and principles were sought. The dominance of von Baer in comparative embryology has never been challenged. Description and comparison received a great impetus in the last half of the nineteenth century from the then new theory of evolution; it was hoped that the full evolutionary history of an animal would be revealed in its embryonic development (p. 18). The third stage, experimental and analytical, is exemplified by Roux and Spemann in Europe and Morgan and Harrison in this country. It is the most vigorous and promising branch of contemporary embryology.

GENERAL FEATURES OF DEVELOPMENT

A multicellular animal begins its development as a fertilized (*i.e.*, activated) egg. Further progress depends upon: (1) *cell proliferation;* (2) *growth;* (3) *morphogenesis*, or molding of the body and its organs; (4) *histogenesis*, or cell specialization into tissues; and (5) *integration,* to produce a unified, working organism.

CELL PROLIFERATION

All cells arise from pre-existing cells by cell division. Although a direct fission of the nucleus and cytoplasm is described in certain old or specialized cells, this style (*amitosis*) plays little or no rôle in development. The ordinary method of cell division (*mitosis*) has several distinctive features. These include the reappearance from a state of dispersion of a characteristic number of chromosome bodies, their growth and splitting into double structures, and the separation and accurate distribution of these components to the two daughter cells. Each new cell acquires one complete set of chromosomes.

It seems like a long span from the egg to the trillions of cells that comprise the completed body of man, yet this prodigious final number can be attained quite readily by repeated cell division. So rapid is the doubling process that some 45 generations (2^{45}) of mitoses are sufficient. Of course, this theoretical product is not realized in any such mathematically precise fashion, since some cells multiply much more slowly than others while cell death also occurs along the way.

GROWTH

Growth may be defined as a developmental increase in mass. It is a fundamental property of life and an important factor in development. Without growth no organism could exceed greatly the size of the egg from which it came. Since all living organisms consist basically of cells and these have definite size limitations, increase in bulk during development naturally is conditioned by cell proliferation which produces more units to participate in growing. Exceptional is the period of cleavage (the initial step in development taken by the fertilized egg), during which the originally overlarge egg subdivides into cells of ordinary size; in this period significant growth does not enter at all.

The Methods of Growth.—Growth is accomplished in several ways. Most important is the synthesis of new living matter (protoplasm) from foodstuffs. In the last analysis, animals depend on plants for their proteins which are the building materials out of which new protoplasm is constructed. Digestive enzymes split the proteins of food into amino acids and these products are used by the cells in the processes of synthesis.

A second method of growth involves water uptake. The amount of water in a living organism is very considerable; in the early weeks of its development the human embryo is nearly 98 per cent. fluid. The colloids within cells and between them have the capacity of imbibing water and swelling. The ability to hold water and release it is governed in part by ionic concentrations.

A third method of growth is by the manufacture and deposit of nonliving substances. This material is of the nature of a protoplasmic transformation or 'secretion.' It is usually located between cells and consists of jelly, fibers or the ground substance of cartilage and bone.

The Measurement of Growth.—The amount of growth is expressed in *absolute* and *relative terms*, but comparisons are more easily made when the latter are employed. Thus the absolute gain in weight of a 10-pound baby and a 100-pound youth might be 1 pound each, whereas the relative gains (expressed as percentages of the initial weights) would be 10 per cent. against 1 per cent. It is the same with *growth rates*. The absolute rate, in terms of any chosen unit of time, is the amount of increase during any period divided by the length of that period. But comparisons are more instructive if relative growth rates are computed. This is done by dividing each absolute rate by the initial value (in weight, volume or length); the result expresses the relative rate in terms of the unit of measurement used. Such computations show that a newborn rabbit and pig, though widely different in weight, grow at the same relative rate, whereas the newborn sheep grows eighteen times faster than the human newborn which originally equals it in weight.

The growth of one part often appears to be quite out of step with the growth of another part or of the organism as a whole. Yet, in general, such relations of size or weight at any period fit into a simple type of mathematical formula which takes into account the amount of divergence between the growth progress of each part. For example, the facial region of a baboon outgrows the cranial region so enormously that the newborn and adult skull seem to be unrelated. Yet the dynamics of skull growth is a harmonious process throughout, and a formula may be devised that fits any stage.

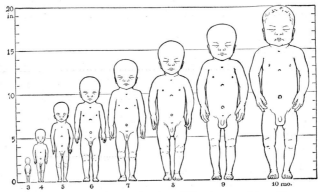

FIG. 3.—Diagram illustrating the changes in size of the human fetus (Scammon and Calkins).

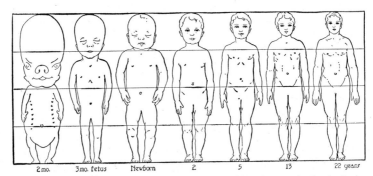

FIG. 4.—Diagram illustrating the changing proportions of the human body during prenatal and postnatal growth (Scammon).

Differential Growth.—The development of an organism is characterized by a progressive alteration of form and proportions, both externally and internally. It is obvious that uniform growth cannot produce these changes. Actually diversity of form is acquired through differential rates of growth operating in various regions and directions. These rates may vary among individuals according to circumstance, but the ratios between the growth rates of different parts of the body are relatively constant. It is these fixed relations that produce similar final form in the countless individuals of any species. And this is accomplished in spite of the fact that different parts of the body appear and begin to grow at different times.

The variance in starting times and growth rates is responsible for what may be called the _growth pattern_.

The changes in the proportions of the body and its parts, due to unequal growth, are produced by: (1) local differences in the growth intensity; (2) growth gradients; (3) reduction of the early dominance of anterior over posterior levels; (4) functional demands; and (5) influence of the growth rate of a neighboring part. The visible way in which differential growth accomplishes the progressive modeling of external and internal form can be illustrated sufficiently through two specific examples. Figure 144 shows stages in the emergence of the limbs from initial, bud-like swellings. Figure 408 illustrates the early form changes undergone by the brain while advancing toward its final shape.

Many pertinent data have been collected concerning the growth rates of the human body and its organs during prenatal and postnatal development. Analyses of these data have brought to light definite growth tendencies and patterns. Some of the more general conclusions, as presented by Scammon, will be summarized in the paragraphs that follow.

Changes in Size and Form.—The growth and external changes in a fetus subsequent to the second month are illustrated in Figure 3. If an adult maintained the chubby newborn shape, his weight would be twice the amount it actually is. Figure 4 shows the proportions of the body at various devlopmental periods, all drawn to the same height. Note: the great decrease in the size of the head; the constancy of the trunk length; the early completion of the arms and the tardier growth of the legs; the upward shift of the umbilicus and symphysis pubis; the downward trend of the midpoint of total length.

Certain of these facts are plainer when tabulated:

CHANGES IN RELATIVE SIZE OF THE PARTS OF THE BODY
In per cent. of the total body volume

Age	Head and Neck	Trunk	Arms	Legs
Second fetal month....................	43	52	3	2
Sixth fetal month....................	36	44	7.5	12.5
Birth..............................	32	44	8	16
Two years..........................	22	51	9	18
Six years..........................	15	50	9	26
Maturity...........................	10	52	9	2c

POSTNATAL INCREASE IN THE SIZE OF THE BODY AND ITS PARTS
(In relation to their sizes at birth as unity; the range indicates the minimal and maximal increase of organs within each group)

Voluntary Musculature	Genital Organs	Total Body, Skeleton and Lungs	Lymphoid Organs	Major Viscera	Endocrine Organs	Nervous System
38	28–38	18–23	3–21	12–15	2–13	2–5

Increase in Surface Area.—The relation of surface area to body mass or volume has a profound influence on the rate of both metabolism and heat loss. This relation shifts greatly during the postnatal period. At birth the surface area averages 2200 sq. cm. This is doubled in the first year, trebled by the middle of childhood, and increases rapidly before puberty. At maturity the total postnatal gain is seven-fold. Since, however, the weight of the body has increased some twenty-fold in the same time, it is obvious that there has been a relative loss. Thus, in the newborn there are over 800 sq. cm. of skin per kilogram of body weight, while in the adult there are less than 300 sq. cm. per kilogram.

Increase in Weight.—During prenatal life weight increases six billion times, whereas from birth to maturity the increment is only twenty-fold. In absolute mass, however, 95 per cent. of the final weight is acquired after birth. The ratio of increase during each fetal month to the weight at the beginning of that month is shown in the table on p. 115. It is an astonishing fact that if the body continued to grow even at the greatly reduced rate during the last fetal month, the weight of the adult would be two trillions times that of the earth.

Increase in Length.—Embryos between four and nine weeks old grow 1 mm. each day; for the rest of intra-uterine life the daily gain in sitting height is about 1.5 mm. Growth in length and in weight have certain features in common, although the relative increase in length is obviously smaller since weight measures mass which extends in three dimensions. The ratio of the increase in length each week or month to the length at the beginning of that period is shown in the table on p. 115. During the first year after birth, length increases 50 per cent. The total postnatal increment is 3.3 times the length at birth. Throughout most of childhood the linear increase is very slow (6 to 7 cm. a year), but at the prepubertal period there is an acceleration; as with weight, this is begun and ended earlier in girls than in boys. Growth in length is complete at about 18 years in females and soon after 20 in males. The body is heaviest in proportion to its length during late fetal life and early infancy. From the middle of the first year until after puberty there is a decline in this ratio. Thereafter there is an increase in relative mass which may continue throughout life. Except at the pubertal period, girls are relatively lighter than boys.

Growth of the Organ Systems.—The *skeleton* grows rather slowly until the last two fetal months, whereupon it shows an acceleration. At birth it constitutes from 15 to 20 per cent. of the body weight. Postnatal growth of the skeleton apparently parallels that of the body as a whole. The *musculature* likewise grows slowly at first, but represents about 25 per cent. of the weight of the newborn and 40 to 45 per cent. of the adult. The *blood vessels* show the same general trend. The *central nervous system*, on the other hand, is relatively huge in the young embryo. It decreases from about 25 per cent. in the second month to about 15 per cent. at birth and 2.5 per cent. in the adult. The *peripheral nervous system* likewise undergoes a considerable reduction in relative weight during the postnatal years. The *skin* (including the subcutaneous fat) increases in relative weight up to birth (26 per cent.) and shows little change thereafter. As a whole, the *viscera* decrease slowly and steadily in relative weight after the first two embryonic months. In the second prenatal month these organs comprise about 15 per cent. of the total body weight; there is a reduction to about 9 per cent. at birth and 5 to 7 per cent. in the adult.

Growth of the Organs.—Although the general course of relative growth in the individual organs follows that of the visceral group as a whole, each has its characteristic curve. Every fetal organ tends to increase more or less rapidly to a maximum relative size, and then to decrease throughout its subsequent history even to maturity.

During fetal life the curves of absolute growth are much alike. The various organs have an initial period of slow increase, followed after the fifth month by a terminal phase of rapid growth. This uniformity, however, disappears at birth when most of the organs can be arranged in four main groups; their postnatal growths are shown graphically in Figure 5.

Factors Controlling Growth.—Certain factors make growth possible and control it. Among these, the following require comment:

The Constitutional Factor.—Every animal species has its characteristic rates and limits of growth. Under identical conditions of development the speed of growth is approximately the same in all individuals of a species, and there is little difference in the final size attained. This is due to inherited qualities that predispose toward a definite basic rate of cell division and growth. It should be emphasized, however, that the original rate undergoes characteristic alterations in different regions of the embryo as the cell strains specialize.

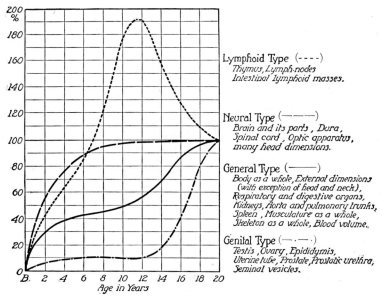

Fig. 5.—Chart showing the course of postnatal growth in the various organ types (Scammon). Growth is calculated in relation to adult weights as 100 per cent.

Temperature.—Within limits, the growth rates vary with the temperature. Each species has its critical maximum and minimum at which development ceases. Somewhere between these extremes lies the most favorable temperature.

Nutritional Factors.—New protoplasm has to be created throughout life, and the amino acids are the building materials out of which this synthesis is accomplished. The body can make some of its own amino acids, but others must be obtained in the food proteins. Certain of them favor growth, but not tissue differentiation. The requirements for growth through new tissue-building are more exacting than those that suffice for the maintenance and repair of protoplasm already on hand. At least one amino acid is required in the diet of the growing young beyond those that the adult needs in its diet to repair tissue losses due to functioning.

Food must not only be suitable but also adequate in amount if growth is to occur. There is a minimum below which growth fails. Above this level growth accelerates, but it cannot exceed an optimum rate, characteristic of the organism, even if an excess of food is available.

Growth-Promoting Factors.—Certain substances which are not foodstuffs further the processes that result in the production of new protoplasm.

The Embryonic Factor.—Tissues cultivated outside the body thrive better if juices extracted from an embryo are added to the nutrient medium. These extracts increase mitoses and shorten the time taken by each mitosis. There is a strong suggestion that definite cytoplasmic co-enzymes are involved. Since cell proliferation is a prerequisite to the growth of an organism, the presumed similar influence of this factor within an embryo is significant though indirect.

Hormones.—Some of the secretions elaborated by the ductless glands are regulators of growth. The thyroid hormone raises the rate of cell metabolism, presumably by acting as a catalyst to increase oxidative processes. It is essential for maintaining a normal level of metabolism. In deficient or excess amounts growth may be affected, but the results vary with the kind of animal and tissue. Thus a young mammal, deprived of its thyroid, remains small and undeveloped in some ways, whereas a tadpole grows slowly. When an excess is fed to a tadpole, only certain parts of the body respond by unusual growth.

One of the hormones produced by the anterior lobe of the hypophysis stimulates the growth of various tissues. Removal of the hypophysis in young animals results in retarded growth, while injections of the growth hormone into normal animals lead to generalized gigantism. Another hypophyseal hormone stimulates specifically the gonads, while the ovarian follicles, thus made to grow, control and maintain the cyclic growth of the genital tract.

Vitamins.—These are accessory food substances which, on the whole, animals cannot make and have to obtain in their plant foods. Their actions are after the manner of chemical catalyzers, and the amounts required are insignificant in comparison to the effects induced. In the absence of vitamin A the young animal fails to gain weight, although its skeleton does grow. Vitamin B_2 exerts a specific influence on growth, and without it growth cannot take place.

Growth-Arresting Factors.—Birds and mammals cease growing when they have attained a certain characteristic age and size. Even cold-blooded animals, which grow throughout their entire life spans, do so at greatly reduced rates. Embryonic cells, grown in tissue culture and supplied with adequate food, have an infinite capacity for continued proliferation and growth. Why, then, does growth of the same cells in an organism become slowed or limited?

The total agencies determining growth rates and size limitation are many and unlike, so that a few comments must suffice. There is a fundamental antagonism between cell differentiation and cell proliferation, since the factors that promote differentiation make proliferation increasingly difficult (p. 16). Many cells reach a level of specialization at which they rarely divide, and some never do so; all this is bound up with the general phenomenon of aging. As cell differentiation proceeds during development, increasing numbers of them pass beyond the stage where mitosis is easy or even possible. This automatically decreases the rate of relative growth. Another check on growth is cell destruction; the growth of certain organs, such as epidermis, blood and some glands, is offset by cell losses. Again,

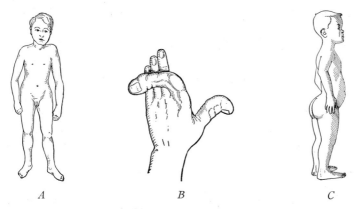

| A | B | C |

Fig. 6.—Growth irregularities. *A*, Unilateral gigantism, or hemihypertrophy; *B*, localized gigantism; *C*, achondroplastic dwarf.

the cessation of growth in the long bones of birds and mammals is apparently due to hormonal interference.

Abnormal Growth.—The mass of an individual is largely set by the size of his skeleton, to which the soft parts conform. Gigantism (*macrosomia*) and dwarfism (*microsomia*) designate conditions that lie outside the normal size range.

General gigantism, or excessive height, is due to an abnormal length of the long bones and, to a less extent, of the vertebræ. It usually starts before birth, and the oversized newborn continues to grow at more than the average rate. On the other hand, an hereditary predisposition toward gigantism may be aroused into action at some time during childhood or adolescence by an infectious disease or other agent. In rare instances, the growth is unequal in the two halves of the body (Fig. 6 *A*) and gigantism may even be confined to specific regions (*B*). The basic cause of gigantism is an overproduction of the growth hormone secreted by the hypophysis. As growth proceeds, a second factor comes into play as a contributing cause. This is a delay in the closure of the growth centers (epiphyses) at the ends of the bones, which extends the normal growth period. An hereditary influence is usually a factor in the production of giants, and endocrine disturbances tend to show in the family line.

Dwarfism is commonly caused by undersecretion of certain endocrine glands. In one form deficient secretion of the growth hormone of the hypophysis is responsible. The under-size may date from birth, or retardation may follow an infectious disease occurring at about the time of puberty. The proportions of the skeleton are not far from normal. Another type, related to the thyroid, is characterized by short arms and legs. The centers of ossi-fication of these parts appear late and growth is sluggish. Such dwarfs are known as *cretins;* they tend to overweight and low mentality. Other types of dwarf are related to constitutional causes (defective genes), congenital syphilis and dietary deficiencies. *Achondroplastic dwarfs,* of unknown cause, have short extremities, a relatively large head and protruding buttocks and abdomen (Fig. 6 *C*).

MORPHOGENESIS

The fertilized egg subdivides into numerous cells, more suitable in size to serve as the building units of the future embryo. At this point

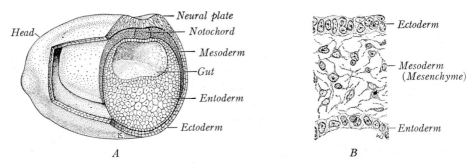

FIG. 7.—Germ layers of early embryos. *A*, Stereogram of the head half of a frog embryo (× 15). *B*, Section from an early human embryo (× 400).

differential cell movements arrange the formative cells into three super-imposed plates, the *primary germ layers*. From their positions they are termed the *ectoderm* (outer layer), *mesoderm* (middle layer) and *entoderm* (inner layer) (Fig. 7 *A*.) While the ectoderm and entoderm remain chiefly as sheets exposed on one surface (*i.e., epithelia*), the mesoderm forms most of a diffuse spongework of cells that is a primitive filling-tissue known as *mesenchyme* (*B*). Such are the materials out of which the embryo organizes.

Differentiation has two meanings. One refers to a change in the shape and organization of the body and its parts (*morphogenesis*), and the other to a change in the substance and structure of the cells themselves (*histogenesis*). Differentiation, in general, is favored by the thyroid influence and by certain amino acids. Morphogenesis includes all of the changes during development that mark the molding of the body and its organs into form and pattern. The processes employed by morphogenesis are relatively simple acts. Although diverse in nature they occur in orderly and logical sequence, each part merely using whatever method may be appropriate to its needs at the moment. Viewed as a whole, the assumption of form starts simply, becomes rapidly a scene of seeming confusion as many changes get under way, and then gradually stabilizes as the principal maneuvers are executed. Following this early period of great activity of diverse kinds, the later and longer periods of development are characterized by a much more leisurely perfecting of form.

The more important of the morphogenetic processes are the following (Fig. 8): (1) *cell migration;* (2) *cell aggregation*, forming (a) masses, (b) cords and (c) sheets; (3) *localized growth*, resulting in (a) enlargements of various kinds and (b) constrictions; (4) *splitting*, which includes the delamination of single sheets into separate layers, the cavitation of cell masses and the forking of cords; (5) *folding*, including circumscribed folds which produce (a) evaginations, or out-pocketings, and (b) invaginations, or in-pocketings. Differential growth, resulting in enlargements and folds of all sorts, is the

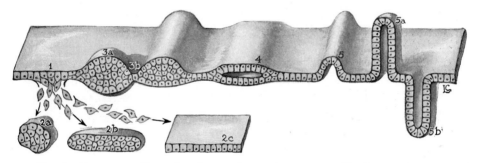

Fig. 8.—Stereogram illustrating the morphogenetic processes. Numbered as in text.

chief process utilized by the embryo in molding its general form and producing new organs. The word *primordium* (or its German equivalent, *anlage*) is a term applied to the first beginnings of a future organ or part before it has taken on its characteristic features. Thus the ectodermal thickening in front of the optic cup is the primordium of the lens, as is the arm bud of the arm.

HISTOGENESIS

All the cells of a germ layer are at first alike in visible structure and lack of specific shape, but they progressively assume distinctive characters which permit their fates to be foretold. At this early period of differentiation in form and structure they are often designated by the suffix *-blast*. Thus a neuroblast will in due time complete its differentiation into a nerve cell, and a myoblast into a muscle cell. The specializations that cells undergo in form and structure are conformable with the particular functions they will perform and, in fact, anticipate these functions. Cells of the same specialized type occur in larger or smaller groups and, thus set apart, come to be known as tissues. There are four main groups of *tissues*. Each of the germ layers gives rise to sheet-like *epithelia;* in addition, the ectoderm forms *nervous tissue* while the mesoderm produces the different kinds of *muscle* and the various *connective tissues*. The total process by which cells differentiate into distinctive kinds and assume specific tissue characters is included in the term *histogenesis*. The histogenesis of an individual tissue summates all the departures it has made from the kind of cell it once was. In doing this the specific differences that separate it from other specialized cells which it once resembled are brought into sharp relief.

Illustrative of histogenetic differentiation is the history of the originally single-layered ectoderm. These cells proliferate and gradually change their form and character as they produce the layers of the epidermis (Fig. 370). More specialized are the hairs, nails, lens of the eye and enamel of the teeth. Glandular derivatives of the ectoderm vary from the sweat and grease glands of the skin to the more highly organized tissue of the mammary gland, salivary glands and anterior lobe of the hypophysis. Other local specializations produce the sensory epithelium of the organs of smell, taste, hearing and vision, and the smooth muscle elements of the iris. Part of the primitive ectoderm becomes the thickened neural plate, from which both nerve cells and supporting elements arise; a diagram of the lineage of these cells will illustrate a typical course of cell diversification during histogenesis (Fig. 387).

Cell growth and division are an integral part of the complete picture of tissue differentiation as it actually operates. Both daughter cells of a mitosis may continue to divide and grow; both may enter on differentiation; or one may continue as a proliferative cell and the other begin its differentiation. A differentiating cell may, for a time at least, interrupt its specialization and return to cell division. Cell differentiation within an embryo proceeds on different time schedules. Some lines advance steadily and rapidly toward their end stages. Other strains start later, are characteristically slower or indulge in rest intervals. Individual cells of many lines undergo arrest before completing their differentiation and persist indefinitely as *reserve elements*. Their differentiation, and usually division, can be resumed at any subsequent time at the call of an appropriate stimulus. In a tissue such as the epidermis the basal cells continue as proliferative stem cells throughout life. From them arise cells which move to higher levels and progressively specialize, die and shed. In nervous tissue, on the other hand, all of the neuroblasts differentiate into mature neurons and a loss can never be replaced.

There is a certain antagonism between cell division and cell differentiation. Cells undergoing rapid division are in a state of turbulence which is unfavorable to cytoplasmic specialization. On the other hand, cells that are producing cytoplasmic elaborations of a physical nature tend to lose the plasticity that is requisite to mitosis. The cell types resulting from the processes of differentiation are discrete entities, without transitional forms; that is, an intermediate between a muscle cell and nerve cell is never seen. Neither can one region of a cell specialize in one direction (*e.g.*, muscle) and another region in a different direction (*e.g.*, nerve). Once a cell becomes committed to any type of differentiation it cannot at the same time engage in another kind, nor can a cell abandon its original line of specialization and change to a different course. Moreover, any particular course of differentiation must be pursued in the distinctive way that characterizes the species to which an embryo belongs.

The path followed by cells during histogenesis shows certain trends which become evident when the conditions at the beginning and at the end of differentiation are contrasted:

Trends from Earlier Stages of Cells toward Later Stages (after Weiss)

From	Toward
uniformity (of size, structure and capacities)	diversity
irregularity (of shape)	regularity
vagueness (nondistinctive shape and qualities)	definiteness
dispersion (through whole embryo or part)	localization
variability (random arrangements or patterns)	stability
generality (primitive characteristics and qualities)	specialization
plasticity (or adaptability)	rigidity
mobility (ameboid and other shifts of position)	immobility
simplicity (of structure and function)	complexity

INTEGRATION

Morphogenesis and histogenesis are decentralizing processes which resolve the early embryo into a mosaic of organs and parts. During the course of development the organs become independent of former unifying controls, existent from the time of the egg. Although the new organs and organ systems possess structural coherence and unity, they need to be reintegrated into co-operative working mechanisms. This control is supplied in part by the system of _endocrine glands_. Their rôle in activating, synchronizing and co-ordinating, by making use of the body fluids as carriers of their specific chemical substances, is important both among the later developmental phenomena and in ordinary physiological action. The other integrating instrument is the _nervous system_ which constitutes the primary mechanism of physiological control and co-ordination.

The supplying of organs with adequate nervous, vascular and hormonal influences is a decisive factor in causing development to pass from a *prefunctional period*, which is preparatory and anticipatory in nature, to a *functional period* of actual (or potential) performance. The time of this transition varies greatly in different organs; growth and differentiation continue into the functional period.

ANCESTRAL REPETITIONS

The *theory of recapitulation* long taught that an individual in the course of its development passes through successive stages that approximate the series of adult ancestors from which it is descended. This repetition of ancestral stages was said to be crowded back in development and abbreviated, but nonetheless to present phylogeny in review. The theory would insist, for example, that the embryonic organs and parts of a mammal pass through adult fish-like, amphibian and reptilian phases before the mammalian states are attained. It also asserts that the various adult types of ancestors have been able to leave their imprint on the style of development used by their descendants. In short, during its life history 'every animal climbs up its family tree.' This doctrine goes beyond the facts.

Embryos of different groups do resemble one another in the early stages of their developments, but this resemblance tends to diminish progressively as they advance toward their final forms. Moreover, a fish, reptile and mammal do not start alike and pass through the same stages; they are individualistic from their beginnings. The similarities that exist are good proofs of a common origin, while the repetition of like ancestral features in the development of different animals is due to the presence of the same hereditary factors in the several kinds of fertilized eggs and the development of these eggs under conditions that permit those features to appear. An embryo of a reptile, bird or mammal does not possess gill arches like an adult fish, but only like those of a fish at a corresponding stage of development. All that can be maintained is that the development of any individual may more or less recapitulate the style of development that its ancestor used. Stages may be omitted, sequences altered, larval specializations interpolated and new structures developed.

Some of the structures appearing during development are apparently useless survivals (*e.g.*, tail), but caution is indicated in judging individual cases since it is doubtful whether any part is retained for long in the evolutionary time scale unless it is either useful or wholly insignificant. For example, the first kidney (pronephros) formed by the embryo of a higher vertebrate does not function as such, yet its tubules unite to produce a duct which grows caudad. If the progress of this duct is blocked, the second kidney (mesonephros) and permanent kidney (metanephros) never develop because an essential stimulus is lacking. Certain ancestral organs abandon their original embryonic function, yet are retained and utilized for new purposes (*e.g.*, mesonephric tubules and ducts become the permanent sex canals of the male). Other parts make their appearance, only to change at once into quite different structures (*e.g.*, gill pouches into thymus and parathyroids); since these are necessary organs it is understandable why in this instance the embryonic pouches appear even though they are never respiratory in function.

Some embryonic organs neither disappear nor take on permanent function, but rather persist throughout life as _vestiges;_ nearly 200 such have been listed for man. Many of these are doubtless on their way toward elimination from the developmental course. Somewhat different are _atavistic characters_, or ancestral reversions. These are features that normally have been dropped from development but may, on occasion, reappear. They are due to the inheritance of genes which are able to reassert themselves whenever the proper embryonic conditions are re-established.

The various ancestral, embryonic traits that recur in human development represent features that first appeared in lower embryos of the vertebrate stock and have persisted as survivals. Such common characters argue eloquently for common ancestry. However incomplete their developmental review may be, the fact remains that the stages encountered constitute the only record that supplies any significant information as to how the human species may have reached its present state.

TERMS DESCRIBING ANATOMICAL RELATION

Adjective	Adverb Denoting Fixed Relation	Adverb Denoting Progress Toward	General Region of Body Referred To
dorsal	dorsally	dorsad	Back surface.
ventral	ventrally	ventrad	Front surface.
cranial	cranially	craniad	Head end. ('Rostral' used mostly in descriptions of the head to indicate snoutward.)
cephalic	cephalically	cephalad	
rostral	rostrally	rostrad	
anterior	anteriorly	(anteriorly)	
caudal	caudally	caudad	Tail end.
posterior	posteriorly	(posteriorly)	
median	....	....	In the midplane.
mesial	mesially	mesad	Toward the midplane.
medial	medially	medially	
lateral	laterally	laterad	Away from the midplane.
proximal	proximally	proximad	A more central part.
distal	distally	distad	A more peripheral part.
sagittal	sagitally	....	Any plane parallel to long axis and dividing embryo into right and left portions.
frontal	frontally	....	Any plane parallel to long axis and dividing embryo into dorsal and ventral portions.
coronal	coronally		
horizontal	horizontally	....	Any plane at right angle to long axis.

TERMINOLOGY

In describing development it is necessary constantly to employ words denoting the position of one part with reference to another, or to the body as a whole. The logical usage tabulated here is common to embryology and comparative anatomy. The terms *superior* and *inferior, anterior* and *posterior*, as used in adult human anatomy, are unfortunate choices based on man's erect posture and peculiar locomotion.

A few examples will illustrate the proper application of these terms: The backbone lies *dorsally;* the breast bone is *ventral* to it. The neck attaches to the *cranial* end of the trunk, while the latter extends *caudad* from the neck. The nose occupies the *sagittal* plane; it is *mesial* to the cheek which for its part is placed more *laterally*. The wrist is *distal* to the elbow, while the elbow is *proximal* to the *wrist*. A nerve is traced *distad* toward its ending. (Sagittal, frontal and horizontal planes lie with respect to each other as do any three adjoining surfaces of a cube.)

RECOMMENDATIONS FOR COLLATERAL READING

History of embryology:
  Meyer. 1939. The Rise of Embryology. Stanford Univ. Press.
  Needham. 1934. A History of Embryology. Cambridge Univ. Press.
Fundamentals of early development:
  Kellicott. 1913. A Textbook of General Embryology. Holt.
  Pincus. 1936. The Eggs of Mammals. Macmillan.
  Weiss. 1939. Principles of Development. Holt.
  Wilson. 1925. The Cell in Development and Heredity. Macmillan.
Human development:
  Hamilton, Boyd and Mossman. 1945. Human Embryology. Williams and Wilkins.
  Keibel and Mall. 1910–12. Human Embryology. Lippincott.
  Keith. 1933. Human Embryology and Morphology. Arnold.
Human postnatal development:
  Scammon. 1923. Vol. I, Chapter III in Abt's 'System of Pediatrics.' Saunders.
Human malformations:
  Schwalbe. 1906–37. Die Morphologie der Missbildungen des Menschen. Fischer.
Experimental embryology:
  Huxley and DeBeer. 1934. Elements of Experimental Embryology. Macmillan.
  Needham. 1942. Biochemistry and Morphogenesis. Macmillan.
  Spemann. 1938. Embryonic Development and Induction. Yale Univ. Press.
  Weiss. 1939. Principles of Development. Holt.
Gradients in development:
  Child. 1941. Patterns and Problems of Development. Univ. of Chicago Press.
Physiological embryology:
  Windle. 1940. Physiology of the Fetus. Saunders.

CHAPTER II

THE SEX CELLS

The development of a multicellular animal is prefaced by the formation and ripening of the sex cells which will unite and give it origin. These germ cells, or *gametes*, are generated within the sex glands of the male and female parents and are termed *spermatozoön* and *ovum*, respectively. The ovum, or egg, is a generalized type of animal cell produced in the female sex gland which is named the *ovary*. Quite different is the spermatozoön which, differentiating in the *testis*, or male gland, is a highly modified and atypical cell. It is the purpose of this chapter to describe how these two elements develop and mature.

Origin of the Sex Cells.—First of all, it is important to inquire how closely Weismann's belief in a separate germ plasm (p. 4) agrees with actual observations. In some lower animals certain cells are set apart early as progenitors of the future sex cells, and it can be shown clearly that every egg or sperm arises from these cells and from no others. For example, when an embryo of the worm, Ascaris, consists of but two cells this specialization into germinal and somatic lines is distinguishable; at the 16-cell stage, one cell definitely limits itself to the further formation of nothing but sex cells; it is the first *primordial germ cell.* Similarly, in the early vertebrate embryo there can be recognized large, pale cells (often located at first relatively far from the sex glands) which appear comparable. In man and other mammals they are identified earliest in the yolk-sac entoderm, near the caudal end of the body; from there they migrate forward through the mesenchyme of the mesentery and into the genital ridge which soon becomes the sex gland (Figs. 252 *B* and 259 *A*).

The nuclear behavior of primordial germ cells in vertebrates indicates that they are truly comparable to sex cells, yet their rôle and fate are disputed.[1] Some claim they are indeed the sole progenitors of all future sex cells, even though the early generations of sex cells derived from them may tend to perish and disappear. Others view the primordial cells as an ancestral type of parent germ cell that either is no longer concerned with the actual formation of present-day eggs and sperms or that at least shares this function with cells from another source. These latter elements are held to originate by the proliferation of indifferent cells located in the 'germinal epithelium' which surfaces the sex gland. It makes no practical difference whether the sex cells are special elements set apart at an early

moment or 'ordinary' cells at a later time, since all cells of the body contain precisely the same complement of chromosomes and genes.

   The Course of Differentiation.—The sex cells of all animals undergo a
similar history in achieving maturity. Even the consecutive stages which
an egg and sperm pass through in their individual developments are fundamentally comparable. The general process of egg-formation is *oögenesis;*
that of sperm-formation is *spermatogenesis.* Each shows in succession three
equivalent stages (Fig. 9): (1) a period of *cell proliferation*, during which the
primitive germ cells divide repeatedly; (2) a period of *growth*, marked by
rapid enlargement of the cells so produced; and (3) a period of *maturation*,
which involves fundamental nuclear changes and is limited to the final two

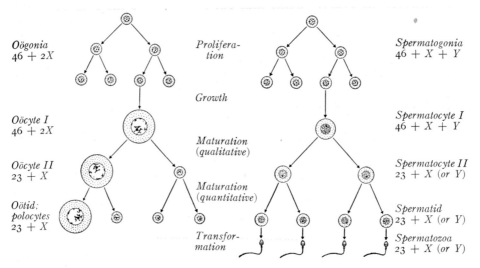

Oögonia
46 + 2X

Proliferation

Spermatogonia
46 + X + Y

Growth

Oöcyte I
46 + 2X

Maturation
(qualitative)

Spermatocyte I
46 + X + Y

Oöcyte II
23 + X

Maturation
(quantitative)

Spermatocyte II
23 + X (or Y)

Oötid;
polocytes
23 + X

Transformation

Spermatid
23 + X (or Y)

Spermatozoa
23 + X (or Y)

FIG. 9.—Diagrams comparing oögenesis and spermatogenesis. The assortment of human
chromosomes is indicated at each stage.

divisions. At the end of maturation the development of an egg is complete
and it is ready to function; the male cells, on the other hand, must pass
through an additional stage (*transformation*) which converts them from
ordinary appearing cells into specialized, motile spermatozoa.

   The process of maturation would be of the greatest importance if only
for the following reason: Since normal reproduction depends upon the union
of male and female sex cells, it is manifest that without some special provision this union would necessarily double the number of chromosomes at
each generation. Such progressive increase is, however, prevented by the
events of maturation which reduce the number of chromosomes in each sex
cell to one-half that characteristic of the species. The details of this process
will be described in later paragraphs.

Chromosome Numbers.—The cells of every animal species contain a definite and characteristic number of chromosomes. This number is identical for all the somatic cells of any animal and for its immature sex cells as well. The smallest possible chromosome assortment is two; it is said to occur in one form of Ascaris, a round worm. The largest number known is found in a crayfish, where 208 can be counted. The chromosome enumeration for the human cell has been stated variously, but it is now becoming more and more accepted that the correct number is 48 for both man and woman.[2] It is important to understand that there is a double set of chromosomes in each cell; hence the human assortment contains only 24 different kinds (Fig. 10).

OÖGENESIS

Origin of the Follicles.—During the fetal period of mammalian development, egg cells arise by proliferation within the germinal epithelium which encloses the ovary. Cells, thus cut off, sink into the ovarian cortex and continue to multiply there as *oögonia* (Fig. 11). To what extent the so-called primordial ova, which have migrated into the emerging sex gland at a still younger stage (p. 21), serve as parent cells is debated. In any event, late in fetal life other epithelial cells of smaller size come to encase

FIG. 10.—Chromosomes from a human spermatogonium, arranged in twenty-four pairs (Painter). × 1200. The X–Y pair of sex chromosomes is at the right end of the series.

the oögonia and so produce *primary follicles* (Fig. 260). Shortly after birth the formation of human oögonia comes to a halt. The total number present at this time in each ovary probably varies widely; estimates range from 40,000 to 300,000. One investigator found a steady decline to about 15,000 at puberty, whereas another reported 200,000 in each ovary from a woman of 22 years. Naturally enough, follicles in various stages of regression (*i.e.*, *atresia*) are abundant at all times. Several years after the end of the childbearing span, follicles are no longer seen.

With occasional futile exceptions, there is no advance beyond the stage of the primary follicle until puberty, which occurs at about the fourteenth year. Thereafter, during the next thirty or more years that constitute a woman's reproductive period, larger follicles in various stages of growth are always to be found. These growing follicles are interpreted in two ways. The traditional teaching has been that from time to time some of the primary follicles, among the initial store present from birth, arouse from their dormancy and begin to grow; of these, a certain favored one outstrips the others each month, continues to completion, and expels a so-called ripe ovum. Thus, from the hundreds of thousands of potential eggs originally formed, only a few hundred survive the struggle for existence and eventually reach maturity, whereas all others are doomed sooner or later to death and disappearance. A rival view, which has been gaining in favor, asserts that no egg that is differentiated before birth ever matures. On the contrary, the functional eggs of mammals, like those of many lower animals, are said to proliferate as needed from a rhythmically active germinal epithelium at the surface of the ovary.[3] While this interpretation may be correct for some mammals (opossum; rodents), it is disputed for others. Studies on man are conflicting and the whole matter must remain for the present unsettled.[4,5]

Growth of the Follicles.—All sexually mature mammals produce a crop of enlarging follicles during each cycle of ovarian activity. Most of these follicles, by far, fail to achieve maturity and at some stage of growth succumb to retrograde changes. At the start a human oögonium measures 0.02 mm. in diameter and its follicular covering consists of a single layer of

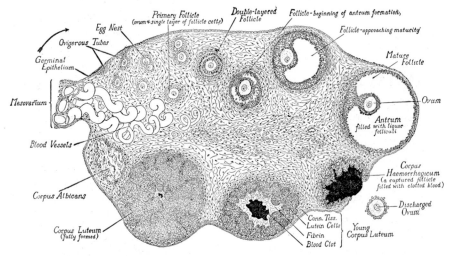

Fig. 11.—Life cycle of an egg and its follicle, shown in a diagram of the mammalian ovary (Patten). Start at the arrow and follow the stages clockwise around the ovary.

flattened epithelial cells (Fig. 11). Through growth the oögonium increases in diameter seven-fold (0.14 mm.), and at the end of the growth period it acquires a new name, *primary oöcyte*. In company with such enlargement on the part of the egg, the follicle cells become cuboidal elements; they proliferate and form a layer, several cells thick. At this time, when the egg is full grown, irregular fluid-filled spaces appear between the follicle cells and then unite into a crescentic cleft (Fig. 11). Progressive enlargement of this cavity converts the original follicle into a definite sac, the *vesicular (Graafian) follicle*, whose cavity (*antrum*) is filled with secreted follicular fluid (*liquor folliculi*). This type of follicle is characteristic of mammals alone.

As the growth of the follicle continues, the oögonium becomes located more and more eccentrically; it is buried in a mound of follicle cells, termed the *cumulus oöphorus* (egg-bearing hillock), situated at any position (Fig. 12). The follicle cells as a whole are arranged as a stratified epithelium, named the *stratum granulosum*. Around this epithelial layer the connective-tissue stroma of the ovary has been differentiating a sheath, the *theca folliculi*. The theca is composed of an inner, cellular and vascular *tunica interna* and an outer, fibrous *tunica externa*. In the final phase of marked growth the superficial portion of the follicle approaches closer to the surface

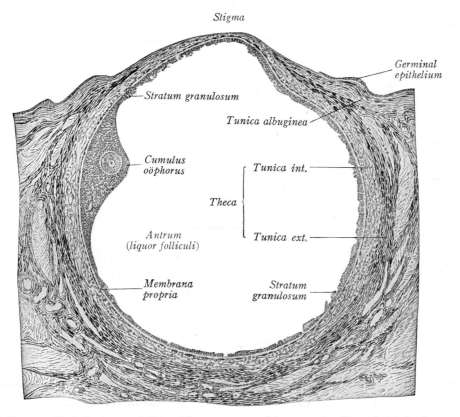

FIG. 12.—Vesicular human follicle with ovum, approaching maturity (Bumm). × about 20.

of the ovary and raises it into a stretched, local elevation. Growth of the follicle is slow at the start, but the advance is rapid in the last day or two before rupture. The full-grown, human follicle is millions of times bulkier than was the primary follicle; its final diameter is about 12 mm.

Probably all mammals develop some follicles that contain more than one egg, but this is infrequent in man. Although such compound follicles conceivably can lead to the production of twins, it is claimed that they usually degenerate. Occasionally an egg has two nuclei; the development of

similar eggs in insects does not result in twinning, and presumably this is
the case in mammals as well.

Maturation.—After an egg has finished its growth and becomes a
primary oöcyte, the succeeding stages of oögenesis are devoted to the important process of maturation. The principal feature of maturation is two
specialized nuclear divisions between which in most animals a resting
nucleus is not reconstituted, as in ordinary mitosis. During these two
divisions each chromosome splits but once, so that each of the four cells
finally formed contains the 'reduced' number of chromosomes; that is, a
complete single set of chromosomes replaces the duplicate set that character-

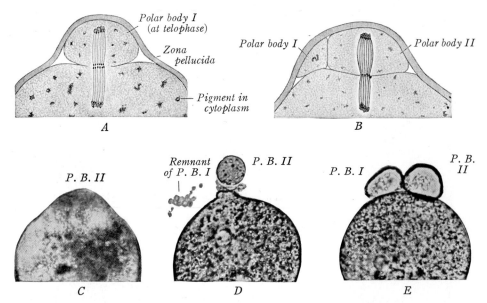

FIG. 13.—Maturation of the mouse ovum. *A, B,* Polar bodies and part of the egg proper,
sectioned (after Sobotta; × 1250). *C–E,* Formation of the second polar body, photographed from
living eggs whose lower hemispheres are omitted. (Lewis and Wright; × 500.)

ized the oögonium and primary oöcyte. This process of reduction, by an
atypical method of cell division, is named *meiosis.*

Maturation of the egg shows another unusual feature. Although the
nuclei of all four cells are equivalent, the cytoplasm is divided very un-
equally so that the end-products are one large, ripe ovum and three rudimentary ova known as *polar bodies,* or *polocytes* (Fig. 9). The latter are
so named because they pinch off at the 'animal pole' of the egg (p. 31).
There is obviously an advantage in concentrating on the production of
but one large, functional egg; it is destined to enter on a prolonged course
of cell division and for this reason should retain all the cytoplasm and yolk
possible. In order to gain this advantage, the definitive ovum develops at

the expense of the three polocytes which, having sacrificed their future, soon degenerate. In most animals the actual subdivision of the first polar body is suppressed, although it may fragment or divide amitotically. This omission is understandable since further cell division would be a superfluous act.

The extrusion of the polar bodies from the egg of the mouse is illustrated in Figure 13. At the end of the division that pinches off the first polar body (*A*) the primary oöcyte becomes a *secondary oöcyte*. The separation of the second polar body is shown as stage *B* and again in *C* and *D*. When both polocytes have become free (*E*) the egg nucleus re-

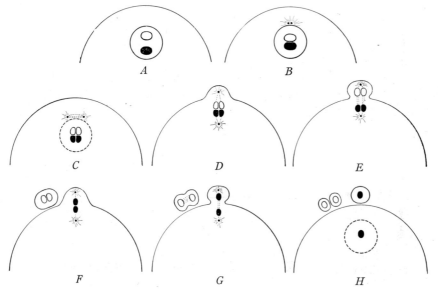

FIG. 14.—Diagrams of the maturation of the ovum in an animal with two chromosomes. *A–E*, Budding off of the first polar body. *F, G*, Formation of the second polar body and subdivision of the first. *H*, Mature egg with polar bodies. (Full explanation in the text.)

constitutes as the *female pronucleus*, considerably smaller than it was before. The ripe ovum is technically an *oötid*, although not often called such. At the close of these maturative events the centrosome disappears and the nucleus, with its single set of chromosomes, is ready to unite with the similarly reduced pronucleus brought in by the sperm. Of practical interest is the fact that most animals whose gametes meet inside the body of the female expel technically unripe eggs from the ovary. Only the first polocyte is cut off before the egg is set free, whereas the second never appears unless fertilization by a spermatozoön follows. This is another instance of economy of effort.

Chromosome Behavior.—The formation of the polar bodies, and especially the distribution of the chromosomes during meiosis, can be explained with the aid of diagrams (Fig.

14). For simplicity only two chromosomes are drawn (*A*). In reality these are a pair, one member (*e.g.*, black) having been inherited from the father of the present individual, the other member (*e.g.*, white) from the mother. During the prophase of the first meiotic division the two chromosomes come to lie side by side (*B*). Each chromosome then splits accurately along its length in such a way that the two halves are identical in their genetic value. Each split-pair is called a *dyad*, whereas the two dyads comprise a quadruple group known as a *tetrad* (*C*). The tetrad next undergoes a division which is accompanied by the budding off of the first polar body (*D, E*). At this division one dyad (the split-halves of one complete chromosome) passes into the polar body, and the other dyad remains behind in the egg. It is a matter of chance orientation during the formation of the meiotic spindle that determines whether the dyad from the paternal or maternal member of the original chromosome pair remains in the egg. Since this first division reduces the original pair of chromosomes of the egg to a single (though split) chromosome, it is termed *reductional;* since whole chromosomes have been separated, the division is qualitative in nature.

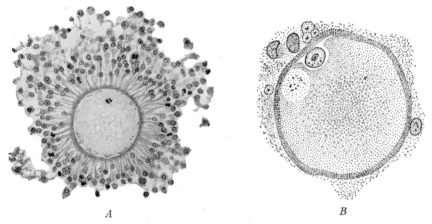

A   *B*

Fig. 15.—Maturation of the human ovum. *A*, Primary oöcyte, with cells of the corona radiata, from a large, unruptured follicle (Stieve; × 155); near the top of the egg are the chromosomes of the first meiotic spindle. *B*, Secondary oöcyte, recovered from the uterine tube (after Allen; × 500). The first polar body has been cut off and the chromosomes left behind were ready to enter the final division had fertilization occurred.

The second meiotic division follows. One half of the remaining dyad (called a *monad*) passes into the second polar body and the other monad stays in the egg (Fig. 14 *F–H*). Meanwhile, in theory at least, the first polar body undergoes a similar division (*G, H*). This type of division is *equational*, since each daughter chromosome is the split-half of a single chromosome and each is, therefore, the exact equal of the other. The equational division differs in no essential way from an ordinary mitosis.

The tetrad, therefore, proves to be a group of four chromosomal elements peculiar to meiosis. The splitting of individual chromosomes during the prophase is characteristic of an ordinary mitosis as well, but the mating and separation of whole chromosomes of a pair, combined with this splitting, occurs in meiosis alone. The reduction of the original number of chromosomes characteristic of a species to one half that number is also expressed by saying that the *diploid* (double) number has been reduced to the *haploid* (single) number. Every chromosome pair of a primary oöcyte exhibits the same behavior during meiosis as did the example whose history has just been traced. In certain animals the sequence of events is reversed, the first division being equational and the final division reductional; the outcome is the same. Some further information concerning the significance of meiosis in heredity will be given at the end of this chapter.

Human Maturation.—There are a few observations on the progress of maturation before the follicle bursts. Figure 15 *A* shows the chromosomes of a primary oöcyte arranging in the meiotic spindle that will lead to the formation of the first polar body. Other ovarian oöcytes, with the first polar body actually cut off (and the metaphase spindle of the second in a state of arrest), have been described.[6] There is reason for believing that all these events take place during the last day or two before the egg is set free.

A number of free eggs have been recovered by flushing out the uterine tubes (Fig. 15 *B*).[7] These unfertilized specimens show no advance since leaving the ovary. Hence it seems certain that, as in vertebrates in general, the free egg remains unchanged until penetrated by a sperm. This act then furnishes the stimulus for cutting off the final polocyte. The fertilized ovum, with both polar bodies present, has been observed in Tarsius, a low primate. Since the full number of human chromosomes is 48, the reduced number in the mature ovum is 24 (Fig. 9).

The Mature Ovum.—Although always relatively large, the final size of a ripe ovum is correlated with the amount of yolk substance stored in it and not with the size of the animal producing it. The smallest known egg is that of the mouse (0.07 mm.); the largest have a diameter measurable in inches (birds; sharks). Most animal ova are nearly spherical in form and all possess the usual cell components (Fig. 16). The *nucleus*, also spheroidal, is bounded by a *nuclear membrane* and contains a *chromatin network* and one or more *nucleoli*. The nucleus is essential to the life, growth and reproduction of a cell, while its chromatin bears the hereditary qualities. The function of the nucleolus is unknown. The abundant *cytoplasm* is distinctly granular and contains few to many nonliving *yolk granules*. In addition, there are such characteristic 'organoids' as the *mitochondria* and *Golgi apparatus;* until the egg is finally ready for fertilization there is also a minute *centrosome*. These organoids are living, self-perpetuating parts, specialized beyond the general cytoplasm. The yolk is nutritive; the centrosome is active during cell division only, but the functions of the other cytoplasmic constituents are imperfectly understood.

The yolk, or *deutoplasm*, consists of fatty and albuminous substance aggregated as rounded granules. It serves as nutriment for the developing embryo. Since no type of ovum is totally devoid of yolk, this material is useful in classifying eggs. One classification is based on the relative abundance of yolk (*i.e.*, small-, medium-, or large amount). Still more significant in relation to the mechanics of development is the distribution of yolk

within the cell: (1) Those ova that contain little yolk tend to have it dispersed rather uniformly, and are accordingly termed *isolecithal* (*i.e.*, equal
yolk) (Fig. 16 *A*). Examples are found among the invertebrates and in all
but the lowest mammals; such embryos have no need for much yolk since
they either attain an independent existence quickly or are soon sheltered
and nourished within the uterine wall of the mother. (2) As the yolk becomes more abundant it tends to concentrate in one hemisphere, and the

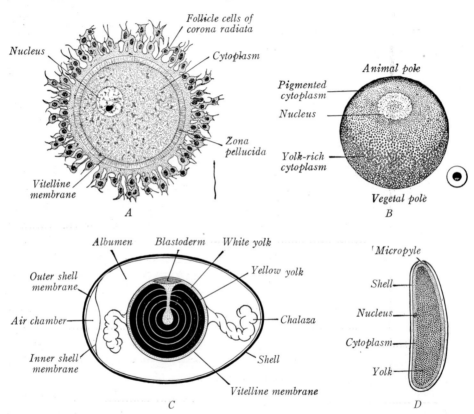

FIG. 16.—Representative types of ova. *A*, Isolecithal human ovum (× 200); at the lower
right a human sperm cell is drawn to the same scale. *B*, Moderately telolecithal egg of the frog
(after Morgan; × 15); at the lower right is a frog's egg surrounded by jelly (× 1). *C*, Highly
telolecithal egg of the hen (after Lillie; × 1). *D*, Centrolecithal egg of the fly (× 35).

ova are then said to be *telolecithal* (*i.e.*, yolk at end) (*B, C*). Many invertebrates and all vertebrates lower than marsupial mammals illustrate this
type. The large, yolk-rich eggs of fishes and amphibians are familiar to
all. The so-called 'yolk' of the hen's egg is actually a complete cell, taking
the form of a highly telolecithal ovum; its huge size and yellow color are
due to the enormous amount of stored yolk-substance. Similar in nature
is the egg of monotreme mammals, such as the duckbill. (3) Among the

arthropods the arrangement of yolk is distinctive. It is massed centrally and is surrounded by a peripheral shell of clear cytoplasm. Such eggs are *centrolecithal* (*D*).

Eggs possess *polarity* which is made manifest in various ways. The *animal pole* is the site where the polar bodies pinch off. This general region of the egg tends to have the highest activity capacities and thus may be more vigorous when development gets under way. At the other end of the polar axis is the *vegetal pole*. Its territory tends to be more sluggish and is concerned with the development of nutrient organs. Cytoplasmic components, such as pigment and yolk, are often disposed in a polarized or stratified way. This is well illustrated in telolecithal eggs, whose animal pole is more protoplasmic and whose vegetal pole is more yolk laden; the nucleus lies nearer the animal pole.

The eggs of most animals become enclosed within protective membranes, or envelopes, which are *primary*, *secondary* or *tertiary* in character. The delicate *vitelline membrane*, innermost in position and elaborated by the egg cytoplasm, is a primary membrane (Fig. 16 *A*). The follicle cells about the ovum usually furnish some kind of secondary membrane; the conspicuous *zona pellucida* is commonly assigned to this group (*A*). Tertiary membranes may be added by the oviduct as the egg passes through it. The jelly around the frog's egg (*B*), the albumen about the rabbit's egg, and the albumen and shell of the hen's egg (*C*) are of this sort.

The Human Ovum.—There is little difference in the size of the eggs formed by the various placental mammals; mouse, man and whale are nearly equal in this respect. Such an egg is small in comparison with many ova; yet when set beside ordinary cells it is truly large, since it is just visible to the naked eye as a tiny speck. The diameter of a normal human ovum, freshly discharged, is about 0.135 mm. Calculation shows that all the eggs necessary to replace the present population of North America could be placed in a cubical vessel three inches square.

The human ovum contains yolk granules and conforms closely to the isolecithal mammalian type (Fig. 16 A). The vitelline membrane is represented merely by the limiting cytoplasmic boundary and is not a definite envelope in the ordinary sense. Outside the ovum proper lies a thick, tough and highly refractile capsule, the zona pellucida; it increases the total diameter of the egg to about 0.15 mm. Abnormal eggs with giant or double nuclei occur, but they are uncommon.

SPERMATOGENESIS

The Course of Differentiation.—The sex cells of male vertebrates develop within thread-like testis tubules (Fig. 258). The latter originate as cellular cords that grow out of the germinal epithelium which covers

the sex gland of an embryo. Such a solid cord contains cells of two types
(Fig. 17 *A*). The larger are stem cells which proliferate and become *spermatogonia;* the smaller are indifferent, supporting cells. Until the time of
sexual maturity these are the only elements to be seen, but then a renewal
of proliferative activity advances the testis to its full functional state. Also
at puberty the solid epithelial cords first become hollow in man (*B, C*).
Two types of cell are then recognizable in the relatively thick wall of a
tubule: (1) The male *sex cells*, in various stages of development, arranged
in a layered fashion; they are all descendants of the spermatogonia.   (2)

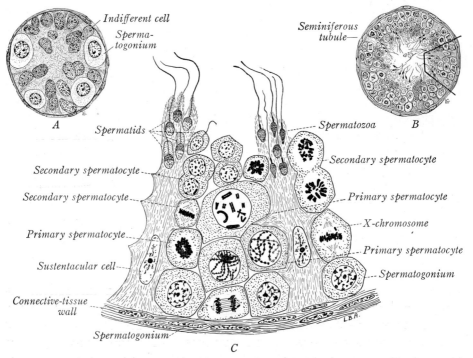

FIG. 17.—Human testis tubules, in transverse section. *A*, Newborn (× 400); *B*, adult (× 115);
C, detail of the area outlined in *B* (× 900).

Tall *sustentacular cells* (of Sertoli), derived from the indifferent cells; they
act as columnar supports and apparently serve as nurse cells.

   As spermatogenesis gets under way some spermatogonia remain as
stem cells, while others enter upon a growth period at the end of which they
are called *primary spermatocytes* (Fig. 17 *C*). Up to this stage each cell
still contains the full number of chromosomes typical for the species. Next
follow the two meiotic divisions which accomplish maturation. Each
primary spermatocyte divides into two *secondary spermatocytes*, and each
of these, in turn, into two *spermatids*. During these two divisions the cells

not only decrease progressively in size, but also the number of chromosomes is reduced to half the original number. That is, the double set is reduced to a single set in a way identical with that already described for the egg (p. 28). Finally, all the spermatids attach to Sertoli cells, from which they appear to receive nutriment, and gradually transform from typical cells into mature *spermatozoa*. Nothing corresponding to this period of transformation occurs in the development of an egg. When it is complete, the spermatozoa detach and are set free inside the seminiferous tubule. A comparison between oögenesis and spermatogenesis is shown diagrammatically in Figure 9.

Human Spermatogenesis.—The process of sperm formation begins at puberty, extends far past the corresponding time limit in the female, and may persist even into extreme old age. In man, like other animals that do not have a special breeding season, spermatogenesis is continuous. Its progressive course runs in recurring waves up the long testis tubules, so that at any horizontal level of a particular tubule all the stages are not encountered at one time. The duration of a spermatogenetic cycle at any level is some three weeks. The events of human spermatogenesis are typical and agree with the general description already given.

All the spermatogonia carry the full number of 48 chromosomes. At the end of the growth period, simple enlargement has changed these cells into so-called primary spermatocytes. Figure 18 A shows such a cell, with the chromosomes arranged as *tetrads* in 24 mated pairs, preparatory to the first meiotic division. The *centrosome* (two centrioles) lies between the nucleus and the *Golgi apparatus*. The latter consists of a dark-staining periphery and a paler interior which contains granules within vacuoles. *Mitochondria* take the form of coarse granules scattered throughout the cytoplasm. At the division of the primary spermatocytes into secondary spermatocytes, the 24 tetrads separate into two groups, each with a single set of 24 chromosomes already split as *dyads*. Since this division disjoins whole chromosomes of each pair, it is reductional. The secondary spermatocytes then divide equationally into spermatids, each dyad separating into two *monads*. At the end of meiosis, therefore, each spermatid contains 24 single chromosomes.

The four spermatids derived from each spermatogonium complete their development by undergoing a direct transformation (*spermiogenesis*) into highly specialized spermatozoa. This involves a remodeling of cell shape and a superficial disguising of certain of the typical cell components, as is illustrated in Figure 18 B-H.[8] The nuclear history is simplest, the open-structured nucleus merely condensing and reshaping into the main bulk of the sperm head. In the young spermatid the Golgi material, which has become dispersed during the spermatocyte divisions (B), assembles on the

surface of the nucleus (*C*) and a distinct bead within a vacuole is again
seen in the midst of darker-staining material. The bead applies itself
against the nuclear membrane (*D*) and soon spreads to constitute the
acrosome, or *anterior cap*, which covers the apical half of the head (*E-G*).
At the same time a *postnuclear cap*, of uncertain origin, appears like a thickening about the base of the nucleus (*D*) and grows upward (*E*, *F*) until
it meets the anterior cap (*G*, *H*). The peripheral Golgi substance about
the vacuole (*D*) detaches, passes down the side of the nucleus (*E*) and
finally is cast off along with an unused remnant of cytoplasm (*F-H*).
Meanwhile the centrioles have migrated to the margin of the cytoplasm

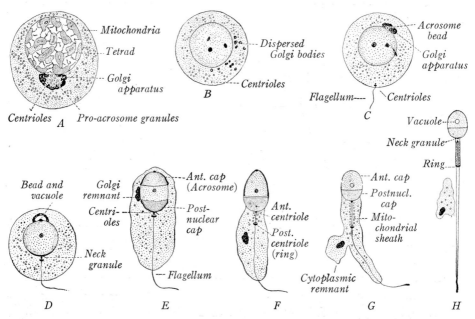

FIG. 18.—Stages in human spermatogenesis (adapted after Gatenby and Beams). × 1000–2500.
A, Spermatocyte; B, spermatid; C–G, transformation stages; H, spermatozoön.

(*B*), and from them jointly there grows out a thread-like *flagellum* (*C*).
The outermost centriole becomes ring-shaped and the two then move inward to the nucleus, opposite the primitive acrosome (*D*). Subsequently
the ring (posterior centriole) grows (*E*) and slips down the thread a distance
(*F-H*). The other, or *anterior centriole*, remains as a granule, located close
to the nucleus, and continues its direct connection with the flagellum.
Some stages (*D*, *E*) show another particle, not centriolar in nature, that
seems to be the rudiment of the later *neck granule* (*H*) (*cf.* Fig. 20). The
mitochondrial granules gather about the flagellum in the region between
the two centrioles (*F*, *G*). The cytoplasm is pulled closely around the

nucleus, but continues as a fairly conspicuous sheath most of the length of the flagellum (*G, H*).

The Spermatozoön.—In a few invertebrates only does the mature male element, or spermatozoön, resemble a typical cell. Most are slender, elongate structures which develop a huge, cilium-like lash; this whips back and forth to accomplish the active swimming that characterizes the cell. Unlike the egg, which is the largest cell of an organism, the sperm is among the smallest in mass. The extremes of length in animals range from 0.018 mm. in Amphioxus to 2.25 mm. in a toad. Some curious types occur, but the commonest shape is that of an elongate tadpole, with an enlarged *head*, short *neck* and thread-like *tail*. The head shows many variations in form (rod; lance; spiral; sickle; spoon; sphere; cone); the tail may bear along its length a fin-like, undulatory membrane.

The Human Spermatozoön.—At one time human sperm cells were regarded as parasites, and under this misapprehension the name spermato-zoa, or 'semen animals,' was given them. The spermatozoön of man is of average size and shape (Fig. 19). Although its length is nearly one-half the diameter of a human ovum, the relative volume is only as 1:85,000 (Fig. 16 *A*). All the sperms required to produce the next generation in North America could be packed into a spherical vessel having the diameter of an ordinary pinhead. The tiny size

FIG. 19.—Human spermatozoa, in edge and flat view. × 700.

of spermatozoa makes their structural details difficult to interpret; later studies have somewhat altered and simplified previous descriptions (Fig. 20) :[3]

a. The *head* measures nearly 0.005 mm., or one-twelfth the total sperm length of 0.06 mm. It appears oval in flat view, pear-shaped in profile. The interior of the head contains the tightly packed nuclear elements of the sperm cell; it is homogeneous in structure, except for a frequently found vacuole. The anterior half of the head is invested with the cap-like *acrosome,* while its posterior half is similarly covered with the *postnuclear cap.* In addition, some have described a superficial network of intersecting fibrils.

b. The short *neck* begins with a problematical *neck granule*, in contact with the head, and extends to the *anterior centriole.*

c. The *body,* often considered to be a 'connecting piece' belonging to the tail, is slightly longer than the head. Its extent is limited by the two centrioles, the posterior one being modified into a *ring, or annulus.* The central core (*axial filament*) is beset with *mitochondrial granules* which some have described as linked into a spiral thread.

d. The *tail* shows two different portions: (1) The tapering *chief piece* constitutes three-fourths of the total length of the sperm. It consists mainly of a cytoplasmic sheath which is a continuation of a similar sheath in the neck and body. (2) The *end piece*, or terminal filament, is a thinner short thread. It is usually said to be the naked termination of the *axial filament*, or flagellum, which begins with the anterior centriole and courses the entire length of the body and tail.

Atypical spermatozoa occur in all individuals. These may include giant and dwarf forms, badly modeled specimens and elements with more than one head or tail.

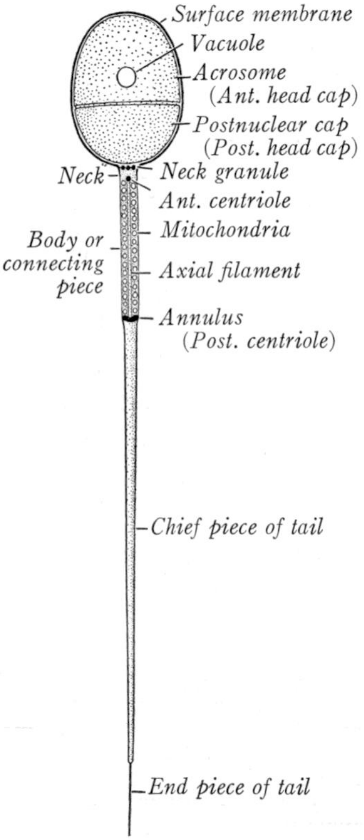

Comparison of the Egg and Sperm.—The dissimilar male and female sex cells of animals are admirably adapted to their respective rôles. They illustrate nicely the modifications that accompany a physiological division of labor. Each has the same amount and species-kind of chromatin, although in the sperm it is more compactly stored. Both cells are thus capable of participating equally in heredity, but in certain other respects each is specialized both structurally and functionally.

The ripe egg contains an abundance of cytoplasm, and often a still greater supply of stored food (yolk). As a result, it is large and passive, yet closely approximates the typical cell in all features except that the previously active centrosome has disappeared. Only in some invertebrates, however, is the egg by itself normally capable of cell division and development.

FIG. 20.—Structure of the human spermatozoön (after Gatenby and Beams). × 1700.

On the other hand, the sperm is small and at casual inspection bears slight resemblance to an ordinary cell. Its cytoplasm is reduced to a bare minimum; it contains a centrosome (in the form of centrioles), but no yolk. Structurally all is subordinated to a motile existence. Functions such as constructive metabolism and cell division are sacrificed. Correlated with the small size of sperms goes an extraordinary increase in numbers, for the greater the total liberated, the more surely will the egg be found. Hence, apart from its rôle in heredity, the chief function of the sperm is to seek out the egg and activate it to divide.

COMPARISON OF THE EGG AND SPERM OF ANIMALS IN GENERAL

Features Compared	Ovum	Spermatozoön
Size	Large	Small
Shape	Spheroidal	Elongate
Quantity	Less than sperms (Sometimes but few)	Large numbers (Often millions)
Motility	Lacking	Flagellate
Protection	Egg envelopes	None
Cytoplasm	Bulky	Minimal
Yolk	Little to much	Lacking
Centrosome	Disappears	Retained (centrioles)
Mitochondria	Diffuse	In body
Golgi apparatus	Diffuse	In acrosome
Nucleus	Open structured	Condensed
Nucleolus	Typical	Indistinguishable
Sex determining rôle	Rarely two kinds (Moths; birds)	Usually two kinds ('Male' and 'female' sperm)

THE SIGNIFICANCE OF MITOSIS AND MEIOSIS

The complicated events of an ordinary mitosis and the equational division of meiosis serve the purpose of dividing accurately the chromatic substance of the nucleus in such a way that the chromosomes of each daughter cell may be identical, both in number and composition. This is important since it is believed that self-perpetuating particles, or *genes*, in the chromosomes are the hereditary determiners, and that these are arranged in definite linear order in particular chromosomes. Before a chromosome splits, each gene in it divides and one daughter gene goes into each daughter chromosome. It is estimated that the vinegar fly, Drosophila, has about 4000 genes.

Although a gene is too small to be seen, the existence of many genes and their constant positions in specific, recognizable chromosomes have been demonstrated convincingly in Drosophila through extensive breeding experiments. Remarkable confirmation of these experimental proofs is afforded by the discovery of giant, compound chromosomes in the salivary glands of this insect (Fig. 21). Both the number and position of distinctive bands in these chromosomes correspond well with charts that plot the positions of genes as deduced from breeding experience. Such a band is not a single gene but a horizontal alignment of casings, containing similar genes in a bundle of identical, unseparated chromosomes. The gene has a diameter of about 0.00002 mm. and is probably a protein molecule; it acts as an organic catalyst and may be an enzyme.[9] The gene is the smallest living thing that is known to grow and reproduce its kind exactly. It exerts its directive influence on the cytoplasm.

At meiosis there is a side-by-side association of like chromosomes (one member of each pair having come from the father, the other from the mother of the preceding generation) (Fig. 22 A). Each member of a chromosome pair carries the same general set of hereditary characters as does its mate. The individual genes of any gene pair within the two chromosomes, however, may be like or unlike in their power of inducing the alternative expressions of a particular character (*e.g.*, for eye color they might be brown-brown, blue-blue or brown-blue). The reducing division of meiosis separates whole chromosomes of each pair, but chance alone governs the actual distribution of the paternal or maternal member of any pair to any particular daughter cell. Reduction obviously halves the chromosome number characteristic for the species, and as a result each daughter cell receives a single (but complete) assortment of chromosomes instead of the double set. The significance of the second, or equational division of meiosis, beyond accomplishing mere cellular multiplication, is obscure. In the end, each gamete receives one complete set of genes contained within a complete, single set of chromosomes.

In man nearly seventeen million different final combinations of chromosomes are possible through reduction alone. Vast as this number is, it represents only part of the full picture since the possible recombinations at an ensuing fertilization are measured by the square of seventeen million. A further increase in new hereditary combinations is made possible by

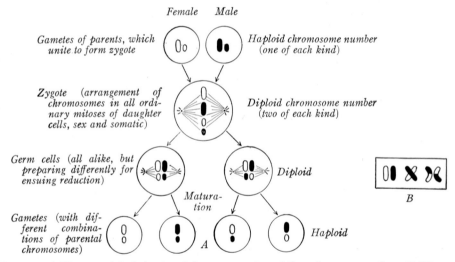

FIG. 21.—Giant, compound sex chromosome from the salivary gland of the vinegar fly, Drosophila (after Painter). × 1000. Twenty-one known characters are identified with bands (genes) in the spaces indicated by vertical lines.

FIG. 22.—*A*, Diagram of the behavior of chromosomes traced through one generation. *B*, Diagram of stages in a 'cross-over.'

the phenomenon of 'crossing over.' At the stage of chromosomal conjugation in meiosis the two chromosomes of a pair sometimes intertwine, and this may result in an interchange of corresponding parts (Fig. 22 *B*). The several factors just mentioned furnish a basis for variations in the hereditary pattern.

REFERENCES CITED

1. Everett, N. B. 1945. Biol. Rev., **20**, 45–55.
2. King, R. L. and Beams, H. W. 1936. Anat. Rec., **65**, 165–175.
3. Swezy, O. 1933. Quart. Rev. Biol., **8**, 423–433.
4. Evans, H. M. and Swezy, O. 1931. Memoirs Univ. California, **9**, 119–224.

5. Uffernorde, H.   1934.   Zentralbl. f. Gynäk., **58**, 1442–1449.
6. Hamilton, W. J.   1944.   Jour. Anat., **78**, 1–4.
7. Hamilton, W. J. *et al.*   1943.   Jour. Obstet. and Gynec. Brit. Emp., **50**, 241–245.
8. Gatenby, J. B. and Beams, H. W.   1935.   Quart. Jour. Micr. Sci., **78**, Pt. 2, 1–29.
9. Gulick, A.   1938.   Quart. Rev. Biol., **13**, 140–168.

CHAPTER III

THE DISCHARGE AND UNION OF SEX CELLS

When the eggs and spermatozoa of animals are ripe they are released from their respective sex glands. In one way or another the sex cells are brought together, whereupon successful ones meet and unite. These activities are known as *ovulation, semination* and *fertilization*.

OVULATION

The discharge of the ovum from its follicle comprises *ovulation*. A few animals breed continuously, but most commonly there is a seasonal or annual spawning period. The several mammalian groups show all gradations between ovulation every few days and an annual breeding period. As a whole, lower mammals ovulate spontaneously at the time of sexual excitement, known as the period of heat or *estrus;* only then will the female receive the male. A few, however, such as the rabbit, have 'provoked ovulation'; that is, copulation is a necessary prerequisite to ovulation, and it is the sexual excitement brought on by the copulatory act that sets into motion the complex events that end with ovulation. Except in the special case of identical twinning, a separate egg is ripened and expelled for each individual developed. It follows that multiple ovulation characterizes many mammals and is an occasional occurrence in man.

In primates ovulation is periodic, at intervals of about four weeks, and spontaneous. There is no period of heat, and hence the urge to mate is not limited to the time of ovulation. The human female begins to ovulate at puberty (about fourteenth year) and continues until the menopause (about forty-seventh year). Although some large Graafian follicles can be found rather constantly in the ovary between later fetal life and puberty, such precocious follicles eventually degenerate with their contained eggs. As a rule only one follicle and egg mature each month, the ovaries alternating with irregular and unpredictable sequence.[1] Thus, from the hundreds of thousands of potential ova provided, only about 200 ripen in each ovary during the thirty-odd years of sexual activity. There are, nevertheless, many thousands of follicles that reach various degrees of advancement during this period and then, as *atretic follicles*, decline and disappear.

Follicle Rupture.—The completed human follicle, some 12 mm. in diameter, causes the surface of the ovary to bulge locally (Fig. 23 *A*). Here the ovarian wall is stretched thin and at its apex there is a clear,

avascular spot named the *stigma*. Internally the follicle contains fluid
which has been secreted against pressure. Since the follicle enlarges greatly
in the last hours of its existence, it would seem that bursting is the result
of a sudden increase in follicular fluid, against whose pressure the wall
cannot adjust itself.[2] This rupture, however, is only the final act of a progressive growth process which leads to cellular, secretory and vascular
changes. The general course of events resembles somewhat the development and rupture of a boil.

The act of ovulation has been observed repeatedly in the rabbit and
sheep (Fig. 24).[3, 4] During the final few minutes the thin stigma dilates
into a pimple-like cone. Rupture at the tip follows quickly, but it is not
explosive. The thin, stretched apex merely opens, the fluid content of the

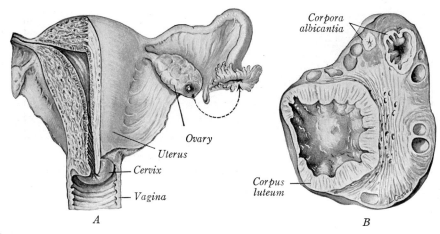

FIG. 23.—*A*, Ovary, with ruptured follicle, and its associated genital tract (× ⅘). *B*, Hemisected
ovary, with corpus luteum of pregnancy (× 1.5).

follicle flows slowly out and the follicle gradually collapses. Carried along
with this fluid-wave is the egg, which now tears away from its previously
loosened cumulus oöphorus. The adhering follicular cells, immediately
investing the egg, constitute the *corona radiata* (Fig. 16 *A*).

Egg Transport.—Ovulation discharges the egg into the peritoneal
cavity, but actually the 'cavity' which it enters is a mere space bounded
by the moist surfaces of those organs in the immediate vicinity of the ovary.
Some observers claim that the fringed end of the uterine tube embraces
the ovary and sweeps over its surface at the general time of ovulation.[5]
It is, therefore, possible that the liberated ovum passes almost directly
into the tube without ever gaining the body cavity in any real sense. Both
the beating cilia of the tubal lining and the augmented waves in the muscular
wall of the tube at this period have been held responsible for directing the

egg into the oviduct and then transporting it downward (Fig. 25). Perhaps
ciliary activity is more effective in picking up an egg, but there are rather
good reasons for thinking that the peristaltic movements are more important
in moving it down the tube (p. 117).

It is known that a pregnant uterine tube can occur on one side while
the sole corpus luteum (a later stage of an ovulated follicle) is located in
the opposite ovary. Also there are records of the removal of one tube and
of the opposite ovary, which still was followed by pregnancy. These facts
make it certain that the short-lived egg at times gets across to the tube
of the other side. Movements of the pelvic viscera might be thought to
accomplish this transport in an accidental manner; on the other hand,
several observers have seen a human uterine tube in intimate contact with
the surface of the opposite ovary, so the transfer may be quite direct.[6]

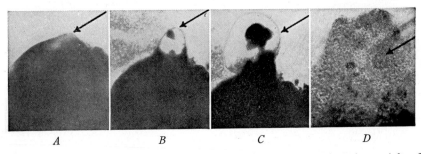

| A | B | C | D |

FIG. 24.—Ovulation in the rabbit, recorded in frames from a motion picture (after Hill).
A, Follicle, with beginning cone (arrow). *B*, Large cone, containing some blood. *C*, Follicular
rupture; extrusion of gelatinous material and blood. *D*, Exudate, attached to follicle (below)
and containing ovum (at arrow).

The Corpus Luteum.—Following ovulation the collapsed and emptied
Graafian follicle transforms into a new ovarian structure, named the *corpus
luteum* (*i.e.*, yellow body) (Fig. 11). It is peculiar to those vertebrates
that bring forth living young,[7] and is especially characteristic of mammals.
The presence of a corpus luteum is a positive indication of previous ovulation; an expert can estimate the age of a corpus luteum with fair accuracy
from its state of development. The so-called lutein tissue, which characterizes the corpus luteum, comes chiefly from the enlargement of the stratum
granulosum cells of the old follicle. Within a few days the corpus luteum
organizes into a prominent, highly vascularized mass whose structure is
typically that of an endocrine gland. There was little or no bleeding into
the collapsed follicle at the time of ovulation, but a significant amount of
blood (*corpus hæmorrhagicum*) may appear within the central cavity somewhat later during the stage of vascularization.

The subsequent history of the corpus luteum varies only in the final
size and length of life attained. When pregnancy does not supervene, this

endocrine body is called a *corpus luteum of menstruation*, or false corpus luteum; in this instance it reaches full size (1–2 cm.) and maturity in ten days. Degeneration then enters (shortly before the next menstrual bleeding) and a rapid decline follows. Among the signs of involution is the increase of a fatty pigment which gives the human corpus luteum its characteristic yellow color. Replacement of the regressing corpus luteum by fibrous tissue produces a white scar, the *corpus albicans* (Fig. 11); several months elapse before all traces of it have disappeared. When conception occurs, the *corpus luteum of pregnancy* (so-called true corpus luteum) continues to grow until, at the thirteenth week, it reaches a final diameter of 2 to 3 cm. (Fig. 23 *B*). Slow regression enters in the last half of pregnancy and the mass eventually converts into a typical corpus albicans.

The Time of Ovulation.—Both human ovulation and menstruation begin with puberty, recur at about twenty-eight-day intervals, and dis-

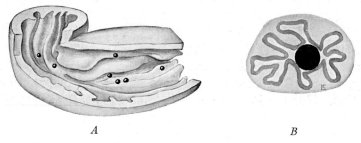

A   *B*

FIG. 25.—*A*, Reconstruction of a segment of the uterine tube of a rat, cut away to show the exact positions of seven eggs (after Huber; × 30). *B*, Human ovum and lining of the lower uterine tube, drawn to scale in transverse section (× 42).

continue during pregnancy and at the menopause. It is natural that some relation in timing should be inferred. For many years ovulation and menstruation were supposed to take place synchronously, like estrus and ovulation in lower mammals. But when actual data were collected it became apparent that this assumption is untrue. In reality the time of ovulation is about midway between two menstrual periods. Numerous sources of evidence, both direct and indirect, point to this conclusion.[8]

The monkey has a menstrual cycle identical with that of woman. In this mammal the time of ovulation can be detected by palpation of the ovary through the rectum.[9] Hundreds of cycles, checked by daily palpation, have showed follicle collapse to occur only between days 8 and 23 (counting from the first day of menstruation); 86 per cent. ovulated on days 10 to 14, and 44 per cent. on days 12 and 13.

About a dozen human eggs have been recovered from the uterine tube on days 14 to 19 and one on day 21. The average time at which freshly ruptured follicles have been observed in ovaries, inspected at operation, is on days 14 to 16. One may, perhaps, conclude that about the fourteenth day is the commonest date for human ovulation. Nevertheless, the monkey demonstrates that considerable latitude must be expected on each side of this mean. How much this is, and to what degree irregular ovulations occur, is not known.

If it is true that ovulation is usually limited to relatively few days at the middle of the human menstrual cycle, then the accumulated clinical records, which cite the eighth day as the time when coitus proves most fruitful, must be faulty. Even allowing for a considerable scattering of dates, due to constant irregularity on the part of some women and occasional variation on the part of others, there is definite conflict with the belief of some clinicians that women have become pregnant on every possible day of the cycle.[10] Any attempt to reconcile these divergent conclusions on the basis of a long survival period (in a potent, waiting condition) of the sperm, egg or both elements, runs contrary to all present evidence. A full understanding of these matters must await additional, reliable data.

Egg Viability.—How long the human egg retains its ability to receive a sperm and then start developing cannot be stated with certainty. In lower mammals the period is brief—a matter of hours rather than days. Similarly, the monkey becomes pregnant only when mated near its time of ovulation. For the human ovum it is now generally believed that the fertilizable period cannot be much more than one day.

If a mammalian egg does not become fertilized, it degenerates while in the oviduct. In the guinea pig this decline becomes visible within 24 hours after ovulation, whereas functional deterioration enters as early as eight hours.[11] Most of the unfertilized eggs that have been recovered from the uterine tubes of both the monkey and man showed signs of degeneration.

SEMINATION

In most aquatic animals the eggs and sperm are discharged externally at about the same time and place. Their meeting depends largely upon chance, enhanced by the production of immense numbers of sex cells. Some animals increase the certainty of such cell union by *pseudocopulation;* thus the male frog clasps the female and pours his spermatic fluid over the eggs as they are extruded. On the other hand, many invertebrates and most vertebrates, including all reptiles, birds and mammals, have their sex cells unite in the genital tract of the female. This is brought about by the sexual embrace termed *copulation*, or *coitus*. Its biological purpose is to introduce spermatic fluid into the female, and this deposit constitutes *semination*. In general, those animals whose offspring reach maturity with reasonable surety (as the result of internal fertilization and parental care after birth) produce far fewer eggs than do those that leave fertilization to chance and development to hazard. The codfish lays 10,000,000 eggs in a breeding period, an oyster 50,000,000; by contrast, in certain birds and mammals only a single egg is matured at a time. Yet the end result is the same, since all animal types maintain their numbers equally well.

Sperm Storage.—At the conclusion of spermiogenesis the spermatozoa of mammals detach from the Sertoli cells. Clusters are moved along the efferent ductules into the epididymis where they separate but remain motionless. The sperms accumulate in the epididymis (which is traversed in the guinea pig in about 15 days); any storage in the seminal vesicles is incidental.[12] A physiological ripening, both as regards motility and fertilizability, takes place in the epididymis as the sperms are forced onward by newer arrivals. Spermatozoa gradually attain their full functional state, retain it for a limited period, and, if not discharged, then slowly decline in vigor until death and resorption supervene.

Ejaculation.—At the male climax, during coitus, ejaculation occurs. Involuntary muscular contractions forcibly eject the older spermatozoa, along with the secretions of several accessory glands which discharge at the same moment. The aggregate mass is the *seminal fluid*, or *semen*. It is a mixture composed chiefly of the secretions of the seminal vesicles, prostate and bulbo-urethral glands, in which are suspended the spermatozoa. The volume of the ejaculate is about 3 c.c. and in it swim some 350,000,000 sperms. An acid environment, such as the vagina where the seminal fluid is first deposited, is deleterious or fatal to spermatozoa; a neutral medium, as furnished by the uterus and tubes, is more favorable.

Sperm Transport.—The outstanding functional feature of spermatozoa is their lashing, flagellate swimming which resembles that of a tadpole. This property is confined to the tail, and its center of control is apparently located in the body of the sperm (anterior centriole?).[13] Movement is first exhibited after ejaculation when the hitherto quiescent sperm cells are aroused to maximum motility by the combined ingredients of the seminal fluid at body temperature. Forward progress of the human spermatozoön is at the rate of 1.5 to 3 mm. a minute which, in relation to their respective lengths, compares well with the swimming ability of man. On the whole, spermatozoa swim in an aimless fashion; but under certain, perhaps artificial, conditions they orient passively against a feeble current (rheotaxis) and then continue to swim a spiral course upstream.

These innate activities, however, play but little part in the transport of sperms through the female genital tract.[14] Passage from vagina to uterus is apparently the result of muscular movements of the cervix, and the time occupied is less than a minute in some mammals. The journey through the uterus is similarly accomplished, in some animals at least, by muscular propulsion; spermatozoa of the dog appear at the ends of the uterine horns within one minute after ejaculation occurs. On the other hand, spermatozoa of the rabbit consume two hours in traversing the uterus; possibly this is because their own motive power is unaided.

In the uterine tube the upward progress, as studied in the rabbit, is of quite a different nature, although again the spermatozoön is a passive passenger.[15] Muscular constrictions in the wall of the tube subdivide its lumen into temporary chambers in which the spermatic fluid is churned and distributed through the action of ciliary currents and countercurrents; against these, flagellate swimming is of no avail. By the forming and re-forming of such compartments at different levels there is an interchange of contents from one to the other, and thus sperms move in a random manner both up and down the tube. Rabbit spermatozoa complete the tubal portion of their journey in two hours, or four hours from the time of coitus. Sharply contrasted are the ram, dog, guinea pig and rat in which the time spent after ejaculation in reaching the vicinity of the ovary is about twenty minutes.[16] The total period required by human spermatozoa in reaching their destination is unknown, but it cannot be more than a few hours at most. Direct observations on the method of transport are wholly lacking.

Sperm Vitality.—Two important questions arise in connection with the activities of spermatozoa in the female genital tract. One concerns the time limit in which the sperm lives and moves; the other, and far more important query, is how long such an element actually retains its ability to unite with an egg and activate it. Adequate observations on many animals indicate that these two periods are not co-extensive. Motility is a function of the tail, which is largely an accessory; the mere fact that a sperm swims does not necessarily imply that it can still fertilize. For example, rabbit spermatozoa retain their motile capacity after 60 days' retention within the male sexual ducts, whereas they prove fertile only to the thirty-eighth day. Furthermore, when once the rabbit semen gets into the genital tract of the doe it loses its ability to fertilize within 30 hours and the unused sperms usually die within two days.

It seems certain that this more rapid loss of fertilizability and life after spermatozoa enter the female mammal is due partly to a rapid decline in vigor in these specialized elements which, possessing but a limited amount of stored energy, have hitherto been spared from rapid katabolism by their inactivity. In addition, there are other factors, such as the deleterious effect of secretions from the female tract and the astonishing susceptibility of sperms to the slightly higher temperature of the interior of the body in comparison to that of the scrotum.

Semination of the mare as long as six days before ovulation occurs can result in pregnancy.[17] This period of fertilizability, however, is far exceeded by some bats, inasmuch as coitus occurs in the autumn whereas ovulation and fertilization are delayed until the end of hibernation in the spring.[18] Among other vertebrates the hen is known to retain functional sperms in its oviducts for as long as three weeks, while a period of four years has been claimed for the terrapin. Also in some invertebrates long life for the sperm is well authenticated, female ants and bees retaining functional spermatozoa for several years.

The data for man are based partly on knowledge but mostly on inference. Some observations following castration imply that the spermatozoa already present in the male sexual ducts may remain alive for months. Human sperms also have been kept alive in salt solution for fourteen days, and an equal length of life and function within the female tract has too often been inferred. This both lacks support from what is known on other mammals, and is inconsistent with the results gained from attempts to recover spermatozoa from the uterine tubes of healthy women. They disappear from the tubes within two or three days after coitus.[19] There is no good reason for believing that the duration of fertilizing capacity extends beyond a day or two. That the sperm may lie in wait for the egg, or the reverse, for any considerable period of time is contrary to experience, since the human species is relatively so infertile.

FERTILIZATION

The formation, maturation and meeting of the male and female sex cells are all preliminary to their actual union into a combined cell, or *zygote*, which definitely marks the beginning of a new individual. This penetration of ovum by spermatozoön, and the coming together and pooling of their respective nuclei, constitutes the process of *fertilization* (Fig. 26). In practically all animals fertilization also supplies the stimulus that starts the ovum dividing and thus sets off development in the ordinary sense. The eggs of certain invertebrates (rotifers; crustaceans; insects), however, develop regularly without being fertilized. This method is styled *parthenogenesis* (virgin origin), and in such cases there is often but one polar cell and no reduction in the number of chromosomes. Only rarely is the sperm of one species able to fertilize successfully the egg of another species. The hybrid progeny is usually infertile, like the mule, but often possesses greater size and vigor than either parent.

The Events of Fertilization.—Both the male and female sex cells have to be in a proper state of maturity if union is to occur. The time when the egg becomes fertilizable varies slightly in different animal types; it may be before maturation begins, after it is completed or at any intermediate stage. In vertebrates the first polar body has already been extruded; not until then does penetration by the sperm begin. In mammals the second polar spindle is also present but in a state of arrest (Fig. 15 B). Only during the preliminary events of fertilization does this second meiosis go through to completion. For its part, a spermatozoön to be successful must still possess high motility and, like the egg, must be in the functionally potent phase intermediate between under- and over-ripeness.

Penetration.—Random movements bring the sperm cells in contact with an egg. There is no real proof of any actual chemical attraction, but the secretions of some eggs may serve to trap sperms accidentally entering their sphere of influence; a positive tactile response (thigmotaxis) also keeps the sperm head in contact with anything touched. The spermatozoa of

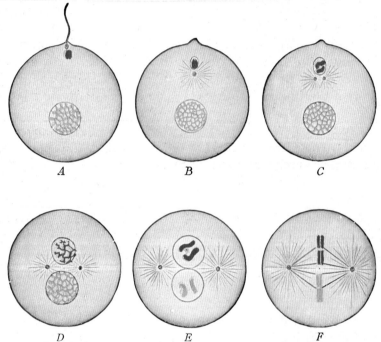

A B C

D E F

FIG. 26.—Semidiagrammatic stages of the events in fertilization (Howell, after Boveri). The chromatin of the ovum is colored blue, that of the spermatozoön red.

mammals secrete a substance that causes dispersion of the cells of the corona radiata still adhering to the egg.[20] They then propel themselves past any cellular remains of the corona and attach to the surface of the egg membrane. Only motile sperms are able to effect this attachment. The mammalian sperm head penetrates the zona pellucida, after which the lashing movements quickly cease and the successful male element is passively engulfed by the egg cytoplasm and drawn inward, tail and all (Figs. 26 A and 27 A). Competing, unsuccessful spermatozoa are commonly seen embedded in the zona pellucida (Fig. 34 A). In a few lower forms the tail detaches and is left outside the egg.

The eggs of mammals and many other animals can be entered at any point by a sperm. On the other hand, sperms avoid the yolk-laden pole of an egg like that of the frog. Even more severe restrictions attend the eggs of fishes, molluscs and insects that are invested with heavy membranes; these egg capsules usually have a definite, funnel-shaped aperture, the *micropyle*, through which the male cell must enter (Fig. 16 *D*). In many animals, including mammals, only one sperm normally gains entrance into an egg; others, endeavoring to penetrate, are thereafter excluded in

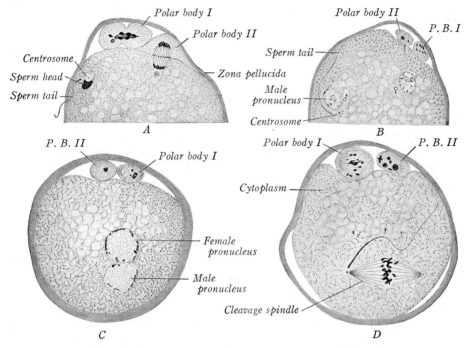

FIG. 27.—Fertilization of the ovum of the bat (after Van der Stricht). × 650. *A*, Entrance of spermatozoön, as second polar body cuts off. *B*, Male (♂) and female (♀) pronuclei, about to approach. *C*, Pronuclei, ready to merge; centrosome present at left of pronuclei. *D*, Spindle of first cleavage division.

some incompletely understood way. If accident or reduced vitality admits more than one sperm, the condition is termed *polyspermy;* development then is abnormal and soon ends except in some eggs (for the most part, those heavily laden with yolk) which regularly exhibit polyspermy. In all such instances, nevertheless, only one sperm actually unites with the egg nucleus; all others perish more or less promptly, without having contributed in any significant way to the main course of development.

Behavior of the Pronuclei.—The sequence of events in fertilization proper is illustrated in Figures 26 and 27. Once within the periphery of the egg, the sperm head rotates, end-for-end, and advances toward the center of the egg. During this journey the head swells, becomes open-structured, and converts into a nucleus of typical appearance which is given the special name of *male pronucleus*. At about this time the tail detaches from the rest of the spermatozoön, but it does not disappear from sight until somewhat later. Both the mitochondrial granules and the Golgi substance of the sperm disperse into the egg cytoplasm and fragment.[21] During the progress of these events the final maturation division of the egg has been completed and the now smaller, reconstituted egg nucleus (*female pronucleus*) made ready for union. To this end the two pronuclei approach and meet. In some animals they actually fuse and so produce a *cleavage nucleus*. In others, including mammals, each pronucleus loses its nuclear membrane and resolves its chromatin into a complete single set of chromosomes. Each set then enters into the first cleavage division as a unit (Fig. 26). Meanwhile a centrosome, presumably the anterior one of the sperm, appears between the chromosome groups and divides into two. After all of these preliminaries the first cleavage spindle soon organizes with the double set of male and female chromosomes arranged midway as an equatorial plate. The full chromosome number, temporarily halved in each gamete by maturation, is thus restored. Fertilization is now complete and the egg, freed from its previous restraints, divides in the ordinary mitotic way. In the rabbit the total events of fertilization occupy ten hours.

The Results of Fertilization.—It is worth while to emphasize again that the male and female cells, merging in fertilization, are each in a sense defective but complementary to the other. Thus the general cytoplasm and yolk are supplied by the egg alone, whereas the sperm probably brings in the functional centrosome (except in parthenogenesis when it must arise within the egg). Both the egg and sperm contribute equally to the requisite nuclear substance, and both contribute mitochondrial and Golgi bodies. By such pooling of the materials of the two sex cells there results a new, joint product, again characteristic of the species.

The fundamental results of fertilization are: (1) Reassociation of the male and female sets of chromosomes. By bringing together equivalent chromatin contributions from two different parents (and thus restoring the typical number of chromosome-pairs) there is furnished a physical basis for biparental inheritance and for variation. (2) Activation of the ovum into cell division, or *cleavage*. As the result of the first cleavage mitosis, and all subsequent ones, every cell of the developing body receives a sample of each kind of chromosome pooled at fertilization. It should be clearly understood, however, that mitotic activation is not dependent on the presence of two pronuclei or on their union, as natural or artifically induced parthenogenesis proves. Such union is, nevertheless, an end and aim of normal fertilization.

Human Fertilization.—Oöcytes have been removed from large ovarian follicles, subjected to spermatic fluid and then incubated; in a few instances they advanced through the first or second cleavage division.[22] A stage showing actual pronuclei has also been announced.[23] There is no hesitancy in believing that the essential course of events in man agrees with that in other mammals.

The meeting and union of the human sex cells is believed to take place normally in the upper third of the uterine tube. It is altogether certain that fertilization cannot be delayed until the ovum reaches the uterus, since staleness and degeneration enter rather soon. Presumably it does not take place even in the lowest levels of the uterine tube; at least, degenerating human ova have been recovered from the tube, and the unfertilized eggs of most mammals begin to show visible signs of decline by the time they near the uterus. The final fate of unfertilized eggs is dissolution in the uterus.

Superfetation.—To fulfill the requirements of superfetation it is necessary that a pregnant female ovulate, conceive and produce a second, younger fetus. In the early months of human pregnancy superfetation is theoretically possible. A few apparent examples have been recorded for lower mammals and at least one suggestive case for man.[24] However, it is difficult to exclude an interpretation of strikingly unequal twins in which one member has experienced retardation in size and differentiation.

Superfecundation.—This term designates the impregnation by successive acts of coitus of two or more eggs that were liberated at the same ovulation. In those lower mammals that are characterized by multiple births, superfecundation is known to occur; in such instances litter-mates can have different fathers. Its possibility in man cannot be doubted even though no records exist that can be accepted as indisputable proof.

HEREDITY AND SEX

Heredity and Environment.—There is an intimate inter-relation between the developing embryo (and its constituent parts) and the immediate environment which it encounters. Both the directing force of heredity and the molding influences of environment are important features of development, and to weigh one against the other is to lose sight of the integrated process of development as a whole. An altered environment may induce physical changes in the embryo, but the inheritance of such acquired characters as the result of direct action upon the soma still lacks adequate proof. The ineffectualness of somatic mutilations, such as circumcision, even though continued through many generations, is too obvious for extended comment. On the other hand, abnormal environmental influences, such as X-rays, can have a direct effect upon the genes that results in the appearance of new somatic characters known as *mutations*.

The Mechanism of Heredity.—That 'like begets like' has long been known, but the formulation of the principles under which heredity operates (*i.e.*, the science of *genetics*) is a relatively recent achievement. Heredity acts in orderly, often complex, but still predictable ways once the genetic constitution of an animal is understood. Even mutations, which occasionally occur as the result of spontaneous or induced changes within the genes, are not outside the realm of analysis and comprehension. Human inheritance is imperfectly understood, due to the mixed ancestry of man and his unselective mating, yet numerous characters, defects and disease tendencies that follow the typical plan are known. Naturally the operation of heredity is much more easily analyzed in laboratory animals whose stock can be selected and matings controlled. Incidental mention may be made of the fact that the close inbreeding of man or any other animal does not of itself produce degeneracy; it merely provides a better opportunity for the bringing out of certain traits, both desirable and undesirable, with which a common stock may be endowed.

The principles of genetics can be approached only through an understanding of its basis, as founded by Mendel. Experiments show that hereditary characters fall into two opposing groups, the contrasted pairs of which are termed *alleles*. As an example, the hereditary tendencies for brown and blue eyes may be followed. It is believed that there is a pair of particles, or *genes* that is responsible for eye color, that they lie in a specific pair of chromosomes, and that each kind of gene is located normally at a corresponding position in its respective chromosome (Fig. 21). Each chromosome pair in any particular germ cell may possess similar genes (both bearing brown-eyed determiners or both blue-eyed determiners), or the chromosome pair may carry opposing genes (the one bearing brown-, and the other blue-eyed determiners). It is further believed that at meiosis these paired genes separate, each in its respective chromosome, and that one only of any pair is retained in each definitive sex cell.

If all the gametes of both sexes contain nothing but brown (or blue) genes, then the progeny can have only brown (or blue) eyes. But if each parent carries both brown and blue genes then the results are more varied. In this instance some gametes with a brown gene and an equal number with a blue gene develop in both sexes. At fertilization three kinds of combination are possible, as is shown in the following schema where '*B*' represents brown and '*b*', blue:

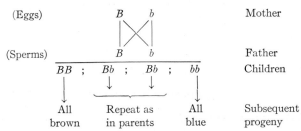

The offspring from two 'brown' gametes (*BB*) will all have brown eyes, and, if interbred, their progeny will likewise inherit brown eyes exclusively. Similarly, the offspring from two 'blue' gametes (*bb*), or their interbred progeny, will include nothing but blue-eyed individuals. The offspring from the brown and blue union (*Bb*) will have brown eyes solely, for brown in the present example is *dominant*, as it is termed. Such brown-eyed individuals, nevertheless, possess both brown- and blue-eyed genes in their germ cells; in the progeny resulting from the interbreeding of this class, the original condition is repeated—pure brown, impure brown which hold blue *recessive*, and pure blues will be formed in the ratio of 1 : 2 : 1, respectively. It is thus seen that blue-eyed children may be born of brown-eyed parents, whereas genetically pure, blue-eyed parents can never have brown-eyed offspring. If offspring carrying *Bb* genes cross with others carrying either *BB* or *bb*, then half of the progeny will be like one of these parents and the other half like the other parent. A cross involving *BB* and *bb* will result solely in *Bb* hybrids.

Sex Determination.—The sex-determining power resides in a chromosome that can be identified in many animals. This chromosome is termed the X- or sex chromosome. It is now agreed that the oögonia of woman, like all her somatic cells, contain 46 ordinary chromosomes and two X-chromosomes. Human spermatogonia duplicate this chromosomal assortment except that there is only one X-chromosome; its mate is a diminutive, inert structure designated as the Y-chromosome (Fig. 10). At meiosis the members of each chromosomal pair are separated and only a single set of chromosomes is retained by any daughter cell. Hence all ripe ova and polar bodies contain 23 + X. On the other hand, reduction in the male produces two classes of spermatozoa; one group has 23 + X, while the other group (equal in numbers) has 23 + Y (Fig. 28). Fertilization by the first kind of sperm cell results in a female (46 + 2 X); fertilization by the second type produces a male (46 + X + Y). It naturally follows that the determination of sex is governed by the chance success of one type of sperm or the other and that it is quite beyond human control. The constant racial preponderance of newborn males over females (106:100) cannot be explained on the basis of any demonstrable advantage possessed by the male-determining sperm. The determiners of various human traits are known to reside in and follow the sex chromosome, and the peculiarities in the transmission of such defects as color blindness and hemophilia are explainable on this basis.

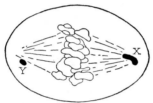

Fɪɢ. 28.—Primary spermatocyte of a male Negro, at the metaphase stage (after Painter). ✕ 2200. In this reductional division the sex chromosomes have separated precociously.

In some animals the X-chromosome of the male is without a mate, and a minority opinion still maintains that this is the condition in man.[25] There is no fundamental difference between the X–O and X–Y scheme of sex determination. In each a double dosage of the X-chromosome is responsible for femaleness, a single dosage for maleness; the presence or absence of Y has no effect on sex determination. In birds, moths, and some fishes the sex-determining system is the exact reverse of that already described, inasmuch as the spermatozoa are all alike in chromosomal constitution while the eggs are of two sorts.

The mere association of sex determination with the occurrence of an identifiable chromosome does not, of course, indicate the full nature of the actual mechanism at work. In reality the details are both varied and complex. In some lower organisms the environment is the decisive factor that directs sex into one channel or the other. On the other hand, sex-regulating genes are highly potent in insects. In vertebrates they are at least chiefly effective in the early stages of development, whereupon their influence is reinforced by the gonadial hormones which superintend the process of sexual differentiation.

REFERENCES CITED

1. Morse, A. H. and van Wagenen, G.   1936.   Amer. Jour. Obstet. and Gynec., **32,** 823–828.
2. Walton, A. and Hammond, J.   1928.   Brit. Jour. Exp. Biol., **6,** 190–204.
3. Markee, J. E. and Hinsey, J. C.   1936.   Anat. Rec., **64,** 309–320.
4. McKenzie, F. F. and Terrill, C. E.   1937.   Univ. Missouri Agric. Exp. Sta., Res. Bull. No. 264, 88 pp.

5. Westmann, A. 1937. Jour. Obstet. and Gynec. Brit. Emp., **44**, 821–838.

6. Caffier, P. 1936. Zentralbl. f. Gynäk., **60**, 2466–2470.

7. Cunningham, J. T. and Smart, W. 1934. Proc. Roy. Soc. London, Ser. B., **116**, 258–281.

8. Hartman, C. G. 1936. Time of Ovulation in Women. Williams and Wilkins, Baltimore.

9. Hartman, C. G. 1944. Western Jour. Surg., Obstet. and Gynec., **47**, 149–184.

10. Fränkel, L. 1938. Rev. obstet. e ginec. São Paulo, **2**, 275–280.

11. Blandau, R. J. and Young, W. C. 1939. Amer. Jour. Anat., **64**, 303–329.

12. Stieve, H. 1930. Bd. 7, Teil 2 in Möllendorff's 'Handbuch der mikroskopischen Anatomie des Menschen.' Springer, Berlin.

13. Cody, B. A. 1925. Jour. Urol., **13**, 175–191.

14. Hartman, C. G. 1939. Chap. 9 in Allen's 'Sex and Internal Secretions.' 2nd ed. Williams and Wilkins, Baltimore.

15. Parker, G. H. 1931. Phil. Trans. Roy. Soc. London, Ser. B, **219**, 381–419.

16. Schott, R. G. and Phillips, R. W. 1941. Anat. Rec., **79**, 531–540.

17. Day, F. T. 1942. Jour. Agric. Sci., **32**, 108–111.

18. Wimsatt, W. A. 1944. Anat. Rec., **88**, 193–204.

19. Belonoschkin, B. 1939. Arch. f. Gynäk., **169**, 151–183.

20. Pincus, G. and Enzmann, E. V. 1936. Jour. Exp. Zoöl., **73**, 195–208.

21. Gresson, R. A. R. 1941. Quart. Jour. Micr. Sci., **83**, 35–59.

22. Rock, J. and Menkin, M. F. 1944. Science, **100**, 105–107.

23. Hamilton, W. J., *et al.* 1945. Human Embryology. Heffer, Cambridge, England.

24. Murless, B. C. 1937. Brit. Med. Jour., 1309–1311.

25. Oguma, K. 1937. Jour. Morph., **61**, 59–94.

CHAPTER IV

CLEAVAGE AND GASTRULATION

The Periods of Early Development.—There is a high degree of unity in the early development of all multicellular animals. The essential identity of gametogenesis, maturation and fertilization has already been emphasized. Further phases of early development, fundamentally similar in all animals, include cleavage and the formation of the primary germ layers.

Promptly following the union of the male and female sex cells, the fertilized egg enters on a series of cell divisions which give the first external sign of development in the ordinary sense of that term. This initial period in the production of a new, many-celled individual is called *cleavage*. By it the egg is subdivided into many smaller cells which typically arrange themselves into a hollow sphere, the *blastula*. An important advance in organization is then accomplished by *gastrulation*, through which the cells of the blastula become redistributed as the *primary germ layers*. These are three in number and from their positions are named *ectoderm*, *mesoderm* and *entoderm*. They contain the material out of which the embryo and all its parts will differentiate.

The Vertebrate Groups.—Although the development of man is the main theme of this book, it is necessary to refer from time to time to conditions in lower animals and particularly in other vertebrates. *Chordates* are animals characterized by the possession of an axial, rod-like support known as the *chorda dorsalis* or *notochord*. Most important of the lower chordates to embryology is Amphioxus whose development has furnished considerable fundamental information. The highest group of chordates is the *vertebrates* whose provisional notochord is replaced by a skull and vertebral column. Vertebrates fall into five classes. The three highest groups possess an enveloping embryonic membrane named the amnion, and this feature is the basis of a convenient classification:

A. ANAMNIOTA (amnion absent).
    1. *Fishes*—lamprey; sturgeon; shark; bony fishes; lung fish.
    2. *Amphibians*—salamander; frog; toad; etc.
B. AMNIOTA (amnion present).
    3. *Reptiles*—lizard; crocodile; snake; turtle.
    4. *Birds*.
    5. *Mammals*.—Characterized by hair and mammary glands.
        a. Monotremes—duck-bill; echidna. Primitive mammals possessing a cloaca, like lower vertebrates. They lay large eggs with shells.
        b. Marsupials—opossum; kangaroo; etc. The young are born immature and are sheltered in a pouch of the skin.
        c. Placentalia. All other mammals; their young are nourished in the uterus by means of a placenta. The highest order is the Primates with specialized 'nails'

55

(lemur; monkey; ape; man). Since the lemurs are considerably different from other primates, the monkey, ape and man are conveniently placed in the sub-order of Anthropoids.

CLEAVAGE

Cleavage progressively splits the fertilized egg into smaller cells, termed *blastomeres*. Cleavage divisions are always mitotic and each daughter cell receives the full assortment of chromosomes, half from each parent. The succession of mitoses tends typically to follow the doubling sequence 2, 4, 8, 16, etc., although in practice the regularity of this series is disturbed sooner or later and thereafter becomes irregular. In most animals the divisions follow in relatively quick succession; in none do the daughter cells grow as a whole, although their nuclei enlarge to a certain extent. Consequently, at each mitosis the blastomeres are reduced progressively in size until finally the size-relation between the originally over-large cell bodies and their nuclei is normal. In a strict sense, therefore, cleavage is a fractionating process which provides mobile building units, rather than a process of truly constructive development. The mass of living substance, available for development, has not increased appreciably when cleavage comes to an end.

The cluster-stage of cohering, sticky blastomeres is sometimes called a *morula* from its general resemblance to a mulberry. By this time the blastomeres tend to be arranged about a central, free space. Their continued subdivision produces the *blastula*, whose central, fluid-filled cavity is the *blastocœle*, or cleavage cavity. In its simple, typical form the blastula is a hollow sphere of cells.

It is the active protoplasm of the egg that accomplishes division. The inert, stored yolk-substance is not involved beyond acting as an impediment which retards the process of mitosis, and even prevents it from extending into overdense regions. In this way the relative amount of yolk and its even or uneven distribution throughout the egg have a profound influence on cleavage and the mechanics of moving the germ layers into their final positions. Yet, in spite of the hindering yolk, the processes at work and the results accomplished are fundamentally comparable in all vertebrate types. The simplest explanation of this basic uniformity is the directing influence of a common inheritance which labors as best it can with eggs variously endowed with yolk.

On the basis of the abundance and distribution of yolk, cleavage is classified as follows:

A. *Total*. Entire ovum divides; *holoblastic ova*.
    1. *Equal*. In isolecithal ova; blastomeres are of approximately equal size; *e.g.*, Amphioxus, marsupials and placental mammals.

2. *Unequal*. In moderately telolecithal ova; yolk accumulated at the vegetal pole retards mitosis, and fewer but larger blastomeres form there; *e.g.*, lower fishes and amphibians.

B. *Partial*. Protoplasmic regions alone cleave; *meroblastic ova*.

1. *Discoidal*. In highly telolecithal ova; mitosis is restricted to the animal pole; *e.g.*, higher fishes, reptiles, birds and monotremes.

2. *Superficial*. In centrolecithal ova; mitosis is restricted to peripheral cytoplasmic investment; limited to arthropods.

Observations on cleavage bring to light certain general principles which can be formulated as rules. Nevertheless, these should not be regarded as invariable laws because they are occasionally disturbed by other, incidental influences.

1. A mitotic spindle occupies the 'center of density' of its protoplasmic mass. (In an isolecithal ovum the spindle is located centrally; in a telolecithal ovum it is nearer the animal pole.)

Corollary: Blastomeres divide into two equal parts unless the yolk is unevenly stored.

2. The axis of a spindle occupies the longest axis of its protoplasmic mass. (Evident in ovoid blastomeres.)

Corollary: The ensuing plane of division cuts across this long axis, and the daughter cells revert to a more spheroidal shape.

3. Each new division plane tends to intersect the preceding plane at right angles. (Acts to maintain the spheroidal shape of blastomeres.)

4. The speed of cleavage is inversely proportional to the amount of yolk encountered. (In telolecithal ova, animal cells divide faster than vegetal cells.)

An understanding of cleavage and gastrulation is best gained through a comparative approach. In this way the increasing influence of yolk can be appreciated and the information obtained from lower vertebrates can be used to explain certain conditions in mammals that otherwise would be puzzling.

Amphioxus.—The almost microscopic egg of this fish-shaped chordate contains a small amount of yolk which is somewhat concentrated at one end, the vegetal pole. Yet for all practical purposes it can be considered isolecithal. Cleavage is total and unequal. About one hour after fertilization the egg divides into two blastomeres, the plane of this first cleavage passing through the egg axis from pole to pole (Fig. 29 *A*). Soon the daughter cells again cleave in a vertical (meridional) plane, but at right angles to the first plane, thus forming four cells (*B*). In the third series of divisions the plane of separation is horizontal (*C*). As the yolk is some-what more abundant toward the vegetal pole, the four mitotic spindles lie nearer the animal pole; consequently, in the resulting eight-celled stage the upper tier of four cells is slightly smaller than the lower four. A return to cleavage in the meridional plane produces a 16-celled morula (*D*). At this time the blastomeres surround a rather definite space at the interior which is the early cleavage cavity, or *blastocœle*. The continuation of practically synchronous cell divisions in alternate planes produces a 32-, 64- and 128-cell stage; during this period the size of the cells is progressively diminished while the central cavity enlarges (*E*). After the seventh set of divisions (128 cells) the regularity of timing is lost. When the embryonic

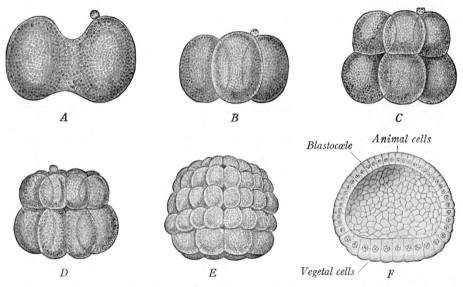

FIG. 29.—Cleavage in Amphioxus, viewed from the side (after Hatschek). × 200. *A*, Two blastomeres, separating, one polar body retained. *B*, Four blastomeres. *C*, Eight blastomeres. *D*, Morula, with sixteen blastomeres. *E*, Young blastula. *F*, Older blastula, hemisected.

mass is about four hours old it consists of 128 or (theoretically) 256 cells and is a diagrammatic *blastula* (*F*). This is a hollow sphere; it is made of a single layer of cells which are arranged about a large blastocœle, filled with a watery jelly.

Amphibians.—Cleavage is total, but unequal. The moderately telo-lecithal egg is 1 to 10 mm. in diameter and contains sufficient yolk to crowd the nucleus and much of the cytoplasm nearer the animal pole (Fig. 16 *B*). As in Amphioxus, the first two divisions subdivide the egg as one would quarter an apple. The spindles for the third cleavage are again nearer the animal pole, but this division takes place in a horizontal plane (Fig. 30 *A*). Hence the upper four cells, thus cut off, are distinctly smaller than the lower four. In the further cleavages that follow, the larger yolk-laden cells divide more slowly than the smaller, more purely protoplasmic ones of the animal pole (*B*). After about 32 cells have been formed, tangential divisions (whose separation planes parallel the surface) begin to occur along with the other types already described. Cleavage ends after about one day with the completion of a quite typical, hollow *blastula* (*C*, *D*); the central *blastocœle* is enclosed by blastomeres which are small at the animal pole and larger and fewer at the vegetal pole. The amphibian blastula differs from that in Amphioxus in two regards: (1) the wall is more than one cell thick; (2) the blastocœle is relatively small and above center.

Birds.—The egg is large and contains a great amount of stored yolk. It represents the highly telolecithal type of egg in which the active cytoplasm localizes as a cap at the animal pole, where the nucleus also is located (Fig. 16 *C*). The huge yolk mass, far more extensive than the vegetal

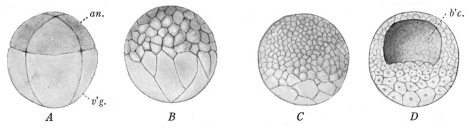

Fig. 30.—Cleavage in the frog, viewed from the side. × 12. *A*, Eight blastomeres, with animal (*an.*) and vegetal (*v'g.*) cells; *B*, about 128 blastomeres; *C*, early blastula; *D*, hemisection of *C*, showing blastocœle (*b'c.*).

hemisphere of an amphibian egg, is a nonliving inclusion and does not participate in cleavage or the formation of the embryo proper. As a result, cleavage is partial and discoidal.

The first two planes of separation are vertical furrows which cross at right angles through the animal pole of the egg but do not extend all the way to the margin of the cytoplasmic cap (Fig. 31 *A*). Succeeding furrows pass first in radial (*B*) and then in circumferential planes (*C*), and the original disc of cytoplasm is transformed into a mosaic of separate nucleated areas, all continuous for a time with the yolk beneath. Following this stage, cleavage divisions also take place in a horizontal plane to produce a certain amount of layering (Fig. 32). The end result, after about one day, is a discoidal plate of cells perched on the surface of the yolk and separated from it by a cleft. At the periphery, the cellular disc progressively gains new cells from a proliferating, syncytial margin that blends into the yolk.

Cleavage thus produces a modified blastula (named a *discoblastula*) in which the cellular cap is termed the *germinal disc* or *blastoderm*. The space between blastomeres and yolk mass is called a *blastocœle*, but its strict homology with that in Amphioxus and amphibians is doubtful. The massive yolk, which serves as a floor to the blastula cavity, is not contained within cells; hence this floor is fundamentally unlike the vegetal hemisphere of the blastula of those lower chordates (Fig. 35 *A–C*).

Mammals.—The eggs of all marsupial and placental mammals are isolecithal and practically microscopic in size (Fig. 16 *A*). Cleavage is total and nearly equal, much as in Amphioxus, but the blastula is con-

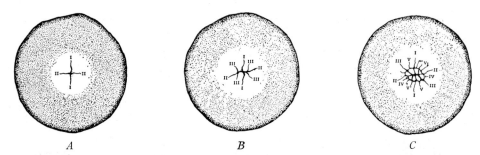

A   B   C

FIG. 31.—Cleavage of the pigeon's ovum, viewed from above (Patten, after Blount). × 4. The order of appearance of cleavage furrows on the blastoderm is indicated by Roman numerals. *A*, Second cleavage; *B*, third cleavage; *C*, fifth cleavage.

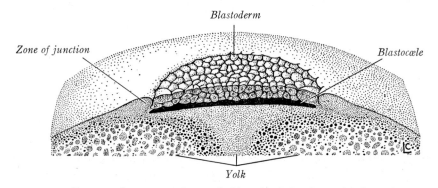

FIG. 32.—Stereogram of an early blastula of the pigeon, hemisected.

siderably different both in arrangement and subsequent developmental course. Subdivision of the mammalian egg begins in the uterine tube, although the later stages of cleavage are completed in the uterus. The process has been studied thoroughly in various common mammals; cleavage in the rabbit has also been carried out in culture and recorded by motion pictures. The extremes of time consumed in completing cleavage are 55 hours for the rabbit and 140 hours for the guinea pig.

As in Amphioxus and amphibians, the first two planes are vertical and the third horizontal. The resulting two-, four- and eight-celled stages are

attained approximately at 36, 48 and 72 hours after copulation. Nevertheless, some cells tend to divide faster than others, so that the exact doubling
sequence often fails (Fig. 33 *B*). In some mammals this difference in the
rate of mitosis is regional and is associated with two cell types which may
be recognizable even at the first cleavage. Darker blastomeres, with slower
cleavage, are destined to become the embryo proper, whereas the clear
cells, with rapid cleavage, differentiate precociously into auxiliary tissue
known as the *trophoblast* (*cf.* Fig. 33). It seems probable that a sorting out
of cell substances, with different prospective values, accompanies even the
earliest step in blastomere formation. At about the 16-cell (morula) stage
the future trophoblast cells begin to flatten against the zona pellucida and
produce a sort of cellular capsule. At the same time pools of clear fluid
accumulate between the more centrally located trophoblast cells (*D*), and
these spaces soon coalesce into a common, central reservoir (*E*). The fluid
is secreted against pressure by the trophoblast cells. By the time some
thirty cells have formed, the embryo is a definite hollow sac known as the

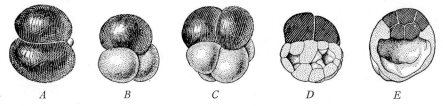

A B C D E

FIG. 33.—Cleavage stages and blastocyst of the pig (Heuser and Streeter). × 240. The dark
cells will give rise to the embryo proper. *D*, *E* are hemisections.

blastocyst or *blastodermic vesicle* (*E*). The cells destined to become the
embryo proper constitute an *inner cell mass;* presently this mass flattens
and is then the equivalent of a blastoderm (*cf.* Fig. 34 *F*, *G*). In Figure
33 *E* trophoblast is lacking above the inner cell mass, but this is merely
because the larger cells of this region are laggard in separating off the
trophoblast cells that belong there. The completed trophoblastic sac is
purely an embryonic adjunct, soon to become associated intimately with
the uterus; it is concerned with protective and metabolic functions.

In certain other mammals, such as the rabbit and monkey, the blastomeres are more nearly equal in size and the trophoblast is already a complete
capsule by the time the inner cell mass is recognizable as such (Fig. 34).
The young blastocyst of all mammals is spheroidal in shape. It grows
rapidly and distends with accumulated fluid; early in this period of enlargement the zona pellucida thins out and disappears.

It is clear that the thin-walled blastocyst is a specialized blastula, but its proper interpretation is not apparent at first glance. Actually the mammalian blastocyst is comparable
to the blastula of the reptile or bird at the completion of blastodermic overgrowth, but with

the yolk removed (Fig. 35 *C*, *D*). The cavity of the blastocyst is not a simple blastocœle, like that of Amphioxus and amphibians (*A*, *B*), but a blastocœle combined with a yolkless yolk-cavity. The trophoblast represents a precocious development of external cells which, in the bird and reptile, gradually envelop the yolk. The more rapid completion of a trophoblastic capsule in true mammals is a necessary preparation for the early association of the embryo-complex with the tissue of the maternal uterus; having discarded yolk as a source

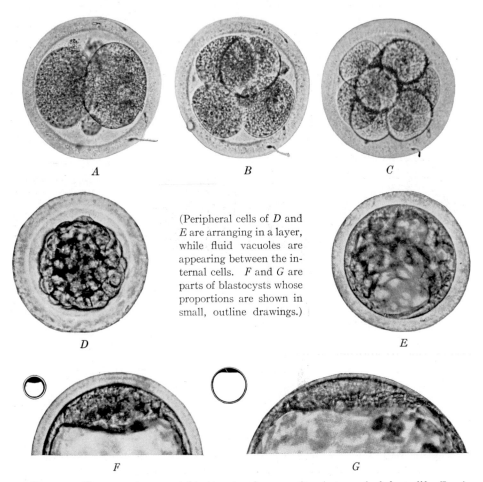

(Peripheral cells of *D* and *E* are arranging in a layer, while fluid vacuoles are appearing between the internal cells. *F* and *G* are parts of blastocysts whose proportions are shown in small, outline drawings.)

FIG. 34.—Cleavage stages and blastocysts of mammals, photographed from life (Lewis, Hartman and Gregory). × 225. *A–C*, Two-, four- and eight-celled stages in the monkey, 30 to 50 hours after ovulation. *D–G*, Morulæ and blastocysts in the rabbit, 45 to 80 hours after ovulation.

of nutriment, the mammalian embryo must establish prompt relations (through its trophoblast) with the mother. In reptiles and birds the embryo-formative region is a superficial blastoderm, while in true mammals its equivalent is the inner cell mass. The higher mammalian ovum, although almost devoid of yolk, thus develops into a 'blastula' fundamentally resembling the type attained by the yolk-laden eggs of reptiles and birds. That this similarity is real and has an evolutionary significance is attested by the occurrence of typical discoidal cleavage and a discoblastula in the highly telolecithal eggs of present-day monotreme mammals.

Human Cleavage.—Stages of cleavage are unknown except for the division of the artificially fertilized and cultured human ovum which has been carried to the three-cell stage.[1] In the monkey and the low primate, Tarsius, cleavage groups, morula and blastocyst have all been studied in detail.[2, 3] Compared with most mammals (*e.g.*, the rabbit, whose blastocyst is 4.5 mm. long when attaching to the uterus) the human blastocyst enlarges slowly. It comes to lie wholly within the uterine wall and at the time of penetration is not much larger than the original egg.

GASTRULATION

Gastrulation is the process by which the three germ layers come to occupy their characteristic positions in the embryo. The relation of these

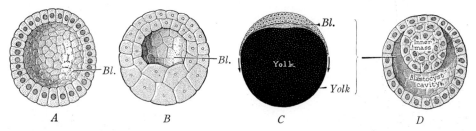

A   *B*   *C*   *D*

Fig. 35.—Blastula types among chordates, shown as hemisections. *A*, Amphioxus; *B*, amphibians; *C*, reptiles and birds; *D*, mammals. *A* and *B* are fundamentally comparable; *C* is a discoblastula; *D* is a modification of *C*, with loss of yolk. *Bl.*, Blastocœle. Arrows on *C* indicate the expanding blastoderm.

layers, one to another, is indicated by their names: *ectoderm* (outer skin); *mesoderm* (middle skin); and *entoderm* (inner skin).

The blastula possesses polarity and bilateral symmetry. It contains cell areas which, in normal development, become the germ layers and give rise to different parts of the embryo. Maps of these prospective regions have been made by staining trial areas on living blastulæ with nontoxic dyes and then discovering what they become. In this way the locations of the prospective ectoderm, mesoderm and entoderm have been mapped, as well as such prospective organs as the neural plate and notochord.

The events of gastrulation have been clarified by the simultaneous staining of these presumptive regions with dyes of different colors and then following their movements to their later positions. These studies prove the essential similarity of gastrulation in the various chordate groups and have changed certain time-honored interpretations. The chief difference encountered among vertebrates is the way in which entoderm becomes segregated; these variations are related to the different physical forms that the blastula assumes.

Amphioxus.—Since the animal pole of the blastula corresponds roughly to the front end of the future embryo, Figure 36 is drawn with the main axis horizontal. Stages *A* and *B* show a late blastula mapped with the cell-territories whose normal fates can be foretold.[4] About the animal and vegetal poles are the future *ectoderm* and *entoderm*, respectively. In between is a girdling zone which is subdivided into prospective *mesoderm, notochord* and *neural plate.* Gastrulation begins about five and one-half hours after fertilization when the blastula contains some 500 cells. An inbuckling (*i.e., invagination*) of the vegetal cells is followed by an inrolling (*i.e., involution*) of cells around the margin of the double-walled cup thus being

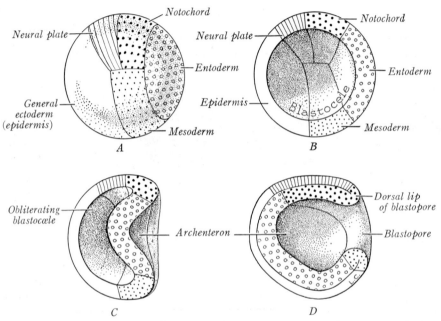

FIG. 36.—Stereograms of gastrulation in Amphioxus. × 350. *A*, Blastula, with areas indicated whose normal fates are known. *B*, Hemisection of *A*. *C, D*, Early and later gastrulæ, hemisected, during invagination and involution.

formed (*C*). The continuation of these movements carries entoderm, mesoderm and notochord to the interior and obliterates the original blastula cavity (*D*). The new, central cavity is the provisional gut or *archenteron*, and its mouth is the *blastopore*. At this period the young embryo is termed a *gastrula* (*i.e.*, little stomach).

Involution took place around the circular margin, or lip, of the blastopore. Backward growth of this lip-region next elongates the cup and unequal growth elevates the blastopore (Fig. 36 *D*). The roof of the archenteron consists of a median strip of notochordal cells, flanked on each side by a strip of mesodermal cells. The sides and floor of the cavity are bounded by entoderm. The notochord soon cuts off as a solid, cellular rod. The mesodermal strips likewise fold off and become a middle layer on each side of the notochord. The entoderm then closes in the dorsal defect caused by the loss of the notochord and mesoderm and thus produces the definitive, tubular *gut*. The cells left on the outside of the gastrula are ectoderm; dorsally they constitute the *neural plate* in contrast to the general covering of the embryo which will become *epidermis*.

The mechanics of invagination is not well understood. Involution and other shiftings of cell territories in chordates result from active mass movements of the cells themselves; although cell division continues during gastrulation, it is not the prime factor responsible for these mass migrations.

An earlier concept of the germ layers can be revised somewhat.[5] Originally it was believed that the blastula is wholly ectodermal, that part of it becomes the entodermal lining of a then two-layered embryo, and that one or the other of these layers next gives rise to mesoderm and so produces a three-layered embryo. As logical as this interpretation once seemed (and to this concept Amphioxus apparently lent support, because for a time the

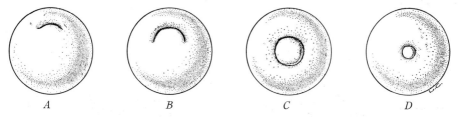

FIG. 37.—Gastrulation in a tailed amphibian, viewed from the vegetal pole. × 10. Successive stages illustrate the early lip of the blastopore (*A*), its completion (*B, C*) and its overgrowth of the yolk-rich cells (*B–D*).

mesoderm is a part of the primitive inner layer of the gastrula) it is no longer tenable. There is no one-layered or two-layered stage in the sense implied. All three germ-layer territories exist potentially in the blastula before gastrulation begins. These regions are then moved to their later positions and superposed as distinct layers through the devices of gastrulation.

Amphibians.—Simple invagination of the vegetal hemisphere, as in Amphioxus, is not mechanically possible and gastrulation is accomplished largely by involution. The first indication of gastrulation is a local groove well below the equator of the blastula (Fig. 37 *A*). This deepening groove is covered by a lip-like fold of the blastula wall. The pocket itself marks the beginning of an *archenteron;* the mouth of the pocket is the *blastopore* and the margin of the fold is the dorsal lip of the blastopore. The early, short groove is extended progressively into a crescent, then a horseshoe (*B*), and finally a circle (*C*). At the sides are the so-called lateral lips of the blastopore and below is the ventral lip. Involution takes place at all points along this circular blastoporic lip, but chiefly at its dorsal portion. Cells of the blastula wall move downward along meridians, pass around the lip of the fold in an undertucking manner, and continue to migrate as an internal layer. In the end a broad, girdling zone of the vegetal hemisphere involutes around the margin of the blastopore and into the interior. To compensate for this loss, the cells of the animal hemisphere spread and overgrow the vegetal hemisphere (*C, D*). In this way the entire surface becomes clothed with ectoderm. This process of expansion is often called *epiboly*.

The amphibian blastula has been well mapped for prospective organ-forming regions, some of which are shown in Figure 38.[6] An important landmark is the sinuous line that demarcates the involuting material (prospective *entoderm* and *mesoderm*) from the prospective *ectoderm* which does not involute (*A*). The chorda-mesoderm material forms a girdling band that encircles the yolk field (*B*). It should be noted that the areas that will become axial organs (like the neural plate, notochord and somites)

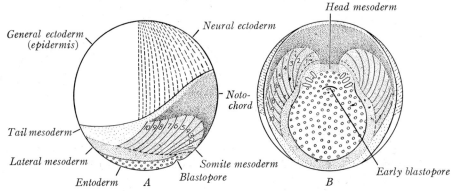

Fig. 38.—Maps of prospective parts of embryos of tailed amphibians at the beginning of gastrulation (after Vogt). *A*, Side view; *B*, view from vegetal pole.

have their greatest extent at this period in a direction opposite to their ultimate cranio-caudal (roughly, pole to pole) orientation.

When *involution* begins at the dorsal lip of the blastopore, the first cells turned in are those of the future entoderm that lie just above the lip (Fig. 38 *B*). Next to follow is head mesoderm and then notochordal material near the midplane. As the blastopore extends and assumes the shape of a crescent, horseshoe and circle, the more lateral notochordal material and that of the somites and unsegmented mesoderm will be tucked in progressively. During these movements toward the interior, a dye-marked circular area becomes elongate, and this expansion (in a longitudinal direction) continues after involution takes place. Hence *elongation*, which affects practically all parts of the gastrula during gastrulation, is a second basic movement of gastrulation. As the various areas pass around the blastoporic lips, their more lateral parts (*e.g.*, the lateral wings of the notochordal area) move toward more median positions in the interior. This mesial *convergence* of more lateral areas, including parts like the neural area that remain on the outside, toward more median locations is the third basic movement of gastrulation. These three types of movement characterize gastrulation in all chordates.

The internal changes and relations during gastrulation can be followed in Figure 39. Stages *A–C* show the progressive enlargement of the archen-

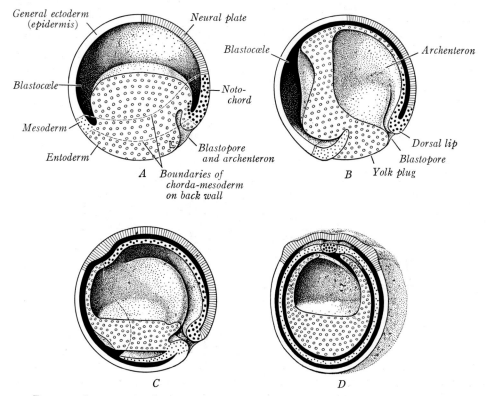

FIG. 39.—Stereograms of gastrulation in tailed amphibians (after Hamburger 'Manual of Experimental Embryology,' University of Chicago Press). *A–C*, Early to late stages, showing the movements of areas differentially marked on the cut surfaces of longitudinal hemisections. *D*, Caudal half of stage *C*, shown by a transverse hemisection.

teron and the corresponding obliteration of the blastocœle, the withdrawal of the yolk to the interior and its changing position, and the internal spread of the chorda-mesoderm. Stage D is a model, in transverse section, of the caudal half of stage *C* (*i.e.*, a direction toward the blastopore is caudad). Gastrulation ends with the general ectoderm (future *epidermis*) and *neural plate* left on the outside; the *notochord*, in a median dorsal location, is flanked by wing-like plates of *mesoderm;* lining the archenteron in front and on the sides is involuted *entoderm;* the floor of the archenteron is the main mass of large-celled entoderm which does not involute but merely elevates into the interior; the roof of the archenteron is still incomplete at this period, but growth and fusion of the dorsolateral walls will soon cover in this gap. Gastrulation in amphibians differs from that in Amphioxus in two important respects: (1) invagination plays no significant rôle; (2) the notochord and mesoderm are not continuous with the entoderm to produce a temporary, composite internal layer.

Birds.—The inert yolk mass is proportionately so enormous that it cannot participate, even passively, in gastrulation. For this reason the events of gastrulation are confined to the germinal disc which contains the cells of all three future germ layers. The process, as a whole, takes place in two stages: (1) first the *entoderm* separates from the rest of the disc: (2) then the cells of the *chorda-mesoderm* move into position between the entoderm and the residual outer layer which henceforth is *ectoderm*.

It is now generally agreed that cells located at the lower surface of the germinal disc of the blastula split away to produce the entodermal

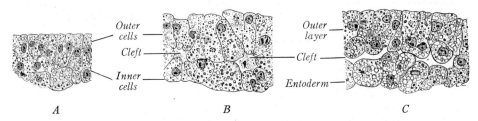

FIG. 40.—Entoderm formation in the chick, shown by vertical sections through the germinal disc (after Peter). × 340. *A*, Early segregation of the future entoderm. *B*, *C*, Later stages of actual separation into two layers.

layer (Fig. 40).[7] A forward movement of the entoderm helps to complete a central, deficient area. Later contributions to the entoderm from cells migrating from the outer layer directly[8] and by way of the primitive streak[9] (see beyond) have also been described. A full understanding of these matters awaits further studies.

The separation of the entoderm from the rest of the germinal disc makes it possible to interpret the resulting stage as a tardy blastula which, though flat, is comparable to those of lower forms.[10] The upper cellular plate would then correspond to the animal hemisphere of a typical blastula, the entoderm to the vegetal hemisphere, while the newly created cleft between these layers would be the blastocœle. Under this interpretation the noncellular mass of yolk has no counterpart in Amphioxus or amphibians and is a new auxiliary feature. Moreover, the original cleft produced during cleavage, now located between the entoderm and the yolk, would not be a true blastocœle; neither is it an archenteron in the ordinary sense, since it is not an invagination cavity.

A surface map of the blastoderm, after entodermal delamination has occurred, is shown as Figure 41 *A*. The relative positions and shapes of

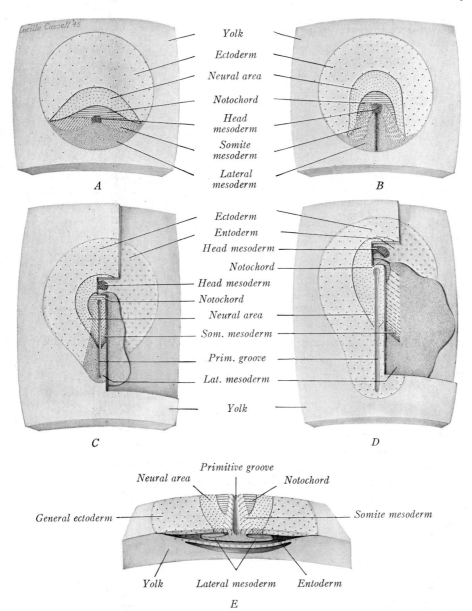

Fig. 41.—Gastrulation movements in the chick (largely after Pasteels). *A*, Map of prospective parts, differentially marked on the surface of an early blastoderm. *B*, Formation of the early primitive streak. *C, D*, Passage of chorda-mesoderm to a middle level. *E*, Transection through middle of streak, stage *C*.

the areas occupied by prospective ectoderm (future epidermis and neural plate), notochord and mesoderm, are strikingly similar to those of the amphibian blastula (*cf.* Fig. 38). The only real difference is in the shapes

5

of the areas containing lateral mesoderm, and this difference naturally results from the absence of a surface entodermal field in the bird. The mass movements which take place during gastrulation are also of the same nature as those described for the amphibian: convergence; involution; and elongation.[11] All of the areas swing, or converge, toward the midline (Fig.

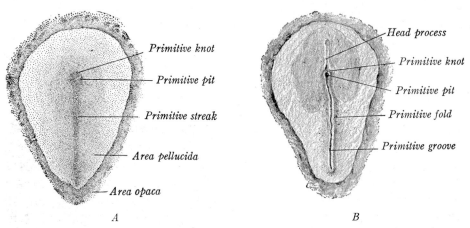

A

B

FIG. 42.—Blastoderms of the chick, in surface view. × 16. A, Stage of the primitive streak; B, stage of the head process.

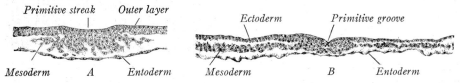

FIG. 43.—Involution and spread of mesoderm in the chick, shown in transverse sections through the primitive streak. × 165. A, Early streak; B, later streak.

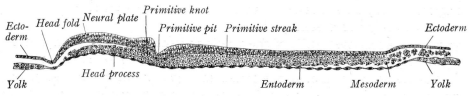

FIG. 44.—Head process and primitive streak of the chick embryo, shown in longitudinal section. × 100.

41 B); the chorda-mesoderm involutes at the midline and then spreads as a middle layer (C–E); after these shifts are completed there is considerable elongation of all areas.

Involution of the chorda-mesoderm takes place through a thickened axial band in the upper layer known as the *primitive streak*. This linear massing of cells is a result of the convergence of mesoderm from each side toward the midline (Fig. 41 *B*). Another result of this convergence is a change of shape of the several surface areas; their lateral halves swing toward the midline and thus become roughly parallel. The future *lateral mesoderm* lies nearest the primitive streak and is the tissue that gave it origin. It continues to migrate and approach the primitive streak from each side; as it arrives at the midline its cells turn downward through the streak and then diverge, right and left, as they spread laterad between the surface layer and the entoderm (*C, E*). A small area of prospective *head mesoderm* next turns in but, on account of its previous position ahead of the primitive streak, it advances in a forward (anterior) direction (*B–D*). The prospective *notochord* and the paired areas of *somite-mesoderm* follow

(*C, D*). At the completion of gastrulation, the residual outer layer is definitive *ectoderm*. The originally crescentic area representing the *neural plate* converges to become a tear-shaped field within the general ectoderm (*A–D*).

The primitive streak is a stretched and seam-like blastopore through which the involution of chorda-mesoderm occurs. The fact that it has no open mouth and may not be related to the segregation of entoderm does not alter the homology. The primitive streak acquires a knob at its forward end (Fig. 42 *A*); this is the *primitive knot* (of Hensen) which is said to be originally a separate mass.[12] A shallow *primitive groove* presently courses

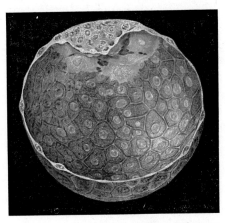

Fig. 45.—Blastocyst of the monkey at nine days, hemisected (Streeter). × 200. Entodermal cells have appeared at the under surface of its inner cell mass, and similar cells occur (by spreading?) on the nearby wall of the blastocyst.

lengthwise along the middle of the streak and ends close to the knot in the *primitive pit* (*B*). This groove results from the active involution of cells. Transverse sections through the streak show the involuting and spreading mesoderm (Fig. 43). A longitudinal section demonstrates the relation of the notochord (also at this period called the *head process*) to the primitive knot and the latter to the primitive streak (Fig. 44). While gastrulation is going on, the originally circular blastoderm elongates and acquires a pear-shaped outline (Fig. 42 *B*).

Mammals.—As in birds, gastrulation occurs in two stages. The first phase takes place when certain cells appear on the under surface of the inner cell mass and arrange themselves into a definite sheet, the *entoderm* (Figs. 45 and 46 *A*). In monotremes[13] and marsupials[14] these cells are smaller and darker ameboid elements which move out of a common layer to a deeper position. In placental mammals the entodermal cells detach from the inner cell mass. This has been called delamination, but the process may involve a strict segregation in which cells specializing toward entodermal fates are sorted out from others that are prospective ectodermal, mesodermal and trophoblastic elements.[15]   In most mammals the entoderm

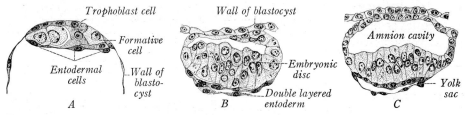

Trophoblast cell   *Wall of blastocyst*

Formative cell

Amnion cavity

Entodermal cells   *Wall of blastocyst*

Embryonic disc

Double layered entoderm

Embryonic disc

Yolk sac

A   *B*   *C*

FIG. 46.—Entoderm formation in the monkey (after Streeter and Heuser.) *A*, At eight days (× 250); *B*, at eleven days (× 250); *C*, at twelve days (× 200).

spreads rapidly and lines the blastocyst as a relatively large sac (Fig. 53 *A*). In primates there is a temporary structure which might be interpreted as a similar, large yolk sac (Fig. 61), yet this homology is both affirmed and denied by those who have studied it most.[15]   In any event, only the ento-

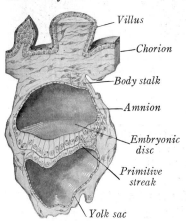

Villus

Chorion

Body stalk

Amnion

Embryonic disc

Primitive streak

Yolk sac

FIG. 47.—Reconstruction of the right half of a human embryo of fourteen days. × 105.

dermal cells under the inner cell mass persist, and these apparently fashion themselves into a smaller, definitive yolk sac (Figs. 46 *B*, *C* and 47).

The remaining cells of the inner cell mass become a plate containing the progenitors of future ectodermal and mesodermal cells (Fig. 46 *B*, *C*). Directly beneath is the layer of entoderm that serves as a roof to the yolk sac. These two layers make up the earliest *embryonic disc*, or blastoderm (Fig. 47). The second phase of gastrulation is concerned with the segregation of the mesoderm and notochord as definite parts, located at a middle level.

Technical difficulties have not permitted the mammalian blastoderm to be marked with dyes and mapped. Yet there is reason to suspect that the areas of presumptive epidermis, neural plate, mesoderm and notochord, and the movements and involution of mesoderm, are similar to those which have been determined for the chick (*cf.* Fig. 41).

A typical primitive streak appears caudally on the upper surface of the embryonic disc (Fig. 48 *A*). The spread of *mesoderm* through the primitive streak is illustrated in section by Fig. 48 *B* and in surface view by Fig. 49 *A–D*. The appearance of the *primitive knot* and the growth of the *notochord* (or head process) from it are indicated in Fig. 49 *D, E*. At the conclusion of these movements to a middle level, the residual upper layer

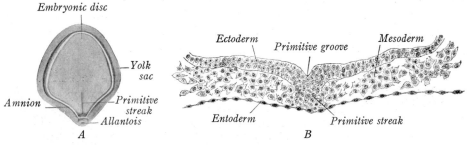

FIG. 48.—Human embryo of sixteen days (after Streeter). *A*, Dorsal view of the embryonic disc (× 25). *B*, Transverse section through the primitive streak (× 185).

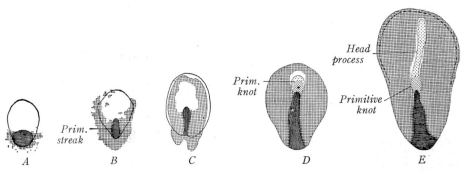

FIG. 49.—Embryonic discs of the pig, mapped to show the spread of mesoderm (cross hatched) and the growth of the primitive streak and head process (Streeter). × 25.

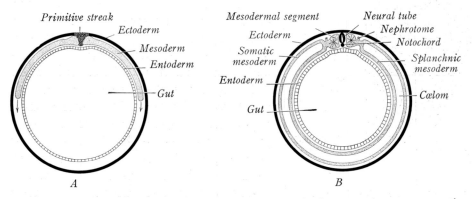

FIG. 50.—Spread and differentiation of the mesoderm, shown in diagrammatic transverse sections of a mammalian embryo at different periods (after Prentiss).

of the embryonic disc is general ectoderm (prospective *epidermis*) and the material of the future *neural plate*.

In most mammals the mesoderm grows rapidly and extends beyond the region of the embryonic disc. Continuing to expand around the wall of the blastocyst, it fills in the space between the trophoblast (usually rated as ectoderm) and the temporarily large sac of entoderm until its peripheral margins meet and fuse (Fig. 50 *A*). This peripheral tissue is *extra-embryonic mesoderm*, which will clothe such auxiliary structures as chorion, amnion, body stalk and yolk sac; it takes no part in forming the embryo proper. In primates, extra-embryonic mesoderm appears before the mesoderm of the embryo becomes recognizable as such. It arises as cells that separate away from the trophoblast of the original blastocyst wall (Fig. 61), and thus has a separate origin from the mesoderm of the embryo itself.[16]

Human Gastrulation.—The youngest human embryo known is a blastocyst in which a layer of entodermal cells has just become segregated from the inner cell mass (Fig. 60).[17] At this stage a cleft is separating a layer of cells, which make up the auxiliary membrane known as the amnion, from the rest of the inner cell mass. This leaves a cellular plate, beneath the cleft, which contains the formative cells that will give rise to the definitive ectoderm and mesoderm of the embryo (Fig. 47). The stages that follow (primitive streak; head process) are well known (Fig. 48). During this period the cells of the mesoderm and notochord move to their characteristic positions and the three primary germ layers are thereby established.

EARLY DEVELOPMENT COMPARED IN DIFFERENT VERTEBRATE TYPES

Animal Type	Type of Egg	Cleavage	Blastula	Blastula Cavity	Method of Gastrulation	Comment on Gastrulation
Amphioxus	Isolecithal (little yolk).	Total; nearly equal.	Sphere; wall a single layer.	Spherical and large.	Invagination; involution via blastopore.	Early inner layer, a composite.
Amphibians	Telolecithal (moderate yolk).	Total; unequal.	Sphere; wall layered and unequal.	Spherical and small; eccentric.	Involution via blastopore.	Germ layers separate from start.
Birds	Telolecithal (massive yolk).	Partial; discoidal.	Cell-disc, on massive yolk.	Shallow; overlies yolk?	Delamination; involution via primitive streak.	Occurs in two stages.
Mammals (except lowest)	Isolecithal (little yolk).	Total; nearly equal.	Blastocyst, with inner cell mass.	Merged with blastocyst cavity.	Delamination; involution via primitive streak	Occurs in two stages.

DERIVATIVES OF THE GERM LAYERS

Since the ectoderm covers the body it is primarily protective, but it also gives origin to the nervous system and sense organs. The entoderm, on the other hand, lines the primitive digestive canal and has nutritive relations; later it also becomes respiratory. The mesoderm, occupying an intermediate position, naturally is related to skeletal support, muscular movement, circulation, excretion and reproduction.

It was formerly believed that the germ layers are rigidly specific in their formative potentialities, but this concept has undergone some revision in so far as vertebrates are concerned. Experiments prove that when a portion of one germ layer is transplanted, at an early stage, into another layer it takes part in the specific organ development that is characteristic of its new site. Hence the germ layers possess a greater versatility than they ordinarily show. In normal development, however, these layers serve as assembly grounds out of which the constituent parts of the embryo emerge in a definite and rigid program of origins.

The subjoined table lists the derivatives of the three germ layers as they arise in normal development.

THE GERM-LAYER ORIGIN OF HUMAN TISSUES

Ectoderm	Mesoderm	Entoderm
1. Epidermis, including: Cutaneous glands. Hair; nails; lens. 2. Epithelium of: Sense organs. Nasal cavity; sinuses. Mouth, including: Oral glands; enamel. Anal canal. 3. Nervous tissue, including: Hypophysis. Chromaffin tissue.	1. Muscle (all types). 2. Connective tissue; cartilage; bone; notochord. 3. Blood; bone marrow. 4. Lymphoid tissue. Epithelium of: 5. Blood vessels; lymphatics. 6. Body cavities. 7. Kidney; ureter. 8. Gonads; genital ducts. 9. Suprarenal cortex. 10. Joint cavities, etc.	Epithelium of: 1. Pharynx, including: Auditory tube, etc. Tonsils; thyroid. Parathyroids; thymus. 2. Larynx; trachea; lungs. 3. Digestive tube, including: Associated glands. 4. Bladder (trigone?) 5. Vagina (all?); vestibule. 6. Urethra, including: Associated glands.

REFERENCES CITED

1. Rock, J. and Menkin, M. F. 1944. Science, 100, 105–107.
2. Lewis, W. H., Heuser, C. H., et al. 1941. Carnegie Contrib. Embryol., 29, Nos. 180, 181, 7–55.
3. Hubrecht, A. A. W. 1902. Verhandl. kön. Akad. v. Wetensch. te Amsterdam, 8, Sect. 2, No. 6, 1–113.
4. Conklin, E. G. 1932. Jour. Morph., 54, 69–151.
5. Oppenheimer, J. M. 1940. Quart. Rev. Biol., 15, 1–27.
6. Vogt, W. 1929. Arch. f. Entwickl.-mech. d. Organ., 120, 384–706.
7. Peter, K. 1941. Ergeb. d. Anat. u. Entwickl., 33, 285–369.

8. Pasteels, J. 1940. Biol. Rev., **15,** 59–106.
9. Hunt, T. E. 1937. Anat. Rec., **68,** 449–460.
10. Pasteels, J. 1945. Anat. Rec., **93,** 5–21.
11. Pasteels, J. 1937. Arch. de Biol., **48,** 381–488.
12. Spratt, N. T. 1942. Jour. Exp. Zoöl., **89,** 69–101.
13. Flynn, T. T. and Hill, J. P. 1942. Proc. Zoöl. Soc. London (Ser. A), **111,** 233–253.
14. Hill, J. P. 1910. Quart. Jour. Micr. Sci., **56,** 1–134.
15. Heuser, C. H. and Streeter, G. L. 1941. Carnegie Contrib. Embryol., **29,** No. 181, 15–55.
16. Hertig, A. T. 1935. Carnegie Contrib. Embryol., **25,** No. 146, 37–82.
17. Hertig, A. T. and Rock, J. 1945. Carnegie Contrib. Embryol., **31,** No. 200, 65–84.

CHAPTER V

THE FETAL MEMBRANES OF VERTEBRATES

Before continuing with the description of the embryo proper it is desirable to examine the conditions under which vertebrate embryos develop and the ways in which they cope with the problems of protection, food and oxygen supply, and the elimination of wastes.

The eggs of fishes, amphibians, reptiles, birds and monotreme mammals are laid, whereupon they undergo development at a suitable temperature in water, earth or air. It is quite different with marsupial and placental mammals, since the embryos of these animals develop within the uterus of the mother. Such wide environmental differences, faced by vertebrate embryos, are correlated with considerable diversity in both the number and nature of their so-called fetal membranes. These are auxiliary organs which have arisen for the protection of the embryo and especially to provide for its nutrition, respiration and excretion until the time arrives when independent existence can be safely attempted.

The embryos of fishes and amphibians develop rapidly to free-swimming larval stages. Because of this precocity they need no auxiliary organs other than a supply of yolk sufficient to last until independent foraging can be carried on. In amphibians and some fishes the yolk is contained in large cells which make up the thick floor of the gut. In sharks and bony fishes the gut- and body wall come to enclose a bulging yolk mass. The lack of protection to the individual embryo is offset by the production of great numbers of embryos, so that survival over accidents and enemies is adequate.

Reptiles, birds and mammals are in a relatively advanced state of development at hatching or birth. Several auxiliary organs are produced which are of use during the prenatal period alone. Especially in higher mammals has the abandonment of yolk for a physiological dependence on the mother led to the greatest elaboration of these structures. The full set of fetal membranes includes the *yolk sac, amnion, chorion, allantois, umbilical cord* and *placenta*. Yet the function of no one of these organs is fixed unalterably; only the amnion is relatively stable. The embryos of this group are produced in small numbers and gain protection by such means as a heavy shell, parental incubation and development within the body of the mother.

REPTILES AND BIRDS

The history of the fetal membranes is correlated with the presence of an enormous mass of yolk and an embryonic life spent within a shell. Although the original blastoderm is a small disc, it spreads by peripheral growth (Fig. 52 B) and eventually covers the entire surface of the egg. But only the most central region is directly concerned with embryo formation. All the remainder of the blastoderm is *extra-embryonic*, and it is this portion that furnishes most of the fetal membranes. The extra-embryonic blastoderm consists of *somatopleure* (ectoderm and somatic mesoderm) and *splanchnopleure* (entoderm and splanchnic mesoderm), separated by a space which is *extra-embryonic cœlom* (*cf.* Fig. 50 B).

The Yolk Sac.—As the embryo enlarges, its circular connection with the extra-embryonic blastoderm grows at a slower rate. This produces a 'constriction' of the splanchnopleure where it joins the rapidly elongating gut. The region of constriction soon lengthens into a tubular *yolk stalk*, whereas the remainder of the extra-embryonic splanchnopleure encloses the massive yolk as the *yolk sac* (Fig. 51). Vitelline blood vessels, arising in the splanchnic mesoderm, ramify on the surface of the yolk sac, and through them absorbed yolk substance is conveyed to the chick during the incubation period (Fig. 52 B). Shortly before hatching, the shriveled yolk sac slips through the navel into the belly cavity.

The Amnion and Chorion.—These membranes are concentric sacs which arise by folding of the extra-embryonic somatopleure. The double-layered somatopleure is first thrown up into two crescentic folds. The earliest fold to appear is located just in front of the embryo; later, a second fold arises just behind the embryo (Fig. 51 A). These two folds advance like two hoods drawn over the head and the caudal region, respectively (B). When they meet, the completed circular fold closes in from all sides over the embryo, as would a bag pursed by draw-strings. The concluding step is the fusion of the several layers located at the margin of the fold (C). The result is the production of two separate, compound membranes (D).

The inner membrane is the *amnion*. It is lined with ectoderm and covered externally with somatic mesoderm. As the body of the embryo takes form, the amnion is continuous with the belly wall at the umbilicus. The amnion is a thin, transparent sac which soon fills with a fluid transudate. Within this amniotic fluid the embryo is suspended, and thus immersed and buoyed up it avoids drying, mechanical injuries and deforming adhesions. At the same time the early, soft embryo is able to maintain its shape free from distortion, to develop and grow unimpeded, and to change its position. The amnion lacks blood vessels, but muscle fibers differentiate in its mesodermal layer and produce rhythmic contractions which agitate the embryo gently and perhaps help prevent adhesions.

The outer sac of somatopleure is the *chorion* (sometimes called the *serosa*), whose component layers are in reverse order to those of the amnion. That is, ectoderm is the covering and mesoderm the lining layer. The chorion lies next the shell, encloses both the embryo and all its other fetal membranes, and is separated from them by the extra-embryonic cœlom. The functions of the chorion can best be explained in connection with the allantois with whose later history it is so closely associated.

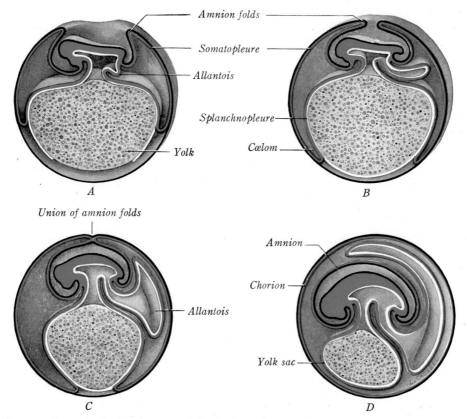

FIG. 51.—Stages in the development of the fetal membranes of the chick. The stereograms are sagittal hemisections. Ectoderm, black; mesoderm, red; entoderm, white.

The Allantois.—This accessory organ was primarily evolved by reptiles and birds as a temporary sac for urinary storage. It arises as an outpouching of the ventral floor of the gut, near its hind end (Fig. 52). Since the gut wall is splanchnopleure, this diverticulum necessarily consists of the same layers (entoderm and splanchnic mesoderm) as it pushes outward into the extra-embryonic cœlom. There it forms a dilatation which develops rapidly into a large *allantoic sac*, connected to the hind-gut by the narrower *allantoic stalk* (Fig. 51 A–C). The expanding sac flattens and spreads throughout the extra-embryonic cœlom (*D*) until, like the chorion, it finally lines the entire shell. Fusion of the outer wall of the allantoic sac with the overlying chorion produces a functionally common membrane in contact with the porous shell. The blood vessels ramifying in the combined meso-dermal layer of these two membranes are situated favorably to serve as intermediaries in gaseous interchanges; accordingly, the allantois becomes the functional 'lung' of the embryo through which oxygen is delivered to the blood and carbon dioxide is extracted from it. The allantoic cavity not only continues to act in its primitive capacity as a reservoir for the excreta of the kidneys, but part of its wall assists also in the absorption of albumen. Shortly before hatching, the allantois dries up, detaches and follows the yolk sac into the belly cavity.

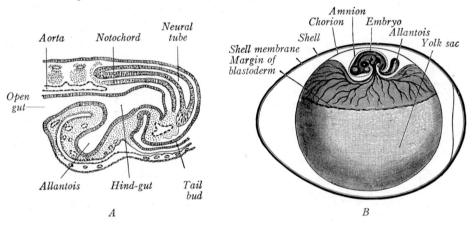

FIG. 52.—Fetal membranes of the chick. *A*, Origin of the allantois, shown in a sagittal section, at three days, through the caudal end of the body (× 30). *B*, Relations of the embryo and its membranes, at five days (after Marshall; × 1).

MAMMALS

Since the mammalian embryo depends on the mother for food and oxygen and must provide for the elimination of its wastes, the fetal membranes begin to develop even while the uterine relation is being established. There is considerable variety in the size, relations and functional rôle of each of these membranes.[1, 2] Some even show differences in the manner of origin. Only the monotremes, whose conditions of development are similar, follow the exact pattern established by reptiles and birds.

The Yolk Sac.—Marsupial and placental mammals lack an actual yolk mass, yet a typical, stalked *yolk sac* appears and produces a complete vitelline circulation in quite young embryos. The early history and relations of this organ vary. In the majority of mammals the entoderm spreads just beneath the trophoblastic capsule and for a time lines it as a relatively large sac (Fig. 50 *A*); when the extra-embryonic mesoderm and cœlom appear between the two, the entoderm becomes clothed with the splanchnic mesodermal layer (B). After a time the growth of the yolk sac slows, and it then reduces in relative size as the allantois comes into prominence. In sharp contrast, the definitive yolk sac of primates is small from the first and remains a comparatively diminutive vesicle within the large chorionic sac (Figs. 47 and 79).

The splanchnic mesoderm, surfacing the yolk sac, is the layer that bears the vitelline blood vessels. Many embryos with a highly developed yolk sac establish an intimate association with the uterus by means of a continuous nutritive path which is brought into existence through the union of the yolk sac and chorion. In this way there is formed a *yolk-sac placenta*, which, however, is usually transitory.

The Amnion and Chorion.—Many mammals produce an amnion by folding, but the details of the process vary. In some (rabbit; carnivores) the early trophoblast overlying the embryonic disc disappears. The ex-

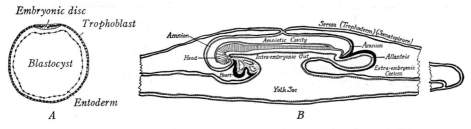

FIG. 53.—Fetal membranes of pig embryos, shown in sagittal section. *A*, Blastocyst, at eight days (× 80). *B*, Diagram, at eighteen-somite stage (Patten; × 8); most of the long chorionic (or serosal) sac has been omitted.

posed disc is then a plaque of special formative cells inset into a spheroidal sac of trophoblast (Fig. 53 *A*). Soon the mesoderm appears and its somatic layer combines with the ectodermal trophoblast to produce the extra-embryonic somatopleure. The amnion presently arises by the simple folding of this somatopleure, as in reptiles and birds (B). Also as in these animals, the amnion is important chiefly as a container of the buoyant amniotic fluid. The *chorion* is merely the rest of the original trophoblastic capsule, now underlaid with extra-embryonic somatic mesoderm; the region above the embryo (A) is closed in by the outer layer of the amnion fold (B). The chorion often enlarges rapidly; in the pig it reaches the astonishing length of one meter by the time the embryo is at the stage of the primitive streak. The chorion has a diverse history, but in all mammals above marsupials it becomes functionally important by differentiating *chorionic villi* and entering into the composition of a placenta (Fig. 55).

Certain other mammals (guinea pig; hedgehog; anthropoids) acquire an *amnion* quite simply and at a very early stage. The primitive amnion cavity arises as a cleft that separates the inner cell mass into two parts: one is the prospective embryo; the other is nonembryonic, auxiliary tissue (Fig. 54). Thus the floor of the enclosed space is the main plate of the embryonic disc; the sides and roof comprise the thinner 'ectoderm' of the membranous amnion. When soon a layer of somatic mesoderm covers this ectodermal dome of the early amnion (Fig. 64 A, B) the structural outcome is identical with the type of amnion derived by folding. The *chorion* of this group of animals is merely a later stage of the original trophoblastic capsule (subsidiary 'ectoderm') to which a lining of somatic mesoderm has been added (*A*).

Still other mammals (pig; deer; rat) combine the two methods of amnion formation already described. The inner cell mass first hollows and then its roof ruptures; after this the definitive amnion develops by folding.

The Allantois. — Many mammals, like reptiles and birds, produce a prominent *allantois* by the sacculation of gut-splanchnopleure into the

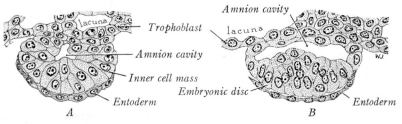

FIG. 54.—Amnion formation in the monkey, shown in sections (after Heuser and Streeter). × 330. *A*, At ten days; *B*, at eleven days.

extra-embryonic cœlom (Figs. 53 *B* and 55 *A*). For example, in carnivores and ungulates it becomes very large, lines the chorionic sac and fuses with it (Figs. 55 *B* and 57 *A*); a goat embryo of two inches has an allantois two feet long. The further history of such conspicuous bladders is a part of the story of the placenta, and will be discussed under that heading. Here it need only be mentioned that the urinary wastes actually collect in the allantoic sac and are not excreted through the placenta.

By contrast, edentates, rodents and primates tend to have a vestigial allantois. In anthropoids it is a tiny, entodermal tube which pushes into the body stalk even before the hind-gut develops. The *body stalk* is a bridge of mesoderm which from a very early period connects embryo to chorion in seeming anticipation of the arrival of the tubular component (Fig. 64 *B–D*). Blood vessels accompany the allantois and extend to the chorion which becomes vascularized through their branches. The entodermal diverticulum itself is functionless and soon regresses, but the blood vessels persist. They become the important umbilical arteries and veins which connect the fetus with a more efficient type of placenta than those that combine a typical allantois with the chorion.

The Placenta.—The marsupials, after an extremely brief gestation period, give birth to immature young. It is easy to understand, therefore, why their chorion as a whole never advances beyond a smooth membrane in close apposition with the vascular uterine lining. The yolk sac of marsupials is large and in some forms it unites with the chorion, apparently to serve as a transitory *yolk-sac placenta*. Nevertheless, marsupials are classed as aplacental mammals.

In all higher mammals (placentalia) the chorion bears vascular villi (Fig. 55 *B*), and these engage the uterine mucosa in a more or less intimate relation which persists throughout pregnancy. Such a functional association

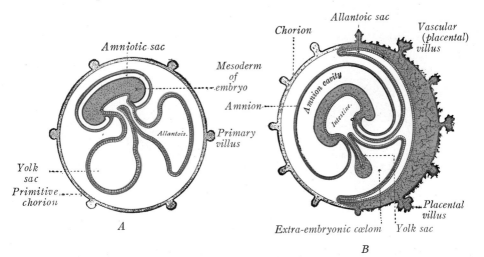

FIG. 55.—Diagrams of the fetal membranes of most mammals, in sagittal section (Heisler, after Roule). *A*, Early stage, with relations much as in the chick. *B*, Later stage, with the fetal basis of an allantoic placenta. Ectoderm, black; mesoderm, red; entoderm, green.

of the fetal chorion (including usually the allantois which fuses with it) and the maternal uterus results in the production of an organ, the *placenta*, specialized to take care of the nutrition, respiration and some or all of the excretion of the embryo.

The shape of the placenta and its size relative to the whole chorionic sac depend upon the final distribution of villi upon the surface of the sac. On this basis four main types have been recognized: (1) *Diffuse.*—Lemurs (among primates) and some ungulates (pig, horse and others) have villi scattered diffusely over the entire chorion, and their placentas are correspondingly expansive (Fig. 56 *A*). In the pig the 'villi' prove on closer inspection to be irregular, folded elevations, located on larger folds several millimeters wide (*B*). In the lemur and horse there are short, branched villi, separated by smooth interspaces. (2) *Cotyledonary.*—True villi occur also in the ruminant (cud-chewing) group of ungulates, such as cattle, sheep and deer. These villi are grouped in well-scattered, prominent rosettes, known as *cotyledons*, which are separated by stretches of smooth chorion (*C*). (3) *Zonary.*—The villi of carnivores occupy a girdle-like band about the middle of the chorionic sac (*D*). (4) *Discoid.*—In general, the villi of insectivores, bats, rodents and primates are limited to one or two disc-shaped areas. The human chorion is originally diffuse, but its villi soon become reduced to a single circular patch (Fig. 100).

Placentas can also be arranged in a structural series, based both on the degree of physical intimacy existing between chorion and uterus, and

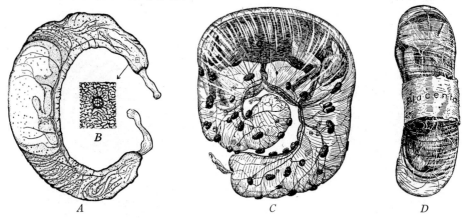

FIG. 56.—Types of chorionic sacs in mammals. *A*, Diffuse distribution of 'villi' in the pig (Patten). *B*, Detail of the rectangular area on *A*. *C*, Villous rosettes (cotyledons) in the lamb (Schultze). *D*, Zonary girdle of villi in the puppy (Corning).

particularly upon the histological relations at the zone of junction of these two components:

1. The simplest placental condition is illustrated by ungulates, such as the pig or horse, and by lemurs. The allantois, developing as in the bird, expands and comes everywhere in contact with the chorion (Fig. 57 *A*). Fusion of these two membranes then follows (*B*); this combines their respective mesodermal layers, and allantoic blood vessels soon spread through the new, common stratum. Meanwhile, the external ectoderm of the chorion has applied itself against the uterine epithelium and the simple chorionic villi fit into corresponding pits in the mucosa of the uterus (*B*). A relationship of this type is called an *epithelio-chorial placenta*.

At the two surfaces of epithelial contact is found nutritive 'uterine milk,' composed of secretions and transudates; it is absorbed by the chorionic villi. Nutritive substances and oxygen from the maternal blood must pass out of the uterine vessels and through both layers of epithelium before entering the allantoic vessels. Over the same path gaseous wastes

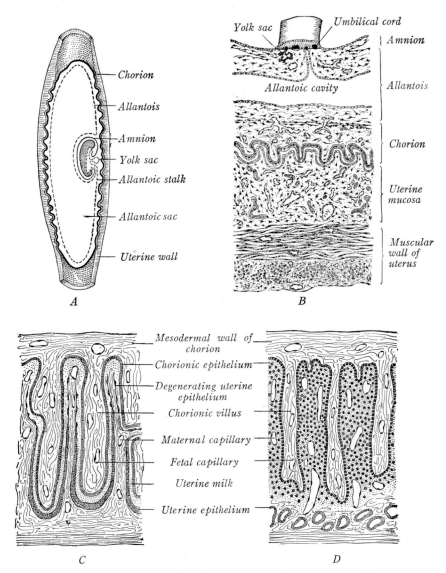

FIG. 57.—Structure of some mammalian placentas, shown by sections. *A*, Diagram of ungulate (pig) placentation. *B*, Detail of the pig's placenta (Patten; × 35). *C*, Detail of a ruminant's (cow) placenta (after Corning; × 10). *D*, Detail of a carnivore's (cat) placenta (after Corning; × 75).

from the embryo travel in the reverse direction. The allantois has, therefore, become important not only as an organ of respiration and excretion (including the storage of urinary wastes), as in reptiles and birds, but also as a participant in nutrition. Since the placenta has taken over the function belonging to the yolk sac of lower vertebrates, the omission of yolk material from the eggs of higher mammals is understandable.

2. The general type of ungulate placenta, just described, is modified slightly by an advance in the subgroup of ruminants (Fig. 57 C). In these mammals the prominent villi of the rosettes occupy deeper pits in the uterine lining. More important still, in the elevated portions of the uterine mucosa, between the villi, there is a local destruction of the uterine epithelium which allows the chorionic ectoderm to come into direct contact with the vascular maternal connective tissue (*syndesmo-chorial placenta*). At the end of gestation, however, the chorionic villi of both types of ungulate placenta are merely withdrawn and the maternal mucosa is not torn away and lost.

3. In carnivores the fetal-maternal union in the region of the villous girdle is much closer than in the ruminant (Fig. 57 D). Nevertheless, the

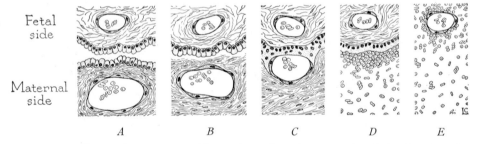

FIG. 58.—Placental types, arranged in a series to show the progressive elimination of barriers between the maternal and fetal circulations (mostly after Flexner and Gellhorn). *A*, Epithelio-chorial; *B*, syndesmo-chorial; *C*, endothelio-chorial; *D*, hemo-chorial; *E*, hemo-endothelial.

erosion of the uterine mucosa spares the endothelium of its blood vessels so that the syncytial chorionic epithelium, packed about the maternal vessels, is still separated from the uterine blood stream (*endothelio-chorial placenta*). At birth there is destructive separation of the placenta, through which the fetal layer with its enclosed maternal vessels splits off from a deeper zone of maternal tissue. This basal zone, which is left behind, has not entered into the pregnancy alterations as have the more superficial levels; it brings about the regeneration of the mucosa in the placental area.

4. A still more intimate placental relation occurs in lower rodents, insectivores, bats and anthropoids; it is characterized by a more thorough erosion of the superficial uterine mucosa (*hemo-chorial placenta*). One type (*labyrinthine*) is like the endothelio-chorial placenta of carnivores except that the endothelium of the uterine vessels is lost and the maternal blood circulates in channels within the fetal syncytium. In the anthropoid type (*villous*) the chorionic villi are free, branching tufts which dangle in cavern-

ous spaces and are directly bathed by maternal blood issuing from opened vessels (Fig. 105). The fusions between chorionic and uterine tissues are such that at birth the placenta tears away as a unit, leaving behind a deeper regenerative layer of less modified mucosa.

5. In higher rodents (rat; guinea pig) is found the nearest approach to actual intermingling of the blood of the two circulations (Fig. 58 E).[2] The chorionic villi reduce to bare blood vessels whose endothelial walls alone separate the fetal blood from the maternal sinuses (*hemo-endothelial placenta*).

The progressive elimination of barriers between the maternal and fetal circulations in the five types of placenta can be followed easily in the series of diagrams shown as Fig. 58.

It is clear that the chorion serves many mammals (*e.g.*, ungulates; carnivores) by bringing the allantois into close relation with the uterine wall. Sharply contrasted is the condition in anthropoids and rodents where the chorion assumes all the placental functions, while

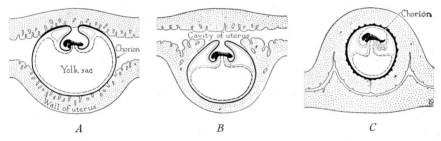

FIG. 59.—Variations in the depth of implantation among mammals (after Mossman). *A*, Superficial (rabbit); *B*, eccentric (ground squirrel); *C*, interstitial (hedgehog).

the superseded allantoic sac becomes vestigial or even lacking. Of course, it may be argued that the allantoic vessels are the most important component of the allantois, that these vascularize the chorion of placental mammals in general, and hence that a placenta is fundamentally chorio-allantoic even though the allantois, as a sac, is insignificant.[2]

There is some evidence that the rate of transfer of substances from the blood of the mother to that of the fetus increases as the number of layers to be passed decreases.[3] The ascending order of efficiency is the same as the order in which the structural types of placenta have just been discussed. It is also natural to assume that this structural series, with a progressive thinning of the fetal-maternal barrier, indicates the evolutionary sequence. Yet this may not be the case, since the epithelio-chorial type is widely scattered and tends to occur in mammals highly specialized in other respects. Arguments have even been advanced in favor of erosive placentation as the primitive type.[4]

Depth of Implantation.—The relation of the chorionic sac to the uterine wall varies greatly among placental mammals. In general three types of implantation may be distinguished, although transitional conditions occur (Fig. 59): (1) *Superficial*. Growth of the sac brings it into contact with the

Type of Mammal	Shape of Placenta (Villous Distribution)	Type of Placenta	Relation of Uterus to Chorion	Loss of Maternal Tissue at Birth
Monotremes	....	....	....	....
Marsupials	Avillous	Aplacental (Temporary semiplacenta in some)	Epithelio-chorial (Temporary)	None (In some, fetal tissue is retained)
Ungulates in general	Diffuse	Semiplacenta (Apposition)	Epithelio-chorial	None (Nondeciduate)
Ruminant ungulates	Cotyledonary	Semiplacenta (Slight fusion)	Syndesmo-chorial	Slight (Semideciduate)
Carnivores	Zonary	True (Fusion)	Endothelio-chorial	Moderate (Deciduate)
Anthropoids	Discoid	True (Fusion)	Hemo-chorial	Extensive (Deciduate)
Higher rodents	Discoid, cup or spheroid	True (Fusion)	Hemo-endothelial	Moderate (Deciduate)

Type of Mammal	Origin of Amnion	Yolk Sac	Yolk-sac Placenta	Allantois	Chorio-allantoic Placenta
Monotremes	Folding	Large (Much yolk)	....	Large	....
Marsupials	Folding	Large	Present (In some)	Small	None (One exception)
Ungulates in general	Folding	Small	Present (Early)	Large	Present
Ruminant ungulates	Folding (Preceded by cavitation in some)	Small	Present (Early)	Large	Present
Carnivores	Folding	Medium	Present (Early)	Large	Present
Anthropoids	Cavitation	Small	None	Vestigial	None*
Higher rodents	Folding or cavitation	Large (Specialized)	None	Small or lacking	None*

* Except that primitive allantoic vessels vascularize the chorion.

lining of the main uterine cavity; this type is also known as central implantation (ungulates; carnivores; monkey). (2) *Eccentric.* The sac lies for a time in a fold or pocket which then closes off from the main cavity (beaver; squirrel). (3) *Interstitial.* The sac penetrates into the substance of uterine lining (hedgehog; guinea pig; some bats; ape; man).

REFERENCES CITED

1. Grosser, O. 1927. Frühentwicklung, etc. Bergmann, München.
2. Mossman, H. W. 1937. Carnegie Contrib. Embryol., **26,** No. 158, 129–246.
3. Flexner, L. B. and Gellhorn, A. 1942. Amer. Jour. Obstet. and Gynec., **43,** 965–974.
4. Wislocki, G. B. 1929. Carnegie Contrib. Embryol., **20,** No. 111, 51–80.

CHAPTER VI

HUMAN EMBRYOS AND THEIR MEMBRANES

PERIOD OF CLEAVAGE (FIRST WEEK)

The subdivision of the fertilized egg into blastomeres and their re-arrangement into a hollow blastocyst occupy the first week of human development. A previous chapter has described the way in which cleavage breaks down the mammalian egg into cells of suitable size to serve as building units. With the production of a typical *blastocyst* this process of size reduction nears its end. At this stage the cells of the future embryo-proper are segregated as an *inner cell mass*, whereas the capsule-like wall of the blastocyst is auxiliary tissue, the *trophoblast*, which will establish nutritive and other relations with the uterus. Information furnished by studies on the monkey and other mammals indicates that the first three days of human development are spent in descending the uterine tube, during which time cleavage has produced about twelve blastomeres. The next three days are passed in the uterine cavity as a free morula and blasto-cyst. At the end of the first week the blastocyst attaches to the epithelial lining of the uterus and begins to sink into the soft tissue beneath. No human specimens illustrative of this entire period are known, except a somewhat abnormal morula and artificially fertilized eggs which achieved the two- and three-cell stages. Cleavage stages and the blastocyst, as they occur in the monkey, are shown in Figures 34 *A–C* and 45.

PERIOD OF THE TWO-LAYERED EMBRYO (SECOND WEEK)

It will be remembered that gastrulation segregates the embryo-forma-tive cells of the inner cell mass into three germ layers which are advan-tageously situated to begin the building of the body and its organs. If cleavage can be compared to the quarrying of building stones, then gas-trulation is the cartage of these units to convenient working points on the site of a future edifice. In mammals gastrulation occurs in two stages and it is the first of these, entoderm formation, that ends the first week and ushers in the second week of human development.

The youngest human embryo known is not more than seven and one-half days old.[1*] Its inclusion within the lining of the uterus had not been

---

* The assigning of ages to recovered embryos is an approximation which may err as much as 10 per cent. from the true age. The ages given here to specimens of the third and fourth weeks are slightly younger than many authorities have favored in recent years and slightly older than some now advocate.

completed (Fig. 60). Several important advances in this specimen mark a stage of development beyond that of the simple blastocyst. The *tropho-blast* (*i.e.*, the blastocyst wall) is much thickened where it has come in contact with the connective tissue of the uterus. Here most of the cells have lost their boundaries and become a syncytium. In the region of the inner cell mass a cleft was separating the *amnion*, which like the trophoblast is auxiliary tissue, from the embryo-formative cells. The latter constitute the *embryonic disc*. It consists of a thicker plate of potential ectodermal and mesodermal cells, not yet recognizable as such, and a definite layer of segregated *entoderm* which faces the cavity of the trophoblastic sac.

The next described specimen, not more than nine days old, lies almost wholly within the uterine lining (Fig. 89 *D*).[1] The chief change is in the syncytial trophoblast which has become thick and spongy through the appearance of irregular spaces; some of these connect with maternal capil-

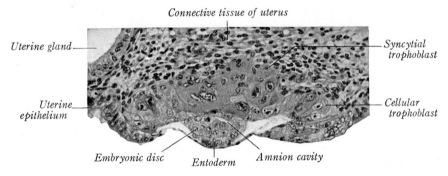

FIG. 60.—Section through a human embryo of seven days, partly implanted in the uterine wall (Hertig and Rock). × 200.

laries. The innermost part of the trophoblastic capsule, next the central cavity of the blastocyst, is not syncytial but consists of discrete cells.

In stages at 11 and 12 days, primitive *mesodermal cells* are differentiating everywhere from the cellular layer of trophoblast (Fig. 61).[2] Some believe that the innermost of these cells have united and produced the so-called *exocœlomic membrane*, which bounds the main cavity of the sac and is continuous with the entodermal cells.[2, 3] Others interpret the membrane as a provisional yolk sac of entoderm, reminiscent of the larger early yolk sac of lower mammals.[4] The mesodermal elements are all extra-embryonic, the main plate of the embryonic disc not having begun the segregation of embryonic mesoderm from ectoderm.

By the thirteenth day a definite *yolk sac* has appeared, presumably by a separation or segregation of cells from the entodermal layer present in earlier stages on the under surface of the embryonic disc (*cf.* Fig. 46).[4] The entoderm in the region of the disc is a thick layer, whereas the sac proper is thin. So different is the appearance of these latter, flat cells that it has even been proposed that they may be mesodermal in origin.[3] The temporary exocœlomic membrane has largely disintegrated as such, while the primitive extra-embryonic mesoderm as a whole is consolidating into

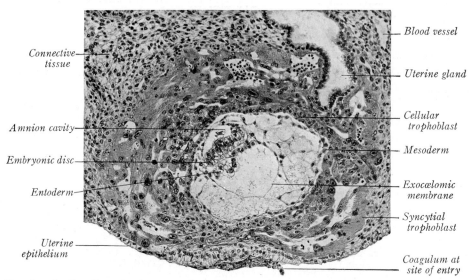

Connective tissue

Amnion cavity

Embryonic disc

Entoderm

Uterine epithelium

Blood vessel

Uterine gland

Cellular trophoblast

Mesoderm

Exocœlomic membrane

Syncytial trophoblast

Coagulum at site of entry

FIG. 61.—Section through a human embryo of eleven days, implanted in the uterine wall (Hertig and Rock).   × 110.

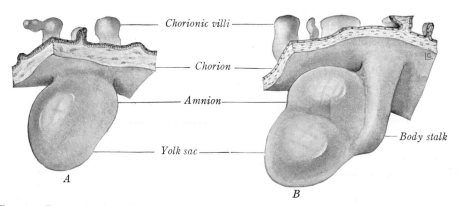

Chorionic villi

Chorion

Amnion

Yolk sac

Body stalk

A

B

FIG. 62.—Reconstructions of the exterior of human embryos. *A*, At fourteen days (× 80); *B*, at sixteen days (× 95).

a definite layer beneath the trophoblast. Some of this mesoderm is beginning to extend as stubby cores into the trophoblastic cords; this marks the beginning of true *chorionic villi* (Fig. 64 *A*). The entire capsule of mesoderm and trophoblast can now be called the *chorion*, and its cavity the *extra-embryonic cœlom*.

The appearance of an embryo at the end of the second week is shown in Figures 62 *A* and 63 *A*. The circular embryonic disc still lacks separate ectodermal and mesodermal layers, although there are slight indications that a primitive streak is organizing. At its peripheral margin, the disc is continuous with the amnion above and the yolk sac below. The extra-embryonic mesoderm can be designated regionally by special names. The layer that now clothes the yolk sac is *splanchnic mesoderm*, while the layer covering the amnion and lining the chorion is *somatic mesoderm* (Fig. 64 *A*). The roof of the dome-like amnion is attached broadly to the chorion by mesoderm. The epithelial covering of the chorion and lining of the amnion are usually classified as *extra-embryonic ectoderm*, by analogy with lower forms.

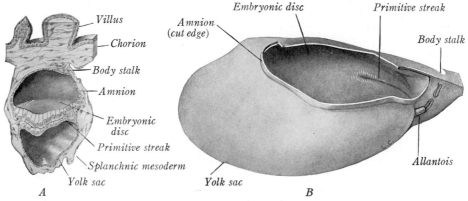

Fig. 63.—*A*, Right half of a human embryo (Brewer) of fourteen days. × 85. *B*, Human embryo (Mateer-Turner) of sixteen days, viewed from the left and above. × 35.

PERIOD OF THE THREE-LAYERED EMBRYO (THIRD WEEK)

At 16 days a well-formed *primitive streak* is evident caudally on the surface of the pear-shaped embryonic disc (Fig. 63 *B*). A transverse section shows the *mesoderm* spreading from the streak as a prominent layer between the *ectoderm* and *entoderm* (Fig. 48). This segregation of embryonic mesoderm signifies that the second phase of gastrulation is in progress. The amnion roof is now free and only a bridge of mesoderm, the *body stalk*, connects the caudal end of the embryo with the chorion (Fig. 62 *B*). The *allantois* is a slender, entodermal tube which has extended into the mesoderm of the body stalk (Fig. 64 *B*). The chorionic villi branch, and blood vessels are appearing in the mesoderm of the villi as well as in the mesoderm of the chorion proper, body stalk and yolk sac.

Stages at 18 days possess a *head process* which extends forward from the primitive knot at the front end of the primitive streak (Fig. 65 *A*). The originally solid head process of the previous day has become tunneled by a *notochordal canal* and the floor of the canal is disappearing (Fig. 66). As a result, there is a temporary communication at the site of the primitive pit between the cavities of the yolk sac and amnion; this passage is known as the *neurenteric canal*. At the caudal end of the primitive streak, the

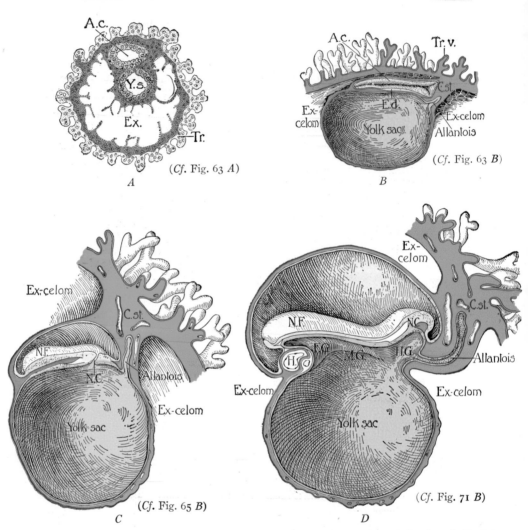

(*Cf.* Fig. 63 *A*)

A

(*Cf.* Fig. 63 *B*)

B

(*Cf.* Fig. 65 *B*)

C

(*Cf.* Fig. 71 *B*)

D

Fig. 64.—Human embryos of the third week (Scammon in Morris). *A*, Section; *B–D*, right halves of models. *A.c.*, Amnion cavity; *C.st.* body stalk; *E.d.*, embryonic disc; *Ex.*, extra-embryonic cœlom; *F.G.*, fore-gut; *H*, heart; *H.G.*, hind-gut; *M.G.*, mid-gut; *N.C.*, neurenteric canal; *N.F.*, neural folds; *Tr.*, trophoblast; *Tr.V.*, chorionic villi; *Y.s.*, yolk sac.

ectoderm and entoderm fuse as the *cloacal membrane*. The primitive streak was the first landmark that revealed the polarity of the embryonic disc. The head process extends the defining of the median plane of the future embryo, and the two together divide the embryonic disc into precise right and left halves. The developmental potencies of a chick blastoderm at this period, tested by grafted pieces, are indicated in Figure 67.

An embryo of 19 days ends the presomite period (Figs. 64 *C* and 65 *B*). It is slipper-shaped in outline and there is slight constriction of the somewhat convex embryo from the yolk sac. Growth has elongated the portion

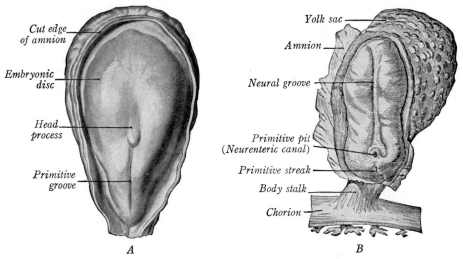

FIG. 65.—Human embryos, with amnion cut away, viewed from above. *A*, At eighteen days (Heuser; × 45); *B*, at nineteen days (v. Spee; × 23).

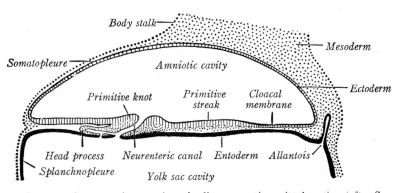

FIG. 66.—Human embryo, at nineteen days, in diagrammatic sagittal section (after Scammon).

of the embryo ahead of the primitive knot. A median strip of ectoderm in this region is thickened as the *neural plate;* a definite *neural groove* courses along its length. The floor of the head process has disappeared, leaving the roof as the *notochordal plate;* this plate soon rounds up into an axial rod, the *notochord.* The *fore-gut* is beginning to form and there are slight indications of the future *heart.* This stage of embryonic development is often called a *neurula;* it designates a third period beyond the stages of the blastula and gastrula.

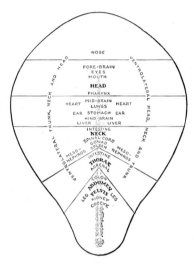

FIG. 67.—Location of prospective organs at the stage of the head process, as tested by cultivating pieces of the chick blastoderm (after Rawles).

A GRADED SERIES OF PRESOMITE EMBRYOS AND THEIR DIMENSIONS

AUTHOR AND DESIGNATION OF EMBRYO	CHORIONIC SAC		YOLK SAC	EMBRYONIC DISC*	ESTIMATED AGE
	Aver. ext. diam. (mm.)	*Aver. int. diam. (mm.)*	*Max. diam. in. (mm.)*	*Length × width*	*(In days)*

I. Primitive Streak Absent

A. *Amniotic cavity; entoderm; solid trophoblast*

Hertig and Rock (C.C. 8020), 1945....................	.22	.15	Unformed	.08 × .09	7

B. *Extra-embryonic mesoderm; spongy trophoblast*

Hertig and Rock (C.C. 7699), 1941....................	.75	.36	Unformed	.09 × .14	11

C. *Yolk sac; chorionic villi differentiating*

Linzenmeier, 1914...........	1.04	.63	.10	.11 × .21	13

* The horizontal measurements of the amnion are either the same, or nearly the same, as those of the embryonic disc.

II. Primitive Streak Present

A. Beginning primitive streak

Brewer (U.C. 1496), 1938....| 2.8 | 1.5 | .2 | .21 × .18 | 14

B. Primitive groove, pit and knot; embryonic mesoderm; villi branching

Streeter (Mateer), 1919 .....| 6.8 | 4.7 | 1.5 | .92 × .78 | 16

C. Solid head process; cloacal membrane; allantois

Thompson-Brash, 1923......| 7.2 | 5.7 | .9 | .9 × .9 | 17

D. Notochordal canal tunneling head process

Ingalls (W. R. 1), 1918......| 7.9 | 6.7 | 2.5 | 2.0 × .8 | 18

E. Neural folds; neurenteric canal; fore-gut indicated

Spee (Glæ), 1889; 1896......| 9.3 | 7.8 | 2.1 | 1.5 × .6 | 19

PERIOD OF THE EMBRYO WITH SOMITES (FOURTH WEEK)

Vertebrate Characteristics.—Since the embryo is now ready to enter into body building, it is worth while to have in mind some of the chief features that characterize vertebrates in general:

1. A tubular *central nervous system,* wholly dorsal in position.
2. An *internal skeleton,* composed of living tissue.
3. A *mouth,* closed by a lower jaw.
4. A *pharynx,* which differentiates gills or lungs.
5. A ventral *heart,* connecting with a closed system of *blood vessels.*
6. A *cœlom,* or body cavity, which is unsegmented but is divided into compartments for the heart and abdominal organs (and, in higher vertebrates, for the lungs as well).
7. The *limbs.* Two pairs, with an internal skeleton.

The Primitive Body Plan.—During the fourth week of human development all of the parts just listed (and many others) make their beginnings. Certain items in this foreshadowing of the future organization of the body require comment and illustration (Fig. 68).

The Neural Tube.—The neural plate folds into a tube which detaches from the general ectoderm and becomes the nervous system. This includes the *brain, spinal cord* and *nerves.*

The Notochord.—This cord of mesodermal cells runs axially between the neural tube and gut. It serves as a primitive 'backbone' and is later surrounded and replaced by the vertebral column.

The Gut.—The roof of the entodermal yolk sac folds into a tubular gut which becomes the digestive tract and respiratory system. The pharynx of fishes and aquatic amphibians opens to the outside by gill slits; incomplete homologues appear in the embryos of reptiles, birds and mammals.

The Somites.—These primitive segments lie alongside the spinal cord in pairs and are a prominent feature of vertebrate embryos (Fig. 72). They arise when transverse clefts subdivide the thickened mesoderm next the midplane into block-like masses. Each somite gives rise to a muscle segment supplied by a spinal nerve, while each somite pair also collaborates in producing a vertebra. At the level of any pair of somites lie primitive kidney tubules, and also blood vessels arising from the aorta. This whole group of associated, mesodermal structures is repeated serially throughout much of the embryo's length.

This segmental arrangement brings to mind the serial divisions, or *metameres,* of an earthworm's body. In the worm each metamere similarly contains a ganglion of the nerve cord, a muscle segment, and pairs of nerves, blood vessels and excretory tubules. Such serial repetition of homologous parts is called *metamerism*. Hence the vertebrate embryo is also fundamentally metameric, even though much of its segmentation is lost as development advances. Just as a worm grows by adding new metameres at its tail-end, so the somites and associated structures of the vertebrate embryo appear first in the head region and are added progressively tailward. But there are these differences between the metamerism of a worm and of the vertebrate embryo: in the worm it is complete, and both external and internal; in the vertebrate it is incomplete ventrally, and purely internal.

The Nephrotomes.—A short plate of cells extends ventrolaterad from each somite. From these serially arranged plates will develop the urogenital glands and their ducts.

The Lateral Mesoderm.—The remainder of the mesoderm of the embryo, ventrolateral to the nephrotomes, is not segmented. It splits into two layers, the *somatic* and *splanchnic mesoderm*. From the first, the ectoderm and somatic mesoderm are closely associated. They constitute a natural unit, named the *somatopleure*, which produces the lateral and ventral body wall of the embryo and continues beyond the embryo as the amnion and chorion. In a similar way, the entoderm and splanchnic mesoderm combine as the *splachnopleure*. It

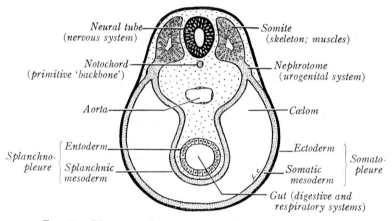

FIG. 68.—Diagrammatic transverse section of a vertebrate embryo.

forms the gut and lungs. The splanchnopleure of the young embryo is continuous with that of the yolk sac.

The Cœlom.—The space between the split layers of lateral mesoderm is the *cœlom*, or body cavity. In mammals the cœlomic cavity of the chorionic sac, and the mesoderm of the chorion, amnion and yolk sac which faces this cavity, exist before there are corresponding developments within the embryo itself. These external representatives of cœlom and mesoderm are designated as extra-embryonic. Until the body wall closes off, there is direct continuity between the cœlom inside and outside the embryo. The original cœlom within the embryo becomes subdivided into separate compartments for the heart, lungs and abdominal viscera. The surface layer of the mesoderm, which everywhere bounds the cœlom, is termed *mesothelium*.

Vessels.—Tiny spaces, appearing within the mesoderm (mostly of the spongy type known as mesenchyme), link into vascular networks which spread rapidly in the chorion, yolk sac and embryo proper. They become the *heart*, *blood vessels* and *lymphatics*. Their thin, lining layer is *endothelium*.

During the fourth week there is an average increase in total length from about 2 to 5 mm., but size alone is too variable among the smaller specimens to constitute a reliable index of development. Better correlated with the degree of development is the number of mesodermal somites. These make their appearance progressively; they begin to appear at the end of the third week and attain nearly their full number (about 40) during the fourth week. Such momentous changes characterize this period that the embryo advances from a simple disc to a relatively complex organism.

Some of the head of an embryo arises from the material of the embryonic disc in the region cephalad of the early primitive knot. But shortly after the primitive knot is formed the primitive streak begins to shorten and the knot moves caudad, paying out in its wake most of the notochord and the floor of the neural tube (Fig. 69).[5, 6]   Simultaneously with this retreat the somite-pairs appear in steady succession on each side of the notochord, organizing from the appropriate mesoderm brought in by the movements of gastrulation. By the time the majority of somites have formed, the surviving primitive knot and streak is a compact mass of

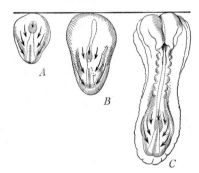

FIG. 69.—Diagrams of the caudal growth of the body, partly at the expense of the retreating primitive knot (Streeter). The primitive knot is stippled.

tissue located at the caudal end of the embryo and known as the *end bud* or *tail bud* (Figs. 70 *D* and 73 *A*). The tail, at least, traces origin from this swelling in which separate germ layers cannot be recognized. Some have argued that the lower trunk as well differentiates from an 'indifferent' material in the end bud.[7] Others believe that there is no real difference between this region and those at more cephalic levels, except that from the first the germ-layer materials are crowded and condensed progressively in a caudal direction in a way that hides their identity. In other words, the gastrulation movements (and the resulting segregation of ectoderm, mesoderm and entoderm) are fundamentally the same with respect to all levels of the future embryo.[6]

The most important maneuver in the establishment of general body form is the transformation of the flat embryonic disc into a roughly cylindrical embryo attached to the yolk sac by a narrower stalk. Three factors co-operate to produce this change: (1) There is more rapid expansion of both the embryonic area and the yolk sac in contrast to a slower rate of growth at the region of transition between the two. The enlarging embryonic area, bound at its more sluggish, inelastic periphery, at first buckles upward and then overlaps the slower growing margin; the latter becomes a zone of 'constriction' between embryo and yolk sac (Fig. 65). Since the growth is particularly rapid at the future head- and tail-ends, the embryo soon becomes elongate (Fig. 71). The entire process can be described as one of internal growth resulting in folding; the embryo enlarges somewhat as does a soap bubble blown from a pipe. (2) In conjunction with the overgrowth just described, there is important underfolding, most evident at the front and hind ends of the embryo.[8] As the neural axis elevates and projects forward beyond the margin of the embryonic disc, the future

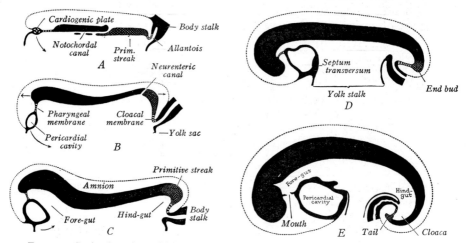

FIG. 70.—Sagittal sections of human embryos to illustrate the reversal occurring at the cranial and caudal ends. × 20. *A*, At presomite stage; *B*, at one somite; *C*, at six somites; *D*, at twelve somites; *E*, at twenty-two somites. Arrows show growth directions.

pharyngeal membrane and the cardiac area swing beneath, as on a hinge (Fig. 70 *A–C*). In doing this the cardiac area, originally ahead of the pharyngeal membrane, necessarily becomes the more caudal of the two in position, while the amnion and the yolk sac (originally at the rim of the disc) then attach caudal to the pericardium (*D*, *E*). Caudal growth of the end bud brings about a similar reversal at the caudal end of the embryo (*A–E*). As a result, the cloacal membrane and body stalk turn under onto the ventral side. (3) Finally, a certain amount of true constriction, through growth, purses all these parts at the site of the future umbilicus (*C–E*).

Throughout the entire period during which the body and its parts are being laid down, development and differentiation appear first in the head region and then advance tailward. For this reason, many structures that extend longitudinally for an appreciable distance show progressive stages of development at successively higher levels in the same embryo.   The size advantage initially gained by the head-end as a whole is relinquished only

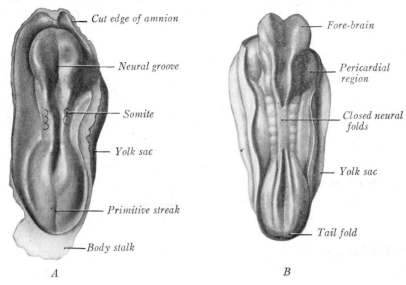

FIG. 71.—Human embryos of twenty-one days, in dorsal view (Streeter).   A, Ingalls embryo of 1.4 mm., with three somites (× 42).   B, Payne embryo of 2.2 mm., with seven somites (× 27).

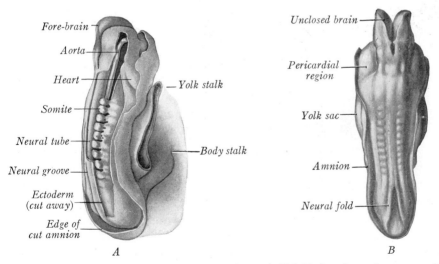

FIG. 72.—Human embryos of twenty-two days.   A, Veit-Esch embryo of 2.3 mm., with nine somites, partially dissected and viewed from the right side (× 25).   B, Corner embryo of 1.7 mm., with ten somites, in dorsal view (Streeter; × 34).

slowly.   A further tendency toward progressively graded development is expressed from the mid-dorsal line in lateral directions.   Such relations are the visible expressions of gradients in growth and differentiation.

Returning now to the consideration of representative embryos, it will be simpler from this point onward in development to concentrate first on

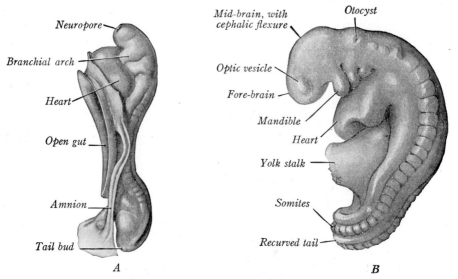

FIG. 73.—Human embryos of twenty-four and twenty-six days, viewed from the left side. A, Atwell embryo of 2.6 mm., with nineteen somites (Streeter; × 23); B, 3.6 mm. embryo, with twenty-five somites (× 16).

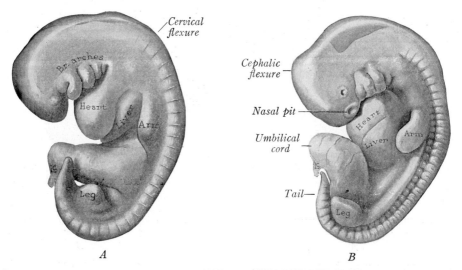

FIG. 74.—Human embryos of four and five weeks, viewed from the left side. A, At 5 mm. (× 12); B, at 8 mm. (× 7.5).

the advances made by the embryo itself. After these changes have been carried up to the time of birth, the later histories of the fetal membranes will be described.

Rapid, differential growth of the embryo about to enter the fourth week causes it to take a cylindrical shape (Figs, 71 and 72). *Neural folds,* rising high and uniting in a progressive manner, roll up a *neural tube* in which a larger *brain region* becomes plainly indicated. Many preserved specimens of this period show a markedly concave back, apparently produced artifically by shrinkage of the yolk sac (Fig. 73 *A*). Internally the *fore-* and *hind-gut* elongate into blind tubes (Fig. 64 *D*). The *heart* becomes conspicuous and a system of paired *blood vessels* is established. *Somites* increase rapidly in number.

Later in the week the characteristic features include (Figs. 73 *B* and 74 *A*): a convexly curved back and ventrally flexed *head;* a sharp bend

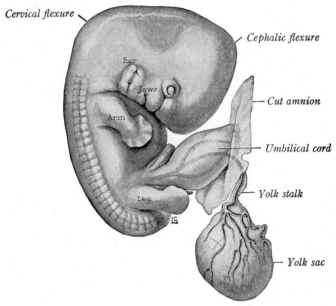

FIG. 75.—Human embryo of six weeks (12 mm.), viewed from the right side.   × 5.

(*cephalic flexure*) at the level of the mid-brain; a broader curvature (*cervical flexure*) in the region of the future neck; a bulging *heart*; a definite *trunk* ending in a conspicuous *tail*. *Sense organs* and *limb buds* are indicated and the *branchial arches* become prominent; the first pair of arches bifurcates into primitive *jaws*. The *yolk stalk*, or connection with the yolk sac, is now relatively small and slender. It is the rapidly elongating neural tube, in contrast to the slower growing ventral surface of the embryo, that produces the characteristic curves and flexures in the embryo as a whole.

PERIOD OF EMBRYO COMPLETION (FIFTH THROUGH EIGHTH WEEK)

These embryos, ranging between 5 and 23 mm., show marked changes. Their external form, although quite unfinished, comes to resemble more the

'human' condition, and after the second month the developing young is
commonly called a *fetus*. This external metamorphosis may be followed
by studying Figures 74 *A* to 77 *E*. It is due principally to the following
factors: (1) Changes in the *flexures* of the body; the dorsal convexity is
lost, the head becomes erect and the body straight. (2) The *face* develops.
(3) The external structures of the *eye, ear* and *nose* appear. (4) The *limbs*
organize as such, with digits demarcated. (5) The prominent tail of the
fifth week becomes inconspicuous both through actual regression and con-
cealment by the growing buttocks. (6) The *umbilical cord* becomes a definite

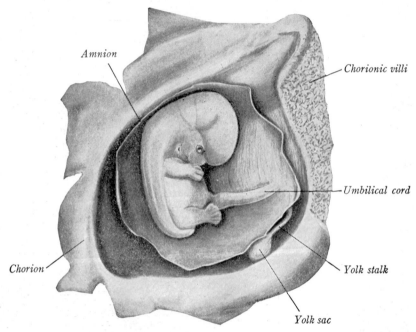

FIG. 76.—Human embryo of seven weeks (18 mm.), with its membranes, viewed from the right
side. × 2. The chorion has been reflected and half of the amnion removed.

entity, its embryonic end occupying a relatively diminishing area on the
belly wall. (7) The *heart*, which was the chief ventral prominence in earlier
embryos, now shares this distinction with the rapidly growing *liver;* these
two organs determine the shape of the ventral body until the eighth week
when the gut dominates the belly cavity and the contour of the abdomen
is more evenly rotund. (8) The *neck* becomes recognizable, due chiefly to
the settling of the heart caudad and the effacement of the branchial arches.
(9) The *external genitalia* appear in their 'sexless' condition. (10) The
neuro-muscular mechanism attains sufficient perfection so that spontaneous
movements are possible.

Almost all of the internal organs are well laid down at two months;

henceforth, until the end of gestation, the chief changes undergone are those of growth and further tissue differentiation.

PERIOD OF THE FETUS

During the *third month* (lunar) the fetus definitely resembles a human being, but the head is still disproportionately large (Fig. 77 *F–H*); the

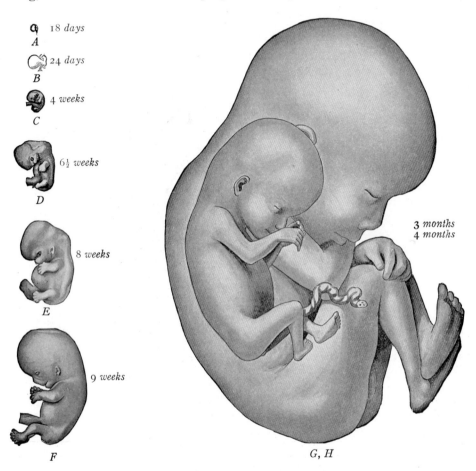

A   18 *days*

B   24 *days*

C   4 *weeks*

D   6½ *weeks*

E   8 *weeks*

F   9 *weeks*

3 *months*
4 *months*

G, H

Fig. 77.—A graded series of human embryos, at natural size.

umbilical herniation is reduced by the return of the intestine into the abdomen; the eyelids fuse, nails begin forming, and sex can now be distinguished readily. At *four months* fetal movements begin to be felt by the mother; the face has a truly human appearance (Fig. 77 *H*). At *five months* hair is present on the head and body. During the *sixth month* the eyebrows and lashes grow; the body is lean but in better proportion. At *seven months* the fetus looks like a dried-up, old person with red, wrinkled

skin; the eyelids reopen.   In the *eighth month* subcutaneous fat is depositing;
the testes are invading the scrotum; infants of this age born prematurely
can usually be reared (incubator babies).   In the *ninth month* the dull
redness of the skin fades, wrinkles smooth out, the limbs become rounded,
and nails project at the finger tips.   During the *tenth month* the body continues to round out, due to the progressive accumulation of fat; the provisional, downy hair-coat begins to shed; the fetus is now 'at full term,'
ready for birth.

The embryos shown in Figures 60 to 76 are drawn at progressively
decreasing magnifications.   In order to obtain a better idea of the actual
and relative sizes of embryos at different periods, the series assembled as
Figure 77 should be studied.   These embryos are all drawn at natural size.

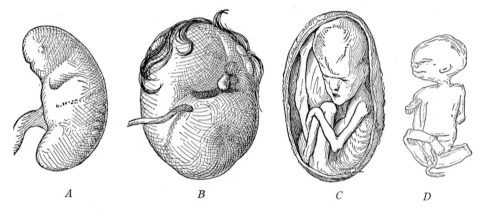

A   *B*   *C*   *D*

FIG. 78.—Malformed human embryos.   *A*, Stunted embryo, with poorly developed external
form (× 4).   *B*, Amorphous fetus, twin to a normal, full-term baby.   Externally there was hair
and a rudimentary mouth and cyclopic eye; internally there were three vertebræ and the base of
a skull, besides much vascular connective tissue and fat and a little muscular and nervous tissue
(× ⅓).   *C*, Mummified fetus, within a calcified gestation sac (× ⅓).   *D*, Fetus papyraceous (× ⅓).

The appended tabulation is designed to present an epitome of human
development for purposes of study and reference.   In the vertical columns
the sequential development of each system is listed.   Of even greater
importance is a study of the horizontal entries which record the correlated
changes throughout the embryo at definite periods.   It is this picture of
parallel development that ordinarily is visualized inadequately.

Anomalies.—Grossly abnormal embryos are not infrequent among those obtained by
spontaneous abortion or necessary operative intervention.   The external body form may
show all gradations from mildly faulty modeling to an amorphous mass that is scarcely
recognizable as a fetus (Fig. 78 *A*, *B*).   Various pathological alterations in the embryo commonly accompany those morbid disturbances that induce its stunting or death.   Degenerative changes are common also in the fetal membranes, although the chorionic sac sometimes
continues to grow for a time quite normally after the embryo has died and even after it has
disappeared.   Many of these imperfect specimens of different kinds result from eggs of such

Table of Developmental Stages

Age in Weeks	Size (C R) in Mm.	Body Form
2.5	1.5	Embryonic disc flat. Primitive streak prominent. Neural groove indicated.
3.5	2.5	Neural groove deepens and closes (except ends). Somites 1–16± present. Cylindrical body constricting from yolk sac. Branchial arches 1 and 2 indicated.
4	5.0	Branchial arches completed. Flexed heart prominent. Yolk stalk slender. All somites present (40). Limb buds indicated. Eye and otocyst present. Body flexed; C-shape.
5	8.0	Nasal pits present. Tail prominent. Heart, liver and mesonephros protuberant. Umbilical cord organizes.
6	12.0	Upper jaw components prominent but separate. Lower jaw-halves fused. Head becomes dominant in size. Cervical flexure marked. External ear appearing. Limbs recognizable as such.
7	17.0	Branchial arches lost. Cervical sinus obliterates. Face and neck forming. Digits indicated. Back straightens. Heart and liver determine shape of body ventrally. Tail regressing.
8	23.0	Nose flat; eyes far apart. Digits well formed. Growth of gut makes body evenly rotund. Head elevating. Fetal state attained.
10	40.0	Head erect. Limbs nicely modeled. Nail folds indicated. Umbilical hernia reduced.
12	56.0	Head still dominant. Nose gains bridge. Sex readily determined by external inspection.
16	112.0	Face looks 'human.' Hair of head appearing. Muscles become spontaneously active. Body outgrowing head.
20–40 (5–10 mo.)	160.0–350.0	Lanugo hair appears (5). Vernix caseosa collects (5). Body lean but better proportioned (6). Fetus lean, wrinkled and red; eyelids reopen (7). Testes invading scrotum (8). Fat collecting, wrinkles smoothing, body rounding (8–10).

Skeletal System

Age	Description
	Head process (or notochordal plate) present.
	Mesodermal segments appearing (1–16±). Older somites begin to show sclerotomes. Notochord a cellular rod.
4	All somites present (40). Sclerotomes massed as primitive vertebræ about notochord.
5	Condensation of mesenchyme presage future bones.
6	First appearance of chondrification centers. Desmocranium.
	Chondrification more general. Chondrocranium.
6	Chondrification. Chondrocranium.
7	First indications of ossification.
8	Ossification centers more common. Chondrocranium at its height.
10	Most bones distinctly indicated throughout body. Joint cavities appear.
12	Carpal, tarsal and sternal bones ossify late; some after birth. Most epiphyseal centers appear after birth; many during adolescence.
16	Blood formation much...
20–40	Blood formation increasing in bone marrow and decreasing in liver (5–10). Spleen acquires typical structure (7). Some fetal blood passages discontinue (10).

Muscular System

Age	Description
	Mesodermal segments appearing (1–16±). Older somites show myotome plates.
4	Premuscle masses in head, trunk and limbs.
5	Myotomes, fused into a continuous column, spread ventrad. Muscle segmentation largely lost.
6	Muscles differentiating rapidly throughout body and assuming final shapes and relations.
7	Definitive muscles of trunk, limbs and head well represented and fetus capable of some movement.
8	Perineal muscles developing tardily.
10	Smooth muscle layers indicated in hollow viscera.
12	Perineal muscles finish development (6).
16	Cardiac muscle appearing in earlier weeks, now much condensed. Muscular movements in utero can be detected.

Circulatory System

Age	Description
2.5	Blood cells and blood vessels present; paired symmetrical.
3.5	Heart tubes fuse, bend, change shape and beat begins. Hemopoiesis on yolk sac. Paired aortæ fuse. Aortic arches and cardinal veins completed; heart shows sinus, atrium, ventricle, and bulbus.
5	Primitive vessels extend into head and limbs. Vitelline and umbilical veins transforming. Myocardium condensing. Cardiac septa appearing. Spleen indicated.
6	Hemopoiesis in liver. Aortic arches transforming. L. umbil. vein and d. venous become important. Bulbus absorbed into right ventricle. Heart acquires its general definitive form.
7	Cardinal veins transforming. Inf. vena cava outlined. Atrium, ventricle and bulbus partitioned. Cardiac valves present. Stem of pulm. vein absorbed into l. atrium. Spleen anlage prominent.
8	Main blood vessels assume final plan. Primitive lymph sacs present. Sinus venosus absorbed into right atrium. Atrio-ventricular bundle represented. Thoracic duct and peripheral lymphatics developed. Early lymph glands appearing. Enucleated red cells dominate in blood. Blood formation beginning in bone marrow. Blood vessels acquire accessory coats.
12	Blood formation active in spleen. Heart musculature much condensed.

Digestive System

Age	Description
4	Jaws outlined. Rathke's sac.
6	Lingual primordia. Foramen cæcum established. Labio-dental appearing. Parotid and submaxillary buds indicated.
7	Lingual primordia fuse into single tongue. Separate labial and dental laminæ distinguished. Jaws formed and ossify. Palate folds present, separated by tongue.
8	Tongue muscles well differentiated. Earliest taste buds indicated. Rathke's pouch detached from mouth. Sublingual gland appearing.
10	Fungiform and vallate papillæ differentiating. Lips separate from jaws. Enamel organs and dentine papillæ forming. Palate folds fusing.
12	Filiform and foliate papillæ elevating. Tooth primordia form prominent cups. Cheeks represented. Palate fusion complete.
16	Hard and soft palates differentiating. Hypophysis acquiring definitive structure.
20–40	Enamel and dentine depositing (5). Lingual tonsil forming (5). Permanent tooth primordia indicated (6–8). Milk teeth unerupted at birth.

Integumentary System

Age	Description
	Epidermis gaining a second layer (periderm).
	Milk line present.
5	Mammary thickening, lens-shaped.
6	Mammary primordium a globular thickening.
7	Epidermis adds intermediate cells. Periderm cells prominent. Nail field indicated. Earliest hair follicles begin developing on face.
8	Epidermis three-layered. Corium and subcutaneous now distinct.
10	Epidermis begins adding other layers. Body hair starts developing. Sweat glands appear. First sebaceous glands differentiating.
12	Vernix caseosa seen (5). Epidermis cornifies (5). Nail plate begins (6). Hairs emerge (6). Mammary primordia budding (5); buds branch and hollow (8). Nail reaches finger tip (9). Lanugo hair prominent (7); sheds (10).

Nervous System

Age	Description
3.5	Neural tube closed. Three primary vesicles of brain represented. Nerves and ganglia forming. Ependymal, mantle and marginal layers present.
4	Five brain vesicles. Cerebral hemispheres bulging. Nerves and ganglia better represented. [Suprarenal] cortex accumulating.
5	Three primary flexures of brain represented. Diencephalon large. Nerve plexuses recognizable. Epiphysis recognizable. Sympathetic ganglia forming, segmental masses. Meninges indicated.
6	Cerebral hemispheres becoming large. Corpus striatum and thalamus prominent. Infundibulum and Rathke's pouch in contact. Choroid plexuses appearing. Suprarenal medulla begins invading cortex.
7	Cerebral cortex begins to acquire typical cells. Olfactory lobes visible. Dura and pia-arachnoid distinct. Chromaffin bodies appearing.
8	Spinal cord attains definitive internal structure.
10	Brain attains its general structural features. Cord shows cervical and lumbar enlargements. Cauda equina and filum terminale appearing. Neuroglial types begin to differentiate.
12	Hemispheres conceal much of brain. Cerebral lobes delimited. Corpora quadrigemina appear. Cerebellum assumes some prominence.
16	Commissures completed (5). Myelinization of cord begins (5). Cerebral cortex typically layered (6). Cerebral fissures and convolutions appearing rapidly (7). Myelinization of brain begins (10).

Sense Organs (Eye, Ear, Nose)

Age	Description
	Auditory... closed, detached. Olfactory placode and differentiate nerve cells.
5	Choroid fissure prominent. Lens vesicle free. Vitreous anlage appearing. Octocyst elongates and buds endolymph duct. Olfactory pits deepen.
6	Optic cup shows nervous and pigment layers. Lens vesicle thickens. Eyes set at 160°. Nasolacrimal duct. Modeling of ext., mid. and int. ear under way. Vomero-nasal organ.
7	Choroid fissure closes, enclosing central artery. Nerve fibers invade optic stalk. Lens loses cavity by elongating lens fibers. Eyelids forming. Fibrous and vascular coats of eye indicated. Olfactory sacs open into mouth cavity.
8	Eyes converging rapidly. Ext., mid. and int. ear assuming final form. Taste buds indicated. External nares plugged.
10	Iris and ciliary body organizing. Eyelids fused. Lacrimal glands budding. Spiral organ begins differentiating.
12	Characteristic organization of eye attained. Retina becoming layered. Nasal septum and palate fusions completed.
16	Eye, ear and nose grossly approach typical appearance. General sense organs differentiating.
20–40	Nose and ear ossify (5). Vascular tunic of lens at height (7). Retinal layers completed and light perceptive (7). Taste sense present (7–8). Eyelids reopen (7–8). Mastoid cells unformed (10). Ear deaf at birth.

Urogenital System

Age	Description
8	Ovary distinct as such. Müllerian ducts, bearing sinus, are to unite as utero-vaginal primordium indicated. Ligaments indicated.
10	Able to secrete. Sinus expands as sac. Duct of opposite degenerating. Uro-urethral and vestibular glands appearing. Urethral sacs forming. Uterine horns absorbed. External genitalia attain distinctive features. Kidney rete tubules; complete male duct. Prostate and seminal vesicle appearing. Hollow viscera gaining muscular walls.
12	Kidney attains typical shape and plan. Testis in position for later descent into scrotum. Uterus and vagina recognizable as such. Mesonephros involuted.
20–40	Female urogenital sinus becoming a shallow vestibule (5). Vagina regains lumen (5). Uterine glands appear (7). Scrotum solid until sacs and testes descend (7–9). Kidney tubules cease forming at birth.

initial poor quality that normal, continued development was impossible. If a dead fetus is retained it usually macerates and resorbs, but it may mummify or even calcify into a *litho-pedion* (*i.e.*, "stone child") and persist indefinitely (*C*). Compression produces a *fetus papyraceous*, or "paper-doll fetus" (*D*).

Malformations of the more specific parts of the body will be described later in conjunction with the detailed development of those regions.

THE FETAL MEMBRANES

The beginnings of the yolk sac, amnion, chorion, body stalk and allantois during the second and third weeks of embryonic life have been described in conjunction with the embryos of those periods. The later

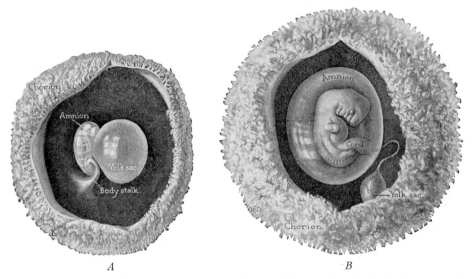

FIG. 79.—Early membranes of human embryos, displayed by opening the chorionic sac. *A*, At 2.6 mm. (× 5); *B*, at 11 mm. (× 2).

histories of these auxiliary organs and the complete developmental course of another, the umbilical cord, will now be traced.

The Yolk Sac.—The entodermal roof of the yolk sac, composed origi-nally of taller cells, provides the primary material from which the gut is fashioned. At first only a slightly narrower region connects the unclosed gut with the yolk sac proper (Fig. 79 *A*). With the further growth of the embryo's body there is progressive constriction of the embryo from the yolk sac. This actual constriction is intensified relatively when both em-bryo and yolk sac continue to enlarge, whereas their region of union lags. The slenderer connection does, however, elongate greatly to become the thread-like *yolk stalk* which soon is incorporated into the umbilical cord (*B*). The yolk stalk detaches from the gut by the end of the fifth week and soon degenerates. Because of its relations, the human yolk sac has sometimes been called the *umbilical vesicle*. It is a pear-shaped sac which attains an average size of 5 mm. by the middle of the second month. It subsequently shrinks somewhat and converts into a solid structure containing detritus. The sac usually persists throughout pregnancy and can frequently be found in the afterbirth, between the amnion and placenta (Figs. 107 and 109 *A*).

Although the human yolk sac is not functional in the sense of storing yolk, it presumably plays some significant rôle that causes it to persist as an early auxiliary organ. The epithelial lining becomes specialized, and blood cells and blood vessels differentiate within the mesodermal covering of the sac. These vessels are of interest as a survival of a necessary nutritional pathway in many vertebrates.

Anomalies.—In 2 per cent. of all adults there is a persistence of the proximal end of the yolk stalk to produce an intestinal pouch, Meckel's *diverticulum of the ileum*. This arises nearly three feet above the beginning of the colon. Although usually a blind sac and less

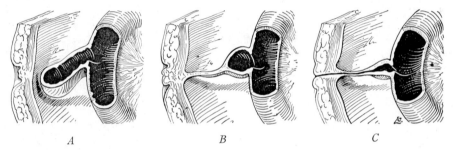

A   B   C

FIG. 80.—Meckel's diverticulum of the ileum. *A*, Ordinary, blind sac. *B*, Diverticulum continued to umbilicus as a cord. *C*, Diverticulum, with fistulous opening at umbilicus.

than ten centimeters long (Fig. 80 *A*), the diverticulum may continue as a cord or band to the region of the umbilicus (*B*). Still more rarely it opens at the navel as a completely pervious duct through which intestinal contents escape; this condition constitutes a fecal *umbilical fistula* (*C*).

Meckel's diverticulum is important surgically since it sometimes telescopes into the intestinal lumen and obstructs it. In other instances when the diverticulum extends to the umbilicus, when its free end fuses to an adjacent peritoneal surface, or when there is a supporting band of mesentery, a loop of the small intestine may become caught and strangulated.

The Amnion.—The margin of the early amnion is attached to the periphery of the embryonic disc, the latter serving as a floor to the amniotic cavity (Fig. 65). As the embryonic disc grows and takes the form of an embryo, this line of attachment becomes limited to the ventral body wall (Fig. 79 *A*) and then decreases in relative size until it bounds the umbilical area. With the development of the umbilical cord, the amnion near the umbilicus applies itself to the cord as an external covering layer (Figs. 79 *B* and 82). The amnion becomes a thin (but tough), transparent, nonvascular membrane. It is lined, next the amniotic cavity, with a single layer of ectodermal epithelium; the external covering is mesodermal connective tissue. The amniotic cavity enlarges rapidly as the fast-growing amnion expands at the expense of the extra-embryonic cœlom, and at the end of the second month fills the chorionic sac (Fig. 82 C). The amnion then fuses loosely with the chorionic wall, the two fibrous layers combining; this naturally results in the obliteration of the extra-embryonic body cavity.

Clear, watery amniotic fluid fills the sac. It is at least mostly of fetal origin, secreted in part by the kidneys and perhaps by the cord, skin and amnion as well, but these problems are not yet wholly solved.[9] During the early months of pregnancy the embryo is suspended in this fluid by its umbilical cord; thus immersed, the flabby embryo maintains its shape successfully and is able to mold further its body form. Also throughout gestation the amniotic fluid performs several mechanical functions: it serves as a protective water cushion which absorbs jolts, equalizes pressures, prevents adherence of the amnion, and permits change of fetal posture. Amniotic fluid is swallowed by the fetus at least as early as the fifth month.[10] At childbirth the amniotic sac acts as a hydrostatic wedge to help dilate the neck of the uterus. During the early stages of childbirth the membranes usually rupture and about a liter of amniotic fluid escapes as the 'waters.' If the tough amnion fails to burst, the head is delivered enveloped in it and this cap is then known popularly as the 'caul.'

FIG. 81.—Vesicular, or hydatidiform mole (DeLee). × ½.

Anomalies.—When the amount of amniotic fluid exceeds two liters the condition is designated *polyhydramnios*. A volume less than one-half liter constitutes *oligohydramnios*, and a marked deficiency may allow the amnion to adhere to the embryo and cause injury. It should be emphasized, however, that the fibrous *amniotic bands*, so-called, which at times interconnect the amnion and fetus appear to be the products of local necroses of fetal tissues, rather than primary amniotic derivatives that cause specific injuries by attaching to the fetus.[11]

The Chorion.—Previous descriptions have traced the differentiation of the primitive capsule of trophoblastic tissue into a shaggy sac which encloses the embryo and all other fetal membranes (Fig. 79). The chief significance of the chorion and its villi is in relation to the development of the placenta. This important topic will be treated in the next chapter.

Anomalies.—Occasionally a degenerating chorionic sac transforms its villi into series of fluid-filled bladders up to the size of a pea (Fig. 81). This constitutes a *vesicular*, or *hydatidi-*

form mole which as a whole may attain huge size. The trophoblast may become a malignant, invasive tumor known as a *chorio-epithelioma*.

The Allantois.—Precocious in origin and insignificant in size, the human allantois does not follow the usual mammalian method of evaginating

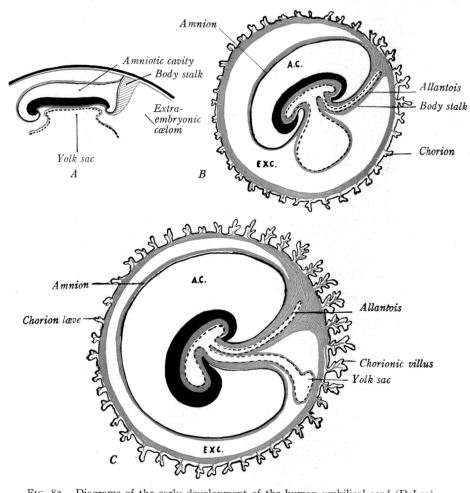

FIG. 82.—Diagrams of the early development of the human umbilical cord (DeLee).
   a.c., Amniotic cavity; *exc.*, extra-embryonic cœlom; solid black, ectoderm; red, mesoderm; dotted black, entoderm.

directly into the extra-embryonic cœlom. Since, however, the body stalk which receives the entodermal, allantoic tube represents mesoderm across which the cœlom has failed to pass (Fig. 64 *B–D*), the fundamental relations are similar to those in lower animals. In fact, the body stalk can be considered as allantoic mesoderm which is established somewhat before the arrival of the entodermal component.

The allantois of man never becomes saccular. Its tiny, entodermal tube extends within the body stalk as far as the chorion, and when the developing umbilical cord includes the allantois as a component, the latter at first is as long as the cord itself (Fig. 82). Soon, however, growth ceases, and interruption and obliteration follow. Allantoic (umbilical) blood vessels continue onto the chorion and vascularize it. When the chorion becomes a part of the placenta, this latter organ performs all the functions of nutrition, respiration and excretion. Physiologically the allantoic tube is a superseded rudiment. The only significant feature of the organ as a

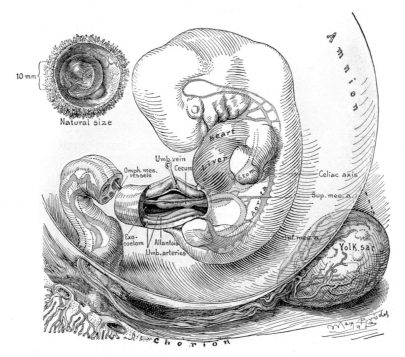

FIG. 83.—Relations of the umbilical cord in a human embryo of six weeks (Cullen). × 6. Near the embryo, the cord has been opened and cut across.

whole lies in the accompanying blood vessels which put the embryo into close physiological relation with the maternal circulation.

Anomalies.—The allantois apparently lies wholly within the umbilical cord and is not responsible for anomalies of the urachus sometimes charged against it.

The Umbilical Cord.—As the embryo enlarges, its ventral unclosed area becomes relatively smaller and even undergoes some constriction (Fig. 82 *A*, *B*). This region, at the junction of embryonic and extra-embryonic territories, is the primitive *umbilicus*. At its margin the amnion and the somatopleuric belly wall become continuous, while through the unclosed umbilical ring extend both the yolk stalk and the body stalk with its included allantois. During the fifth week a cylindrical structure, the *umbilical cord*, comes into existence through the expanding amnion wrapping itself around the body stalk and yolk stalk as it crowds them together (Figs. 79 *B* and 82 *C*).[11, 12] Hence the umbilical cord is an auxiliary organ and not an outgrowth or extension of the body wall. In addition to the components already mentioned, a part of the extra-embryonic cœlom is enclosed within the cord for a time (Fig. 83). The portion of this cœlom nearest the body of the embryo enlarges greatly and during the seventh to tenth weeks contains coils of the intestine which herniate into it. After the

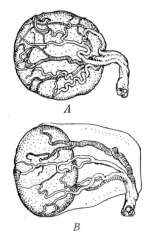

A

B

FIG. 84.—Anomalous insertions of the umbilical cord. *A*, Marginal attachment. *B*, Velamentous attachment on membranes adjoining the placenta.

intestine is withdrawn, the cavity of the cord obliterates by the encroachment of the mesodermal tissue of the cord. Such obliteration marks the disappearance of the last remnant of the extra-embryonic cœlom. Until the end of gestation the umbilical cord continues to connect the fetus with the part of the chorion that constitutes the fetal side of the placenta.

The umbilical cord is covered with the mostly single-layered epithelium of the enveloping amnion. It contains, embedded in mucous tissue, the following structures (Fig. 83): (1) the yolk stalk and its vitelline blood vessels; (2) the allantois; and (3) the allantoic, or umbilical blood vessels (two arteries and a single, larger vein). The *mucous tissue* or jelly of Wharton, peculiar to the umbilical cord, differentiates from the mesenchyme included in the cord at the time of its formation; it is rich in mucoid jelly, poor in fibers and contains neither intrinsic blood vessels nor nerves. In the early months of pregnancy remnants of the yolk stalk, vitelline vessels and allantois are to be seen, and the latter may continue even to birth.

The mature cord is about one-half inch in diameter and attains an average length equal to that of the full-term fetus (about two feet). Its insertion on the placenta is usually slightly eccentric (Fig. 109 *A*). A spiral twist soon appears, which may finally number as many as forty turns. Several explanations have been proposed to account for this spiraling.[13] The blood vessels frequently curl in loops (by stronger local growth or perhaps, in part, by a local unwinding); these cause external bulgings known as *false knots* (Fig. 109 *A*).

Anomalies.—The extremes of length for the human cord range from almost nothing to six feet. Abnormal shortness leads to practical difficulties at the time of delivery, and extreme shortness can cause distortion of the fetus. The production of atrophy and amputation through the cord winding about the neck or extremities of a fetus is often alleged, but without convincing proof. The umbilical cord may attach to the margin of a placenta (Fig. 84 *A*) or even on the adjoining membranes (*B*). Sometimes the fetus slips through a looped cord in such a way as to produce a simple *true knot* (Fig. 109 *A*). Failure of the intestine to retract from its temporary location in the cord results in *umbilical hernia* (Fig. 191 *D*), while a secondary protrusion after the intestine is normally withdrawn can produce the same final condition.

DETERMINATION OF THE AGE OF EMBRYOS

The determination of the exact age of a recovered human embryo is beset with difficulties. For the practitioner it is fortunate that significant errors concern chiefly the rarer specimens of the early weeks. Development starts with fertilization and if this date could be determined reliably, the age-problem would largely disappear. But the available data, usually supplied by the unaided memory of the patient, too often are either incorrect or, at least, open to alternative interpretation as to the probable time of conception. This lack of a reliable starting date for most pregnancies makes further computation but approximate. On the other hand, the terminal age-date of a healthy embryo whose normal growth has been interrupted by operation is definite, and the true age of such a specimen (whether determinable or not) is the interval since fertilization. But some embryos experience a progressively slowing growth rate prior to their operative removal or spontaneous abortion. Moreover, aborted embryos commonly are not only dead, but have been retained in this condition for a time before extrusion occurs. In neither instance is the recovery date of much value with respect to normal age spans.

It is impossible more than to approximate the time of fertilization. Even in fortunate cases when the occasion of an isolated, fruitful coitus is surely known, it can only be assumed that fertilization should have occurred, on the average, one day after such coitus. Accordingly, in the common absence of a reliable coital history it becomes important to determine the probable time of ovulation. If this could be set, the fertilization date would then be indirectly established within a day—for the reason that the egg loses its fertilizability so rapidly. In a previous discussion of the time relation between ovulation and menstruation (p. 43) it was stated that ovulation occurs most commonly at the middle of the menstrual month; nevertheless, it is well recognized that this is at best an average, and oftentimes ova are liberated either earlier or later.

Thus it is approximately correct to compute the age of an embryo *from the fourteenth day after the onset of the last menstruation*. There are, however, two practical difficulties which may make such a reckoning unreliable in any specific case. First, deviation from the average time of ovulation; some clinicians even contend that there is no day of the cycle

6

on which instances of conception have not been proved.[14] Second, bleeding that resembles menstruation (the 'placental sign') not infrequently appears in early pregnancies to obscure the true time of the last normal menstruation.[15]

For ordinary purposes it is both convenient and reasonably accurate to compare a given specimen with a standard age- and size-table. These norms have been established through careful studies on fetuses that were accompanied by fairly adequate clinical histories. It is, however, necessary to understand that such tables merely state averages, whereas the normal size-range varies appreciably above or below the means listed. Furthermore, size alone is rather unreliable as a basis of comparison in the first month; more important is the state of structural development which advances in definite, orderly sequence.

Embryos are measured in two principal ways (Fig. 85). Commonest is the *crown-rump length* (designated *CR*), or sitting height; this is the dis-

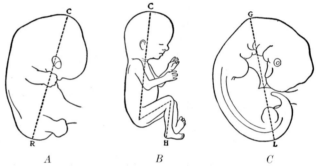

FIG. 85.—Measurement of embryos. *A*, Crown-rump length; *B*, crown-heel length; *C*, neck-rump length, or greatest length.

tance from vertex to breech. The other measurement is the *crown-heel length (CH)*, or standing height. In embryos of about four weeks, when the head is greatly flexed, it is often more practical to use the neck-rump measurement, or *greatest length (GL)*. The table on page 115 lists some statistical averages for human embryos of definite ages. The lengths of embryos between three and eight weeks should be memorized at the outset, because frequent reference will be made to these ages and sizes.

Handy rules for calculating the greatest length in inches of an embryo or fetus (including the legs when this measure increases the total length) are as follows:

For the first five months, add the numbers of the previous months.
Examples: At 1 month = 0 (actually, 0.1 inch)
At 4 months, 1 + 2 + 3 = 6 (actually, 6.2 inches)
For the last five months, multiply the number of the month by two.
Example: At 8 months, 8 × 2 = 16 (actually, 16.1 inches)

RELATIONS OF AGE, SIZE AND WEIGHT IN THE HUMAN EMBRYO

Age of Embryo	Crown-rump Length (mm.)	Crown-heel Length (mm.)	External Diameter of Chorionic Sac (mm.)	Weight in Grams	Ratio of Increase Each Month When Value at Start of Month Equals Unity	
					CR Length	Weight
One week	0.1*	.....	0.2			
Two weeks	0.2*	.....	3			
Three weeks	2.0	.....	10			
Four weeks	5.0	.....	20	.02	49.0	40000.00
Five weeks	8.0	.....	25			
Six weeks	12.0	.....	30			
Seven weeks	17.0	19.0	40			
Second lunar month	23.0	30.0	50	1	3.6	49.00
Third lunar month	56.0	73.0	....	14	1.4	13.00
Fourth lunar month	112.0	157.0	....	105	1.0	6.50
Fifth lunar month	160.0	239.0	....	310	0.43	1.95
Sixth lunar month	203.0	296.0	....	640	0.26	1.07
Seventh lunar month	242.0	355.0	....	1080	0.14	0.69
Eighth lunar month	277.0	409.0	....	1670	0.14	0.55
Ninth lunar month	313.0	458.0	....	2400	0.13	0.43
Full term (266 days)	350.0	500.0	....	3300	0.12	0.38

* Total length of embryonic disc.

Of practical interest is the determination of the date of delivery of a pregnant woman. The average time for delivery is ten lunar months, or 280 days, from the beginning of the last menstrual period. This period of 280 days should not be confused with the duration of pregnancy (*i.e.*, the age of the fetus) which is about two weeks less. Two-thirds of all deliveries vary not more than 11 days above and below the mean of 280. The expected delivery date can be set by counting back three calendar months from the first day of the last period, and then adding a year and one week. This date is, of course, only a forecast based on averages. Since bleeding, which is mistaken for menstruation, sometimes occurs after pregnancy begins and since there is some normal variation in the length of pregnancy, the computation may prove unreliable in any particular case.

For comparison and reference, the gestation periods and average number of young of a few representative mammals are appended (p. 116). Some of these in a sense are premature at birth. The newborn rat is blind, hairless and helpless. At the other extreme, the guinea pig is well developed, able to walk and even to eat solid food. The weight of the newborn in comparison to the mother ranges from 0.1 per cent. in the polar bear to 33 per cent. in the bat.

VIABILITY AND LONGEVITY

The survival-ability of the protoplasm with which a fertilized egg (and hence the future individual) is endowed varies enormously.[16] Some ova succumb early in development and others later; in all, about one pregnancy in three is unsuccessful, largely because the embryos are not vigorous enough to reach birth as living individuals. Moreover, this selective elimination does not cease at birth but continues throughout the life span. A person reaching middle age has realized the expected viability of an egg of average quality; on the other hand, an individual attaining old age comes from an egg with great initial energy, balance and resistance. But not only do ova as a whole differ in endurance, vulnerability and capacity for growth, but the several organs and parts also are similarly variable. Some relatively unimportant organs, such as teeth and hair, suffer a natural early decline, yet this does not matter. When, however, a functionally important organ fails, for whose loss the rest of the body cannot compensate, then life is imperiled. In this instance an otherwise competent human machine meets an untimely death merely because of a single, defective, critical organ, such as the heart. By contrast, frail individuals frequently totter into old age because they are originally well balanced and have no vulnerable weakness.

This concept of the importance of the quality of the eggs from which mankind traces origin is fundamental. To a certain degree its implications are fatalistic, yet there are other interacting factors in the total equation besides the innate quality of inherited protoplasm. Chance and a hostile, local environment may cut short a life intended for long performance. On the other hand, an intelligently ordered existence can do much to conserve constitutional endowments to their full expectancy.

COMPARATIVE DATA CONCERNING GESTATION IN MAMMALS

Animal	Gestation Period	No. in Litter	Animal	Gestation Period	No. in Litter
Opossum	13 days	8	Macacus monkey	24 weeks	1
Mouse; rat	20; 22 da.	6; 8	Man; manlike apes	38 weeks	1
Rabbit	32 days	6	Cow	40 weeks	1
Cat; dog; guinea pig	9 weeks	4– 6	Mare	48 weeks	1
Sow	17 weeks	6–12	Rhinoceros	18 months	1
Sheep; goat	21 weeks	1– 2	Elephant	20 months	1

REFERENCES CITED

1. Hertig, A. T. and Rock, J. 1945. Carnegie Contrib. Embryol., 31, No. 200, 65–84.
2. Hertig, A. T. and Rock, J. 1941. Carnegie Contrib. Embryol., 29, No. 184, 127–156.
3. Streeter, G. L. 1941. Carnegie Contrib. Embryol., 29, No. 181, 37–40.
4. Heuser, C. H. 1941. Carnegie Contrib. Embryol., 29, No. 181, 35–37.
5. Streeter, G. L. 1927. Carnegie Contrib. Embryol., 19, No. 100, 73–92.
6. Pasteels, J. 1937. Arch. de Biol., 48, 381–488.
7. Holmdahl, D. E. 1935. Zeitschr. f. mikr.-anat. Forsch., 38, 409–440.
8. Grünwald, P. 1941. Jour. Morph., 69, 83–125.
9. Needham, J. 1931. Chemical Embryology; vol. 3. Macmillan, N. Y.
10. Reifferscheid, W. and Schmiemann, R. 1939. Zentralbl. f. Gynäk., 63, 146–153.
11. Streeter, G. L. 1930. Carnegie Contrib. Embryol., 22, No. 126, 1–44.
12. Politzer, G. and Sternberg, H. 1930. Zeitschr. f. Anat. u. Entwickl., 92, 279–379.
13. Shordania, J. 1929. Zeitschr. f. Anat. u. Entwickl., 89, 696–726.
14. Weinstock, F. 1934. Zentralbl. f. Gynäk., 58, 2947–2952.
15. Brewer, J. L. 1937. Amer. Jour. Anat., 61, 429–481.
16. Streeter, G. L. 1931. Sci. Monthly, 32, 495–506.

CHAPTER VII

HUMAN PLACENTATION

The subject of *placentation* includes all the events related to the establishment of the embryo within the uterus of the mother, to the development of a placenta, and to the fetal-uterine association throughout pregnancy.

TRANSPORT OF THE OVUM AND BLASTOCYST

The fertilized and cleaving egg is propelled down the central cavity of the uterine tube, guided by the longitudinal folds of its lining membrane

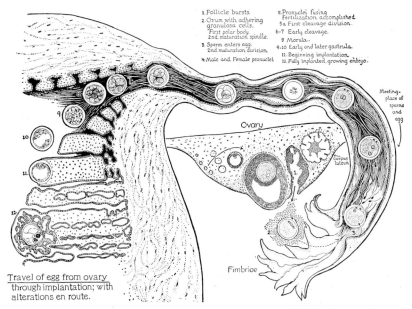

1. Follicle bursts.
2. Ovum with adhering granulosa cells. First polar body. 2nd. maturation spindle.
3. Sperm enters egg. 2nd. maturation division.
4. Male and Female pronuclei

5. Pronuclei fusing Fertilization accomplished.
5a First cleavage division.
6-7 Early cleavage.
8 Morula.
9-10 Early and later gastrula.
11. Beginning implantation.
12. Fully implanted, growing embryo.

Ovary

Meeting-place of sperms and egg

Corpus luteum

Fimbriae

Travel of egg from ovary through implantation; with alterations en route.

FIG. 86.—Stages of the developing human ovum, at various levels in its journey from ovary to uterus (Dickinson).

(Fig. 86). In known mammals, except carnivores, the tubal journey requires three days. That muscular contractions, rather than ciliary activity, are the effective agent is implied by the uniformity of this period of time despite great differences in the lengths of tubes (*e.g.*, mouse; cow), and by differences in the rate of travel from one level of the tube to another. This conclusion has been strengthened by direct observations on rodents.[1, 2] Such muscular force is not directed against the almost microscopic egg itself but against the fluid in which the egg is suspended.

The developing human egg presumably enters the uterus on the fourth day after ovulation, as does the egg of the monkey. The period spent in the uterus as a free morula and blastocyst varies considerably among mammals; in man it is about three days. During this interval there is further transport to the site where attachment and embedding will occur. It is suspected that muscular activity may again be responsible for this transfer.[3]

PREPARATION OF THE UTERUS FOR THE EMBRYO

There is no information as to what determines the site 'selected' by the blastocyst for attachment. If it is not chance there is, at least, no

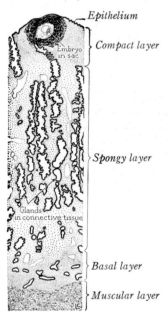

FIG. 87.—Vertical section of the human endometrium, with an implanted blastocyst of eleven days (after Hertig and Rock). × 15.

visible sign of special preparation or predetermination in the area finally used. Instead, the entire lining of the uterus, except in the region of its neck, is in a state of special preparation for the reception of the embryo. This favorable condition is a phase of the monthly cycle of change controlled by the ovarian hormones. The details of these correlated phenomena will be discussed in the next chapter. For the present it is sufficient to state that the lining membrane has thickened markedly (5 mm., more or less); it is well vascularized, and the glands are dilated and contain glycogen and other secreted material.

The uterine lining is a mucous membrane named the *endometrium* (Fig. 87). Its exposed surface is covered with a single-layered epithelium which dips inward at intervals to produce the tubular *uterine glands*. Beneath the surface epithelium and between the glands is a soft, cellular connective tissue. The appearance of the endometrium changes somewhat at different depths. Nearest the uterine cavity is the *compact layer* through which pass the slender necks of the glands. Next deeper is the thick *spongy layer*, characterized by the dilated portions of the glands. Deepest of all is the thin *basal layer* which contains the blind ends of the glands; it does not participate to any extent in the glandular and other changes characteristic of the menstrual cycle and pregnancy. For this reason, the compact and spongy layers are often spoken of as the *functional layer* of the endometrium.

IMPLANTATION

Implantation includes the attachment of the blastocyst to the epithelial lining of the uterus, the penetration of the blastocyst through the epithelium, and its embedding in the compact layer of the endometrium.

The follicular cells that adhere to the freshly discharged ovum, as the corona radiata, are lost during the journey down the tube. Shortly before implantation begins, the encapsulating zona pellucida disappears as well. This release permits the blastocyst to come into direct contact with the uterine epithelium and makes future growth possible. The human blastocyst probably begins to attach on the late sixth or early seventh day after ovulation. Since stages of its attachment and penetration are lacking, reliance must be placed on the detailed information gained from the monkey.[4] The sticky, somewhat swollen blastocyst first adheres to the uterine epithelium (Figs. 88 and 89 *A*). In this region of contact, between the mouths of glands, the trophoblastic wall of the blastocyst thickens and its more superficial cells lose their boundaries and become a syncytium. At the same time the cells of the uterine epithelium in the area of attachment begin to break down, apparently as the result of some influence (digestive

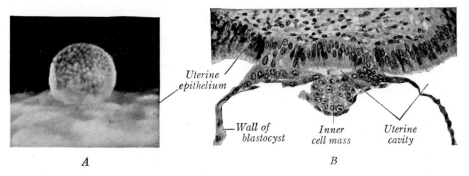

A   *B*

FIG. 88.—Attachment of the blastocyst of the monkey to the uterine epithelium at nine days (Heuser and Streeter). *A*, Total view, from side ($\times$ 50). *B*, Median section of the same specimen, showing fusion at two points. ($\times$ 200).

enzyme?) exerted by the trophoblast. The injured cells are taken up by the trophoblast and digested. This erosion creates a gap in the epithelium through which the invading trophoblast advances and comes into relation with the connective tissue beneath (Fig. 89 *B*).

At this point the series of human specimens begins. The youngest was not more than seven and one-half days old; implantation probably had been in progress for 24 to 36 hours.[5] This blastocyst had advanced through the epithelial gap, was pushing into the soft tissue beyond, but still was largely uncovered (Figs. 89 *C* and 90 *A*). Wherever the trophoblast had made contact with maternal tissues it is mostly syncytial and remarkably thickened (Fig. 60).

The next known stage, two days older, lay largely buried within the compact layer of the endometrium (Fig. 89 *D*).[5] Rapid growth of the trophoblast had produced a thick, spongy shell. The original wall of the blastocyst was composed of distinct cells, but the trophoblastic shell now consists of a relatively thin layer of such cells (*cytotrophoblast*), next the cavity of the blastocyst, and a very thick peripheral layer (*syntrophoblast*)

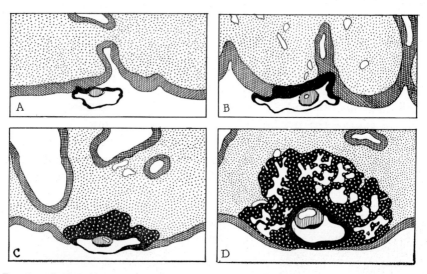

FIG. 89.—Stages of implantation, shown by sections (× 90). *A, B,* Attachment of blastocyst and epithelial erosion in the monkey at nine and ten days (after Wislocki and Streeter). *C, D,* Advance of human blastocyst through epithelial gap and into uterine connective tissue at seven and nine days (after Hertig and Rock). Cellular trophoblast, solid black; syncytial trophoblast, mottled black; epithelium, crosshatched; connective tissue, stippled.

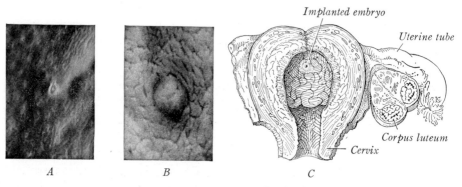

FIG. 90.—Implantation sites of human embryos, in surface view. *A,* At seven days (Hertig and Rock; × 8); *cf.* Fig. 60. *B,* At eleven days (Hertig and Rock; × 8); *cf.* Fig. 61. *C,* At fifteen days (after Ramsey; × ⅔).

in which nuclei lie embedded in a common cytoplasmic mass (Fig. 92). The cellular trophoblast is the parent tissue which produces the synctium by cell division, loss of cell membranes and change in cytoplasmic character.

The appearance of a completely implanted embryo, five to six days after attachment began, is shown in Figures 61, 87 and 90 B.[6] The original point of entry into the endometrium is sealed with a fibrinous and cellular plug known as the *closing coagulum*. The processes of wound healing, already begun, will cause it to disappear in less than a week. It is plain that a blastocyst is definitely oriented during its penetration and afterward. The side bearing the inner cell mass, or future embryo proper, is the surface that attaches, leads the way in penetration and lies deepest when implantation is completed. Figure 90 C illustrates the internal appearance of a uterus, containing an implanted embryo of 17 days (11 days after attachment), at three-fifths natural size. The site of implantation varies some-

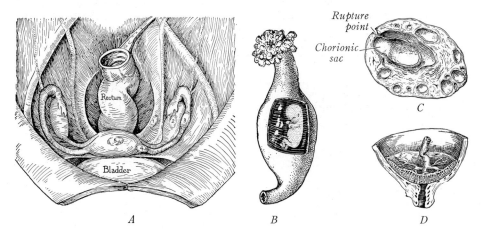

FIG. 91.—Atypical implantation sites in woman. *A*, Diagram, in ventral view, of the locations in which pregnancies may occur: 1, abdominal; 2, ovarian; 3, tubal; 4, interstitial; 5, uterine. *B*, Tubal pregnancy, with a window cut in the tubal wall ($\times \frac{1}{2}$). *C*, Ovarian pregnancy (after Mall and Cullen; $\times \frac{3}{4}$). *D*, Placenta prævia, at the cervix of a hemisected uterus ($\times \frac{1}{5}$).

what, although it is usually at a high level in the uterus, and commonest (and with equal frequency) on either the front or back wall.

Anomalies.—If the fertilized egg fails to reach the uterus, but implants and develops elsewhere, the condition is known as an extra-uterine or *ectopic pregnancy* (Fig. 91 *A*). The commonest ectopic site is the uterine tube (*tubal pregnancy; B*). Primary attachment to the peritoneum (*abdominal pregnancy*) and the development of an unexpelled egg within its ruptured follicle (*ovarian pregnancy; C*) are known also. Continued ectopic growth to maturity is rarely achieved because of the unsuitability of the locations chosen and the inadequacy of the placental arrangements developed at these sites. Pregnant tubes frequently rupture; in some instances the chorionic sac is expelled and secondarily becomes an abdominal pregnancy.

Occasionally the embryo locates in the right or left side of the uterus. Still less frequently it implants near the neck of the uterus, so that the expanding placenta covers the cervical canal (Fig. 91 *D*). This latter condition is called *placenta prævia* (*i.e.*, placenta leading the way).

ESTABLISHMENT OF THE EMBRYO IN THE ENDOMETRIUM

Even as the blastocyst is becoming implanted, its trophoblastic wall (*i.e.*, the future chorion) starts on a course of specialization which will put it in intimate physiological relation with the endometrium. This is not a one-sided adjustment, since the maternal tissues, as well, adapt themselves to the new relations and demands. Both sets of co-ordinated changes lead to the production of the specialized *placenta*, which is the medium of physiological interchange between the mother and fetus throughout the period of pregnancy. The implanted blastocyst is located superficially in the endometrium (Fig. 87). Although it expands greatly as development proceeds, it does not actually encroach beyond the compact layer (Fig. 95).

Trophoblastic Lacunæ.—A prominent feature of the syncytium is the appearance within it of vacuoles which merge and produce irregular cavities, or *lacunæ* (Figs. 89 *D* and 92).[6] This process produces a communicating

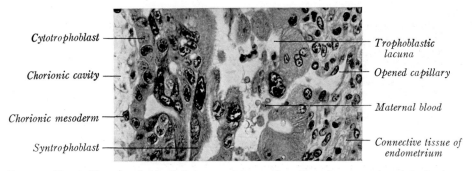

Cytotrophoblast

Chorionic cavity

Chorionic mesoderm

Syntrophoblast

Trophoblastic lacuna

Opened capillary

Maternal blood

Connective tissue of endometrium

FIG. 92.—Trophoblast, trophoblastic lacunæ and a tapped capillary from a section of the implanting sac of a human embryo of eleven days (Hertig and Rock). × 320.

labyrinth which adds to itself progressively by incorporating new lacunæ as fast as they appear in the growing, expanding syncytium. This system of channels, which gives the trophoblast its spongy texture, is the beginning of the future *intervillous space* of the placenta. In the week following implantation this labyrinth becomes well developed.

Vascular Relations.—Connections are quickly established between the trophoblastic lacunæ and the uterine blood vessels (Fig. 92). Although some minute branches of the spiral arterioles are tapped, the chief communications during this early period are with enlarged capillaries, which connect arterioles and venules, and with the venules themselves.[6] Within a week after implantation there are prominent sinus-like venules beneath the embedded sac. At first the blood within the trophoblastic lacunæ is small in amount and relatively stagnant. Later the number of vessels coming directly from arterioles increases and the flow of blood improves (Fig. 95). An outstanding characteristic of all trophoblast is that, like endothelium, it does not provoke blood into clotting. The uterine connective tissue in the vicinity of the young chorionic sac is edematous and contains extravasated blood.

Endometrial Erosion.—The trophoblast is an invasive tissue which spreads peripherally into the maternal tissues. Paralleling this invasion goes a certain amount of destruction of the endometrial tissues; this erosion is characteristic of the *border zone* where trophoblast and endometrium meet. Some dissolution is apparently related to inadequacies of the blood supply, similar to the necrosis that precedes menstruation. Other destruction is due to trophoblastic influence (digestive enzyme?). The erosive processes are declining in intensity by the end of the third week. At all times erosion is a mild process, under control.

Both the cellular and syncytial trophoblast have the capacity of ingesting maternal tissue, although most of this tissue has undergone a

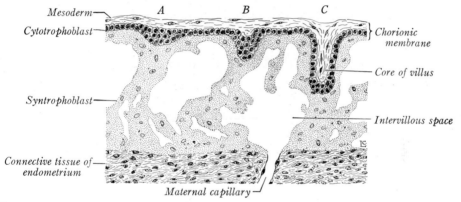

FIG. 93.—Stages in the projection of secondary villi from the chorionic wall of an implanted embryo of two weeks. × about 100.

certain degree of necrosis before phagocytosis occurs. Blood cells of all kinds and reticular fibers are the identifiable elements found most commonly within the young trophoblastic cells.[7] In addition, there is granular and amorphous material in the process of digestion. Such substance (*histotroph*) is presumably utilized for nourishment in the early period of establishment, as is also blood plasma and tissue fluid.

The Chorionic Villi.—The cellular trophoblast of the globular chorionic sac tends to be single-layered, except where proliferation has produced local masses. These masses extend a short distance into the plates and strands of syntrophoblast and indicate a first stage in the development of *chorionic villi* (Fig. 93 A). Just as the cytotrophoblast differentiates the mesodermal lining (future connective tissue) of the chorion, so also it differentiates the core of vascular connective tissue within villi.[8, 9] At first this tissue is only a stubby center at the base of a villus (B) but, as the

cytotrophoblast proliferates and sends columns outward, the axial connective tissue extends likewise (*C*). Continued growth and branching bring
a tuft-like chorionic villus into being (Fig. 94). By the end of the third
week the young villi are becoming well formed and vascularized (Fig. 95).

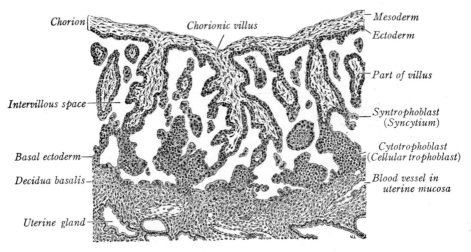

FIG. 94.—Part of the human placental site, at seventeen days, in vertical section. × 65.

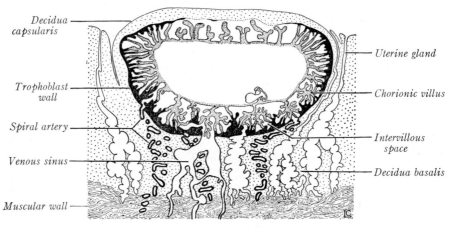

FIG. 95.—Vertical section of an implanted human embryo of twenty-two days, showing the relations of the chorionic sac to the endometrium (after Ortmann). × 2.

Sometimes this definitive type is called *secondary villi* in contrast to the
earlier plates of pure trophoblast which are known as *primary villi*.

Establishment Completed.—Toward the end of the third week the
essential arrangements have been accomplished which make possible the
physiological interchanges between mother and fetus that will characterize
the remainder of pregnancy (Figs. 95 and 101). Blood vessels (allantoic

arteries and veins) pass from the embryo through the body stalk to the connective tissue of the chorion, and then extend into the chorionic villi. This vascularized connective tissue of the chorion and its villi is everywhere covered with trophoblast, which consists of an inner cellular layer and an outer, or superficial, syncytial layer. Trophoblast also forms a carpet over the eroded surface of the endometrium and receives the ends of many villous branches. All this trophoblast bounds the *intervillous space* as a complete, common lining. In these labyrinthine channels maternal blood circulates and bathes the villi. The passage of nutritive substances from the circulating blood of the mother to that of the fetus within the vessels of the villi is often spoken of as *hemotrophic nutrition*. It is contrasted with the early *histotrophic nutrition* in which the damaged maternal tissues, extravasated blood and the stagnant blood in the trophoblastic lacunæ are taken up by the trophoblast.

The fetal-maternal relations during the fourth week are illustrated in Figure 95. By this time the setting is complete for the establishment of a definite placenta, but its history and detailed structure must be postponed until the endometrium as a whole in pregnancy has been described.

THE DECIDUAL MEMBRANES

The mucosal lining (endometrium) of the uterus, already altered in anticipation of pregnancy and utilized as a nesting place by the implanting embryo, rapidly acquires the characteristics of pregnancy and then persists throughout the gestation period. Naturally enough, the greatest disturbance of natural relations occurs in the part of the endometrium where the embryo lies. Yet the remainder of the membrane becomes involved after a time and then experiences characteristic alterations as well.

The fusions that take place between the entire endometrium and the expanding chorion (which eventually comes in contact with it everywhere) lead to a general splitting off of the uterine lining at birth. The mucosa of the pregnant uterus is, therefore, named the *decidua* (*i.e.*, that which falls off). Its preparation for pregnancy, the long deferred loss at delivery and the subsequent repair after childbirth extend and exaggerate the events of an ordinary menstrual cycle. The decidual membranes are actually a direct continuation and further elaboration of the premenstrual (also called 'progravid') type of mucosa.

Even when the early chorionic sac lies embedded within the endometrium, three regions of this thickened membrane can be recognized (Figs. 96 and 97): (1) The *decidua parietalis*, the general lining of the uterus exclusive of the region occupied by the embryo. (2) The *decidua capsularis*, a region covering the chorionic sac and interposed between the sac and the uterine cavity. (3) The *decidua basalis*, a region underlying the chorionic sac and situated between it and the muscular wall of the uterus.

The decidua parietalis, a membrane not directly involved in lodging the embryo, is at first a typical, undisturbed part of the endometrium of

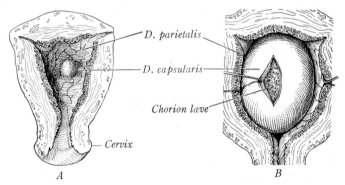

FIG. 96.—Elevation of the human decidua capsularis by the expanding chorionic sac. *A*, At nearly four weeks ($\times \frac{1}{2}$); *B*, at ten weeks ($\times \frac{2}{3}$).

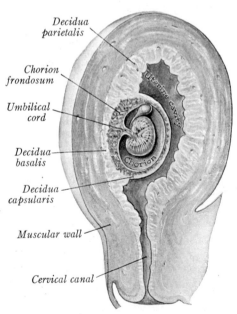

FIG. 97.—Gravid human uterus of five weeks, hemisected to show the decidual relations. $\times$ 1.

pregnancy. Quite different are the other two decidual membranes. Since the chorionic sac separates the decidua capsularis from the decidua basalis, neither of these two membranes contains all the levels of the typical endometrium.

Mention has been made previously of the distinctive vascular and glandular specializations that the endometrium builds up in preparation for pregnancy. Another conspicuous specialization is the *decidual cells*. These are greatly enlarged connective-tissue cells which occur chiefly in the compact layer (Fig. 99). Their course of specialization begins during implantation and, although declining in size and numbers, they remain throughout pregnancy as characteristic constituents of the deciduæ. The decidual cells are large, rounded elements which store glycogen and may contain more than one nucleus. Their size and proliferative increase help account for the thickness of young deciduæ; as a result, the surface of the early decidua parietalis folds characteristically (Fig. 96 *A*). The full significance of the decidual cells is not understood.

The Decidua Parietalis.—The general, nonplacental lining of the gravid uterus has long been called the *decidua vera*, but the term *decidua* *parietalis* is descriptively preferable (Fig. 97). The compact layer becomes thick; it contains the narrower segments of the uterine glands, embedded in large quantities of decidual cells. Its surface epithelium has usually disappeared by the end of the third month, at which time contact with the expanding decidua capsularis takes place. The spongy layer is characterized for a while by the enlarged and sacculated portions of the uterine glands, carried over from their progravid state.

For the first two months of gestation the long axes of the uterine glands stand vertically with respect to the mucosa. Later, as the parietal decidua is stretched (through expansion of the uterus) and compressed (through growth of the sac containing the fetus), the glands broaden and their cavities become elongate clefts parallel to the surface (Fig. 99). The period

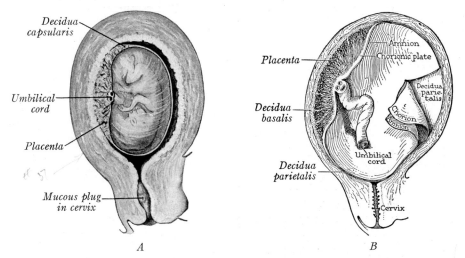

FIG. 98.—Gravid uteri, hemisected to show the obliteration of the uterine cavity. *A*, At three months ($\times \frac{1}{2}$). *B*, At seven months; fetus removed and flaps of the amnion and chorion cut and reflected ($\times \frac{1}{3}$).

of growth and thickening of the decidua parietalis is limited to the first three or four months of pregnancy, during which time it attains a maximum thickness of about one-half inch. Later it becomes thinner, loses much of its early vascularity and exhibits actual regressive changes. The uterine cervix does not elaborate a decidua; its glands, however, do enlarge and secrete a *mucous plug* which closes the uterus during the period of gestation (Fig. 98 *A*).

The Decidua Capsularis.—The superficial portion of the compact endometrium that originally covers the chorionic sac and faces the uterine cavity is the *decidua capsularis*. Growth of the sac causes the capsularis to elevate into a progressively expanding dome (Fig. 96). In the earlier stages of pregnancy blood vessels and some glandular traces occur in the substance of this layer, while its surface epithelium is continuous with that of the decidua parietalis. As the chorionic sac expands, the capsularis grows thin and atrophic (Fig. 99 *A*). At the end of the third month its full surface comes into contact with the decidua parietalis with which it fuses, thereby obliterating the uterine cavity (Fig. 98). During the next three months the capsularis degenerates and disappears; this leaves the chorion free to become adherent to the decidua parietalis for the remainder of pregnancy (Fig. 99 *B*). Long before this, the amnion has fused loosely with the chorion. At term the combined thickness of all these membranes has reduced to 2 mm. or less.

With the obliteration of the uterine cavity at three months, the only cavity within the uterus for the remainder of pregnancy is that of the amniotic sac (Fig. 107).

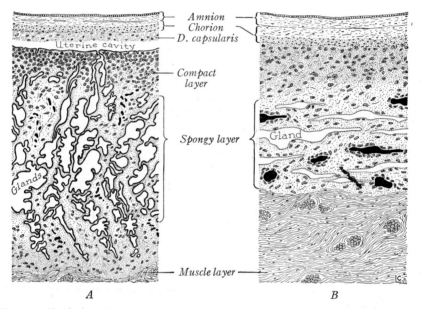

FIG. 99.—Vertical sections through the wall of the gravid uterus. *A*, In the third month, before the obliteration of the uterine cavity ($\times$ 18). *B*, At seven months, obliteration long completed ($\times$ 24).

The Decidua Basalis.—At the site of implantation the chorion lies upon a deeper part of the compact layer, beneath which is the spongiosa (Fig. 95). These two endometrial components specialize in pregnancy as the *decidua basalis*. On the whole, the changes in this portion of the deciduæ parallel those of the parietalis, but the basalis continues until birth as a component of the important placenta.

THE PLACENTA

The first steps leading to the development of a *placenta* have already been described. These include the development of chorionic villi and a labyrinthine intervillous space, and a decidua basalis with blood vessels that supply the intervillous space.

The human placenta is discoid in shape, and this form is determined by the final distribution of villi on the chorionic sac. In the early weeks the villi cover uniformly the entire surface of the chorion and reach 1000 in number. But with continued growth of the chorionic sac, the villi next the stretched decidua capsularis become compressed and their vascularity is reduced. Atrophy produces a perceptibly bare polar spot at two months (Fig. 100 A), while in the fourth month about half of the chorion is naked. The area of chorion lacking in villi is called the *chorion læve* (*i.e.*, smooth chorion). The villi associated with the decidua basalis, on the other hand, persist and give the name *chorion frondosum* (*i.e.*, bushy chorion) to this

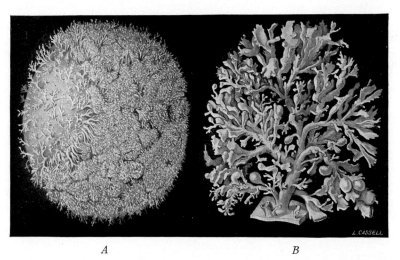

A   B

FIG. 100.—Human chorionic vesicle at nine weeks. *A*, Entire sac, showing the early distinction between the chorion læve and frondosum (× 1). *B*, Detail of a chorionic villus (× 7).

deeper portion of the sac. The area of persistent villi is normally somewhat circular in form, so the human placenta naturally takes the shape of a disc. Since the umbilical cord passes from the embryo to the deeper, now frondose portion of the chorion, it follows that when this latter region becomes a part of the placenta, the cord then attaches to its fetal side and usually near the midpoint.

No adequate conception of the placenta is possible without a clear recognition of its double origin. The chorion frondosum (both the membrane and its villi) is the fetal portion, while the decidua basalis (*i.e.*, mostly the remains of the eroded and altered stratum compactum) is the maternal contribution (Fig. 97). The intervillous space, which to a large degree separates these two components, is an expansion of the cavities arising within the early chorionic trophoblast. The general plan of the placenta is that of two parallel plates (the chorionic membrane and the decidua basalis) between which is a blood sinus (the intervillous space) containing an enormous number of branches belonging to the chorionic villi. In the paragraphs that follow, these components will be described in detail.

The Fetal Placenta.—The chorionic membrane of the placental region comes to be known as the *chorionic plate* (Fig. 101). The surface bordering the intervillous space is covered with trophoblast which has a history like that presently to be described for the chorionic villi. During the last half of pregnancy it is replaced largely by fibrinoid material. Beneath the trophoblast there is a layer of connective tissue which contains blood vessels radiating from the umbilical cord. These belong to the umbilical (allantoic)

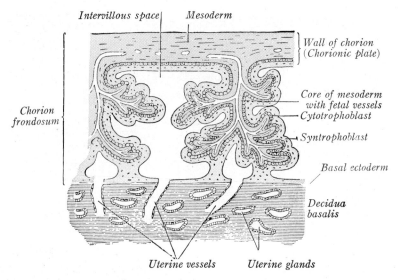

FIG. 101.—Diagrammatic section through an early human placenta (Bryce in Gray).

system of vessels, and the chorionic plate distributes them to the villi. At the end of the second month the expanding amnion comes everywhere into contact with the chorion. The ensuing fusion in the placental area causes the amnion to attach to the fetal surface of the placenta, and this relation persists throughout pregnancy (Fig. 98 *B*).

The *chorionic villi* are the most important part of the placenta because they furnish the means by which all interchanges take place between the mother and fetus. The early villi are compact, bush-like tufts with but few branches, and these are short and plump. Their main stems arise from the chorionic membrane and almost all of the ends (*anchoring villi*) attach to the exposed surface of the compact decidua basalis. Side branching begins in the second month and produces many *free villi* as well (Figs.

95, 100 *B* and 101). During the middle and later months of pregnancy the villi become much more tree-like, arborizing profusely and having longer and slenderer branches (Fig. 105). Fusions with the decidua basalis make some of the branches seem to arise from that layer. All the villi are contained within the huge blood sinus which is the intervillous space.

All parts of the villous tree have the same structural plan (Figs. 101 to 103). At the center is a connective-tissue core, which contains among other cell types some special large cells (of Hofbauer) apparently phagocytic in function. Embedded in this tissue are commonly one or two arterioles and venules. These taper to enlarged capillaries which continue to the villous tips where they complete a continuous system of closed vessels. After the second month more and more of the capillaries come to lie close beneath the surface trophoblast which here is thinned locally.[10] The connective-tissue core is covered with a double layer of trophoblast. Inside, next the connective tissue, is the *cytotrophoblast* with its separate cuboidal cells sharply defined; it is also known as the layer of Langhans. This cellular layer gives rise to syncytium, the *syntrophoblast*, which covers the

FIG. 102.—Tip of a mature chorionic villus, injected to show the relations between arterial (black) and venous (gray) vessels. × 130.

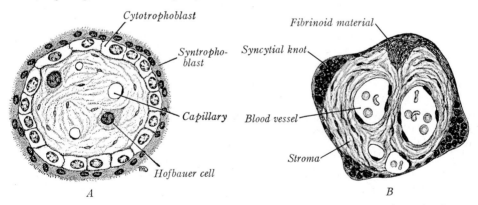

Cytotrophoblast

Syntrophoblast

Capillary

Hofbauer cell

A

Fibrinoid material

Syncytial knot

Blood vessel

Stroma

B

FIG. 103.—Human chorionic villi, in transverse section. × 265. *A*, In the early weeks of pregnancy; *B*, at full term.

villi externally. During the first third of pregnancy the cytotrophoblast of the villi is almost completely used up in the forming of syncytium. In this way the cellular layer becomes progressively scarcer and more interrupted, until finally the syncytial trophoblast is the only epithelial covering

7

of the villi (Fig. 103 *B*). The free surface of the syncytium often bears a striated border like that of certain other absorptive epithelia. At intervals along the older villi (*B*) the synctium aggregates into distinct protuberances with numerous nuclei; these are the *syncytial knots*, characteristic of this layer but of unknown significance.

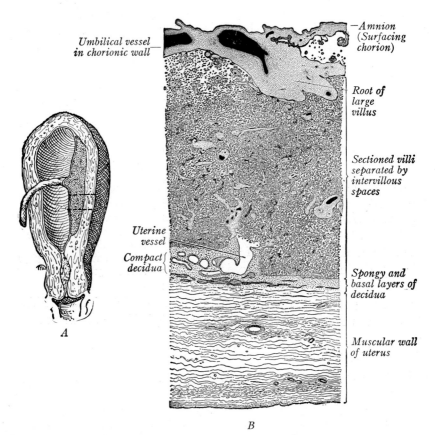

FIG. 104.—Gravid human uterus, in section. *A*, Hemisection, with a mature placenta *in situ*. *B*, Vertical section, at seven months (Minot; × 3.5); the area shown corresponds to the rectangle in *A*.

The territory of a rapidly enlarging villous tree is in time marked off by thin *placental septa* into a distinctive lobule known as a *cotyledon*. Each cotyledon is a natural unit since it contains (besides several minor, free villous trees) a main villous tree which distributes its branches and twigs throughout that particular lobule (Fig. 105). In all there are some twenty cotyledons, incompletely separated by the thin partitions. The placental septa have been described as folds of the decidua,[11] but it is now believed that they are of trophoblastic origin.[12, 13]

Represented in young stages and increasingly abundant in older placentas are irregular masses of stainable substance known as *fibrinoid material*. It occurs as incomplete layers in the chorion and decidua basalis and as irregular patches on the villi (Fig. 103 *B*). This peculiar material has a complex origin to which degenerating decidua and trophoblast contribute.[10]

The intervillous space belongs by origin to the fetal part of the placenta (p. 122), even though it is occupied by maternal blood. For a time the entire sinus is lined with trophoblast; later some of the lining becomes replaced by fibrinoid material. Although greatly choked by villi and subdivided incompletely by septa, the space still represents half of the volume of the total placenta. At the periphery of the placenta there is a specialized part of the intervillous space. This villus-free channel is the *marginal sinus* which encircles the placenta incompletely, but plays a prominent rôle in collecting blood from the main space (Fig. 105).

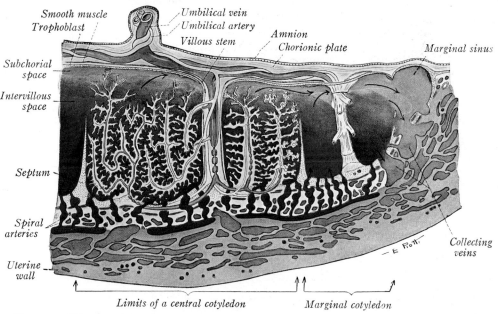

FIG. 105.—Diagram of the circulation of fetal and maternal blood through the human placenta. (After Spanner from Weatherford, Textbook of Histology, The Blakiston Co.)

The Maternal Placenta.—The decidua basalis, as the maternal contribution to the placenta, contains representatives of both the compact and the spongy layer of the progravid endometrium (Fig. 104). The glands of the spongiosa become stretched into clefts by the third month, but there seems to be much variability in their size, shape and even in their persistence during the later months. The part of the decidua basalis that is most intimately incorporated into the placenta is the *basal plate;* in part this is merely another name for the stratum compactum of this region. The basal plate is composed of a connective-tissue stroma containing decidual cells, fibrinoid material and portions of trophoblast originally belonging either to anchoring villi or to the so-called *basal ectoderm*. The latter layer is the residue of the peripheral shell of trophoblast that made junction with the eroded endometrium (Fig. 101). The basal ectoderm covers the basal plate; it decreases in amount as pregnancy continues and at term has a discontinuous distribution.

The blood supply of the intervillous space is indicated in Figure 105. The spiralling uterine arteries pass through the basal plate obliquely, losing their accessory coats as they proceed. They open by slender nozzles into the intervillous space, many to a lobule. Abundant, wide veins drain the more marginal lobules and the marginal sinus, but the central lobules seem to lack all venous connections.[14]

Growth and Maturity.—Growth of the fetus is roughly paralleled by the enlargement of the uterus and placenta. The placenta continues to increase in size throughout pregnancy and after the second month it occupies about 30 per cent. of the internal surface of the uterus.[15] The method by which growth in diameter is accomplished is not well understood. In-

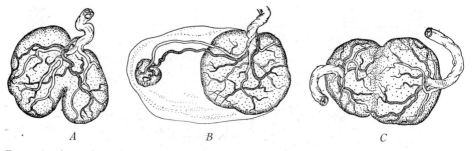

FIG. 106.—Anomalous placentas. *A*, Bilobed placenta; *B*, main and accessory placenta; *C*, fused placentas of ordinary twins.

crease in thickness, resulting chiefly from the elongation of villi, is completed at four months.[15]

The mature placenta makes a prominent, circular patch upon the interior of the greatly enlarged uterus (Fig. 107). Most of its bulk is due to chorionic villi and blood in the intervillous space (Fig. 104). When cut into, the organ is dark red and spongy. It shows various indications of degenerative changes, and some claim that at term the placenta is nearing the end of its functional capacity both because of these alterations and because the trophoblast has lived out its normal life span.[11] The increasing occurrence of fibrinoid substance in older specimens has been mentioned (p. 133); its presence on villi decreases their absorptive surface, and when aggregated constitutes *white infarcts*. *Red infarcts*, caused by massive coagulation of blood in the intervillous space, also are characteristic.

Anomalies.—The umbilical cord may attach atypically to the placenta (Fig. 84). Departure from a circular shape by the placenta is quite common, ranging from an oval contour to other variant forms (*i.e.*, spindle; pear; heart; crescent; ring) which are more rarely encountered. The placenta may be notched, lobed or even divided completely (Fig. 106 *A*). Occasionally there are one or more accessory placentas, of smaller size than the main placenta (*B*). All such specimens are referable either to irregularities in the shape or growth of the chorion frondosum or to the persistence and independent development of more than one patch of chorionic villi. Fused placentas result when ordinary twins become too closely implanted (*C*).

PHYSIOLOGY OF THE PLACENTA

The blood of the fetus and that of the mother circulate independently in totally separate channels, and all interchanges are by diffusion. Fetal blood is pumped into the umbilical artery in the umbilical cord and is distributed by way of the chorionic plate to the villi (Fig. 105). After passing through the capillary mesh of the villi, the blood returns to the fetus in the umbilical veins. Each cotyledon, or lobule, of the placenta contains a main villous trunk which extends to the basal plate. Most of its branches are said to dip toward this compact layer of the decidua basalis and then to recurve backward toward the chorionic plate.[14] The arrangement is somewhat like that of an old-fashioned candelabra and this is the course taken also by the vessels within the villous tree.

Maternal blood enters a cotyledon through the spiral, terminal branches of the uterine arteries (Fig. 105). Their numerous, tiny nozzles open directly into the intervillous space. Blood flows past the branches and twigs of the villous tree and is kept within the cotyledon by the placental septa which separate the cotyledons. Gaining the region just beneath the chorionic plate, which is relatively free of villi, the now impure blood passes in a peripheral direction to the margin of the placenta where it is drained away by the plentiful branches of the uterine veins located there. The force that propels the blood through the cavernous space of the placenta is not surely known. There are difficulties in the way of understanding how the maternal blood pressure can move the large lake of blood that fills the clogged intervillous space. An alternative suggestion is that contraction of smooth muscle in the uterus, chorion and villous trunks is the effective agency in squeezing the placenta and thus promoting a flow of blood.[14] Exact information also lacks concerning the rate of flow. Many believe it is slow, if not semistagnant by ordinary circulatory standards. This might be favorable for some of the activities taking place at the barrier membrane between the maternal and fetal blood. On the other hand, there are penalties (*e.g.*, coagulation; obstruction; infarct formation) which attend such sluggishness. In fact, this handicapping may be so severe that the placenta can scarcely fulfill its normal functions toward the end of pregnancy.

The complete separation of the fetal and maternal circulations is something like that of the blood of the hand (*i.e.*, the villous tree) and a bowl of water (*i.e.*, the intervillous space) in which the hand is immersed. A more precise comparison is furnished by the relation of the intestinal villi to the fluid-content of the gut during digestion. In neither chorionic nor intestinal villi is there direct contact or mixture between the external fluid-mass and the blood within the vessels of the villi. Their only communication is through diffusive interchange. In the placenta the trophoblastic covering of the villus, the connective-tissue stroma and the endothelium of its capillaries all intervene to separate the fetal and maternal blood streams. As pregnancy advances, there is marked thinning of this barrier;[10] this is correlated with an increase in permeability.[16]

Nutritive substances, inorganic salts and oxygen pass from the mother's blood to the fetus, whereas the gaseous and fluid waste-products of fetal metabolism are transferred in the opposite direction. The trophoblast is the living membrane that is chiefly important in these interchanges, both as regards permeability and barrier functions. To a considerable degree it acts like an ordinary semipermeable membrane, and the distribution of substances between mother and fetus is governed by the physical laws of diffusion. In this process the size of the molecule is a determining factor. Gases, the mineral salts of the body, simple sugars such as dextrose, and waste products such as urea all pass through by diffusion. These are examples of substances of relatively small molecular size in solution. But other dissolved substances fail to be transmitted if their molecules are too large. For example, blood proteins with large molecular structure may not enter the villi as such, but are first broken down into simpler products, such as amino acids, of smaller molecular size. This requires a rebuilding by the embryo of its more complex proteins from these transferable components. Fats are not soluble in water and do not pass the barrier as such. They are split into transferable substances and rebuilt by the fetus. There has been much debate as to whether the trophoblast, besides acting as a physical membrane, also exerts some selective regulation over what passes, like that occurring in glandular secretion. There are some evidences of such vital control which suggest that simple physical processes are not the only mechanisms involved in the passage of substances from mother to fetus.[17]

Since the placenta is impermeable to particulate matter even of ultramicroscopic size, it serves as an efficient barrier against the transmission of bacteria. The rare cases of fetal disease of bacterial origin are believed to result from injury to the placenta. By contrast the viruses of smallpox and some other diseases pass readily, as do antibodies such as diphtheria antitoxin and the Rh agglutinins.

Among the activities of the placenta can be mentioned the production and secretion of hormones, the ability to synthesize certain foodstuffs and the employment of enzymes located there. Nerves are completely lacking in the chorion and its villi. There is no possibility of 'maternal impressions' affecting an unborn babe. The total absorbing surface of the chorionic villi at the end of pregnancy is calculated to be 125 square feet.[18] This is fifty times the surface area of the skin of a newborn.

PARTURITION

During pregnancy the uterus enlarges into a huge sac whose muscular coat increases in bulk some twenty-four fold and whose capacity becomes over 4000 c.c. By the sixth month the upper end of the uterus has reached the level of the navel, and at the end of pregnancy it is not far below the breast bone. The fetus assumes the characteristic attitude illustrated in Figure 107. At the time of birth the head is commonest directed downward, but the buttocks may be presented first or the baby may even lie crosswise.

Delivery.—Childbirth, or *parturition*, occurs on the average at the time of the tenth missed mensis following conception—that is, 280 days after the last menstrual period. The causes that induce 'labor' are obscure, but the process consists of a protracted series of involuntary muscular contractions of the uterus, termed 'pains,' combined with reflex as well as voluntary contractions of the abdominal muscles. These bring about a dilatation of the uterine cervix, the bursting of the bulging fetal membranes ('bag of waters'), and cause the extrusion ('delivery') of the child. With

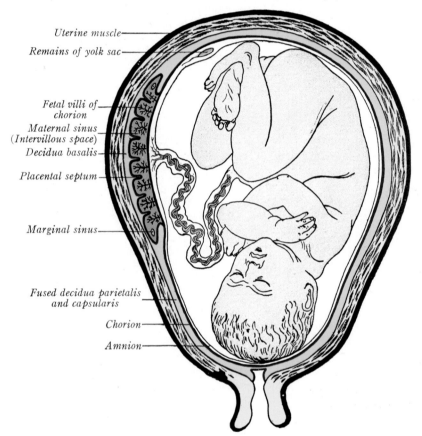

Uterine muscle

Remains of yolk sac

Fetal villi of chorion

Maternal sinus (Intervillous space)

Decidua basalis

Placental septum

Marginal sinus

Fused decidua parietalis and capsularis

Chorion

Amnion

FIG. 107.—Diagrammatic longitudinal section of the uterus, illustrating the relation of an advanced fetus to the placenta and other membranes (Ahlfeld).

the rupture of the membranes the amniotic fluid is expelled but the fetal membranes themselves remain behind, attached to the deciduæ. Within a few minutes after the birth of the baby the pulsation in the exposed cord slows; the cord is then tied and severed. The stump of the cord gradually shrivels and eventually becomes a depressed scar, the *umbilicus* or navel.

The reduction in size of the emptied uterus leads to the detachment of the placenta, whereupon the pull of the placenta progressively detaches the other deciduæ (Fig. 108 A). The plane of separation of all these membranes lies usually in the spongy layer where there are only thin-walled partitions between the stretched glands (B). Soon after the birth of the baby there enters a second series of uterine contractions. Through them the placenta and its associated membranes (the 'afterbirth') are forced out. Restoration and repair of the endometrium proceeds rapidly, and from the deep spongy and basal layers regeneration is nearly completed within a week.

The Afterbirth.—The expelled placenta is a thick, circular disc which averages seven inches in diameter, one inch in greatest thickness, and weighs a little over one pound (Fig. 109). Its entire margin is continuous with the ruptured and cast-off sac that formerly contained the fetus. This

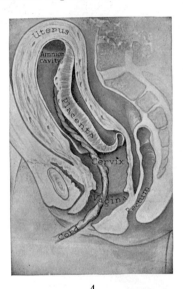

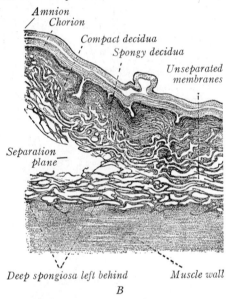

FIG. 108.—Separation of deciduæ after childbirth. A, Placental detachment by means of escaping blood. B, Partially separated decidua parietalis, in vertical section (Broman; × 5).

membrane results from the fusion of the several components that led to the obliteration of the uterine and chorionic cavities (p. 128). Its constituent parts, from within outward, are: (1) the nonplacental amnion; (2) the chorion læve; (3) the decidua capsularis (no longer recognizable); (4) the decidua parietalis. The cast-off placenta shows an amniotic or fetal surface, and a uterine or maternal surface. The fetal surface was primarily chorionic but, like the other deciduæ, it is now covered with smooth, glistening, adherent amnion. Usually near but not quite at the center of the fetal surface is attached the umbilical cord, already described at length (p. 111). The torn, maternal surface of the placenta is irregularly rough, reddish gray in color and bears blood clots. It exhibits incomplete lobular areas which correspond to the cotyledons.

Anomalies.—Childbirth may be early or late by as much as fifty days, but most of the apparent wide departures from the average duration of pregnancy are due to miscalculations. The termination of pregnancy at still younger stages, when the fetus is not viable, is designated an *abortion* or *miscarriage*. It probably occurs in at least 20 per cent. of all pregnancies.

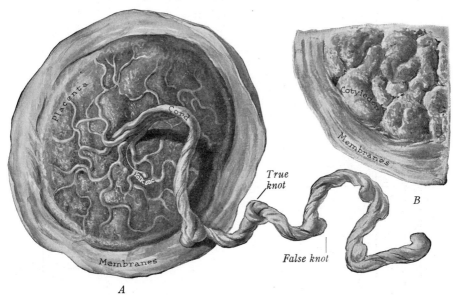

Fig. 109.—Mature human placenta and its associated membranes, after expulsion. × ⅓. *A*, Fetal surface; *B*, quadrant of the maternal surface.

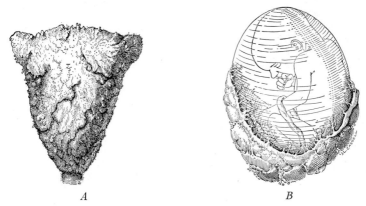

Fig. 110.—Aborted fetuses within intact membranes. *A*, At two months, the castoff deciduæ comprising the external tunic (× ⅖). *B*, At four months (× ⅓); the placental area, showing cotyledons, is below.

Abortion may follow as a natural consequence upon the death of the fetus through poor placentation or disease; these factors, and others, may induce bleeding and uterine contractions, and thus cause the detachment of a living fetus. Sometimes the aborted deciduæ are discharged as a whole, and in younger specimens they may retain the shape of the uterine cavity (Fig. 110).

IMPORTANT FACTS CONCERNING HUMAN DECIDUÆ AND FETAL MEMBRANES

Organ	Origin	Composition	Location	Fate	Function
A. Fetal membranes:					
1. Yolk sac	Fashions from early entodermal layer.	Entoderm and splanchnic mesoderm.	Yolk stalk, within umbilical cord. Yolk sac, between amnion and placenta.	Disconnects from gut early. Stalk disappears early. Sac may persist.	Roof forms the gut. Early blood cells and vessels arise on yolk sac.
2. Allantois	Diverticulum of hind-gut region of the yolk sac.	Entoderm and splanchnic mesoderm.	First lies within body stalk; later within umbilical cord.	Epithelium disappears early (except traces). Blood vessels persist.	Vessels connect fetal circulation with the placenta.
3. Amnion	Differentiates between inner cell mass and trophoblast.	'Ectoderm' and somatic mesoderm.	Encloses embryo and umbilical cord. Attaches to embryo at the umbilicus.	Persists until birth. Fuses with chorion. Covers fetal surface of placenta and afterbirth.	Contains fetus, immersed in amniotic fluid. Sole cavity of later pregnant uterus.
4. Chorion	Trophoblastic capsule of blastocyst.	'Ectoderm' (trophoblast) and somatic mesoderm.	Encloses embryo and all other fetal membranes.	Frondose part becomes fetal placenta. Smooth part fuses with d. parietalis. Cast off after birth.	Placental area is the fetal organ for nutrition, respiration and excretion.
5. Umbilical cord	Amnion wraps about yolk stalk and body stalk.	Chiefly, allantoic vessels and connective tissue enveloped by the amnion.	Connects belly wall with the fetal side of the placenta.	Cut off after birth. Lost with placenta.	Vascular pathway between fetus and placenta.
B. Maternal membranes:					
1. D. parietalis	Progravid endometrium continued into pregnancy.	Compact and spongy layers (i.e., the 'functional layer' of endometrium).	Nonplacental lining of uterus.	Stretches but persists. Fuses with d. capsularis and then with chorion. Splits off in spongiosum as part of the afterbirth.	Potential, but unused, placental site. Contributes to growing placental margin?
2. D. capsularis	A part of the endometrium of pregnancy, split and elevated by the chorionic sac.	A more superficial part of the compact layer.	Between chorion and cavity of the uterus.	Pressed into union with d. parietalis. Soon becomes unrecognizable.	Covers and holds implanted chorionic sac in place. No lasting function.
3. D. basalis	Endometrium of pregnancy beneath the implanted chorionic sac.	Deeper compact layer and all of the spongy layer.	Between chorion and the muscular wall of uterus.	Splits in spongiosum and is lost with rest of placenta.	Supplies maternal blood to the placenta.
C. Placenta	A local association of fetal and maternal tissues.	Chorion frondosum and decidua basalis.	Usually on front or back wall of the uterus.	Cast off as unit after birth. (Continuous with d. parietalis and chorion læve at the placental margin.)	Vital intermediary organ between fetus and mother. Produces hormones and, probably, enzymes.

REFERENCES CITED

1. Burdick, H. O. *et al.* 1942. Endocrinology, **31**, 100–108.
2. Alden, R. H. 1942. Anat. Rec., **84**, 137–169.
3. Hartman, C. G. 1944. Western Jour. Surg., Obstet. and Gynec., **52**, 41–61.
4. Heuser, C. H. and Streeter, G. L. 1941. Carnegie Contrib. Embryol., **29**, No. 181, 15–55.
5. Hertig, A. T. and Rock, J. 1945. Carnegie Contrib. Embryol., **31**, No. 200, 65–84.
6. Hertig, A. T. and Rock, J. 1941. Carnegie Contrib. Embryol., **29**, No. 184, 127–156.
7. Brewer, J. 1937. Amer. Jour. Anat., **61**, 429–481.
8. Hertig, A. T. 1935. Carnegie Contrib. Embryol., **25**, No. 146, 37–82.
9. Wislocki, G. B. and Streeter, G. L. 1938. Carnegie Contrib. Embryol., **27**, No. 160, 1–66.
10. Wislocki, G. B. and Bennett, H. S. 1943. Amer. Jour. Anat., **73**, 335–449.
11. Grosser, O. 1927. Frühentwicklung, etc., Bergmann, München.
12. Spanner, R. 1935. Morph. Jahrb., **75**, 374–392.
13. Stieve, H. 1940. Zeitschr. f. mikr.-anat. Forsch., **48**, 287–358.
14. Spanner, R. 1940. Zeitschr. f. Anat. u. Entwickl., **105**, 163–242.
15. Stieve, H. 1940. Anat. Anz., **90**, 225–242.
16. Flexner, L. B. and Gellhorn, A. 1942. Amer. Jour. Obstet. and Gynec., **43**, 965–974.
17. Needham, J. 1931. Chemical Embryology; vol. 3. Macmillan, N. Y.
18. Christoffersen, A. K. 1934. Comp. rend. Soc. Biol., **117**, 641–644.

CHAPTER VIII

REPRODUCTIVE CYCLES AND THEIR HORMONAL CONTROL

Previous chapters have described the periodic maturing of eggs and their reception by the well-prepared uterus. The purpose of the present chapter is to examine the mechanisms by which these and other co-ordinated, reproductive phenomena are controlled.

REPRODUCTIVE CYCLES

Periodic breeding among animals and plants is familiar to everyone. The egg-laying cycle varies from the daily regularity of the hen to the seventeen-year periodicity of a locust. Many animals and plants time their breeding with respect to the seasons in order to take advantage of favorable temperature and food for their young. Somewhat similar is the annual breeding of many wild mammals; it is so timed that the young are born when food is abundant for the mother. Some marine forms have their reproductive cycles tuned to the tides and even to definite phases of the moon. Other animals, freed of such seasonal, tidal or lunar influences, are nonetheless cyclic, and this is true of various domesticated mammals and of primates. The reproductive rhythm of female rats and mice repeats at intervals of five days; the guinea pig, every 15 days; the sow, mare and cow, every three weeks; the monkey and human, every four weeks; the chimpanzee, every five weeks; the cat and dog, twice or thrice a year. In mammals that breed once annually the testes exhibit a period of activity and a long interval of inactivity during which sperm production ceases and the testes decrease greatly in size. In domesticated mammals and primates spermatogenesis is continuous, but the individual testis tubules exhibit wave-like cycles of activity.

The Estrous Cycle.—Among mammals, other than primates, the recurring periods of sexual excitement in the adult female are known as 'heat.' The biological term is *estrus,* and the correlated phenomena of the reproductive system from one period of estrus to the next make up the *estrous cycle.* These events can be understood better by recounting what takes place during the typical cycle of a specific mammal, the sow. For 18 days she follows her ordinary routine and shows no interest in the boar. But during the next three days she becomes restless and sexually excited. If a boar is present, he is accepted; the mating normally results in pregnancy, whereupon the cycles cease until after the young are born. If there is no mating, or an infertile one, the cycles continue at the usual intervals of three weeks throughout the year.

Examination of the ovaries of the sow on different days of the cycle shows that a definite series of events takes place (Fig. 111). During the days of sexual inactivity, known as the _diestrus_, the ovarian follicles are all small. About two days before estrus numerous follicles begin to grow, and on the first day of estrus there are large vesicular follicles with maturing eggs. Late in the second day of estrus the follicles rupture, expel the eggs and straightway begin to transform into corpora lutea. These structures attain full development by the seventh day after ovulation. If the eggs are not fertilized, the corpora lutea retain their functional state for seven more days and then begin to degenerate. While degeneration is still in progress, the development of a new crop of follicles is under way and the

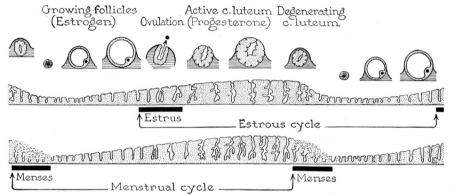

FIG. 111.—Diagram showing the correlation of events in the ovarian follicle, in the endometrium of mammals below primates and in the human endometrium (partly after Corner).

cycle repeats. If the eggs are fertilized, the corpora lutea continue on into pregnancy and the cycles cease.

Examination of the uterus during a cycle reveals another regular sequence of events (Fig. 111). During the growth and ripening of the ovarian follicles there is growth and change in the endometrium. During the period of the developing and mature corpus luteum the endometrium specializes further in a way that will fit it for pregnancy. If the eggs are not fertilized, the endometrium returns to its original condition as the corpora lutea decline, only to repeat the whole series of changes in the next cycle. If the eggs are fertilized, the endometrium retains its specialized state which is both favorable to pregnancy and necessary for its occurrence.

These several phenomena are all co-ordinated in perfect timing. The eggs are matured just when the sow becomes sexually excited and receptive to the boar; this ensures fertilization and early development. The uterus is prepared at the right time to receive and nourish the embryo; this ensures continued development. If pregnancy occurs, the cyclic happenings are suppressed and favorable ovarian and uterine states are retained; if it does not occur, the cycle repeats again and again.

The conditions existing in the sow illustrate the fundamental plan of the cycle among mammals. There are minor peculiarities in each mammalian type, and there are also major variations. For example, a few animals, such as the cat, ripen follicles in every cycle, but the follicles do not burst unless mating occurs. The rabbit exceeds this by not even ripening its follicles in the absence of mating; thus it remains in a state of prolonged estrus.

The Menstrual Cycle.—The greatest departure from the basic plan of the mammalian reproductive cycle is found in man, apes and the higher monkeys. In these forms the periodic growth of the follicle and corpus luteum is quite typical, as are the correlated changes in the endometrium. But an outstanding peculiarity is that the regression of the corpus luteum, about two weeks after ovulation, is accompanied by a destructive breakdown of the endometrium with hemorrhage. This periodic loss of tissue and blood is *menstruation* (Fig. 111). It is the most conspicuous feature of the cycle and it has no counterpart in lower mammals. Since, however, the estrous cycle of lower mammals has an equally prominent event, estrus, during which ovulation occurs, it was natural to think that the two happenings are similar and that ovulation in the higher primates occurs at the time of menstruation. Only in recent years have these errors been corrected.

The human cycle averages about 28 days in length, but some individuals run to shorter cycles and others to longer ones. There is a popular impression that the cycle is normally regular, but this is far from the truth. If two-thirds of all the cycles of any individual keep within a range of four to six days about her average, it is as good a performance as can be expected.[1] No instance of perfect regularity for any considerable period of time has ever been reported. In view of the biological mechanism (hormones) that controls the menstrual cycle no such case is to be expected.

The events of a menstrual cycle can be described as occurring in four stages (Fig. 112). These phases are timed from the start of visible flow, which counts as day one. Former accounts of the cycle have been modified considerably,[2] partly because of direct observations made on pieces of endometrium grafted onto the iris of the eye of the monkey and viewed through the transparent cornea.[3]

1. *Repair* (days 5–6). During the five days of actual menstruation the compact layer and most of the spongy layer are lost by sloughing. But even before all bleeding has ceased, epithelial cells begin to leave the remnants of the glands located in the basal and spongy layers. These cells glide over the denuded surface and epithelize it anew.

2. *Proliferation* (days 7–15). This phase completes and extends the postmenstrual repair. It coincides with the growth of a new set of follicles in the ovary. The glands proliferate, lengthen rapidly and produce a thin secretion. Connective-tissue cells also multiply and differentiate a new mesh of reticular fibers. The endometrium increases from 1 mm. in thickness to 2 mm. or more.

3. *Secretion* (days 16–28). Another term is the progestational stage. It parallels the growth and functional life of the corpus luteum. Although the glands no longer proliferate, they elongate further, swell and become tortuous (Fig. 87). Throughout much of their length they show sacculations, distended with a thicker mucoid secretion rich in glycogen. Peculiar spiral arterioles, continuing their upward growth, break up into capillaries that supply the superficial two-thirds of the endometrium; the basal one-third is supplied by ordinary, straight branches of the uterine arteries. By

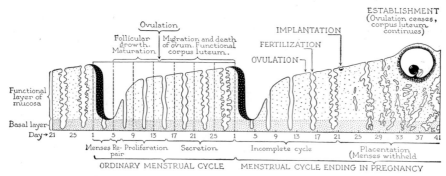

FIG. 112.—Graphic presentation of the relations existing between human ovulation, menstruation and pregnancy (modified after Schröder).

the end of this period the endometrium has doubled its previous thickness, due largely to the increase of secretion and to edema fluid.

4. *Menstruation* (days 1–5). Hours before the onset of active menstruation, the spiral arterioles constrict one by one and cause the endometrium to blanch. Accompanying this local anemia the mucosa shrinks and death of the blood-deprived tissues follows. At times the spiral arterioles relax locally, blood escapes from the injured vessels, and sooner or later this non-coagulating blood discharges into the cavity of the uterus. Fragments of the disintegrating endometrium slough away down through the levels supplied by the spiral arterioles.

Anovulatory Cycles.—At times the ovarian follicle fails to rupture and expel its egg. In this event there is, of course, no corpus luteum and no secretory phase of endometrial upbuilding. Yet menstruation follows the ending of the proliferative phase. It is typical in all respects except that it occurs in an endometrium brought only through the proliferative stage. Such menstruation without ovulation occurs most frequently in girls beginning their menstrual career, in women approaching the end of their reproductive capacity (menopause) and during the nursing of infants.

Estrous and Menstrual Cycles Compared.—The estrous and menstrual cycles are alike in having (Fig. 111): (1) a period of growth of the ovarian follicle and ripening of the egg, accompanied by heightened hormone (estrogen) output from the ovary and proliferative growth of the endometrium; (2) ovulation which ends this period; and (3) a period of the corpus luteum, with the production of a luteal hormone (progesterone) and the resulting progestational growth which makes the endometrium suitable for pregnancy.   They are unlike in several respects: (1) in the estrous cycle the animal has a definite period of heat, during which ovulation occurs and the male is accepted; (2) in the menstrual cycle, ovulation is unaccompanied by heat or limited mating and the end of the luteal phase is signalized by tissue loss and bleeding; and (3) the two cycles, as described, occupy different positions with respect to the sequence of uterine changes.

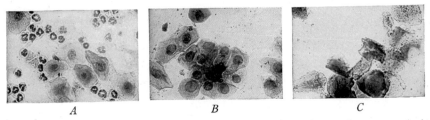

A   *B*   *C*

FIG. 113.—Vaginal cycle of the rat, as shown by smears (Fluhmann).   × about 500.   *A*, At interval; *B*, just before estrus; *C*, during estrus.

The Vaginal Cycle.—The changes that characterize the female sexual cycles are not confined to the ovaries and uterus.   The epithelial lining of the uterine tubes and vagina undergoes cyclic alteration as well.   Clearest and most noteworthy are the rhythmic changes in the vagina of rodents (Fig. 113).[4]   Just before estrus the epithelial cells proliferate and begin to specialize.   During estrus they cornify and shed in great numbers; migrating leucocytes, present at other times, disappear temporarily just before and during estrus.   By examining vaginal washings the exact stage of the cycle can be determined at any time.   Such tests are of the utmost importance in experimental work because these animals give no other clear signs of their estrous state, as, for example, do the sow by excitement or the bitch by genital swelling.

In primates, unfortunately, the vaginal changes are less extensive and distinct.[5]   Normal ovarian activity as against total inactivity can be detected, but the diagnosis of ovulation cannot yet be made as a routine laboratory test.

The Mammary Cycle.—In lower mammals, growth changes and

regression take place in the mammary gland in co-ordination with the ovarian cycle.[6] Controlled observations on periodic epithelial growth in the human are lacking, but the breasts do become larger and firmer (due to blood engorgement and, perhaps, edema of the connective tissue) preceding menstruation. During pregnancy there is remarkable growth of the ducts and secretory end-pieces. After the nursing period, regression returns the glandular elements to the resting state.

THE HORMONES CONCERNED WITH REPRODUCTION

The preceding paragraphs have presented the main events of the reproductive cycles in a purely descriptive way, scarcely hinting at the forces that impel and control them in their orderly and well co-ordinated sequences. These agencies are hormones—chemical substances produced in ductless glands, distributed through the blood stream and capable of arousing into action certain specific tissues that come under their influence. It is to the hormones concerned with reproduction that attention must now be directed.[7, 8]

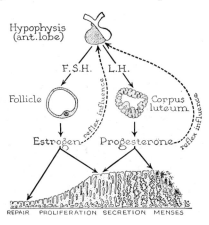

Fig. 114.—Diagram of the hormonal influence of the hypophysis on the ovary, and of the ovary on the uterus and hypophysis.

The Pituitary Hormones. — The hypophysis, or pituitary body, is a small gland attached to the under side of the brain. It consists of two parts, or lobes. The anterior lobe is a derivative of the primitive mouth, and certain basophilic cells distributed through it are the elements that secrete the *gonadotropic hormones*. There is rather good evidence for the existence of two distinct hormones (Fig. 114).[8] One, the *follicle-stimulating hormone* (F. S. H.) causes the normal growth of the ovary and testis and their coming into function at puberty. The periodic development of small follicles to the point where they contain full-sized eggs (primary oöcytes) is a self-contained activity. But it is the follicle-stimulating hormone that makes the solid follicles grow into vesicular follicles with ripe eggs; it is a basic factor in producing ovulation; it causes the follicles to secrete the estrogenic hormone. In the male the same hormone governs spermatogenesis. In view of its influence on the gonads of both sexes, *gametokinetic hormone* would be a more appropriate designation. The second pituitary product is the *luteinizing hormone* (L. H.). It aids in bringing about ovulation. Under its influence the emptied vesicular follicle transforms (*i.e.*, luteinizes) into a corpus luteum.

In the male it controls the activity of the interstitial cells which are presumably the source of the male hormone. Again it will be noted that the name given this hormone is inadequate.

Abundant proofs of these several effects have been supplied through experiments in which the hypophysis has been removed, transplanted or used in the form of extracts as a substitute for normal pituitary control. This endocrine organ, therefore, is the seat of control without which the ovaries and testes cannot function. Through the gonads it also governs secondarily the cyclic phenomena of the female reproductive tract, the functional state of the male accessory glands (prostate and seminal vesicles) and the secondary sexual characters. These pituitary hormones are proteins, and the isolation of the luteinizing hormone in pure form has been accomplished.[9]

The Ovarian Hormones.—These are two in number. One, *estrogen*, is especially associated with the follicles, both large and small. The other, *progesterone*, is a product of the corpus luteum (Fig. 114).

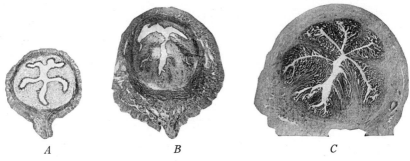

A   B   C

FIG. 115.—Influence of ovarian hormones on the uterus of the rabbit, shown by transverse sections (*B, C*, Bouin and Ancel). × 9. *A*, Immature rabbit. *B*, Growth to adult state, caused by estrogen. *C*, Progestational (secretory) changes, caused by progesterone.

Estrogen.—In the prepubertal period of mammals the uterine tubes, uterus, vagina and mammary glands, all of which have remained small and relatively undeveloped since birth, grow rapidly to nearly the adult size and the external sexual characters become established (Fig. 115 *A, B*). At puberty the uterine, vaginal and mammary cycles begin. These phenomena are dependent on the ovaries, as experiments utilizing castration, the grafting of ovaries into castrates, and the injection of ovarian extract into castrates all prove. The retention of the mature state of the reproductive tract and mammary glands fails after castration, and marked atrophy follows. But the castrate condition can be prevented or corrected by ovarian transplants or by the administration of ovarian extract. Similar treatment of an immature mammal brings about precocious growth and maturity of the reproductive tract and mammary glands.

The hormone responsible for the several effects just mentioned is called *estrogen* because it produces most of the characteristic features of the estrous or menstrual cycle. Estrogen occurs in the ovary in general (including, to a slight degree, the corpus luteum), and there is some suspicion that it is made by the internal theca of the follicles.[10] Estrogen is finally lost from the body by being excreted in the urine. Actually 'estrogen' is a collective term because a considerable group of related, chemical substances produces similar effects. They are all organic compounds, belonging to the sterols, which can be isolated in pure crystalline form. *Estradiol* is apparently the actual substance secreted by the ovary. Estrogenic compounds also have been synthesized in the laboratory; the most important of these products is *stilbestrol*.

As is characteristic of hormones, tiny amounts of an estrogen produce large effects. For example, *estrone* is an estrogen recoverable from pregnancy urine. The administration of 0.00001 milligram of estrone daily for three days can produce the characteristic estrous changes in a castrated mouse. Six million of these doses would equal an ordinary United States postage stamp in weight. The daily output of the more potent estradiol from both ovaries of an adult woman has the same effectiveness as 0.3 milligram of estrone.

Like other hormones, the group of estrogens is selective in its action. Their influence is directed chiefly at the reproductive tract and mammary glands. Injection of estrogen into an immature mammal or an adult that has undergone castrate atrophy of the reproductive tract causes the blood vessels of the uterus to dilate, cell proliferation to increase and the glands and muscle to enlarge. Hence estrogen acts on the uterus by bringing it to the full adult condition and by maintaining it there (Fig. 115 *A*, *B*). It is responsible for the proliferative stage of the estrous or menstrual cycle (Fig. 114). The vagina also responds by growth and epithelial specialization. Before puberty the mammary glands are in a rudimentary state of development, even the ducts being nothing more than short, little-branched sprouts. Under the influence of estrogen the nipples enlarge and the ducts grow and branch into the tree-like system that characterizes the mature, nonpregnant mammal (Fig. 118 *A*, *B*).

Progesterone.—The growth and change in the uterus that characterize the full estrous and menstrual cycle are not due wholly to the influence of estrogen. On the contrary, the culminating events that make the endometrium suitable for pregnancy (whether pregnancy occurs or not) are directed by the corpus luteum (Fig. 114). Its hormone, *progesterone*, implies by its name that it causes the progestational specialization that favors gestation; the last part of the word also indicates that the hormone is chemically a sterol. This progestational development comprises the final, progressive changes in the endometrium which have already been described as the secretory phase (Fig. 115 *C*). Removal of the developing corpora lutea prevents this portion of the estrous or menstrual cycle from appearing. Under these conditions pregnancy cannot occur. For one thing, the endometrium fails to become sensitized in such a manner that it can react to the presence of an embryo by collaborating in the formation of a placenta.

Actually, however, there is no invading embryo in this type of experiment because the blastocysts die while still free in the uterus, awaiting the time for implantation. They die for the lack of chemical substances secreted by the glands of the endometrium under the influence of progesterone. Hence, in the normal course of events, the corpus luteum prepares and sensitizes the endometrium for pregnancy; endometrial secretions nourish and protect the embryo before implantation occurs; and the uterus reacts to the stimulus of implantation by forming a placenta. In some mammals the corpus luteum is necessary for the maintenance of pregnancy, and its removal leads to resorption or abortion of the fetuses. Such is not the case in primates, once the embryo is well established.

Pure progesterone in crystalline form can be isolated from corpora lutea. Properly used with estrogen, it is able to bring the uterus of an immature mammal or of a mature castrate to its full functional state. When an animal is castrated just after mating, the injection of progesterone can replace the action of the corpora lutea and embryos can then be carried successfully to birth. Progesterone has not been synthesized from simpler substances, but it is being made by altering other sterols such as cholesterol. The daily output

Fig. 116.—Friedman test for pregnancy (Fluhmann). At left, control ovaries; at right, multiple ovulation induced by pregnancy urine.

of progestrone is much greater than that of estrogen but the latter is far more potent, weight for weight, in producing its characteristic effects.

The Placental Hormones.—A gonadotropic hormone is formed by the trophoblast of the embryo even before there is a placenta as such.[11] Known as the *anterior pituitary-like hormone*, it is lost to the body in the urine of the mother. Its concentration there is sufficient so that the injection of pregnancy urine into a mature rabbit will induce ovulation (ordinarily dependent on coitus) in about ten hours. This response provides the basis for the Friedman test for pregnancy which is highly reliable even in the first month of pregnancy (Fig. 116). The normal function of this placental hormone is not known.

The human placenta contains *estrogen* in large amounts, as does also pregnancy urine. Since removal of the ovaries during pregnancy does not stop the formation of these substances (*estriol*, in the placenta; *estrone*, the elimination product), and since there is a sharp decline of estrone in the urine after delivery, it would seem that the placenta is the source.

A small amount of *progesterone* is found in the human placenta, and there is some reason for suspecting it is made there. This might explain why human pregnancies, once well begun, continue to completion even when the ovaries are removed.

The Testicular Hormone.—Through the ages it has been known that castration of the male suppresses the development of the secondary sexual characters, causes atrophy of the accessory reproductive organs, and in vertebrates in general, including most mammals, leads to loss of the sex drive. The aggressive bull and docile ox illustrate the castrate change. The relation of these conditions to a hormone produced in the testis is firmly established. The weight of evidence favors the interstitial cells, located in groups between the seminiferous tubules, as the secretory agents. *Testosterone* has been prepared from testis tissue, and the slightly different and much less potent *androsterone* from the urine. Both have been purified in crystalline form and both have been prepared artificially by the degradation of cholesterol. The collective term for these hormones is *androgen*, meaning 'promoting masculinity.'

Many substances with androgenic properties are known, most in the long list being artificial creations of the laboratory chemist. When testis extracts or pure androgens are administered to immature mammals they stimulate the growth of the accessory reproductive organs; in castrated adults they restore these atrophied organs and the mating urge. In many wild species with a rutting season, the male hormone is secreted especially at that time; contrariwise, the interstitial tissue undergoes regression in the long interval between seasons and the accessory glands shrink. There is no sharp line of distinction between androgens and estrogens. Their chemical constitution is closely similar and in large doses each can produce certain effects of the other. Both are present in the urine of each sex.

THE HORMONAL CONTROL OF REPRODUCTIVE CYCLES

Not only do the several hormones produce characteristic effects on the reproductive system, but also these hormones are linked in action. Some of them complicate the system of control by acting reflexly on the hypophysis. The reproductive cycles, in all their essentials, can be imitated by injecting hormones into experimental animals.

The Ovarian Cycle.—The rhythmic action of the ovary, with its sequence of maturing follicles and developing and waning corpora lutea, is believed to be due to an interplay or see-saw action of the gonadotropic hormones of the hypophysis and the ovarian hormones (Fig. 117). The follicle-stimulating hormone ripens the eggs and follicles, and thus causes more estrogen to be secreted by the enlarging follicles. The increasing estrogen has a dual effect on the hypophysis; it inhibits the formation of the follicle-stimulating hormone and so indirectly checks its own production; at the same time, it stimulates the secretion of the luteinizing hormone. Ovulation occurs when the secretion of follicle-stimulating hormone is still high and the output of luteinizing hormone is beginning to increase; it is apparently due to the combined action of these two hormones. The rising level of luteinizing hormone changes the emptied follicle into a corpus luteum, from which progesterone is secreted. This latter hormone, in turn, depresses the formation of the luteinizing hormone and the corpus luteum goes into a decline. But meanwhile the supply of estrogen has reached a low level, its repressive effect on the hypophysis has ceased and a new crop of follicles is developing. And so the cycle repeats, the ovary helping govern its own cyclic activity (Fig. 114).

This summary fails to account satisfactorily for some peculiar cycles like those of the rabbit or the annual cycle of many wild mammals. A nervous factor acting on the hypophysis also seems to play a part, and its relative importance varies in different species. Proper amounts and proportions of the pituitary hormones are necessary to produce the typical growth, rupture and luteinization of the follicles. A proper reactiveness of the follicle is also an important factor.

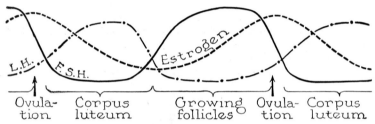

FIG. 117.—Diagram of the hormonal control of the ovarian cycle. See explanation in text.

The Uterine Cycle.—The rhythm of the uterus is controlled directly by the ovarian hormones. During the follicular phase of the ovary (estrogen formation) the proliferative growth occurs in the endometrium. During the luteal phase of the ovary (progesterone formation) the secretory or progestational changes take place. If pregnancy does not occur, the corpus luteum declines and disappears after a relatively brief existence, and the uterine cycle repeats. If pregnancy does occur, the corpus luteum persists and the endometrium remains in a specialized state, but ovulation ceases. These effects are probably the result of placental hormones influencing the ovaries by way of the hypophysis.

The peculiar feature of the higher primate type of uterine cycle is the destruction, with bleeding, that brings the progressive changes to an end. Why this occurs in some primates alone and what purpose it performs are unknown, but an explanation of its cause can be given. In an anovulatory cycle the endometrium is brought only through the proliferative stage; when the supply of estrogen then reduces to a certain level (see ovarian cycle, above) the endometrium is no longer able to maintain itself and menstruation occurs. In an ordinary ovulatory cycle there is no bleeding during the proliferative phase because the ovaries are supplying estrogen; there is no bleeding in the secretory stage because the corpus luteum is supplying progesterone. With the decline of the corpus luteum, however, the hormonally sustained endometrium is left temporarily without support and consequently breaks down.

The Vaginal Cycle.—The proliferation and cornification of the epithelium are dependent on the rise of estrogen in the body, corresponding to the final period of rapid follicular growth. Desquamation and leucocytic infiltration occur as the estrogen declines and its effect wears off, thus returning the lining to its 'inactive' diestrous condition.

The Mammary Cycle.—During the pubertal period, the duct system grows to adult size under estrogen stimulation (Fig. 118 A, B). Only in pregnancy is this degree of differentiation exceeded appreciably. Then the terminal twigs branch and bud off secretory end-pieces (C). This response in many animals requires the action of progesterone, while in a few species

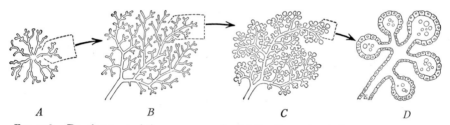

A   B   C   D

Fig. 118.—Development of the mammary gland (after Corner). A, Immature state. B, Effect of estrogen in bringing the duct system to the adult, virginal state. C, Further branching of ducts and budding of secretory end-pieces in pregnancy. D, Prolactin effect in causing secretion. The enclosed area of A grows into B, the enclosed area of B into C, etc.

estrogen stimulation alone is adequate. In still other mammals progesterone is not necessary, but apparently is a helpful aid; the human, like the monkey, may prove to be in this group. The actual secretion of milk is brought about by a hormone, *prolactin*, produced by the acidophilic cells in the anterior lobe of the hypophysis (D). Prolactin is a protein which has been isolated in pure form.[9] The glands are capable of secreting milk in the second half of pregnancy. The reason why the flow is withheld until after childbirth is because lactation is inhibited by the estrogen secreted by the placenta. When nursing and the suckling stimulus cease, and milk is no longer withdrawn, the secretory end-pieces undergo a degeneration and the gland returns essentially to the virginal state.

The Total Reproductive Period.—The growth and coming into function of the gonads and accessory reproductive organs, and the development of the secondary sexual characters, all depend in the last analysis on the gonadotropic hormones of the hypophysis. What actuates them to become effective at a certain time (*puberty*) cannot be said. It is a part of the larger plan of growth and maturing of the body, and the reproductive powers are wisely withheld until the parents are relatively far along in their own developmental course. The normal loss of the reproductive capacity comes earlier in female mammals than in males. Known in woman as the *menopause*, it is marked by the cessation of all cyclic, reproductive activities. Involution and atrophy of the ovaries, reproductive tract, external genitalia and mammary glands follow on the withdrawal of estrogen support, and sex desire ultimately wanes. In the male the decline of spermatogenesis and the secretion of testicular hormone is individually variable and less determinate than in the female.

REFERENCES CITED

1. Arey, L. B.   1939.   Amer. Jour. Obstet. and Gynecol., **37,** 12–29.
2. Bartelmez, G. W.   1937.   Physiol. Rev., **17,** 28–72.
3. Markee, J. E.   1940.   Carnegie Contrib. Embryol., **28,** No. 177, 219–308.
4. Stockard, C. R.   1932.   Sect. 40 in Cowdry's 'Special Cytology.' 2nd ed.   Hoeber, N. Y.
5. de Allende, I. L. C., *et al.*   1945.   Carnegie Contrib. Embryol., **31,** No. 198, 1–26.
6. Loeb, L.   1932.   Sec. 41 in Cowdry's 'Special Cytology.'   2nd ed.   Hoeber, N. Y.
7. Corner, G. W.   1943.   The Hormones in Human Reproduction.   Princeton Univ. Press, N. J.
8. Allen, E., *et al.*   1939.   Sex and Internal Secretions.   Williams and Wilkins.   Baltimore.
9. Chow, B. F.   1944.   In 'Advances in Protein Chemistry,' 153–185.   Academic Press, N. Y.
10. Stafford, W. T., *et al.*   1942.   Anat. Rec., **83,** 193–207.
11. Jones, G. E. S., *et al.*   1943.   Bull. Johns Hopkins Hosp., **72,** 26–38.

CHAPTER IX

EXPERIMENTAL EMBRYOLOGY

Descriptive and comparative embryology offer no explanation as to how and why the steps in development happen when and as they do. Such information comes from experiment. This youngest and most vigorously prosecuted field of embryology is commonly called *experimental embryology;* other terms are developmental mechanics, causal embryology and analytical embryology. Its contributions to an understanding of dynamic causation are already impressive.

THE METHODS OF ATTACK

A biological experiment consists in altering some condition under which a state exists or a process proceeds and then studying the results. The object of experiments in development is to reduce causation to its simplest terms. These results provide, bit by bit, the elements upon which synthesis and comprehensive understanding are based.

One line of experiment tests the dependence of the developing egg or embryo on its environment. The several physical and chemical environmental agents are called *external factors*. Their effects are naturally seen best in those organisms that are directly exposed to their influences; the embryos of viviparous animals, and especially mammals, are less subject to variations of the environment. The external factors of chief importance are the following: (1) *Mechanical*, such as pressure, gravity and centrifugal force. (2) *Physico-chemical*, such as pH and osmotic pressure. (3) *Radiational*, such as heat, ultraviolet rays and X-rays. (4) *Chemical*, through ionic effects. It is not necessary to itemize the detailed effects of these factors which have been tested by adding or subtracting them, one at a time, from the normal environment. Some are requisite to normal development; most, either in excess or deficiency, cause abnormal development of various kinds. These agents also become useful as tools in conducting experiments. For example, the centrifuge disarranges the constituents of the egg and redistributes them into layers according to their specific gravities; heat or ultraviolet rays can be used to kill local regions of the cytoplasm; X-rays or radium emanations can destroy the nucleus; excess sodium chloride can prevent the closure of the spinal cord; calcium-free sea water causes cleavage stages to separate into their component blastomeres.

A second line of attack tests the relations existing between the embryo as a whole and its parts, and the influence of component parts one on another. These interactions and influences are called *internal factors*. Their effects are tested by subtracting parts, by altering relationships through interchange or substitution, and by adding parts or wholes. The terminology and procedure are as follows: (1) *Isolation*. This is carried out by removing a part or region and allowing it to develop in its natural medium (*e.g.*, sea water) or, as an *explant*, in an aseptic, nutrient medium (*i.e.*, tissue culture). When introduced into a reasonably indifferent environment provided by another embryo (*e.g.*, belly cavity; chorio-allantoic

8

membrane) it is called an *interplant*. (2) *Defect*. The egg or embryo, after the excision or destruction of a local region, becomes a defect experiment. An egg nucleus can be destroyed by X-rays or sucked out with a micropipette. Cytoplasmic areas can be destroyed by local pricking, heat or ultraviolet treatment. A fine hair can be employed to cut or constrict. Tiny knives, glass needles and scissors are used for excising the parts of embryos. Some regions are differentially susceptible to toxic substances. (3) *Recombination*. Blastomeres can be displaced into strange positions. The grafting of an excised part into the place left by the removal of another part is *transplantation*. When the substitution or exchange is from one individual to another, the embryo supplying the transplanted part is the *donor;* the one receiving it as a graft is the *host*. (4) *Addition*. *Implantation* is the addition of a part, as a supernumerary structure, to an embryo complete in every way. *Fusions* of whole eggs or early cleavage stages can be accomplished; the surgical union of older embryos is called *parabiosis*.

Eggs and embryos of various kinds have served as experimental material, but echinoderms and amphibians are prime favorites. The embryos of birds can be used to some extent, whereas the manner of development of mammals and the unfavorable stickiness of their tissues at operation present formidable difficulties.

AN INTERPRETATION OF EARLY STAGES

Organization of the Egg.—The ripe egg exhibits a degree of organization. Fundamentally important is its *polarity*, with a main axis connecting the two poles. The animal pole possesses higher activity capacities and tends to be near the future apical or anterior end of the embryo; these capacities decrease in gradient fashion to the vegetal pole. Polarity, or axiation, is impressed from without on the ovarian egg, and the animal pole is the end of the egg which was most active in physiological exchanges during oögenesis. Also of great significance is the establishment of *bilateral symmetry*. Innumerable planes, which could divide the egg into physiological halves, pass through the primary axis of the egg connecting the two poles. Not all meridians are exactly equivalent and a certain one comes to possess a slight advantage over the others, due to influences impressed on it while in the ovary. The existence and localization of such a plane can be revealed by susceptibility experiments. This differential in favor of bilateral symmetry is not often over-ridden by factors acting at the time of fertilization and afterward, but there is some evidence that the point of entry of the sperm may shift the still labile plane of symmetry in the egg of the common frog to a new position.

The cytoplasmic cell body is not homogeneous. There is a greater concentration of pure protoplasm (building material) at the animal pole, whereas reserve materials (such as yolk) favor the vegetal pole. Moreover, the interior differs from the surface. The internal core of cytoplasm is semifluid; the peripheral shell, more gelatinous. A gel condition favors regional differentiations, and such not only occur but even become visible in some eggs. They are characterized by pigmentation, different colloidal consistency or other features. These stratifications and distributions, however, are the result and not the cause of polarity. Following their disturbance by centrifuging, the original axis of polarity still governs further development (Fig. 119).

The Initiation of Development.—The free, unfertilized egg undergoes progressive 'aging.' A demonstrable result is an increasing coarseness and aggregation of cell colloids over their previous finely dispersed state; with this congealing tendency goes a reduction in vigor and plasticity. *Fertilization* reverses these trends, thus rescuing the egg from impending senescence and death and bringing about cell rejuvenation. Within limits, an over-ripe egg will still receive a sperm and develop. But as staleness advances, development is progressively poorer; malformations increase and viability of the embryo decreases.[1] It is obvious, however, that fertilization must do more than rejuvenate; it must also activate. What the inciting factor may be is not clear, although a primary effect seems to be the liberation of an acid within the cytoplasm. This in turn, induces physico-chemical changes which lead to complex chemical reactions of unknown character. Among

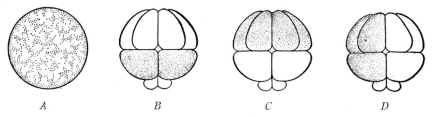

| A | B | C | D |

FIG. 119.—Persistence of polarity in centrifuged eggs (Morgan and Spooner). *A*, Distribution of yolk and pigment granules in the normal egg of the sea urchin. *B–D*, Retention of main axis, with tiny blastomeres at the original vegetal pole, in 16-cell cleavage stages, regardless of the dislocation of the heavier granules and lighter clear oil and protoplasm.

the changes, the cytoplasmic colloids become more viscous and stable, while in some forms, including vertebrates, permeability and cell respiration increase greatly.

One set of chromosomes, from either parent, is adequate for development. That the female pronucleus is not essential to cleavage is proved by the fact that spermatozoa will activate eggs from which the nucleus has been removed or in which the nucleus has been made degenerate through radium treatment. Even an enucleate, cytoplasmic fragment of some eggs will receive a spermatozoön and develop into a larva. On the other hand, a sperm with its nucleus fatally damaged by radium (so that it is inactive, like a foreign body) is still able to enter an egg and stimulate it to develop. Even in the absence of sperms, the eggs of many invertebrates and vertebrates can be made to develop readily through chemical or other stimulation (*artificial parthenogenesis*). Adult frogs have been reared from eggs induced to develop parthenogetically by pricking with a needle; normal rabbits

have been born from eggs stimulated by various artificial means.[2] These
several facts show that the ability to develop is a fundamental property
of a ripe egg and that the actual union of the male and female pronuclei
is not the factor that sets off development. Neither does the entering
sperm supply a specific substance that is necessary for egg activation; it
only releases those reactions within the egg upon which development
depends. The egg, therefore, is the essential primordium of the future
embryo; it is indispensable, while the sperm is dispensable.

Cleavage and Gastrulation.—By means of *cleavage* the egg is subdivided into smaller building units. The pattern depends on the position
and orientation of the mitotic spindle at each division, on the rate of
mitosis in different regions, and on shifts of the blastomeres after they are
cut off. The physical constitution of the cytoplasm and spindle, the amount
and distribution of yolk and the influence of surface tension are known
factors in determining pattern. Deviations from the general rules of

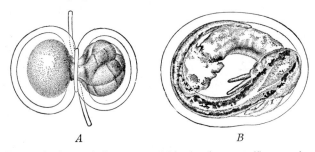

A   *B*

FIG. 120.—The equivalence of cleavage nuclei in development (Spemann). × 13. *A*, Constriction of the egg of the newt had confined the nuclei (and cleavage) to the right half; at this
point one nucleus was permitted to pass into the left half and the ligature was tightened to produce separation of the halves. *B*, Later identical larvæ, derived from the two halves.

cleavage (p. 57) doubtless have logical explanations, based on asymmetrical, protoplasmic organization or forces, and on local differences in vis-
cosity and other qualities. Blastomere shifts that go beyond the adjust-
ments which are made in conformity with local surface tensions, are akin
to those mass movements that take place in the multicellular blastula
during *gastrulation*. The latter result from a 'flowing' of cell groups in
which the individual cells are mere passengers. Such gastrulation movements are a function of the blastula as a whole, analagous to ameboid
movements in a single cell but even less well comprehended. The results
of gastrulation are eminently practical: the cells of the blastula segregate
at convenient levels as the germ layers, thereby distributing in some cases
cells already specialized and with closed fates; but in vertebrates, the cells
lack specific and irrevocable assignments as yet and merely acquire positions
that are advantageous in a future program of specialization and morphogenesis.

Cleavage, no matter how orderly it may be, is not a mechanism primarily designed to distribute particular qualities to the blastomeres which, carrying out irrevocable assignments, then give rise to particular parts of the embryo. The idea that specific qualities are distributed through the nuclear divisions of cleavage can be disproved by experiment. For example, a half egg, made to receive but one of 16 cleavage nuclei, develops into a normal individual; hence the daughter nuclei cannot be qualitatively unlike (Fig. 120). That cleavage is not a specific device for subdividing the egg cytoplasm in such a way that the various blastomeres receive portions with rigidly different, developmental qualities follows from certain facts: in many animals one of the first two blastomeres is able to develop into a whole embryo, while later blastomeres can have their normal fates swerved to other ends. Although the blastomeres sometimes do receive cytoplasmic allotments of different character, it is the organization of the cytoplasm that governs these distributions and the cleavage pattern. The latter is a

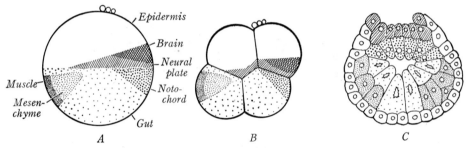

FIG. 121.—Organ-forming areas in the egg of the tunicate, Styela (after Pasteels, Vanderbroek and Conklin). A, Map of fertilized egg, showing the locations of prospective parts. B, C, Eight-cell cleavage stage in side view and transverse section of larva, showing the fates of the mapped regions.

somewhat incidental instrument which leads to the organization of the embryo, rather than being the primary cause of its organization.

Organ-forming Regions.—In the normal course of development, the egg breaks up into blastomeres and these become first germ layers and then definite organs and parts of the embryo. Complete *cell lineages* can be followed in some lower forms with a rigid style of cleavage and few and distinctive cells; but in vertebrates the blastomeres and cell groups of the blastula can be traced to their destinations only by marking them with vital dyes which stain the cytoplasm without injuring it. This continuity, though not exact spatial correspondence, between definite territories of early and late stages may even be presaged to a certain extent in some fertilized eggs by localized substances, different in color or texture. In these cases a distinctive area may prove to be the precursor of a specific portion of the later embryo (Fig. 121). It should be emphasized, however, that not every structural differentiation within such egg cytoplasm has functional significance for organ formation. In fact, visible granules, like pigment and yolk, are not factors to this end as dislocation by centrifuging proves (Fig. 119), although they may serve normally as markers of significant territories. For this reason, and since so little is known about actual protoplasmic differentiations, it is better to avoid the term 'organ-forming substances.'

Any correspondence between specialized regions of the egg and later organs is, of course, not preformation in the gross sense (p. 4). It is merely a *prelocalization* of distinctive regions whose normal (*i.e.*, presumptive) fates can be foretold. For the moment, the existence of these regions of the egg or early germ can be considered as having only a descriptive or topographical meaning. Whether their developmental possibilities just

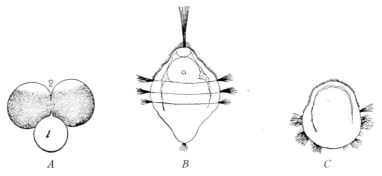

A   B   C

Fig. 122.—Mosaic development in the mollusc, Dentalium (Wilson). *A*, Egg, with so-called polar lobe (*l*) protruded, in the first cleavage division. *B*, Normal larva. *C*, Defective larva resulting from the removal of the polar lobe at stage *A;* the apical organ and region below the main zone of cilia are lacking.

equal or transcend their routine developmental performance, will be considered next.

THE CONCEPT OF POTENCY

Potency refers to the total range of developmental possibilities which an egg, blastomere or part is capable of realizing under any condition, either natural or experimental. In some animals (*e.g.*, tunicates; molluscs; annelids) cleavage follows a precise pattern (*i.e.*, *determinate cleavage*) and each blastomere has its characteristic position and unalterable fate (Fig. 121). The cleavage group or blastula is a mosaic in which the component blastomeres have received assignments according to an inflexible plan already completed at the time of fertilization. This parceling-out process means that each blastomere at some period becomes the precursor of a definite part of the embryo. Destruction of such a blastomere results in a defective larva (Fig. 122). An isolated blastomere of the two-cell stage develops into a half-larva; later blastomeres have still more restricted possibilities. This is *mosaic development;* the potencies of the blastomeres just equal the fates which they achieve.

In other animals (*e.g.,* vertebrates) the plan of cleavage is less rigid (*i.e., indeterminate cleavage*). Although normal development demonstrates a general relation between blastomere position and fate, still the blastomeres possess more capabilities than they ordinarily show. For example, the destruction of a blastomere with a certain presumptive fate or its dislocation to a strange position is followed by readjustments and substitutions which produce a normal embryo. A first blastomere of a mammal, when isolated, can alter its usual destiny and develop into a perfect (but small) embryo, while two fertilized eggs, made to cohere like a two-cell stage, produce a single, giant embryo.[3] Even a symmetrical half of an amphibian blastula will give rise to a whole embryo. This is *regulative development;* the potencies of the blastomeres are greater than their normal performance would lead one to suspect. A vertebrate embryo, as a whole, does not consist of organ-specific districts until relatively late; in an amphibian this is at the neurula stage.

All gradations exist between determinate, mosaic eggs and indeterminate, regulative eggs. But in every case, development eventually attains the unalterable, mosaic state, so that the differences observed between the eggs of different animals are those that accompany an early or late loss of regulative plasticity. Even the mosaic egg of a tunicate is regulative before fertilization occurs; halves, cut in a meridional plane and fertilized, become complete larvæ. The existence of regulation, as shown by the production of a whole embryo from a half egg, a single blastomere or a half blastula, or from the union of two eggs, is proof that the embryo is not preformed in the egg but rather that it develops epigenetically (p. 4).

THE PROBLEM OF DETERMINATION

At some time during development every embryonic region loses its originally extensive potentialities and becomes limited to a specific line of action and structural differentiation. This fixation of fate by the assumption of an irrevocable assignment is known as *determination.* It may already be settled in the fertilized egg, so that cleavage is a matter of parcelation and later development is a program of realization (extreme mosaic eggs); or determination may only be getting into full swing during gastrulation (regulative eggs, including the eggs of vertebrates). The progress that determination has made at any period is learned by testing potencies. For example, when areas of prospective epidermis and neural plate are exchanged at the beginning of amphibian gastrulation, each differentiates into tissue appropriate to its new site (Fig. 123). A similar interchange at the neurula stage, however, results in the neural tube containing an insert of epidermis, and the skin an island of neural tissue (Fig. 124). Hence, between the early gastrula and the early neurula stage, developmental plasticity and the capacity of adaptation have been lost to these parts; that is to say, they have been determined.

Experiment proves that determination appears in different regions at different times; it is established gradually and always proceeds from the general to the particular. Determination is a 'receiving of an irrevocable instruction,' whereas differentiation of form and tissue is the visible carrying out of this assignment. Only rarely among animals are the early, determined cells recognizable structurally from their neighbors.

The developmental history of a limb of an amphibian illustrates the course of determination and its results: The egg and blastula gain an animal and vegetal hemisphere and bilateral symmetry. Cell groups move into position as segregated germ layers, whose cells at first are undetermined and interchangeable. A diffuse, fore-limb field becomes estab-

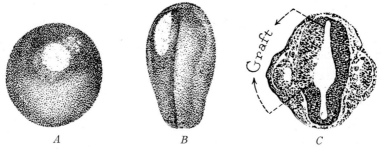

A   B   C

FIG. 123.—Plasticity of parts prior to their determination (Spemann). *A*, Early gastrula of a pigmented amphibian containing, within its prospective brain region, a substitute graft from the prospective belly epidermis of a pale species ($\times$ 20). *B*, Embryo, with graft, at neurula stage ($\times$ 20). *C*, Transverse section through the head of the later embryo; the transplant has been influenced by its surroundings to differentiate into an inset of pale brain tissue ($\times$ 60).

lished in the mesoderm. Centrally within this larger, potential limb district the actual limb bud appears as a localized mass. Although irreversibly determined as a limb (as proved by its self-differentiation after explantation into tissue-culture medium), the bud still possesses regulative ability; if it is halved, two fore limbs develop; if an extra bud is grafted in, the materials merge and make one limb. Moreover, the field retains for a time reserve capacities; if the bud is removed, the field becomes a whole once more and another limb bud can develop in it. At this stage, the limb is determined as an organ, but its cells still lack specific assignments; their determination is an affair of local subfields in which they happen to lie. Overlapping, competing subfields are established for the upper arm, forearm and hand. Mesenchymal condensations then signify the definite localization of these parts. Finally, progressive form- and tissue differentiation serve as visible indices of the terminal determinations.

How is determination brought about? It has already been shown (p. 158) that the cleavage pattern and qualitative differences in the cell nuclei must be excluded from consideration. Determination is the result of progressive change within the cytoplasm and has chemical differentiation as its basis. This internal chemo-differentiation may set the fates of the cells within a local region alone, whereupon these cells are able to self-differentiate. Or a cell group may also emit a chemical substance that affects specifically an adjoining region so that it becomes determined in a way it otherwise never would; in this instance differentiation is dependent on an outside stimulus. Self- and dependent differentiation are not mutually exclusive; an organ that gets its start through dependence soon acquires the power of self-differentiation and becomes independent. Critical study has revealed more and more cases of seemingly pure self differentiation to be dependent in their earlier periods.

Embryonic Induction.—The specific, morphogenetic effect brought about by a chemical stimulus transmitted from one embryonic part to another is known as an *induction* or *evocation*. The part exerting this influence is an *inductor* or *organizer*, and the chemical substance emitted is

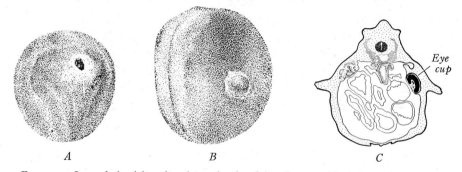

A   *B*   *C*

FIG. 124.—Loss of plasticity after determination (after Spemann). *A*, Neurula of toad, from which the eye region of the brain has been removed. *B*, The portion taken from *A* has been transplanted into the flank of another neurula of equal age. *C*, Transverse section through the resulting tadpole; the transplant has become an eye cup in strange surroundings.

an *evocator*. Induction is an important and widespread mechanism of determination. It occurs especially in organs assembled as a composite from different sources and is useful in bringing about orderly development and the correct timing and fitting together of parts.

Inductive effects have been studied most thoroughly in amphibians. The first part to exhibit organizer activity is the future chorda-mesoderm tissue that rolls around the dorsal lip of the blastopore. This tissue, passing to the interior of the gastrula, underlies the dorsal ectoderm like a tongue and is in contact with it. In this region of contact, the ectoderm first thickens into the neural plate and then folds into the neural tube. That it has been subject to induction can be proved by experiment: if contact between the ectoderm and chorda-mesoderm is prevented, the neural plate fails to develop; if the dorsal lip of the blastopore is implanted under strange ectoderm, it brings about the formation of a neural plate there. This neuralizing effect, however, has further consequences, and it will be instructive to follow one particular sequence of provable inductions to its end. The swelling forebrain, reacting to the influence of the head mesoderm, produces a pair of lateral bulges (the eye vesicles) that become the stalked eye cups. Each vesicle induces the adjacent ectoderm of the head to thicken into a lens plate (Fig. 462 A) which then folds into a lens vesicle (B, C) and pinches off. The lens, in turn, causes the pigmented epidermis over it to clear and to become the corneal epithelium (Fig. 463). In this sequence of inductions there are, at least, inductors (or organizers) of the first, second and third order.

After the extirpation of an inductor (e.g., eye vesicle), the usual response (e.g., lens formation) fails. This type of experiment, however, does not show that the inductive effect is more than an arousing into action of a tissue already prepared to respond in a particular way. That the eye vesicle can actually 'instruct' adjacent ectoderm is proved by implanting a vesicle beneath the ectoderm of the belly, or by substituting belly ectoderm for the normal lens ectoderm. In both experiments a lens differentiates from the strange ectoderm that normally would never display this activity. That the normal, presumptive lens ectoderm is not at first predisposed toward lens formation can be proved by supplying it with eye- or nose inductor, whereupon it responds by forming these parts. The testimony of these several experiments in favor of the epigenetic mode of development is unanswerable.

In order to produce an induction, the tissue of the inductor must be in contact with the region stimulated. This is because the chemical substance (the *evocator*) that mediates the response passes by diffusion from cell to cell. An inductor acquires inductive power and retains it for a time. Strange tissue, grafted into an inductor becomes imbued with the power residing in that region. So does an induced early organ, which may be made to induce another organ like itself. Similarly, an embryonic region is capable of responding to a particular inductor for a limited time only; during this reactive period, when determination is established and the course of differentiation set, the tissue is said to possess *competence*. Although an inductor gives a cue or order, the competent tissue carries it out in its own way. For example, when body ectoderm of a frog is grafted onto the future mouth region of a newt, a mouth is induced; but it is a frog's mouth, with horny jaws instead of teeth.

The Organizer.—The prospective chorda-mesoderm tissue is the original focus (organization center) with respect to which the rest of the embryo integrates. This can be proved by grafting the dorsal lip of a gastrula into the belly region of another gastrula (Fig. 125 A, B). It sinks beneath the surface and self-differentiates into a mesodermal axis (notochord and segmentally arranged somites, together with kidney tubules and lateral mesoderm). A neural axis is induced from the host ectoderm above it (*C*), while additional mesodermal organs may be induced from host tissue and an accessory gut may form from the host entoderm beneath. As development proceeds, a secondary embryo arises which remains attached to the primary embryo, derived from the host gastrula (*D*). It is this master organizing-power (self-differentiation combined with complex inductions) that makes the primordial chorda-mesoderm be recognized as the *primary organizer*, or, as it is often called, *the organizer*. Given the opportunity and materials, it will cause a whole embryo to be formed.

An organization center has also been discovered in some invertebrates and in fishes and birds. The primitive streak of a bird is a modified blastopore through which the prospective chorda-mesoderm passes during gastrulation. It induces the formation of the neural plate, and when trans-

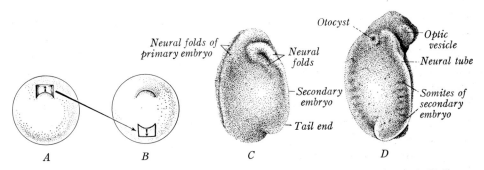

FIG. 125.—Induction of a secondary embryo by an extra, primary organizer. *A, B,* Transplantation of the dorsal lip of an early gastrula of the newt to the future belly region of another gastrula. *C, D,* Stages of the resulting primary embryo, with a secondary embryo attached to it (Bautzmann; × 13).

planted induces the appearance of a secondary embryo, as in amphibians. The entoderm, which precedes the primitive streak in time of appearance, is the inductor of the primitive streak.[4] Little is known of the mammal beyond the facts that a chick primitive streak will induce a neural plate in a rabbit blastoderm and a rabbit primitive streak acts similarly in a chick blastoderm.[5]

The influence of the primary organizer is two-fold. The chorda-mesoderm contains a chemical substance, or evocator, that causes competent ectoderm to form a neural plate and tube. But when chorda-mesoderm, killed by heat or chemicals, is implanted under strange ectoderm the result is similar. Moreover, dead tissue from other regions of the embryo and from all kinds of animals, embryonic or adult, has the same effect. Tissues that are ineffective when living may become inductors when dead. A neutral substance, such as agar, soaked in an extract from a known neural inductor and used like an implant may induce a neural plate. These results imply that the essential agent in neural inductions is a widespread chemical substance that is also contained in every part of an embryo. Yet in life it is only set free by the chorda-mesoderm, whereas elsewhere it exists apparently in an inactive or bound state. The kind of effect described thus far is one in which a competent tissue is activated into doing something within the range of its emerging field powers. But there is more to organizer action than the mere eliciting of a specific activity in a field, without displaying any itself. The primary organizer is also able to impose pattern upon the region that comes under its influence. A neural plate that is induced by a dead organizer lacks the regional specializations, such as brain or spinal cord, that characterize the different levels of an embryo. The living organizer, on the contrary, is able to instruct the neural plate in such a manner that it carries out regional assignments at appropriate levels and produces a neural tube as a whole. This means that the plate of chorda-mesoderm exerts different pattern-forming influences along its length; proof is supplied by appropriate transplantation experiments. Similar, dual influences of simple induction and regional individuation are doubtless exerted by inductors lower in grade than the primary organizer.

The Rôle of Genes.—The same assortment of chromosomes and genes is present in every cell of the embryo and, by themselves, they are incapable of initiating the processes of development and differentiation. Genes can only produce their effects when particular environmental conditions have been created with which they can interact. This may be quite early, since the gastrula of a hybrid-cross may show characteristics that belong to the species that supplied the sperm. It seems highly probable that genes can affect organizers, as they more certainly do the fields where differentiation and pattern are being worked out. There is also a suspicion that genes control the processes that bring a tissue into a competent state.

It would appear that the cytoplasm provides the fundamental mechanism for bringing about development, whereas the genes act as directing and controlling agents. Unfortunately, most of the information concerning the effects of genes comes from the later periods of development when details are being worked out. Such details are complex; wing differentiation in the vinegar fly has been analyzed into 16 separate processes, under the control of some 40 genes. Genes act by affecting the rates at which reactions go on in the embryo. Catalysts, inhibitors or hormones are produced or inhibited, masked or unmasked.

Hormonal and Nervous Influences.—Hormones play a rôle in development, especially in its later phases. They, however, are not primary, creative factors of development. On the contrary, when certain parts of the fetus have arrived at a proper state of differentiation (including hormone sensitivity) they merely react to the chemical stimulation supplied by the hormone substance. Nervous excitation is not a factor in the differentiation of tissues and organs. For example, a muscle or even a whole limb can develop fully in the complete absence of nerve. Through its inductive power, however, the nervous system does influence the development of the nose, eye and ear.

THE GRADIENT THEORY

Embryos and many adult animals show gradients of physiological activity. The principal one parallels the main axis of the body and has its high point at the anterior (apical) end and its low point posteriorly. When a worm is cut in two at any intermediate level, each piece retains an anterior-high and posterior-low polarity essentially like the original worm. The anterior piece grows a new tail, and the posterior piece a new head. The gradient theory first points out the agreement in space and orientation between morphological and physiological polarity. It then asserts that the significant gradient is metabolic in nature and that the relative intensity of metabolism at the two end-stations on a gradient is the cause of a head and tail existing and reconstituting where they do.

An egg first shows an animal-vegetal polar gradient. At gastrulation the organization center appears within another gradient field. As the embryo progresses, antero-posterior, dorso-ventral and medio-lateral gradients can be demonstrated, as well as gradient fields where the various organs are emerging. The gradient theory claims that the gradients call forth developmental activity, are the real organizers, and determine pattern. The fate of any cell depends simply on its relative position in the gradient system, and the kind of tissue differentiation at any point is set by the relative intensity of protoplasmic activities at that point.[6]

This ambitious theory which attempts to unify regeneration and development on a simple, common basis, emphasizes facts of fundamental importance concerning the existence of certain gradients and their correlations. It is with the specific interpretation of gradients as the causative factors of determination that objections have been raised. Is the significant gradient metabolic, and more especially oxidative? Is metabolic activity an instrument of determination or a mere indicator of the intensity of development? Are gradients more than attributes of activity? How can qualitative differences arise from an influence that differs only in strength? How can a continuous gradient produce wholly discontinuous formations such as the nose, eye and ear? How can a gradient at best do more than activate, leaving determination still resident in the regions stimulated?

TWINNING AND DUPLICATION

Experimental Twinning.—Organization into an embryo requires the presence of the primary organizer. The formation of separate embryos from isolated, early blastomeres of regulative eggs depends on whether or not these blastomeres contain (or are able to differentiate) organizer substance. In the sea urchin any one of the first four blastomeres includes a sample of the egg from pole to pole and will form a perfect, but small, larva. Subsequent cleavage restricts the organizer material to the vegetal blastomeres, and especially to tiny 'micromeres' at the vegetal pole (Fig. 119); even blastula-halves that contain both animal and vegetal cells will regulate into complete larvæ. In amphibia, the site of the primary organizer is indicated by a less pigmented territory that appears above the equator of the egg just after fertilization. If the first cleavage furrow transects this *gray crescent*, each of the resulting blastomeres, when isolated, can form an embryo; otherwise the blastomere containing the crescent is the only one that so develops. It follows that only when a blastula or early gastrula is halved in such a manner that each part contains some of the primary organizer (dorsal lip of the blastopore) will twin embryos result (Fig. 126).

A double 'monster' forms when the primary organizer of an amphibian is made to separate partially into two chorda-mesodermal tongues (Fig. 127 A, B). Double twins can also be produced by grafting together two half gastrulæ, each containing its blastopore (C, D). Depending on the angle the two dorsal lips make with the new main axis, such embryos can be made to have two heads or two tails. A most interesting cruciate (cross-

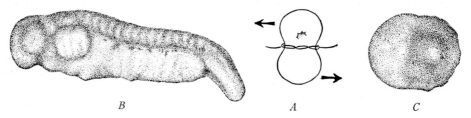

B   A   C

FIG. 126.—Dependence of organization on the primary organizer (Spemann, 'Embryonic Development and Induction,' Yale Univ. Press.) A, Gastrula of newt, about to be separated into halves. B, Well-proportioned embryo derived from dorsal half containing the organization center. C, 'Twin,' without exterior differentiation, derived from ventral half.

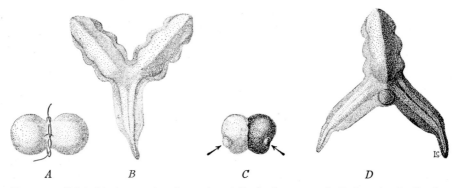

A   B   C   D

FIG. 127.—Jointed twins, produced experimentally in the newt. A, B, Anterior duplication, resulting from a constriction that causes the primary organizer to split into two tongues. C, D, Posterior duplication, resulting from the fusion of parts of two gastrulæ whose normal, main axes are indicated by arrows (after Spemann).

shaped) type results when the dorsal lips face each other directly. The two developing axes then meet head on and make an embryo with fused heads and partly separate bodies (cf. Fig. 132 A). But each head is a joint product, the left half from one individual and the right half from the other; and the midplane of the heads is at right angles to that of the facing bodies. Other types of crossed doubling are produced when a fertilized egg is inverted during the first cleavage. The heavier yolk settles, and traces of it interfere with gastrulation. Twinning can be enhanced in fishes, amphibians and birds by depressing certain environmental factors (temperature, oxygen, etc.) at the time of gastrulation. This tends to abolish the supremacy of the original axis, and leads to its replacement by other, more or less independent axes.

Organ primordia also possess regulative capacity for a time. A part of the anlage contains all the factors necessary to the formation of a whole and tends to produce a whole. This capacity can lead to duplication. The heart of an amphibian arises as two plates that normally meet in the midplane to form a tube. If the fusion of these bilateral primordia is prevented, each forms a separate, complete heart. On the other hand, a single organ can subdivide; when a limb bud is split lengthwise and the halves are prevented from reuniting, two perfect limbs are obtained. Subdivision may divide an organ field, even before it is visible as such; thus a transplant from the early eye field may form an eye in addition to the one produced from the undisturbed, residual tissue.

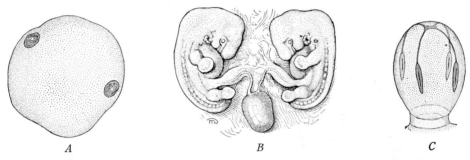

A   B   C

FIG. 128.—Early twin embryos. *A*, Blastocyst of a sheep, with two embryonic discs (after Assheton; × 15). *B*, Twin human embryos of 12 mm., with individual yolk stalks attached to a common yolk sac (× 2.3). *C*, Chorionic vesicle of the armadillo, containing four embryos at the stage of the primitive streak (after Patterson; × 2.3).

Natural Twinning.—The unaided isolation of blastomeres to produce separate twins is not known to occur in vertebrates. Since the cleavage cells of mammals are contained within the thick, tough zona pellucida until the blastocyst stage is achieved, this method of twinning seems unlikely. There are several other methods by which twins may originate spontaneously: (1) two blastoderms (or inner cell masses) arise by subdivision or segregation, and each develops an embryonic axis (Figs. 128 *A* and 129 *A*); (2) separate organization centers appear on a single blastoderm (Fig. 129 *B*); (3) a single organization center subdivides by fission or budding. Whether any particular specimen of sporadic twinning that is recovered at a later date (Fig. 128 *B*) belongs to type (2) or (3) cannot be established. The Texas armadillo, which produces quadruplets regularly (Fig. 128 *C*), utilizes first (2) and then (3). Joined twins (Fig. 129 *C*) probably result: (*a*) from incomplete subdivision of an embryonic axis, rather than (*b*) from the secondary fusion of separate axes. In the last analysis, twinning of any sort must be interpreted in terms of organization centers—whether separate from their first establishment as such, partially fused, or primarily single but with incomplete to complete subdivision. The critical time for twinning is before gastrulation (1, 2) or during gastrulation (3, a, b).

The frequency of multiple births varies considerably in different countries and races. As the term is popularly employed, twins occur among

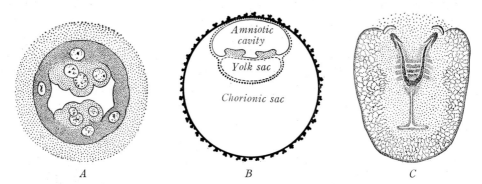

FIG. 129.—Manner of origin of single-egg twins (after Streeter, Corner and Tannreuther). *A*, Hypothetical stage of separate inner cell masses in a mammalian blastocyst. *B*, Hypothetical stage of two embryonic axes on a single embryonic disc. *C*, Partially double embryo of the chick.

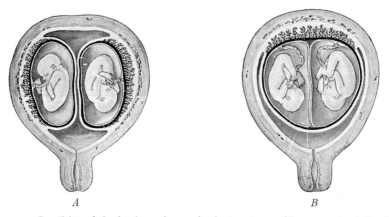

FIG. 130.—Condition of the fetal membranes in the two types of human twins (after Bumm). *A*, Ordinary, double-egg twins with individual chorions and placentas. *B*, True or single-egg twins, with a single chorion and placenta. Cut surfaces: deciduæ, thick white; amnions, thin white; chorions, black.

American whites once in 87 confinements; triplets have a frequency of 1 : $(87)^2$ and quadruplets 1 : $(87)^3$. Six appears to be the maximum number of simultaneous births that is well authenticated. A distinction must be drawn between false and true twins. The simultaneous birth of two or more human babies is most commonly due to the development of a corresponding number of eggs which were discharged from separate follicles, became fertilized by different sperms and implanted individually in the uterus (Fig. 130 *A*). Such *ordinary* or *fraternal twins*, triplets, etc. are contained within individual chorions. The fusion of these separate sacs into one is not known to occur in man where the intervening decidual tissue may block actual merger, just as it does in specimens of apparently fused placentas. The individuals may be of the same or opposite sex and they have only the general degree of family resemblance as occurs in brothers and sisters of different ages. Properly speaking they are not twins at all, but merely members of a litter.

Quite different are the true, or '*identical*' *twins* which are always of the same sex and so strikingly similar in physical, physiological and mental traits that only rarely is their diagnosis difficult. This close duplication is enforced by their derivation from a single egg, whereby each member acquires the same chromosomal and cytoplasmic constitution. Because they develop from a single blastocyst, human identical twins are contained within a common chorionic sac and have a common placenta (Fig. 130 *B*). The umbilical cords, however, are usually separate and the same is true of the amnions. The claim that the separation of blastomeres into two units during cleavage results in some identical twins possessing individual chorionic sacs needs more rigid proof than has yet been advanced.[7] At birth the practical diagnosis of single-egg twins is made when they are monochorionic. Triplets, quadruplets, etc. may be all identical or a mixture of identical and ordinary individuals. One third of all American twins are of the one-egg type, whereas in Japan the frequency is said to be three fourths.[8] Multiple ovulation, and hence ordinary twinning, tends to run in some family lines, and probably the same is true of one-egg twinning.

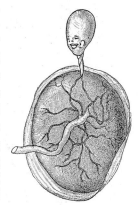

FIG. 131. — Acardiac human fetus, attached to a placenta whose umbilical cord belonged to a full-term, normal twin (after Barkow).

Anomalies.—Sometimes an identical twin is smaller than its mate and incapable of separate existence after birth. In this instance the heart is either rudimentary or lacking, and there is a corresponding degree of dependence on the normal twin for some or all of the blood supply. This supply may be direct, because of union between the two bodies (Fig. 133), or indirect through the medium of a common placenta (Figs. 78 *B* and 131). Such a twin with a deficient heart, or no heart at all, is an *acardius*. It varies in form from moderate deficiencies to complete amorphism.

Very rarely identical twins are conjoined as a 'double monster.' The degree of union may be slight or extensive, and the possession of a single or double set of internal organs varies with the intimacy of the fusion at any level. Union is by the heads, upper trunks or lower trunks; the joining in each case may be by the dorsal, lateral or ventral surfaces (Fig.

132). Sometimes there is a marked disparity in the size of the two components; in such instances the smaller is called a *parasite* (Fig. 133). The general principles of causation, as established by experiment (p. 168), have a special application in birds and mammals. Doubling of the head and upper trunk is due to the chorda-mesoderm splitting into two streams during the forward movements of gastrulation through the primitive streak. Doubling of the lower trunk results somewhat later when the caudally retreating primitive streak and knot produce a forking divergence.

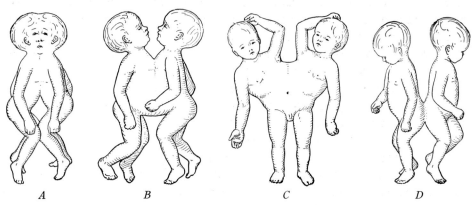

A   *B*   *C*   *D*

Fig. 132.—Symmetrical, conjoined twins. *A*, Ventral union of heads; a similar face occurs on the other side of the head. *B*, Ventral union of thoraces. *C*, Lateral union of lower bodies. *D*, Dorsal union in sacral region.

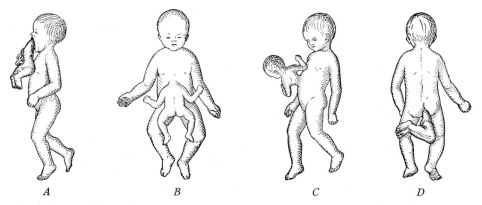

A   *B*   *C*   *D*

Fig. 133.—Unequal conjoined twins, one a parasite. *A*, Attachment to head of host; *B*, *C*, attachment to middle trunk; *D*, attachment to rump.

TERATOLOGY

Teratology is the subdivision of embryology that deals with abnormal development and its end products. It is recognized that the body and its organs always display some individuality in size, form, architecture or position. There are no rigid boundaries to this 'normal variation,' and any competent anatomist can set his own standards of normality. When, however, an organ or organism clearly oversteps what can reasonably be accepted as a permissible range of variation, then the condition is known as an *anomaly* or *malformation*. Continuous gradations connect the normal, slightly abnormal and severely abnormal. Since the roughing out of the human body and its parts occurs largely in the early weeks of development, most anomalies date from that time. Contrasted against these *congenital anomalies*, existing at birth, are those defects which are acquired secondarily through such means as structural weakness and disease. About one newborn in 165 carries a major malformation, either external or internal; the incidence in aborted fetuses is still higher.

Anomalies fall into several categories that indicate the general nature of the defective development:

1. *Developmental Failure.*—The primordium fails to appear, or at least does not develop to a significant degree. *Agenesis* denotes this condition. Examples: absence of arm or kidney.

2. *Developmental Arrest.*—Progressive development falls short of completion; examples: cleft palate; undescended testis. Temporary structures or states persist; examples: anal membrane; umbilical hernia. Normal growth fails; examples: dwarfism; infantile uterus.

3. *Developmental Excess.*—Growth is exaggerated; example: gigantism. Normal numbers are increased; examples: digits; twins. Organs overmigrate; examples: thyroid; ovary. Processes exceed normality; example: obliteration of mesocolon.

4. *Misplacement.*—Organs occupy abnormal locations (but not by arrest of normal shifts). Examples: transposed viscera; palatine teeth.

5. *Fusion or Splitting.*—Examples: horse-shoe kidney: cleft ureter.

6. *Atavism.*—Ancestral recurrences (p. 19). Examples: azygos lobe of lung, as in quadrupeds; elevator muscle of clavicle, as in climbing primates.

In subsequent chapters the more important anomalies will be mentioned and explained. The 'explanation', however, will often be superficial and unsatisfactory because response, differentiation and growth are conditioned by numerous factors. Not only may a specific malformation be produced in various ways, but also the same kind of disturbance may cause different types of malformation. The factors controlling general and differential growth have been discussed already (p. 8 and 11). In the present chapter the importance of potency, inductive stimuli, pattern-forming influences, competence, proper timing and dosage to determination have been made clear. Some abnormalities, ordinarily sporadic, become established in certain lines as hereditary characteristics; mutations of this kind have been induced experimentally by bombarding genes with X-rays. In general, the influence of genes (dominant or homozygous recessive) that affect differentiation and the rate and timing of developmental processes is of the utmost importance. Each developing organ or part passes through an individual critical period (or periods), during which time it is susceptible to influences brought to bear on it. Other parts are not sensitive, at that particular moment, to the same factors. The action of such *differential susceptibility* can be tested in lower forms by altering the external environment. It should be sufficient merely to state that the world-wide superstition that fright or accident to a pregnant mother can 'mark' her unborn babe in a correlated way is not even a possibility.

REFERENCES CITED

1. Blandau, R. J. and Young, W. C.   1939.   Amer. Jour. Anat., **64,** 303–329.
2. Pincus, G.   1939.   Jour. Exp. Zoöl., **82,** 85–129.
3. Nicholas, J. S. and Hall, B. V.   1942.   Jour. Exp. Zoöl., **90,** 441–460.
4. Waddington, C. H.   1933.   Arch. f. Entwickl.-mech. d. Organ., **128,** 502–522.
5. Waddington, C. H.   1937.   Arch. de Biol., **48,** 273–290.
6. Child, C. M.   1941.   Patterns and Problems in Development.   Univ. Chicago Press.
7. Lassen, M. T.   1931.   Arch. f. Gynäk., **147,** 48–64.
8. Strandskov, H. H. and Edelen, E. W.   1946.   Anat. Rec., **94,** 404.

PART II. SPECIAL DEVELOPMENT

CHAPTER X

EXTERNAL BODY FORM

Tissue combination in definite patterns creates still higher units of organization, the *organs*. Groups of organs associate as *organ systems* within the *organism*, or embryo as a whole. The development of an organ is brought about by the co-operative activities of morphogenesis and histogenesis (p. 14 *ff.*). It is usual to refer to these joint efforts as *organogenesis*.

An organ (*e.g.*, the stomach) has one tissue predominantly important (*i.e.*, its lining epithelium), while the others (*i.e.*, the muscular coats and connective-tissue layers) are accessory. Whenever an organ is said to originate from a certain germ layer, only its primary tissue is meant; the stomach, therefore, is entodermal. A few organs, like the teeth and suprarenal glands, have equally important parts derived from two germ layers.

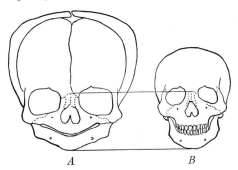

A   *B*

Fig. 134.—Skulls of the newborn (*A*) and adult (*B*), drawn to the same face-height to illustrate the relative loss in size of the neural skeleton (Scammon).

The assumption of the vertebrate type of organization by the embryo and its general shaping into human form were traced in a previous chapter. A systematic examination of the developmental history of the organs and parts that make up man will occupy Part II of this book.

THE HEAD AND NECK

Body-building begins in the head region where it gains an early advantage and acquires a favored blood supply. For a long time the head is disproportionately large. In Figure 74 the future cervical somites are midway along the embryo. The gradual adjustment of size relations may be traced in Figure 4.

The Head.—The cephalic end of an embryo is composed of two portions almost from the start. One is neural in nature and includes the brain, eyes and internal ears, as well as their supporting structures. The other is the facial or visceral part; it contains the upper ends of the alimentary and respiratory tracts. The neural portion is much the larger in young embryos and this supremacy is never lost completely, although the subsequent differentiation and growth of the nose and jaws reduce the early disparity in size (Fig. 134).

Anomalies.—*Cranioschisis*, or open-roofed skull, is usually associated with virtual absence of the brain (Fig. 135 *A*). *Microcephalus* describes a small cranium housing an undersized and underdeveloped brain (*B*). At the other extreme is an abnormally large head (*macrocephalus*) which accommodates a brain swollen by the excessive accumulation of cerebro-spinal fluid; *hydrocephalus* also designates the same condition (*C*). The expanded, macrocephalic cranium bears numerous supernumerary (Wormian) bones in its widened sutures. Various distortions of the normal-sized cranium (asymmetrical; conical; wedge-

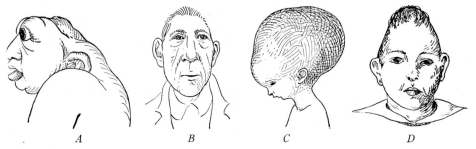

A	*B*	*C*	*D*

FIG. 135.—Malformations of the human cranium. *A*, Cranioschisis, or acrania, in a newborn; *B*, microcephalus; *C*, macrocephalus, or hydrocephalus; *D*, wedge-shaped cranium.

shaped) depend upon the premature closure of some sutures, while growth continues as usual along other bony margins (*D*).

The Branchial Arches and Neck.—The construction of a face and neck is closely bound up with the history of the *branchial arches*. These are bar-like ridges, separated by grooves, which appear on the ventrolateral surfaces of the embryonic head during the fourth week (Figs. 73 and 74). They correspond to the gill-arches of fishes and some amphibians. In these animals the arches actually bear gills and are separated by clefts through which respiratory water flows. Each arch contains a cartilaginous core, and a blood vessel (aortic arch) which interconnects the dorsal and ventral aortæ; in addition, there are appropriate muscles and nerves. The branchial arches of amniote embryos do not acquire gills. The human embryo develops five arches, separated by four ectodermal *branchial grooves*. At the same levels as these external grooves the entoderm of the pharynx pushes aside the mesenchyme and bulges outward to become the *pharyngeal* *pouches* (Fig. 171). The ectoderm of each groove and the entoderm of its complementary pouch then meet and unite; the thin plates thus formed only rarely rupture and complete the gill-slit condition.

The first branchial arch on each side bifurcates into a maxillary and a mandibular process (Fig. 74). The last arch lies caudal to the fourth cleft and is poorly defined along its posterior margin. During the sixth week the second arch overlaps the next three and obscures them (Fig. 74 *B*), the more caudal arches sinking into a triangular depression called the *cervical sinus*. At least that part of the sinus that contains the fourth and fifth arches closes off,[1] whereupon its ectodermal-lined cavity promptly detaches and obliterates (Fig. 75). Thus, after a short existence of two weeks, the branchial arches largely disappear as such and the resemblance to the ancestral gilled condition comes to an end.

Various muscles, bones and blood vessels differentiate from the mesenchymal cores of the arches, while their epithelial covering and lining have

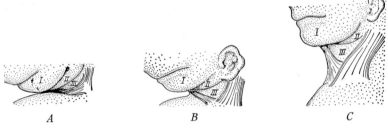

FIG. 136.—Relation of the branchial arches (numbered) to the ventral surface of the human neck (after Frazer).

other, distinctive fates. Moreover, the entodermal pouches, whose later sites can be observed in Figure 137 *A*, give rise to important derivatives. The completion of these transformations marks the appearance of a *neck* which is characteristic of amniotes alone. This part of the body results from an elongation of the region between the first branchial arch and the early pericardium (Fig. 136). The second and third arches, at least, can be seen to contribute to its ventral surface.[1] The heart itself is left behind, but all the structures that connect head with thorax (*i.e.*, vessels; nerves; muscles; digestive tube; respiratory tube) participate in the elongation. The detailed histories of all derivatives from the branchial-arch system will be treated in later chapters, and at present only the final results will be summarized in a table (p. 178).

Anomalies.—Imperfect obliteration of the branchial 'clefts' leads to the formation of cervical (branchial) cysts or fistulæ (Fig. 137 *B*). Some blame the second cleft and the cervical sinus for these abnormalities,[1] while others consider the third pharyngeal pouch (through remnants of its thymic stalk derivative) to be chiefly responsible.[2]

DERIVATIVES OF THE BRANCHIAL REGION OF THE EMBRYO

	ECTODERMAL DERIVATIVES		ENTODERMAL DERIVATIVES			MESODERMAL DERIVATIVES	
Arch or Pouch	Ectodermal Branchial Groove	Ectodermal Covering of Arch	Entodermal Lining of Arch	Entodermal Pharyngeal Pouch	Skeleton	Muscles (and Their Nerves)	Aortic Arches
I	Ext. auditory meatus. Epithelium of: Meatus. Tympanic membrane (external surface).	Epidermis of auricle (ventral half). Maxillary process: Epidermis of upper lip and cheek. Enamel; parotid gl. Mandibular process: Epidermis of lower lip and jaw. Enamel. Submaxillary gland. Sublingual gland. Epithelium of: Vestibule; palate. Body of tongue.	Epithelium of: Some of sides and floor of mouth.	Cavity and epithelium of: Tympanic cavity. Tympanic membrane (internal surface). Auditory tube. Mastoid cells. (Thyroid arises from floor at about this level.)	Maxillary process: Upper jawbone. Palate. Dentine; cementum. Mandibular process: (Meckel's cartilage.) Lower jawbone. Dentine; cementum. Spheno-mandibular ligament. Malleus; incus.	Mastication. M. digastricus (ant. belly). M. tensor tympani. (Nerve V innervates this group.)	Degenerates.
II	(Anomalous cysts or fistulæ.)	Epidermis of: Auricle (dors. half). Upper neck.	Epithelium of: Root of tongue. Pharynx. (In part.)	Palatine tonsil (?): Fossa. Epithelium of: Surface and crypts.	(Reichert's cartilage.) Stapes. Styloid process. Stylo-hyoid ligament. Hyoid (lesser horns).	Expression. Auricular. Epicranial. M. digastricus (post. belly). M. stylo-hyoideus. M. stapedius. (Nerve VII.)	Degenerates.
III	Obliterates in cervical sinus.	Epidermis of: Middle neck.	Epithelium of: Root of tongue. Pharynx; epiglottis. (In part.)	Inf. parathyroid. Thymus. Reticulum. Thymic corpuscles.	Hyoid (body and greater horns).	Pharynx (in part). (Nerve IX.)	Stem of internal carotid.
IV	Obliterates in cervical sinus.	Obliterates in cervical sinus.	Epithelium of: Root of tongue. Pharynx; epiglottis. (In part.)	Sup. parathyroid. Rudimentary thymus.	Thyroid cartilage. Hyo-thyroid ligament (?). Cuneiform cartilage.	Pharynx and larynx (in part). (Nerve X.)	Left: arch of aorta. Right: subclavian (in part).
V	Not formed.	Epidermis of: Lower neck.	(Lungs arise from floor at about this level.)	Ultimobranchial body ('lateral thyroid').	Thyroid cartilage (?). Corniculate, arytenoid and cricoid cartilages.	Larynx (in part). (Nerve X.)	Pulmonary artery. D. arteriosus. (Arch 5 or 6?)

Cervical cysts are closed, epithelial sacs which may be derived either from an ectodermal groove or the complementary, entodermal pouch. (Similar cysts occur also along the mid-dorsal line, where the neural tube was rolled in, and at the seams of fusion of the several facial components.) Incomplete reduction of the branchial 'clefts' gives rise to *cervical fistulæ*, which are of two types: A complete fistula is an open communication between the pharynx and the external surface of the neck (Fig. 137 C); it is due to the total failure of an open cleft to close. Incomplete fistulæ are blind *cervical diverticula* leading outward from the pharynx or inward from the skin of the neck; they correspond to the entodermal pouch or ectodermal groove, respectively.

The Face.—The development of the *face* is managed chiefly by the bulging region ventral to the fore-brain and by the first pair of branchial arches. The emerging eyes and nasal (olfactory) pits are also intimately concerned; in fact, just as the snout constitutes most of the face of low

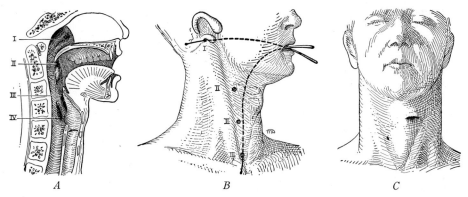

A   *B*   *C*

FIG. 137.—Anomalies of the primitive branchial apparatus in man. *A*, Left half of an adult head to indicate the final sites of the embryonic pouches, *I–IV* (after Corning). *B*, Preferred locations of cervical cysts, diverticula and fistulæ. *C*, Cervical fistula of second pouch origin.

vertebrates, so in mammals a first step in face-construction is the development of the nasal cavities.

An early stage of the face is shown in Figure 138 *A* where the expansive *fronto-nasal process* represents much of the front of the head. The *nasal pits* are present and the first branchial arches have not only bifurcated into *maxillary* and *mandibular processes*, but the mandibular portions have already united as the *lower jaw*. Each nasal pit is soon bounded by a prominent *lateral* and *median nasal process* (*B*); at this period the nasal pits communicate by a groove with the mouth cavity, just as in sharks. Presently the median nasal processes fuse with the maxillary processes (*C*) and become compressed toward the median plane (*D*). The compound product of these unions constitutes the *upper jaw*. Each lateral nasal process likewise joins the maxillary process of the same side. The lateral nasal processes become the sides and wings of the *nose*, whereas superficially the maxillary processes furnish the adjacent *cheek* regions. At the same time, the upper portion of the original fronto-nasal process becomes the *forehead*. Its downward continuation, located between the forehead and median nasal processes, is the so-called *triangular area* (*B*). It elevates slowly into the dorsum (bridge) and the apex of the *nose*. The various fusions between the facial components, as well as similar unions elsewhere in the developing

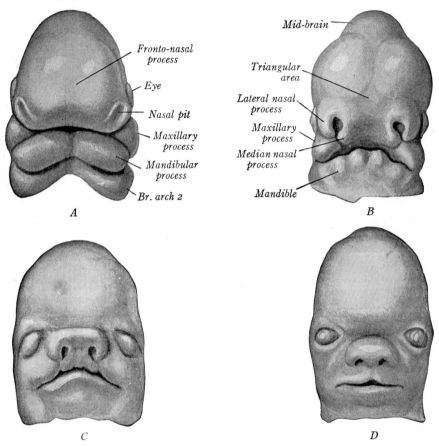

FIG. 138.—Development of the human face (adapted after Peter). *A*, At 6 mm. (× 14); *B*, at 10 mm. (× 11); *C*, at 15 mm. (× 10); *D*, at 20 mm. (× 7.5).

embryo, take place much after the manner of simple wound healing. The final relations of the several components are indicated in Figure 139 *A*.

The development of the human face occurs chiefly between the fifth and eighth weeks. When first formed, the nose is broad and flat, with the nostrils set far apart and directed forward (Fig. 138 *C*). In later fetal months the bridge of the nose is elevated and prolonged into the apex, and the nostrils point downward (Fig. 139 *B*). Accompanying this relative narrowing of the nose, the head broadens behind the eyes and causes them to be directed forward; in this way binocular vision becomes possible in primates. The zone between the median nasal processes is evident as the permanent *philtrum*, or median groove of the upper lip. This median region often continues downward into a distinct *labial tubercle* (Fig. 139 *A*). The lateral margins of the median nasal processes are indicated by angular indentations of the upper lip, best seen when the mouth is either open and

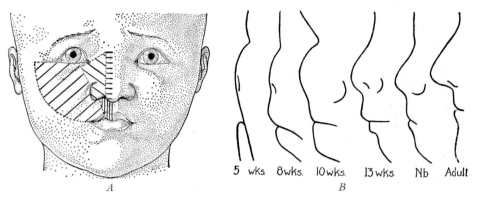

FIG. 139.—*A*, Definitive contributions of the facial components. *B*, Profiles, illustrating the changes in the form and proportions of the face throughout the life span (Scammon).

relaxed (Fig. 140 *A*) or when puckered (*B*). The *lips* begin to split away from the gum regions of the jaws in the seventh week. The original lateral extent of the *mouth opening* is at the point of bifurcation of the maxillary and mandibular processes (Fig. 138 *C*). Later this broad slit is reduced markedly in its lateral extents; in this way the *cheeks* are established and the lips become pursed. The *chin* is a median projection grown forward from the fused mandibular processes. Progressive modeling of the face continues throughout childhood and even until the individual becomes full grown (Fig. 139 *B*).

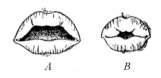

FIG. 140.—Junction of the median nasal and maxillary processes, as marked by angles in the adult upper lip (Lewis). *A*, Mouth open and relaxed; *B*, mouth puckered.

Anomalies.—The relatively frequent occurrence of malformations of the face is explained by the complexity of the developmental processes in this region. General failure of the usual transformations results in a featureless face (*aprosopus*). The lower jaw may be retarded (*micrognathus*) or even absent (*agnathus;* Fig. 141 *A*). The primitive mouth slit sometimes fails to reduce normally (*macrostomus;* Fig. 460); on the contrary, the normal degree of closure may be exceeded (*microstomus;* Fig. 482 *C*) and even complete atresia (*astomus*) is known. Fetal or infantile nose shapes are not infrequently retained.

A median defect of the upper lip or jaw, through incomplete union of the median nasal processes, is a rare anomaly (Fig. 460). Equally rare is imperfect fusion at the midplane between the mandibular processes which fashion the lower lip and jaw (Fig. 141 *B*). *Oblique facial cleft* describes a slanting cleft that extends from the mouth up the cheek (*B*). It is due to the failure of union between a maxillary process and the nasal processes (*cf.* Fig. 139 *A*). Among the commonest of human anomalies is *hare lip*, or *cheiloschisis*. This malformation is poorly termed since it is not median like the notched upper lip of the hare. Hare lip is usually unilateral and on the left side (Fig. 141 *C*) but it may be double (*D*). The defect can involve either the fleshy lip or bony upper jaw alone, or both together. The cause lies in the faulty fusion of the median nasal and maxillary processes. Sometimes the condition of hare lip is also combined with cleft palate. Double hare lip, whether accompanied by cleft palate or not, may result in the incisive bone (*i.e.*, the premaxilla, formed from the median nasal processes) projecting beyond the surface of the face; this defect is designated *wolf snout.*

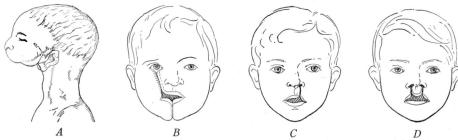

FIG. 141.—Malformations of the human face. *A*, Agnathus; *B*, oblique facial cleft and median cleft of lower lip; *C*, unilateral hare lip; *D*, bilateral hare lip of the type called 'wolf snout.'

FATES OF THE FACIAL COMPONENTS (EXCEPT EYES)

EMBRYONIC PART	FLESHY DERIVATIVES	BONY DERIVATIVES
Frontal process.	Forehead.	Frontal.
Triangular area.	Dorsum and apex of nose.	Nasal.
Median nasal processes.	Fleshy nasal septum. Median part of upper lip and gum; incisive papilla.	Ethmoid (perpendicular plate). Vomer. Premaxilla (incisive bone).
Junction of median nasal processes.	Philtrum and frenulum. Labial tubercle.	
Lateral nasal process.	Side of the nose. Wing of the nose.	Maxillary (frontal process). Lacrimal (?)
Junction of lateral nasal and maxillary process.	Naso-lacrimal duct.	
Maxillary process.	Upper lip and gum, laterally. Upper cheek region.	Maxillary. Zygomatic.
Mandibular processes.	Lower lip, gum and chin. Lower cheek regions.	Mandible.

The Sense Organs.—The eye, ear and nose will be considered in detail in Chapter XXI. The development of the external *nose* has been described in preceding paragraphs dealing with the face. The *eye* makes its appearance in the early weeks, and by the second month lids are present (Fig. 138). For a time the eyes are placed laterally and far apart, but gradually this distance is reduced. The *external ear* is developed around the first branchial groove by the appearance of small tubercles that combine as the auricle (Figs. 75 and 77 *E–G*). The groove itself deepened into the external auditory meatus.

Anomalies.—See Chapter XXI: nose (p. 485); eye (p. 496); ear (p. 506).

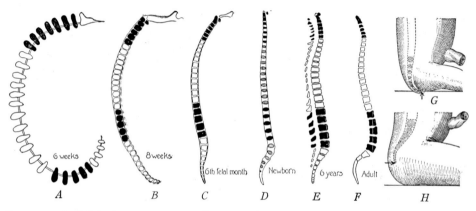

FIG. 142. –*A–F*, Spinal curvatures, at various ages, viewed from the right side (Scammon). *G, H*, Recession of the coccyx (arrow) between the tenth fetal week and birth (Schultz).

THE TRUNK

In young embryos the *trunk* is like a cylinder, flattened by lateral compression (Fig. 74). Its external contour is made irregular by the bulging heart and liver. During the early fetal period these visceral organs become less dominant, and the muscles and skeleton of the trunk also appear. The trunk then acquires an ovoid form, circular in section (Fig. 77). From the third fetal month through early infancy there is relatively little change in the trunk proportions. When erect posture is assumed, the dominance of the thorax and abdomen is reduced and the lumbar region gains in prominence and relative length. The thorax of the newborn is rather conical and thickest below, due to the ribs being more horizontal. In childhood the thorax becomes barrel-shaped—that is, broadest at its middle.

The **C**-shaped curvature of the fetal body straightens in the newborn (Fig. 142 *A–D*). The permanent curves of the spinal column appear partly through the pull of the muscles, and are not pronounced until posture becomes erect (E, F). The embryonic tail is at its relative maximum at the end of the fifth week when it is one sixth the length of the embryo. During the succeeding four weeks it disappears from external view, partly through actual regression; moreover, the coccyx, which represents the remnant of a tail, recedes to a higher position in relation to the buttocks (G, H). The *coccygeal fovea*, or postanal pit, of a newborn marks the site where the coccyx disappeared below the surface (Fig. 143 B).

Anomalies.—A grave defect results from incomplete closure of the body wall along its midventral line (Figs. 143 A and 302 A). This is known as *gastroschisis*, or, if the thorax be involved as well, *thoraco-gastroschisis*. Protrusion of the viscera depends on the degree to which the body wall is deficient and on its extent. A kindred malformation is cleft spine (*rachischisis*), consequent on the failure of the neural tube and vertebral column to close normally (Fig. 143 C).

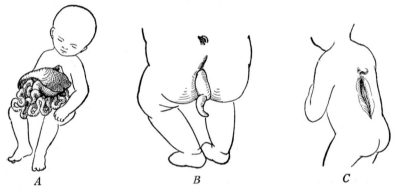

A B C

Fig. 143.—Malformations of the human trunk. A, Gastroschisis, with protrusion of the abdominal viscera. B, Tail of an infant ($\times \frac{1}{4}$); this specimen was 'soft' but slightly mobile, and is shown in its contracted state; above is a coccygeal fovea. C, Rachischisis, or cleft spine.

The embryonic tail has been known to persist and even increase to extraordinary size (Fig. 143 B). Specimens as long as 3 inches have been recorded in the newborn; most of these are soft and fleshy, but a few have contained skeletal elements. Some tumors of the coccygeal region are attributed to the abnormal activity of residual primitive-knot tissue (the end bud).

THE APPENDAGES

The *limb buds* appear late in the fourth week as lateral swellings but, due to the early dominance of the head-neck region, the arm buds seem to be located far down the body (Fig. 74). The distal end of a limb bud flattens (Fig. 144 A, E) and a constriction divides this paddle-like portion from a more proximal, cylindrical segment (B, F). Later, a second constriction separates the rounded part into two further segments (C, G); the three divisions of arm, forearm and hand, or thigh, leg and foot are then respectively marked off. Radial ridges, separated by grooves, first foretell the location of digits (C, G). These elongate into definitive fingers or toes, and rapidly project beyond the original plates; the latter, by a slower rate of growth, become restricted to webs between the basal ends of the digits (*D, H*). The thumb early separates widely from the index finger, and the same is true of the great and second toes.

Of the two sets of limb buds the upper pair appears first, begins its differentiation sooner and is earlier in attaining its final relative size. Not until the second year of postnatal life does the leg equal the arm in length; its continued faster elongation throughout childhood is a conspicuous feature of postnatal development (Fig. 4).

The limbs as a whole undergo several changes of position. At the very start they point caudad, but soon project outward at right angles to the body wall. Next, they are bent directly ventrad at elbow and knee, so that the elbow and knee then point outward (laterad) and the palm and sole face the trunk; naturally the thumb (radial) side of the arm and the

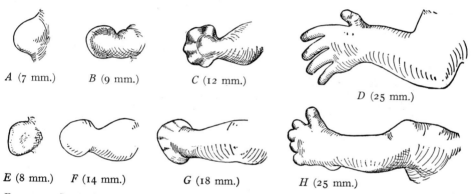

A (7 mm.) *B* (9 mm.) *C* (12 mm.) *D* (25 mm.)

E (8 mm.) *F* (14 mm.) *G* (18 mm.) *H* (25 mm.)

Fig. 144.—Stages in the development of the human limbs between the fifth and eighth weeks. × 6. Upper row, upper limb; lower row, lower limb.

great toe (tibial) side of the leg constitute the cephalic borders of their respective limbs. Finally, both sets of limbs undergo a torsion of 90° about their long axes, but in opposite directions. As a result, the (straightened) elbow points dorsad, the radial side of the arm becomes the outer border (when radius and ulna are parallel), and the palm faces ventrad. Conversely, the (straightened) knee points ventrad, the tibial side of the leg is the inner side, and the sole of the extended foot faces dorsad. By following through these changes it will be seen that the radial and tibial sides of arm and leg are homologous, as are palm and sole, elbow and knee.

Anomalies.—The limbs may either fail to develop at all or become mere stubs (*amelus;* Fig. 145 *A*). Sometimes the proximal segments of an extremity are normal while the distal portion is deficient and tapers to a stump (*hemimelus; A*). The reverse condition has at least the proximal segment missing, whereupon the hand or foot seems to spring directly from the trunk, like a seal's flipper (*phocomelus; B*). More or less complete union of the legs produces the siren or mermaid condition (*sympodia; B*). Rarely the hands or feet have missing digits, including the split or 'lobster-claw' condition (*C*). Opposite in nature is a partial duplication (*dichirus; D*), which is merely an extreme example of the common *poly-dactyly* (*E*), usually characterized by the addition of but a single digit. The bony fusion or fleshy webbing of digits (*syndactyly; F*) favors the union of the middle and third digits. Abnormal shortness of the digits is *brachydactyly;* it is due either to the omission of phalanges or to marked shortness of an otherwise normal set. The opposite tendency is *hyperphalangism,* in which supernumerary phalanges are interpolated in the customary digital series. All of these malformations of hands and feet tend to be strongly heritable.

    Clubhand or *clubfoot* is said by some to result from primary defects in the differentiating limb buds; others urge that clubfoot is essentially a retention of a transitory condition normal to the early fetus.[3] Congenital elevation of the shoulder results from an arrested descent of the upper limb from its cervical, embryonic position. Congenital dislocation at the hip

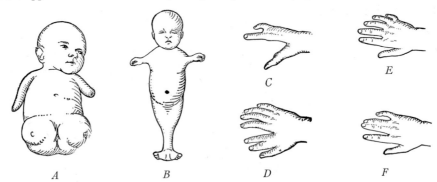

Fig. 145.—Malformations of the human limbs. *A,* Hemimelus in arms and amelus in legs; *B,* phocomelus in arms and sympodia in legs; *C,* cleft, or 'lobster-claw' hand; *D,* dichirus, or double hand; *E,* polydactyly; *F,* syndactyly.

joint comes from a failure of the outgrowths that normally produce a brim about the socket floor. Intra-uterine amputations (at any level) sometimes occur; the cause is intrinsic, due to focal deterioration, and not the result of constriction by a looped umbilical cord or amniotic bands.[4]

REFERENCES CITED

1. Frazer, J. E. 1926. Jour. Anat., **61,** 132–143.
2. Wenglowski, R. 1933. Arch. f. klin. Chir., **100,** 789–892.
3. Böhn, M. 1929. Jour. Bone and Joint Surg., **11,** 229–259.
4. Streeter, G. L. 1930. Carnegie Contrib. Embryol., **22,** No. 126, 1–44.

ENTODERMAL DERIVATIVES

CHAPTER XI

THE DIGESTIVE SYSTEM

The primary tissue of the entire digestive system is entoderm. This epithelial layer originally lines the whole yolk sac, but a regional difference in the shape of the entodermal cells is apparent from the first (Fig. 63A). Those that underlie the embryonic disc (and serve as a flat roof to the early yolk sac) are taller than the rest; they are the ones that are destined to

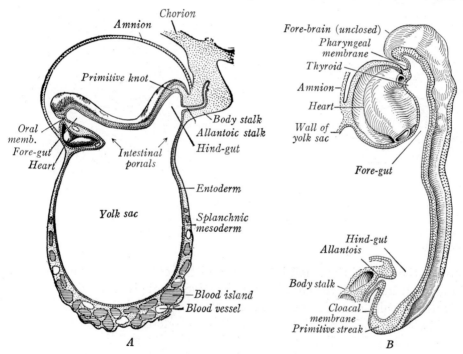

FIG. 146.—Entodermal tract of early human embryos, in sagittal section. *A*, At seven somites (Prentiss, after Mall; × 23). *B*, At ten somites (after Corner; × 30).

become gut-entoderm. When, at the twentieth day, the rapidly expanding embryonic disc begins to fold into a cylindrical embryo (p. 99), its gut-entoderm participates as a component layer. Pushing first into the head end and then into the hind end of the cylindrical body, the entoderm necessarily takes the form of two internal, blind tubes, opening by so-called intestinal portals where they join the yolk sac. The two tubes are named

187

fore-gut and *hind-gut* (Fig. 146). An intermediate region, open ventrally into the yolk sac through the narrower yolk stalk (Fig. 148), is sometimes termed the *mid-gut*, but its existence in man is brief since the yolk stalk constricts rapidly during the fourth week and detaches from the gut at the end of the fifth week. Both the fore-gut and the hind-gut elongate and broaden by interstitial growth, so as to approximate the growth of the embryo as a whole.

The primitive, tubular gut differentiates into the alimentary canal which has three chief segments: the mouth, pharynx and digestive tube. The latter division includes the esophagus, stomach, small intestine and large intestine; it lies in the body cavity and is suspended or held in place by mesenteries (Fig. 207). The fore-gut transforms into mouth, pharynx and digestive tube to a point far along the small intestine. The hind-gut

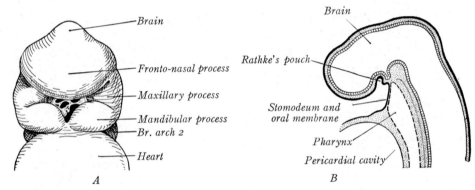

FIG. 147.—Human stomodeum and oral membrane. × 30. *A*, Boundaries of the stomodeum and a partly perforated oral membrane, shown in front view at 2.5 mm. *B*. Relation of ectoderm (full line) and entoderm (broken line) in this region, illustrated by a sagittal section at 2.5 mm.

becomes the rest of the small intestine, and the colon and rectum besides. Throughout its length the entodermal digestive canal gives rise to numerous derivatives, chief of which are the respiratory tract and the thyroid, parathyroids, thymus, liver and pancreas. The entoderm furnishes merely the epithelial lining of the digestive and respiratory tracts, and the characteristic epithelial parts of the other organs. The various glands, both large (such as the liver and pancreas) or small (like the gastric and intestinal glands), are primarily growths from out the lining epithelium. All of the accessory coats of the gut-tube develop from the unsegmented sheets of splanchnic mesoderm and are added as secondary investments.

At each end the gut comes ventrally into direct contact with the ectoderm. The fused plates, thus produced, are the *oral (or pharyngeal) membrane* and the *cloacal membrane* (Fig. 148). The oral membrane makes a floor to an external depression known as the *oral fossa*, or *stomodeum;* this fossa is bounded by the fronto-nasal, maxillary and mandibular processes (Fig. 147) and is brought into existence by the overjutting of these parts as the head grows forward. Midway in the fourth week (2.5 mm. embryos) the oral membrane ruptures and the oral fossa and fore-gut merge (Fig. 148 B). The stomodeum develops into the front part of the mouth which is, therefore, ectodermal.

The caudal end of the entodermal tube becomes the *cloaca*, or common vent. At an early stage it gives off the allantois (Fig. 148) and soon receives

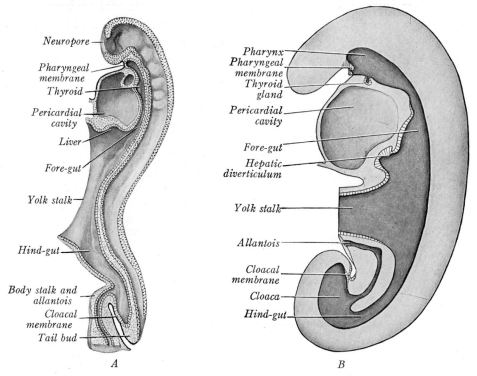

Neuropore
Pharyngeal membrane
Thyroid
Pericardial cavity
Liver
Fore-gut
Yolk stalk
Hind-gut
Body stalk and allantois
Cloacal membrane
Tail bud
A

Pharynx
Pharyngeal membrane
Thyroid gland
Pericardial cavity
Fore-gut
Hepatic diverticulum
Yolk stalk
Allantois
Cloacal membrane
Cloaca
Hind-gut
B

Fig. 148.—Entodermal tract, shown in hemisections of human embryos. *A*, At 2.5 mm., with eighteen somites (× 35). *B*, At 2.5 mm., with twenty-three somites (after Thompson; × 38).

the urinary and genital ducts (Figs. 171 *A* and 182). Even before these connections are complete, the cloaca begins to subdivide into a dorsal *rectum* and a ventral *bladder* and *urogenital sinus* (Fig. 185). By the end of the seventh week the cloacal membrane has separated into an anal and urethral region (Fig. 186); following this the two membranes rupture and disappear, and the division of the cloaca is concluded. Each of the new canals (rectum and urogenital sinus), so formed, acquires thus simply its individual opening to the outside.[1] The end of the hind-gut is then lined for a short distance with ectoderm, and this portion (the so-called *proctodeum*) constitutes the anal canal. It will be noticed that the primitive entodermal tube extends caudad a little beyond the cloacal membrane (Figs. 171 *A* and 182); this *tail-gut,* or *postanal gut,* dwindles during the fifth week and soon disappears. How rapidly all these changes occur may be appreciated by comparing embryos of four weeks (Fig. 184) with those two or three weeks older (Figs. 185 and 186).

THE MOUTH

After the loss of the oral membrane it is impossible to determine the exact junction of ectoderm and entoderm in the mouth. The inherent difficulties are increased by a considerable 'displacement' caudad of the dorsal line of union. The plane dividing ectoderm from entoderm is then a slanting one which passes forward from the beginning of the pharynx to the floor

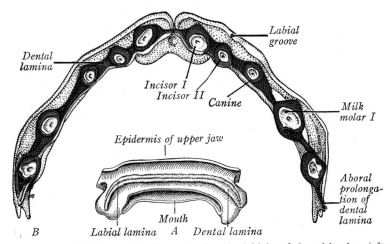

FIG. 149.—Isolated epithelium of the jaws, showing the labial and dental laminæ (after (Röse). *A,* At two months (× 8); *B,* at three months, with primordia of milk teeth (× 9).

of the mouth next the lower gum. This means that the roof and much of the sides of the primitive mouth are ectodermal. Specifically, the nasal passages, palate, front of the tongue and vestibule are considered to be covered with ectoderm; the enamel of the teeth and probably the salivary glands are likewise ectodermal derivatives. Although these various structures do not belong among the entodermal organs, it is simplest to describe them with the digestive and respiratory systems of which they are functional parts. A further derivative of the ectodermal stomodeum is a dorsal inpocketing, known as Rathke's pouch, which becomes the epithelial hypophysis (Fig. 147 *B*). Its point of origin marks the caudal extent of ectoderm in the completed mouth (Fig. 166).

Lips and Cheeks.—Until the end of the sixth week the primitive jaws are solid masses which do not show any subdivision into lip and gum regions, as is the permanent condition in animals below mammals. The separation of a lip from its respective gum is foreshadowed by the appearance of a thickened band of epithelium (Fig. 150 B). This *labial lamina* grows from the ectodermal covering of the primitive jaw into the mesoderm beneath. Following the contour of the jaw, it makes a long, curving band which deepens into a partitioning plate (Fig. 149 A). Progressive disintegration of the more central cells causes each plate to split into two sheets (Fig. 150 A, C). In this manner the *lips* become separate from the *gums* by the tenth week, and the epithelial-lined labial groove, so formed, deepens into the *vestibule*. Mesially the splitting is not so deep, thus leaving the *frenulum*.

The *cheeks* come into existence chiefly through a reduction in the extent of the originally broad mouth opening; this results from progressive fusion of the lips at their lateral angles. The labial and buccal muscles differ-

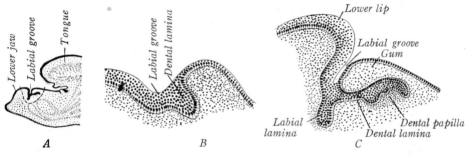

FIG. 150.—Development and relations of the labial and dental laminæ, demonstrated by sections through the human lower jaw. *A*, Sagittal section, at nine weeks, to explain the areas included in *B* and *C* (× 10). *B*, Labio-dental lamina, at seven weeks (Röse; × 90). *C*, Detail at nine weeks, of the area set off in *A* by a broken line (Röse; × 45).

entiate from the mesenchyme of the second branchial arches which migrates between the epidermal covering and mucosal lining of these parts.

The Teeth.—Historically the teeth are products of the skin, and both the epidermis and corium contribute to their formation; but it is the ectoderm that plays the leading rôle and exerts an organizing influence. A tooth is a greatly modified connective-tissue papilla that has both undergone a peculiar ossification into *dentine* and become capped by a hard *enamel* elaborated from the epidermis. In addition, the base encrusts with *cementum*, a bony deposit. The teeth have a double source of origin in the embryo. The enamel is from ectoderm; the dentine, pulp and cement are mesodermal. There are two generations of teeth in man and most other mammals, but no essential difference exists between the development of the temporary (milk) teeth and the permanent ones. Since the primordia of the temporary dentition arise first, they will be described first.

The earliest indication of oncoming tooth development is an epithelial plate, the *dental lamina*, which arises during the seventh week just gumward of the labial lamina, already described (Figs. 149 *A* and 150 *B*). The dental lamina soon becomes a horizontal shelf which projects perpendicularly from the labial lamina and extends well into the substance of the primitive gum (Fig. 150 *A, C*). Each dental lamina thereby courses alongside the curving labial groove and lies just gumward of it (Fig. 149 *A*). At intervals along the epithelial lamina there develops simultaneously a series of knob-like thickenings called the *enamel organs*, which both produce the enamel and serve as the molds for the future teeth (Fig. 151 *A, B*). Early in the third month the deeper side of each enamel organ presses against a dense accumulation of mesenchyme (Fig. 150 *C*); the epithelial surface of contact both buckles inward (*i.e.*, invaginates) and grows around the mesenchymal mound until the whole enamel organ is hollowed like a thick cup (Fig. 151 *C–E*). The concavity, formed in this manner, is occupied by the condensed mesen-

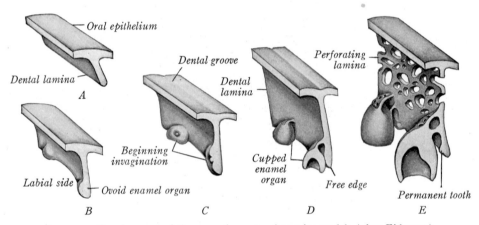

FIG. 151.—Development of the enamel organs, shown by models (after Eidmann).

chymal tissue of the *dental papilla* which is destined to differentiate into dentine and pulp (Figs. 152 and 153). An enamel organ and its associated dental papilla are the developmental basis of each tooth. Ten such primordia of the *deciduous*, or *milk teeth* are present in each jaw of a ten-weeks' fetus (Fig. 149 *B*). The neck of the enamel organs and much of the dental lamina break down in later fetuses (Fig. 151 *E*). However, the original free edge of the lamina persists longer and gives rise to the primordia of the permanent enamel organs.

The Enamel Organ.—This primordium gradually becomes a double-walled sac, composed of an outer, convex wall (*outer enamel layer*) and an inner, concave wall (*inner enamel layer*) (Fig. 152). Between the two is a filling of looser cells (*enamel pulp*) which transforms into a stellate reticulum. The enamel organ first encases the crown portion of the future tooth, molds its shape and deposits enamel there. Later the enamel organ elon-

gates and similarly models the root portion of the dental papilla which
seemingly organizes under its influence (Fig. 155 *A*). In this region it is

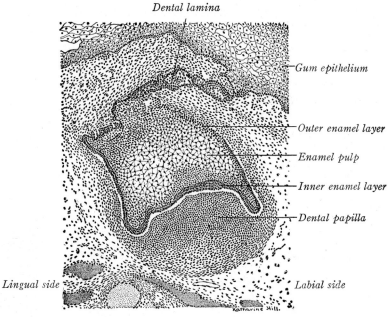

Dental lamina

Gum epithelium

Outer enamel layer

Enamel pulp

Inner enamel layer

Dental papilla

Lingual side

Labial side

FIG. 152.—Primordium of a human tooth, at three months, shown in section (Prentiss). × 70.

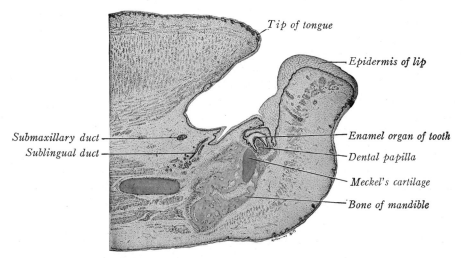

Tip of tongue

Epidermis of lip

Submaxillary duct

Sublingual duct

Enamel organ of tooth

Dental papilla

Meckel's cartilage

Bone of mandible

FIG. 153.—Sectioned human lower jaw, at three months, with a tooth primordium *in situ* (Prentiss). × 14.

called the *epithelial sheath* of the root; here the middle, pulp constituent of
the typical enamel organ is lacking.

Neither the outer enamel cells nor the enamel pulp contribute directly to tooth development, although the building materials of enamel must pass from the nearby blood vessels through their loosely arranged tissue. It is interesting and perhaps significant that the epithelial sheath of the root, lacking pulp, deposits no enamel. In the region of the future crown of the tooth the cells of the inner enamel layer become columnar and are designated *ameloblasts* (enamel formers), for they produce *enamel* at their 'free' surfaces (Fig. 154). The enamel substance arises first as a cuticular secretion from the end of an ameloblast; calcification of this 'Tomes process' is secondary. Continued enamel formation produces elongate *enamel prisms*, one for each ameloblast, which become cemented together (Fig. 155 *C*). As

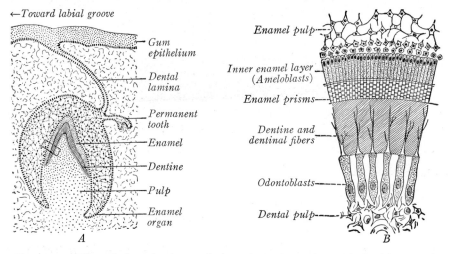

←*Toward labial groove*

Gum epithelium

Dental lamina

Permanent tooth

Enamel

Dentine

Pulp

Enamel organ

A

Enamel pulp

Inner enamel layer (Ameloblasts)

Enamel prisms

Dentine and dentinal fibers

Odontoblasts

Dental pulp

B

FIG. 154.—Differentiation of a human incisor, shown in sections. *A*, Deciduous and permanent primordia, at seven months (× 40). *B*, Detail of the area indicated by a rectangle in *A* (Tourneux; × about 300).

the enamel layer thickens, the ameloblasts retreat in a centrifugal direction until finally the internal and external layers of the enamel organ meet. Enamel is first deposited during the fifth month at the apex of the crown (Fig. 154 *A*); the process spreads downward in a progressive manner so that the ameloblasts of the neck region are the last to become active. Premolar and molar teeth have a separate cap of enamel for each cusp; these eventually meet and merge into a compound crown (Fig. 156). The remains of the enamel organ constitute the transient *dental cuticula* (Nasmyth's membrane), seen on the crown of the newly erupted tooth.[2] The inner enamel cells of the epithelial sheath of the root remain more cuboidal in form and do not produce enamel.

The Dental Papilla.—At the end of the fourth month the superficial cells of the dental papilla organize under the direction of the enamel epithelium[3] and arrange themselves in a definite layer that simulates a columnar epithelium (Figs. 154 and 155 A). These specialized, connective-tissue cells are given the name of *odontoblasts*, but that they are solely responsible for all of the dentine substance has not been demonstrated convincingly. The fibrils of the early dentinal matrix seem to be continuous with those coursing within the papilla as a whole (Fig. 155 B). This soft, fibrillar predentine then calcifies into the definitive *dentine*, or dental bone. Whether the odontoblasts lay down the predentine fibrils is debatable; more likely they are somehow concerned with the subsequent deposit of calcium about them. In any region of the tooth, dentine formation precedes slightly the appearance of enamel; calcification of all the teeth begins in the fifth and sixth fetal months.

As with enamel, the dentine layer is laid down first at the apex of the crown (or cusp) and then progressively toward the root (Figs. 154 A and 156). As the layer thickens, the odontoblast cells retreat before it and so always maintain a more central position. Yet, during the recession, branched processes of the odontoblasts (the *dentinal fibers* of Tomes) are spun out and remain behind in the dentine where they occupy tiny dental canaliculi (Fig. 154 B). The whole odontoblast layer persists throughout life and intermittently lays down dentine, so that eventually the root canal may be obliterated. The crowns of the milk teeth are not completed until 4 to 12 months after birth, and only then is root development begun. As a preliminary the epithelial sheath elongates, and within this tube the primitive connective tissue is stimulated to condense and organize as it did in the crown. The epithelial sheath of a premolar or molar tooth branches and hence the root comes to have fangs. Growth of the roots is completed during the third to fourth year of childhood.

The more central mesenchyme of the dental papilla, internal to the odontoblast layer, differentiates into the *dental pulp*, popularly known as the 'nerve' of the tooth (Fig. 155 A, B). This is composed of a framework of reticular tissue which binds together blood vessels, lymphatics and nerve fibers.

The Dental Sac.—The mesenchymal tissue surrounding the developing tooth is continuous with that of the dental papilla. Outside the tooth it differentiates into ordinary connective tissue which constitutes the so-called *dental sac* (Fig. 155 A). In the region of the future root the dental sac takes on three important functions: (1) Beginning at the time of eruption its inner cells differentiate into a layer of *cementoblasts*. With the progressive disintegration of the epithelial sheath in a downward direction, these cells deposit upon the dentine an encrustation of specialized bone, known as *cementum*. Deposition proceeds from the neck region downward. (2)

During the period of tooth development there has been steady progress in the ossification of the jaw bone. In the region of the teeth the external surfaces of the dental sacs become active in producing alveolar bone; since each tooth comes to be surrounded with spongy bone, it occupies its individual compartment (crypt). As a tooth is cut and its root grows to full length, the bone-lined socket (*i.e.*, *alveolus*) reaches a definitive state.   (3)

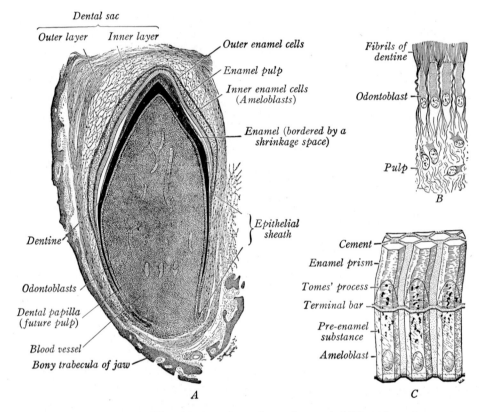

FIG. 155.—Later tooth differentiation, shown in sections. *A*, Milk incisor of a newborn dog *in situ* (Stöhr; × 29). *B*, Relation of pulp fibrils to the fibrillar matrix of dentine (after v. Korff; × 350). *C*, Growth of enamel prisms from ameloblasts (× 1000).

The fibrous sac itself consolidates into the thin *periodontal membrane* which holds the tooth in place by embedding its marginal fibers both in the cement and in the wall of the bony socket.

Eruption.—Progressive growth of the root and other unknown factors combine in pushing the crown out of its bony crypt, through the overlying gum and to the outside. The periods of eruption of the various *milk-* or *deciduous teeth* vary with race, climate and nutritive conditions. Usually they are cut, completed and shed in about the following sequence after birth:

	Erupt	Completed	Shed
Median Incisors..........................	6– 8 months	2 years	7 years
Lateral Incisors..........................	7– 8 "	2 "	8 "
First Molars.............................	12–16 "	2½ "	10 "
Canines.................................	16–20 "	3 "	11 "
Second Molars...........................	20–30 "	3 "	11 "

The Permanent Teeth.—This dentition develops essentially like the temporary set. The enamel organs of those permanent teeth that correspond to the milk dentition arise between the sixth and eighth fetal months in another series along the free edge of the disintegrating dental lamina (Figs. 151 *E* and 156). Located at similar intervals as the deciduous teeth,

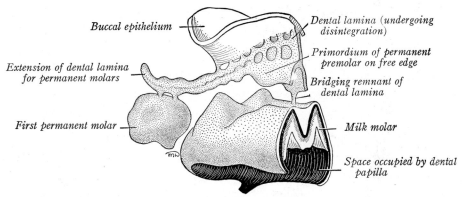

FIG. 156.—Model showing the relation of a human milk molar and a permanent premolar to the dental lamina (adapted after Röse). × 7. At the left a permanent molar is developing from a backward extension of the dental lamina.

they come to lie on the lingual side of them. In addition, three molars not represented in the primary dentition are developed on both sides of each jaw from a backward-growing, free extension of the dental lamina (Fig. 156). The primordia of the first permanent molars are present at birth, those of the second molars six months later, while indications of the third permanent molars, or 'wisdom teeth,' are not found until the fifth year. Provision for the permanent dentition of thirty-two teeth is then complete. The earliest calcification has begun in the newborn, but the last tooth to calcify does not begin until the ninth year.

The permanent teeth grow slowly for a while, but later they progress more rapidly and press against the milk teeth (Fig. 157 *A*). The roots of the latter then undergo partial resorption, whereupon their dental pulp is liberated. The combination of tissue loosening and pressure from the permanent teeth leads to the shedding of the milk teeth. This, in turn, permits the permanent set to remodel and occupy the vacated alveoli, and to erupt. Toward the sixth year, before the loss of the deciduous teeth begins, each jaw may contain twenty-six teeth (*B*). The permanent teeth are cut and completed as follows:

	Erupt	*Completed*
First Molars	6– 7 years	10 years
Median Incisors	6– 8 "	10 "
Lateral Incisors	7– 9 "	11 "
Canines	9–12 "	14 "
First Premolars	10–12 "	13 "
Second Premolars	10–12 "	14 "
Second Molars	11–13 "	15 "
Third Molars (Wisdom Teeth)	17–21 "	18–25 "

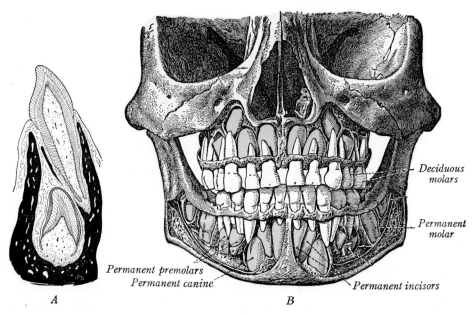

FIG. 157.—Relations of the human deciduous and permanent teeth. *A*, Milk canine, with eroding root, and a permanent canine, at four years, sectioned *in situ* (× 3). *B*, The two dentitions, at five years (Sobotta).

The teeth of vertebrates are homologues of the placoid scales of elasmobranch fishes (sharks and skates). The teeth of the shark resemble enlarged scales, and many generations of such teeth are produced in the adult fish. In some mammals three, or even four dentitions occur. The primitive teeth of mammals were of the canine type, and from this conical tooth the incisors and molars have arisen. Just how the cusped tooth differentiated—whether by the fusion of originally separate units or by the development of cusps on a single primitive tooth—is debated.

SUMMARY OF RELATIONS IN TOOTH DEVELOPMENT

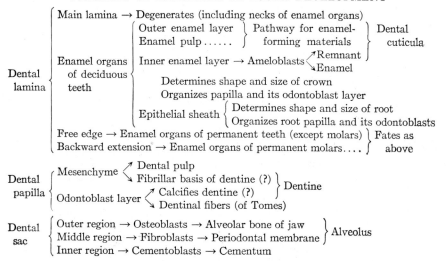

Dental lamina
{
  Enamel organs of deciduous teeth
  {
    Main lamina → Degenerates (including necks of enamel organs)
    Outer enamel layer } Pathway for enamel- } Dental
    Enamel pulp...... } forming materials } cuticula
    Inner enamel layer → Ameloblasts ↗Remnant }
    ↘Enamel
    Determines shape and size of crown
    Organizes papilla and its odontoblast layer
    Epithelial sheath { Determines shape and size of root
    { Organizes root papilla and its odontoblasts
  }
  Free edge → Enamel organs of permanent teeth (except molars) } Fates as
  Backward extension → Enamel organs of permanent molars.... } above
}

Dental papilla
{
  Mesenchyme ↗ Dental pulp
  ↘ Fibrillar basis of dentine (?) } Dentine
  Odontoblast layer ↗ Calcifies dentine (?) }
  ↘ Dentinal fibers (of Tomes)
}

Dental sac
{
  Outer region → Osteoblasts → Alveolar bone of jaw } Alveolus
  Middle region → Fibroblasts → Periodontal membrane }
  Inner region → Cementoblasts → Cementum
}

FIG. 158.—Supernumerary teeth in a milk dentition. An additional incisor (*) occurs in regular line, while an ectopic molar is located on the palate.

Anomalies.—Dental anomalies include irregularities in number, size, shape, structure, position and eruption. There may be a congenital absence (*anodontia*) of some or all of the teeth, or a production of more than the normal number (Fig. 158). Supernumerary teeth in abnormal locations (*e.g.*, the palate) arise from ectopic tooth primordia which have suffered displacement (Fig. 158). Representatives of a third dentition have been recorded, and sometimes fourth molars develop behind the wisdom teeth. Teeth have been observed in which, owing to a defect of the enamel organ, the enamel was wanting. Imperfect teeth are frequently associated with hare lip. Epithelial remnants of the dental lamina may give rise to cysts of various kinds located in the gum.

The Oral Glands.—The glands of the mouth are especially characteristic of mammals, the only animals that chew their food. They are usually regarded as ectodermal derivatives, although the site of origin of the submaxillary and sublingual glands with respect to the vanished oral membrane is not surely known. All of the salivary glands have a common plan of origin and development.[4] The primordium arises as an epithelial bud and grows by branching into a bush-like system of solid *ducts*, whose end-twigs round out into berry-like, secretory *acini* (Fig. 159 *B*). Secondary hollowing of the whole system and specialization of the acinal cells complete the epithelial differentiation. A dense mass of mesenchyme, in which the epithelial primordium lies, furnishes an enveloping *capsule* and subdivides the gland into *lobules*.

The paired *parotid glands* are the first to appear. In the sixth week (10 mm.) a keel-shaped, epithelial flange has been observed, near each angle of the mouth, growing away from the groove that will divide cheek from gum (Fig. 159 *A*). The flange elongates and, in embryos of seven weeks,

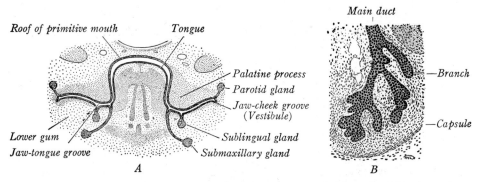

FIG. 159.—Origin and growth of human salivary glands. *A*, Sites of origin, shown by a diagrammatic section across the jaws at about two months (× 15). *B*, Detail of the branching submaxillary gland, at two months (× 70).

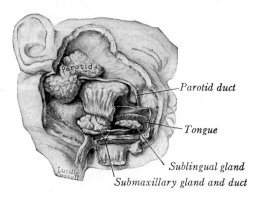

FIG. 160.—Location of the major salivary glands in a newborn. × ½.

separates from the parent epithelium. A tube is then formed by hollowing and this grows backward toward the ear. It soon branches and differentiates into the body of the gland, while the stem portion of the tube becomes the parotid duct opening into the vestibule (Fig. 160). Acinal cells are present at five months but, as with the other glands, differentiation is not complete until some time after birth.

Each *submaxillary gland* also arises at the end of the sixth week (12 mm.) as an epithelial ridge, located in the groove between the lower jaw and the tongue and at one side of the midplane (Fig. 159). The caudal end of the ridge soon begins to separate from the epithelium and extend backward and ventrad beneath the lower jaw; here it enlarges and branches into the gland proper (Fig. 160). The main stalk, separating in a rostral direction, persists as the submaxillary duct and opens at the side of the frenulum of the tongue.

Each *sublingual gland* appears during the eighth week as several solid buds of epithelium growing downward from the groove between the lower jaw and tongue (Figs. 153 and 159 *A*). This group, located just lateral to the submaxillary primordium, consists of the sublingual proper, with its major duct (of Bartholin), and of about ten equivalent smaller glands, each with a minor duct. Growth is slower than in the submaxillary gland. The glands lie alongside the tongue and beneath it (Fig. 160). The major duct opens just lateral to the submaxillary duct, or it may join it.

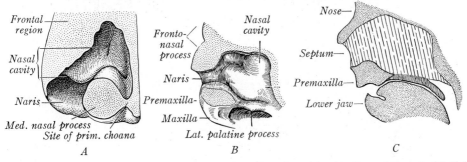

FIG. 161.—Separation of the human nasal- and oral cavities by the palate. *A*, Medial half of the left nasal sac, at 12 mm. (after Shaeffer; × 45). *B*, Lateral half of the right nasal sac, at seven weeks (× 12). *C*, Relation of the fetal palate and nasal septum, demonstrated by a median section (after Frazer).

The smaller oral glands (*labial*, *buccal* and *palatine*) are aggregates that arise at about three months from multiple epithelial buds in their respective locations.

Anomalies.—There may be an absence of any of the salivary glands. Accessory glands occur, as do imperforate ducts which lead to retention cysts.

The Palate.—The mammalian palate is a device for separating the mouth from the nasal respiratory passages and thus subserving the functions of mastication and suction. The two nasal cavities are at first represented by olfactory pits which quickly enlarge into blind sacs, as in adult sharks. The floor of each deepening sac then comes to overlie the roof of the front part of the primitive mouth and is separated from it by a membrane only (Fig. 161 *A*). The thinning membranes rupture during the seventh week and so create two internal nasal orifices, the *primitive choanæ*

(Fig. 163 *A*). For a short time the two choanæ open directly into the primitive oral cavity whose roof is merely the base of the skull; this simulates the permanent condition in amphibia. However, the definitive nasal passages presently become separate by the partitioning off of a portion of the mouth cavity and the adding of this to their original extent. The new passages then communicate with the pharynx by secondary, definitive *choanæ*. The horizontal septum, which thus divides mouth from nasal passages, is the *palate* (Fig. 162 *B*); the details of its formation will next be described.

The primordia of the palate are two shelf-like folds that grow from the maxillary-process components of the upper jaw toward the midplane of the mouth cavity (Figs. 161 *B* and 163 *A*). In their growth mesad

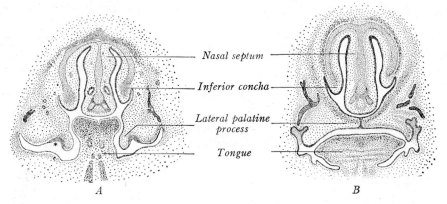

Nasal septum

Inferior concha

Lateral palatine process

Tongue

A   *B*

FIG. 162.—Formation of the human palate, demonstrated by sections through fetal heads. × 11. *A*, At eight weeks (after Keibel); *B*, at ten weeks (after Kallius). An asterisk in *A* marks the region of cell proliferation that swings the palate folds upward.

during the seventh and eighth weeks these *lateral palatine processes* encounter the tongue, which rises high at this period, and are forced to bend downward (Fig. 162 *A*). A little later the tongue is withdrawn, due to its flattening combined with a general sinking of the mouth floor, and the lateral palatine processes are then able to bend upward to the horizontal plane (*B*). This shift in position is presumably due to a faster rate of growth on their under surfaces.[5]

The halves of the palate unite, first with each other and then with the nasal septum. Beginning in the ninth week, this fusion progresses rapidly from in front backward (Fig. 163 *B*). Coincidently bone appears in the front part and forms the *hard palate*. Transverse ridges (to aid in the grinding of food) are developed in the mucosal covering of the hard palates of most mammals; their reduced state in man (more so in the adult than in the fetus) is perhaps correlated with the soft nature of his food (*C*).

More caudad (where union with the nasal septum does not occur; Fig. 161 *C*) ossification fails. This region constitutes the *soft palate;* the halves of its free apex, the *uvula,* are commonly still notched at birth (Fig. 163 *C*). The folds of the soft palate are invaded from behind by tissue from the third branchial arches; this is responsible for those backward prolongations of the palate, known as the *palatine arches,* which delimit oral cavity from pharynx. From the same source comes the mesenchyme that differentiates

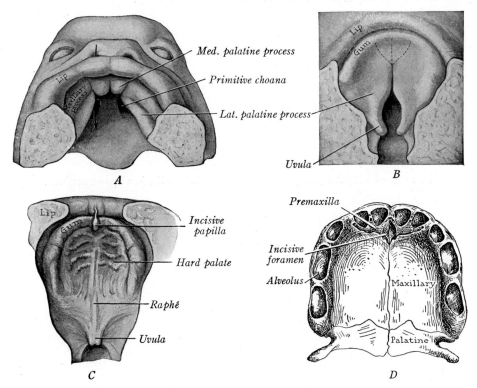

FIG. 163.—Development of the human palate, viewed from the oral side. *A,* At eight weeks (after His; × 9); *B,* at nine weeks (after Peter; × 9); *C,* newborn (× ¾); *D,* infant skull (× 1.5).

into the muscles of the palate. The completed palate shows a median seam, or *raphé,* indicative of its bilateral origin.

The median nasal processes, which participated so conspicuously in the formation of the face, also develop so-called *median palatine processes* (Fig. 163 *A*); the latter do not contribute to the palate itself but become the premaxillary portion of the upper jaw (Fig. 161).[6] Fusion between the median palatine processes and the palate is incomplete, so that in the mid-plane there is a gap, the *incisive foramen,* flanked by the *incisive canals* (of Stenson) (Fig. 163 *D*). These become covered with mucous membrane

10

(*incisive papilla; C*) although they sometimes are still open at birth, as is
the permanent condition in most mammals (*cf.* Fig. 459 *A*).

Anomalies.—The lateral palatine processes occasionally fail to unite properly, thereby
producing a malformation known as *cleft palate,* or *uranoschisis* (Fig. 164). The extent
of the defect varies considerably. In some persons it involves the soft palate alone and
then is median in position. By contrast, clefts in the hard palate tend to lie at one side
of the midline. Both hard and soft palates may be involved in the same individual. Cleft
palate not infrequently is associated with single or double hare lip.

FIG. 164.—Cleft palate, combined with right-sided hare lip, in a human newborn.

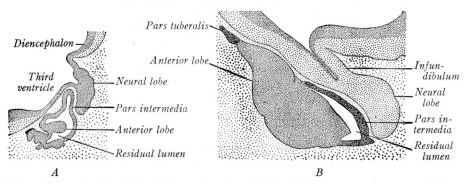

FIG. 165.—Development of the human hypophysis, shown by sagittal sections (after Atwell).
× 35.   *A*, At eight weeks; *B*, at eleven weeks.

The Hypophysis.[7]—The hypophysis, or pituitary body, is an endocrine
gland of double origin. One part, obviously glandular in nature, is epithelial; the other component, not so plainly secretory, is a specialized extension from the brain wall. The epithelial hypophysis develops from the
ectoderm of the stomodeum, which in early stages is adherent to the floor
of the fore-brain (Fig. 182).[8] During the subsequent growth of these parts,
and the filling-in of mesenchyme between them, both layers become drawn
out into hollow diverticula (Fig. 147 *B*).

The stomodeal pocket, known as *Rathke's pouch,* is located originally
just in front of the intact oral membrane. In embryos about 3 mm. long

this pouch is a distinct, shallow sac which quickly enlarges and flattens against the hollow extension from the floor (infundibulum) of the forebrain (Fig. 551). The latter is the future neural lobe of the hypophysis. Meanwhile the connection of Rathke's pouch with the oral epithelium has elongated into a stalk which lags in development and vanishes by the end of the second month (Fig. 165 A). A previous page describes how, after the disappearance of the oral membrane, the stomodeum adds substantially to the primary mouth cavity. In this merger the original, virtually external site of origin of Rathke's pouch comes to be located well back on the roof of the primitive mouth (Figs. 185 and 186). Still later, when the palate separates off the nasal passages, it lies at the dorsal and caudal border of the nasal septum (Fig. 166).

During the third and fourth months the hypophysis attains its characteristic shape and organization (Fig. 165 B). The cavity of the closed pouch becomes the *residual lumen* of the adult gland; the final condition in

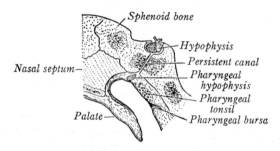

FIG. 166.—Relations of the hypophysis and pharyngeal hypophysis of the newborn, shown in median section. × 1.

man is unique since this lumen becomes reduced to cysts or even obliterates completely.[9] The rostral wall of Rathke's pouch thickens greatly and differentiates into the glandular cords of the *anterior lobe;* these are separated by abundant sinusoids. That portion of the wall between the lumen and neural lobe (originally the apex of the pouch) remains thin and constitutes the *pars intermedia;* in man it forms epithelial cysts, but is not prominent. Another glandular region, the *pars tuberalis*, extends along the rostral border of the infundibulum. It develops from the fusion of a pair of early lateral lobes which bud off from the main pouch, close to the attachment of the temporary epithelial stalk.[7] The tubular primordium of the *neural lobe* is transformed into a solid club, composed of nerve fibers, neuroglial tissue and spindle-shaped cells of uncertain nature. A permanent infundibular stalk connects the neural lobe with the brain.

Anomalies.—The course of the stalk of Rathke's pouch is sometimes perpetuated by a canal in the sphenoid bone. Notable among the accessory glands that may occur along this pathway is a constant mass located between the nasal septum and the pharyngeal tonsil (Fig. 166).[10] It is known as the *pharyngeal hypophysis*.

THE PHARYNX

Because the primitive pharynx is the source of numerous organs, its developmental history is necessarily complex. In spite of this, the fundamental importance of the pharynx would scarcely be suspected from its adult simplicity and unspectacular rôle as a common corridor for crossing pathways for air and food. Most of the developmental complexities occur during the transitional period when the mammalian embryo passes from a stage in which the pharynx is arranged as for branchial respiration to a stage in which the breathing of air is anticipated. Naturally the parts altered most profoundly are the branchial arches and pharyngeal pouches themselves. In addition to the remodeling that is necessary to provide for the mammalian method of chewing and swallowing, various other con-

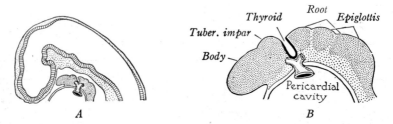

FIG. 167.—The tongue, at about four weeks, in diagrammatic sagittal section. *A*, General relations; *B*, detail of *A*.

versions occur. The pharynx proper becomes a muscular funnel, lined for the most part with a stratified epithelium.

The Branchial Arches.—In a previous chapter (p. 176) were described the general relations and significance of the branchial arches. These ancestral gill arches are converted into numerous things—including the neck, jaws, face and external ear, already discussed (p. 177 *ff.*), and various arteries, muscles, cartilages and bones to be considered in later chapters. On the floor of the pharynx they contribute especially to the tongue. The nearby larynx, also of branchial-arch origin, belongs to the respiratory system.

The Tongue.—This organ develops from the ventral ends of the branchial arches. It consists of two different parts—one oral in origin, the other pharyngeal (Fig. 167). The oral portion, comprising most of the *body*, occupies the definitive mouth cavity. It arises from the mandibular arches, in front of the oral membrane, and hence is covered with ectodermal epithelium. This part of the tongue bears papillæ and is concerned with mastication. The pharyngeal portion is the *root*. It develops primarily from the union of the second branchial arches, but receives important contributions from the third and, apparently, the fourth arch as well. The entodermal-covered root becomes infiltrated with lymphoid tissue and is concerned with swallowing. The junction between ectoderm and entoderm is in front of the row of vallate papillæ, whereas the body and root are demarcated by a V-shaped groove, the *terminal sulcus*, behind them (Fig. 168 *D*).

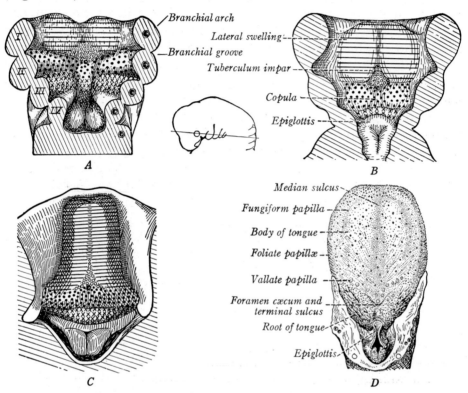

FIG. 168.—Development of the human tongue, viewed from above. *A*, At 6 mm. (key figure shows section planes of *A–C*); *B*, at 9 mm.; *C*, at 15 mm.; *D*, at birth (× 1). Distinctive markings indicate the contributions of the branchial arches. The tuberculum impar is designated by circles, and at its base a larger circle indicates the foramen cæcum.

In embryos of four weeks (5 mm.) the body of the tongue is indicated by three primordia. These are the paired *lateral swellings* of the first branchial arches, which latter have fused as the mandible, and the median, somewhat triangular *tuberculum impar* (*i.e.*, unpaired tubercle) wedged in between them (Fig. 168 *A*). At the same time the future root is represented by a median elevation, brought into existence by the union of the bases of the second branchial arches, and for this reason named the *copula* (*i.e.*, a yoke). Between the tuberculum impar and the copula is the point of origin of the thyroid diverticulum (Fig. 167). This site becomes second-

arily depressed into a prominent pit which occupies the apex of the terminal
sulcus and constitutes the permanent landmark known as the *foramen
cæcum* (Fig. 168 D).

The individual components of the tongue are in process of fusion during
the sixth week. The lateral swellings of the first arches increase rapidly
in size, unite with the tuberculum impar, and nearly enclose it (Fig. 168
B, C). In sharp contrast, the tubercle itself lags in development and
becomes progressively less conspicuous. In the end, it furnishes little or
nothing to the final organ.[11, 12] The plane of union of the two lateral
swellings is indicated superficially by the *median sulcus* and internally by
the fibrous, *median septum*. The copula, together with the adjacent portions of the second branchial arches, enlarges greatly to produce the early
root of the tongue (B). Eventually, however, this territory seems not only
to be encroached upon by the third and fourth branchial arches (which
primarily form the epiglottis; C), but there is a slipping forward of their
mucous membrane as well. This conclusion is supported circumstantially
by the fact that the sensory portions of the trigeminal and facial cranial
nerves (the nerves of the first and second branchial arches) ultimately supply
the epithelium of the body of the tongue, while the glossopharyngeal and
vagus nerves (the nerves of the third and fourth arches) supply the root.
Some stratification of the lingual epithelium occurs as early as the eighth
week.

Continued expansion of the tongue both in length and breadth brings
into existence a deep, ∩-shaped furrow at the front and sides which will
make this organ partly free and highly mobile (Fig. 168 C). At the same
time (seventh week), the tongue elevates and assumes prominence through
the differentiation of striated muscle internally (Fig. 153). This musculature is innervated by the twelfth, or hypoglossal nerve, and both nerve and
muscle belong ancestrally to the region caudad of the branchial arches. It
is believed that during phylogeny the tongue migrated cephalad and invaded the branchial region, retaining its nerve supply the while. Such an
invasion would also explain satisfactorily the forward dislocation of the
mucosa, already mentioned. Nevertheless, it must be admitted that if the
muscle so migrates in present-day embryos, it does this in a diffuse condition which is difficult, if not impossible, to trace. Except for slight indications suggestive of migration,[13] the muscles of the tongue appear to arise
in situ from the mesenchyme of the arches that make up the floor of the
mouth.[14]

The lingual papillæ[15] are confined chiefly to the oral, or masticatory
part of the tongue (Fig. 168 D). In fetuses of 9 and 11 weeks, respectively,
the *fungiform* and *filiform papillæ* may be distinguished grossly as elevations
of the mucosa (Fig. 169 A). The *vallate papillæ*, which are entodermal,

develop along a V-shaped epithelial ridge just in front of the terminal sulcus. At intervals there appear about nine elevations (*B*). In the tenth week a thickened, epithelial ring delimits each elevation; this ring then grows downward and takes the form of an inverted, hollow cone (*C*). During the fourth month circular clefts split each epithelial collar (*D*), thus separating the sides of the vallate papilla from the surrounding wall and forming the trench from which this type of papilla derives its name (*E*). At the same time lateral outgrowths arise from the bases of the epithelial cones and

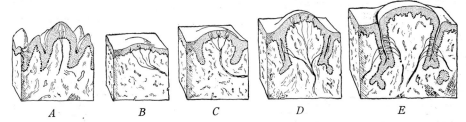

Fig. 169.—Models of developing lingual papillæ. *A*, Filiform and fungiform papillæ, at eleven weeks; *B–E*, vallate papilla, at two to five months. Stages of Ebner's glands in *D, E*.

hollow into the *glands of Ebner*.[16] The *foliate papillæ* develop as parallel folds during the third month (*cf.* Fig. 168 *D*). The taste buds of the mouth begin to be indicated at about eight weeks; the details of their development are given on p. 479. One taste bud occupies the top surface of each fungiform papilla (Fig. 169 *A*), while several buds characterize an early vallate papilla (*C, D*). The latter taste buds vanish before birth and are replaced by definitive buds on the sides and on the trench wall (*E*).

Fig. 170.—Anomalous trifid tongue.

The *lingual tonsil* is foreshadowed in the fifth month by an infiltration of lymphocytes into the root of the tongue, whereas the pit-like crypts do not differentiate until the time of birth (Fig. 180).

Anomalies.—Reduction or absence of the tongue, referable to developmental arrest, and bifid and trifid tips, through persistence of the unfused apical components, are recorded (Fig. 170).

The Pharyngeal Pouches.—The lateral walls of the entodermal pharynx give rise to a series of paired sacculations that extend outward toward the corresponding ectodermal branchial grooves. The early relations between these *pharyngeal (branchial) pouches* and the branchial grooves and branchial arches are illustrated in Fig. 168 *A*. The pairs of pouches arise in succession in a caudalward direction. Toward the end of the fourth week (4 mm.) five sets have been formed, the last pair being atypical and attached to the fourth (Figs. 171 *B* and 172). Meanwhile the pharynx has flattened dorso-ventrally and broadened at its cranial end; as a result, it is triangular in outline.

Each typical pouch develops a dorsal and ventral wing (Fig. 171 *B*, *C*).[17] Also, in expanding, the pouch pushes aside the intervening mesenchyme and comes into contact with the ectoderm of the corresponding

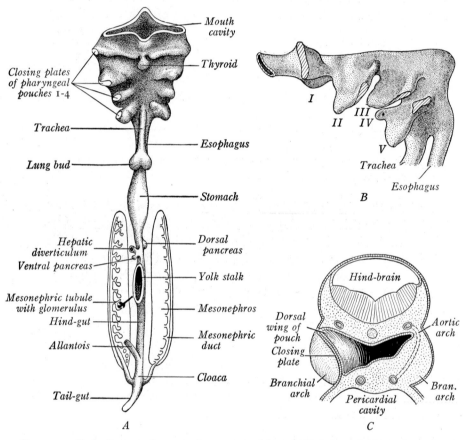

FIG. 171.—Early human pharynx, shown as models. *A*, Entodermal tract, at 5 mm., in ventral view (adapted by Prentiss; × about 25). *B*, Flexed pharynx, at 7.5 mm., viewed from left side (after Kingsbury; × 40). *C*, Pharynx, at 8 mm., in obliquely transverse section (after Frazer).

branchial groove. The two layers fuse and thus produce a *closing plate* (*C*). Although the closing plates become perforate in human embryos only occasionally, each pouch and groove, nevertheless, is homologous to a functional branchial cleft of fishes and tailed amphibia; their transitory appearance is an illustration of an unerased ancestral imprint. The first and second pharyngeal pouches of each side soon open into a broad, lateral expansion of the pharynx (Fig. 172 A). The third and fourth pouches grow laterad and communicate with the pharyngeal cavity through narrow ducts. The fifth pouch is merely a blind diverticulum. As the head region thickens, the ectoderm of the branchial grooves also is drawn out into transient tubes leading inward to the closing plates; most striking are the subdivisions of the cervical sinus (Fig. 172 A).

The fates of the entodermal pouches are varied and spectacular. Although not continuing as parts of the digestive apparatus, their embryonic relations justify their inclusion in the present chapter. The first pouch retains its lumen and differentiates into the *auditory (Eustachian) tube* and the *tympanic cavity* of the middle ear. The second is greatly reduced and becomes the fossa and covering epithelium of the *palatine tonsil*. The third, fourth and fifth lose all trace of a lumen and give rise to a series of ductless

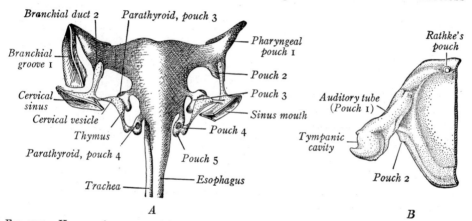

FIG. 172.—Human pharynx, modeled in dorsal view (after Hammar). *A*, At six weeks (× 17); *B*, at eight weeks (× 14).

glands; these are the *thymus, parathyroids* and *ultimobranchial bodies.* Some variations in detail attend the fates of these pouches among various mammals.

The Auditory Tubes and Tympanic Cavity.—It is customary to state that the dorsal wing of each first pouch expands during the eighth week into the *tympanic cavity* of the middle ear, whereas the rest of the pouch is drawn out into an *auditory tube* (Fig. 172 B). However, the unconfirmed claim has been made that the tubo-tympanic region is really more complex than this since it absorbs the second arch and pouch and is then bounded caudally, in part, by the third branchial arch.[18] Simultaneously with the transformation of the first entodermal pouch, the overlying ectodermal groove deepens to produce the *external acoustic meatus.* This canal leads inward to the closing plate which regains a middle layer of mesoderm and persists as the *tympanic membrane* (Fig. 479).

The Palatine Tonsils.—By the growth and lateral expansion of the pharynx, the second pouch of each side is largely absorbed into the pharyngeal wall (Fig. 172). For many years it has been taught that the dorsal (some say ventral) angle of its cavity persists as the *tonsillar fossa*, while the entoderm of the pouch furnishes the covering epithelium of the *palatine tonsil*. Later studies have cast some doubt on such a direct and continuous relation; rather it is urged that the tonsil develops at the general site of the second pouch merely because this is a neutral, favorable position in a region of marked growth shiftings.[19] The crypts arise progressively in fetuses of three to six months as solid ingrowths from the epithelium (Fig. 173 *A*). They branch and hollow secondarily (*B, C*); many of the branches degenerate and reform after birth.[20] Lymphocytes appear in the third month (*B*) and organize as nodules after the sixth month; the arrangement

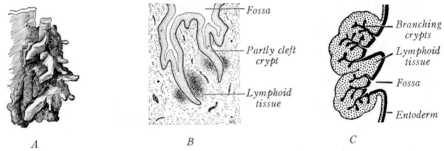

FIG. 173.—Development of the human palatine tonsil. *A*, Model of the crypt system, at fourteen weeks (× 18). *B*, Vertical section, at fourteen weeks (× 35). *C*, Diagrammatic vertical section, at four months.

of lymphoid tissue makes the tonsil temporarily bilobed (*C*). The permanent location and relations of the palatine tonsil are shown in Fig. 180.

Anomalies.—Cervical cysts, blind diverticula and complete fistulæ occur (Fig. 137 *B, C*). They are usually related to the second (or third?) branchial clefts (p. 177).

The Thymus.—Toward the end of the sixth week each third pharyngeal pouch shows a pronounced ventral sacculation (Figs. 172 *A* and 174 *A*), and the whole pouch, accompanied by the detached cervical sinus,[21] is set free in the week following (Fig. 174 *B, C*). At first hollow, these thymic primordia rapidly become solid epithelial bars. The lower ends enlarge and unite superficially during the eighth week to foreshadow the definitive organ; yet the thymus never loses wholly its paired nature (Fig. 175 *A*). The two lower ends are attached to the pericardium and gradually sink with the latter to a permanent position in the thorax (Fig. 176). During this descent the upper ends become drawn out and finally vanish.

By the tenth week the original epithelium is transforming into a syncytium that resembles reticular tissue (Fig. 175 *B, C*). The *thymic corpuscles* (of Hassall) are usually interpreted as compact aggregates of enlarged reticulum cells,[22, 23] although other interpretations are not lacking.[21] In all, over a million are formed.[24] At the end of the third month the thymus becomes increasingly lymphoid and is differentiating into a *cortex* and *medulla (C)*. An origin of the characteristic small cells of the thymus from entodermal reticulum has been asserted frequently,[25] but most investigators view these elements as migratory lymphocytes that invade the organ from without.[26] Lobulation com-

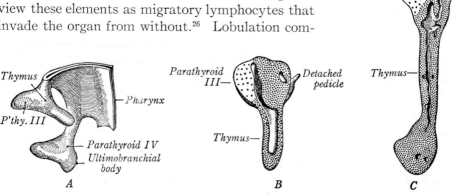

FIG. 174.—The third and fourth pharyngeal pouches of human embryos, shown as models (Weller). *A*, At 10 mm., in ventral view (× 65). *B, C*, Detached third pouches, at 14 mm., hemisected (× 75).

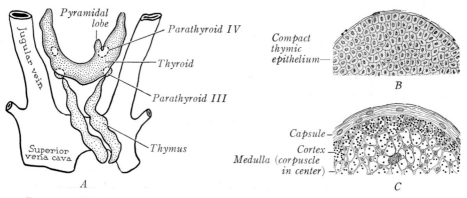

FIG. 175.—Glandular derivatives of the human pharynx. *A*, Thyroid, parathyroids and thymi, at two months, in ventral view (after Verdun; × 15). *B*, Thymus, at seven weeks, in section (× 200). *C*, Thymus, at three months, in section (× 150).

pletes the process of morphogenesis. The thymus enlarges steadily until puberty after which it regresses, although persisting in reduced form even into old age.[27]

The ventral diverticula of the fourth pouches produce rudimentary thymic primordia in some mammals, but such activity in the human embryo is late, inconstant and not thoroughly traced.[52]

Anomalies.—The slender upper ends of the thymus sometimes persist. They either continue the thymus to the level of the thyroid gland or form separate accessory lobes there, depending on whether they persist wholly or in part (Fig. 176).

The Parathyroid Glands.—The dorsal wing of each third and fourth pouch thickens into a solid mass of cells that is prominent at 10 mm. (Figs. 172 *A* and 174 *A*). Each is the primordium of a parathyroid gland. A few days later the two pairs of globular parathyroids (III and IV) are set free from the pharynx, although they still remain connected until the 20 mm. stage with the simultaneously detached thymi and ultimobranchial bodies, respectively (Fig. 174 *B, C*). The pair from the third pouches is drawn down by the migrating thymic primordia (Fig. 177) to the level of the caudal border of the thyroid gland (Fig. 175 *A*). The pair from the fourth pouches does not shift its position appreciably and remains at the cranial thyroid

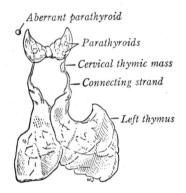

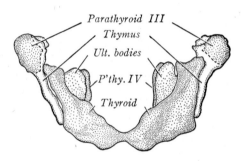

FIG. 176.—Thyroid, parathyroids and thymi of a human newborn, in ventral view. × ⅔.

FIG. 177.—Glandular derivatives of the human pharynx, at 14 mm., shown as a model in ventral view (after Politzer and Hann). × 45.

border.[28] Even at their earliest appearance, the parathyroids are differentiating into distinctive, clear cells; they gradually become well vascularized. All four glands embed superficially in the thyroid capsule.

Anomalies.—Variations in the number, size and location of the parathyroid glands are common (Fig. 176). Both regular (especially parathyroids III) and accessory glands may locate at some distance from the thyroid.

The Ultimobranchial Bodies.—In the fifth and sixth weeks these sacs are often classified as rudimentary fifth pouches, although there is some doubt as to their true status (Figs. 172 *A* and 174 *A*).[29] At the beginning of the seventh week (13 mm.) each ultimobranchial body, joined with the adjacent parathyroid IV, is set free from the pharynx. Meanwhile growth of the thyroid brings its two lobes into contact with the ultimobranchial bodies (Fig. 177). Each of the latter then loses its cavity and is incorporated into the thyroid. Some believe that the final fate of the ultimo-branchial bodies is degeneration;[29, 52] others describe an actual conversion ('induction') of ultimobranchial into thyroid tissue, apparently through the dominating influence of a thyroid environment on a plastic, implanted tissue.[28, 30] Only to this degree, at best, are the ultimobranchial bodies 'lateral thyroid' primordia.

The Thyroid Gland.[31, 32]—The main mass of the thyroid gland develops from the ventral floor of the pharynx. Embryos about 2 mm. long have begun to invaginate an entodermal pocket in the midplane at the level of the first pharyngeal pouches (Fig. 148). This *thyroid diverticulum* quickly becomes a solid mass which lies at the bifurcation of the aortic trunk (Fig. 167) and attaches to the pharynx by a narrower neck (Fig. 171 *A*). Even at this stage (four weeks) the diverticulum may be bilobed (Fig. 178 *A*). The neck is known as the *thyro-glossal duct*, for the reason that it

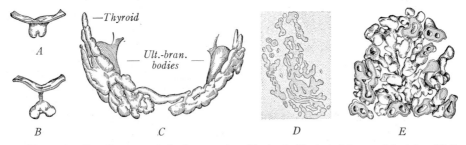

FIG. 178.—Development of the human thyroid gland, illustrated by models (after Weller and Norris). *A*, At 4.5 mm., showing the bilobed primordium attached to the floor of the pharynx (× 40). *B*, At 8 mm., showing the thyro-glossal duct (× 40). *C*, At seven weeks (× 40). *D*, At nine weeks, showing (in section) follicular cavities beginning to appear in beaded portions of the epithelial plates (× 40). *E*, At three months, showing the subdivision of epithelium into follicles, some of which are cut across (× 110).

temporarily connects the primitive thyroid with the tongue which is forming from the pharyngeal floor at the same time (*B*); here it opens at the aboral border of the tuberculum impar (Fig. 167). The thyro-glossal duct soon begins to atrophy (fifth to sixth week),[53] but its point of origin on the tongue is permanently indicated by an enlarged pit named the *foramen cæcum* (Fig. 168 *D*). As soon as it is set free, the thyroid begins to be converted into an irregular mass of epithelial plates (Fig. 178 *C*). Early in the seventh week the gland becomes crescentic in shape and settles to a transverse position with a lobe on each side of the trachea. Actually its shift is illusory and is caused by the forward growth of the pharynx, which leaves the aortic trunk and thyroid behind.

During the seventh week the ultimobranchial bodies come in contact with the main thyroid primordium and fuse with it (Fig. 178 *C*), thus bring-ing its 'descent' to a close. As discussed in a previous paragraph, these bodies rapidly lose their original identity and transform into thyroid tissue. In the eighth week discontinuous cavities begin to appear in swollen, or beaded portions of the solid thyroid plates (*D, E*); these represent the cavities of *follicles* which soon after acquire colloid. By the end of the fourth month this conversion into follicles ends; thereafter new follicles arise only by the budding and subdivision of those already present.

Anomalies.—Persistent portions of the thyro-glossal duct give rise to accessory thyroids, cysts or even fistulæ (Fig. 179). Accessory thyroids may also be derived from detached portions of the main primordium. The variable pyramidal lobe of the thyroid, leading upward from the gland, results from the retention and growth of the lower end of the thyro-glossal duct (Fig. 175 *A*). Over-migration to an abnormally low location sometimes occurs.

The Pharynx Proper.—This funnel-shaped, muscular sac is the residual product after the transformation of its floor and side walls is finished.

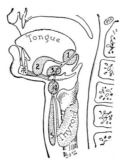

FIG. 179.—Diagram showing the course of the thyro-glossal duct. Along it are indicated the commonest sites (1–5) for cysts (after Chemin).

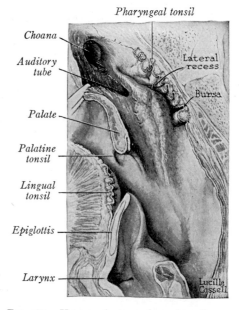

FIG. 180.—Human pharynx, shown in a dissection of the newborn. × 2.

Besides the organs already described, there are a few additional derivatives (Fig. 180):

The Pharyngeal Tonsil.—The entrance to the definitive pharynx is in a sense encircled by a lymphoid ring. In addition to the lingual tonsil below and the paired palatine tonsils at each side, there is still another tonsil mass that lies in the dorsal wall. This *pharyngeal tonsil* starts development in the fourth month; its lymphoid accumulation is a response to local vascularity and freedom from growth tensions.[33] The so-called crypts appear even earlier, but they are merely epithelial folds, wrinkled by the stresses of this region, and the dilated ducts of mucous glands.

The *pharyngeal bursa* is a pit located just below the pharyngeal tonsil. It results from the ingrowth of epithelium along the course of the degenerating tip of the notochord.[34]   Until the end of the second month the latter is fused with the epithelium of the pharynx at this point.

Seessel's pouch is merely the dorsal, blind end of the entodermal fore-gut which, after the disappearance of the oral plate, persists for a short time as a sort of pit (Fig. 541).   It has no further significance.

The lateral *pharyngeal recess* (of Rosenmüller) is not related to the second pharyngeal pouch, as once asserted.

DERIVATIVES OF THE PHARYNX AND ITS POUCHES

Region	Level of Pouch I	Level of Pouch II	Level of Pouch III	Level of Pouch IV	Level of Pouch V
Roof:	Caudal end of soft palate?	Pharyngeal tonsil. Pharyngeal bursa.			
Sides: Dorsal wing of pouch.	Tympanic cavity: Lining of drum. Mastoid cells. (Rest of pouch: Auditory tube.)	Palatine tonsil: Fossa. Epithelium of: Surface. Crypts. (Tonsil develops at site of pouch, but perhaps not from it.)	Inferior parathyroid gland.	Superior parathyroid gland.	An atypical pouch. Derivative: Ultimobranchial body (lateral thyroid).
Sides: Ventral wing of pouch.	Absorbs into tubotympanic walls.		Thymus: Reticulum. Corpuscles.	Rudimentary thymus in some specimens.	
Floor: (Arch relations.)	Tongue body (I, II). Thyroid gland. Foramen cæcum.	Tongue root (II, III). Lingual tonsil.	Epiglottis (III, IV).	Larynx (IV, V). Trachea. Lungs.	

THE DIGESTIVE TUBE

The digestive canal (esophagus, stomach and intestine) exhibits a rather uniform developmental history, except in such details as size, shape, position

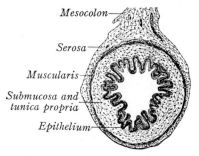

Mesocolon—

Serosa—

Muscularis—

Submucosa and tunica propria

Epithelium—

FIG. 181.—Organization of the human colon at three months, shown in a transverse section (Johnson).   × 33.

and glandular specialization.[35]   It consists of an internal tube of entoderm, which is the primary tissue that becomes the epithelial lining (including glandular ingrowths), and an investing layer of splanchnic mesoderm that specializes into connective tissue, muscle and surface peritoneum (Fig. 181).   In accordance with the principle of developmental direction (p. 100) the higher levels of the digestive tube begin specialization sooner than lower levels and maintain this advantage for some time.   The mucosal lining expands faster than the outer wall and so is thrown into folds;

these anticipate a future distention by food and also provide additional secretory and absorptive surface. Of the two chief muscle coats, the circular layer uniformly develops earlier (seventh week) than the longitudinal layer (twelfth week).

The Esophagus.—Embryos of about 2.5 mm. lack a definite esophagus (Fig. 148), as in fishes, and at four weeks it is still a short tube extending from pharynx to stomach (Fig. 182). However, the esophagus soon elon-

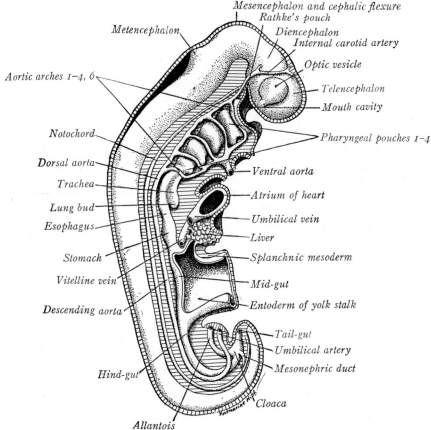

FIG. 182.—Entodermal tract of a 4 mm. human embryo, shown in lateral view (Prentiss, after His). × 25.

gates rapidly, keeping pace with the differentiating neck and the growing heart and lungs alongside (Figs. 185 and 186).

In embryos of six weeks the epithelium has acquired two layers of cells. One week later the epithelium thickens by proliferation, whereupon vacuoles appear in it and increase the size of the lumen (*cf.* Fig. 190 *A*). In this way the lining becomes irregularly channeled, but at no time is it totally occluded like the fetal esophagus of various lower vertebrates. At birth the epithelium numbers ten layers and includes some ciliated cells. *Super-ficial glands* are developing in the fourth month, but the *deep glands* arise much later. As a constituent of the mediastinum, the esophagus never acquires a typical mesentery (Fig. 204).

Anomalies.—There may be stenosis (narrowing) or atresia (no cavity) (Fig. 206 *A*). As the latter condition usually involves the trachea as well, it will be easier to explain after that organ has been discussed (p. 242). The partial epithelial occlusion, normally a transient feature, predisposes toward all these abnormalities.

The Stomach.—The stomach is discernible in embryos of 4 mm. as a spindle-shaped enlargement of the fore-gut, somewhat flattened on its lateral surfaces (Fig. 182). Originally the stomach lies at a high level, but by the end of the seventh week a 'descent' has been completed through a distance of some ten segments to the permanent location in the abdomen (Figs. 184

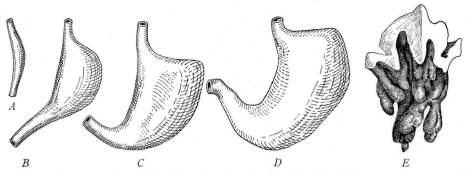

FIG. 183.—Models of the human stomach. *A*, At 5.5 mm. (× 25); *B*, at 9 mm. (× 25); *C*, at 15 mm. (× 25); *D*, at 23 mm. (× 15); *E*, gastric glands, at seven months (after Johnson; × 150).

to 186). Although usually described as a shift caudad, either by active growth or secondary crowding, such descents of the stomach, heart, lungs, and diaphragm are probably better interpreted as relative rather than actual. They result from the forward growth of the head-end of the embryo which leaves these organs behind. Especially are the more dorsal regions of the body concerned in this forward overgrowth, due primarily to the rapid elongation of the neural tube. The simultaneous, but passive, transport cephalad of the dorsally located somites would explain the apparent descent of other relatively fixed organs, since the somites are customarily used as reference points.[36]

During the period of descent (6–7 weeks) the stomach has been undergoing certain changes in shape and orientation (Fig. 183): (1) the entire organ increases in length; (2) the dorsal border grows faster than the ventral wall and so produces the convex *greater curvature* in contrast to the passively concaved *lesser curvature;* (3) the *fundus* arises as a local bulge near the cranial end; (4) the dorsal mesentery, active at this time in forming the sacculated omental bursa, expands rapidly, whereas the ventral mesentery grows slowly.   The last named factors assist in causing the stomach to rotate 90° about its long axis until the greater curvature (primitive dorsal wall) lies on the left and the lesser curvature (primitive ventral wall) is on the right (Fig. 211).   The original right and left surfaces of the stomach, carrying the corresponding vagus nerves, necessarily then become dorsal and ventral; this circumstance logically explains the otherwise puzzling positions of the vagi at this level.   At the time of rotation, the enlarging liver displaces the freely movable cephalic end of the stomach to the left, whereas the caudal end is relatively anchored by the short ventral mesentery and bile duct; as a result, the whole organ extends obliquely across the abdomen from left to right.   The vitelline artery also aids by acting as a block.[54]   All of the factors involved in the rotation and displacement of the stomach are not understood, but, as with intestinal and liver placement, they are at least partly intrinsic and not wholly passive.

The mucous membrane shows two early folds that course along the lesser curvature from esophagus to pylorus.   These ridges delimit a groove, recognizable in the adult as the *gastric canal*.   Mucosal pits (*foveolæ*) are indicated in embryos of seven weeks, and at 14 weeks *gastric glands* begin to bud off from them (Fig. 183 *E*).[37]   Both continue to increase many fold between birth and maturity until the pits total three millions and the glands 14 millions. [38]

Anomalies.—Except for transposition to the right side of the abdomen (Fig. 206 *B*) or a location above the diaphragm, the only striking anomalies are stenosis and atresia. The latter are usually located at the pylorus and are explained on the same basis as the adjacent duodenal occlusion (p. 225).

The Intestine.—In embryos of four weeks (5 mm.) the intestine is a simple tube, beginning at the stomach and ending in the cloaca (Fig. 184 *A*); the latter is already starting to split off a separate rectal canal.   The only recognizable divisions of the intestine at this stage are the *duodenum* (identified by its relations to the primordial liver and pancreas) and the remainder of the intestine which bends ventrad in the midplane and midway receives the attachment of the yolk stalk.   For convenience the segments of the early intestine above and below the yolk stalk are designated the cranial and caudal *limbs of the intestinal loop*.   The intestine is supported from the dorsal body wall by the *dorsal mesentery;* the ventral mesentery exists only in the duodenal region.

From 5 to 9 mm. the ventral flexing of the intestinal loop becomes more marked and the attachment of the yolk stalk to it discontinues (Fig. 185).   At this stage a bulging in the caudal limb indicates the *cæcum*

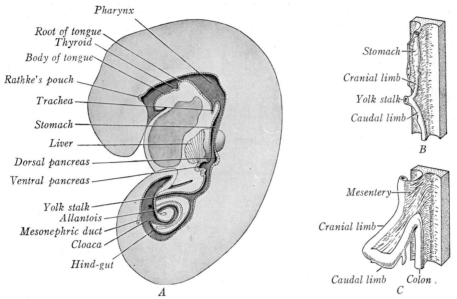

FIG. 184.—Early stages of the human entodermal canal. *A*, At 5 mm. (Prentiss, after Ingalls; × 14). *B*, *C*, Models of the intestine, at 5 mm. and 15 mm., showing rotation.

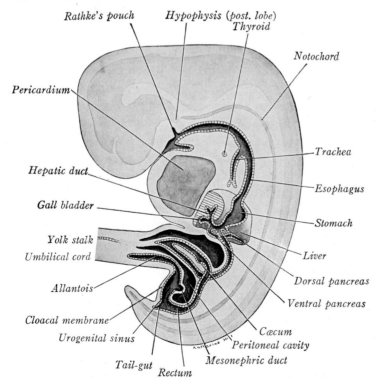

FIG. 185.—Human entodermal canal, at 9 mm., showing exaggerated rotation of the intestinal loop (Prentiss, after Mall). × 9.

and consequently marks the boundary between the *small* and *large intestine.* Succeeding gross changes include the torsion, elongation and coiling of the intestine, and its final placement and fixation.

Following the stage of a distinct intestinal loop comes a torsion about the superior mesenteric artery which courses in the mesentery between the two limbs and serves as an axis of rotation (Fig. 184 *B, C*). The torsion is so exerted that the originally cranial limb is carried from the midplane to the right and caudad of the caudal limb; conversely, the primitive caudal limb shifts to the left and cephalad (Fig. 185). In other words there has

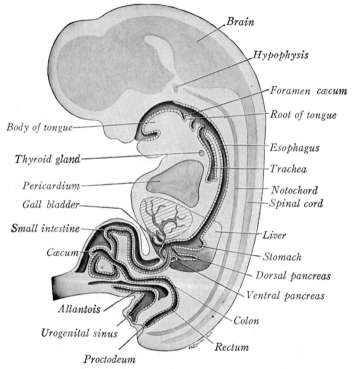

FIG. 186.—Human entodermal canal, at 17 mm., after herniation of the intestine into the umbilical cord (Prentiss, after Mall). × 5.

been anticlockwise rotation, as one views the embryo from the ventral side, during which the two limbs in a sense reverse positions. The intestine is thrown initially into a loop because of accelerated growth in length in comparison to that of the abdomen. The torsion is said by some to result from an internal spiral growth of the gut,[39] whereas others locate the cause in the change of position of the enlarging left umbilical vein which is dragged to the right and caudad by the expanding right lobe of the liver; this would mechanically force the cranial limb of the bowed gut downward and to the right.[40]

When the primary torsion is accomplished, the gut (and especially the small intestine) begins to lengthen so rapidly that the belly cavity can no longer contain it, and at seven weeks the intestinal loop escapes into the umbilical cord, the primary torsion being retained (Fig. 186). This protrusion constitutes a temporary but normal umbilical hernia. Continued elongation of the small intestine leads to extensive coiling (Fig. 187 A), yet the whole complex can be analyzed into six primary loops. By contrast, the large intestine and its associated mesentery grow relatively little at this period. In embryos of ten weeks the abdominal cavity has both increased sufficiently in size and undergone the necessary spatial readjustments so that the intestine can return; this it does rather suddenly, after which the cœlom of the cord is promptly obliterated. The cause of withdrawal is not

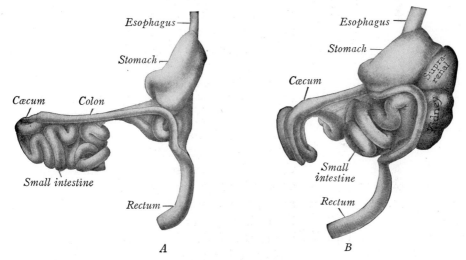

FIG. 187.—Human intestine during herniation (after Bardeen). A, At nine weeks, when protrusion is maximum (× 5). B, At ten weeks, after a partial return of the small intestine (× 4).

well understood; both the pull of the non-herniated gut and retraction from the slower growing mesentery have been suggested,[35, 54] while others hold that the intestine is sucked back by a negative pressure within the growing abdomen brought about by a decline in the growth rate of the liver.[41] The small intestine is the first to re-enter the abdomen. It does this in a progressive manner, the proximal portions leading; the returning coils pass behind the outstretched mesenteric artery, fill the available space on the left side of the abdomen, and press the non-herniated colon also to the left (Fig. 187 B).[41] In the permanent arrangement of the small intestine the primary loops are still recognizable according to Mall, but Pernkopf denies the persistence of any such regularity.[35] The first of these loops is the *duodenum* whose transverse position is due to the downward thrust of the stomach and the anchoring effect of the ventral mesentery and bile duct; the others are divided between the *jejunum* and *ileum*.

Perhaps because of its cæcal swelling, the large intestine is the last to leave the umbilical cord and re-enter the belly cavity. Its tendency to straighten then carries the cæcum across to the right side, close to the crest of the ilium. Here the cæcum becomes fixed in its permanent position.[42] From this point the colon passes obliquely upward to the left of the stomach where it recurves sharply (splenic flexure) into the future descending colon (Fig. 188; in stipple). The latter limb, remaining on the left side, swerves in its sigmoid segment to the midplane where it joins the rectum. As the liver loses in relative size and accordingly 'retreats' cephalad, an hepatic flexure appears in the originally oblique proximal limb of the colon and becomes increasingly sharper. This flexure progressively demarcates an ascending from a transverse colic limb (Fig. 188,*).

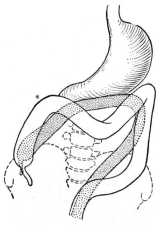

FIG. 188.—Position of the colon in human fetuses. In stipple, the relations at ten weeks on return from the umbilical cord; in outline, the relations during the seventh month with the ascending colic limb and hepatic flexure (*) evident.

The *ascending colon*, beginning to elongate as such in the middle of fetal life, is not completed until early childhood. The original cæcal bulge grows and makes a definite, blind sac that extends the large intestine beyond its junction with the ileum (Fig. 189 *A*). The distal end of this sac lengthens rapidly for a time (*B*), but it eventually lags greatly in thickness (*C*). As a result, the characteristic *vermiform process* of the higher apes and man becomes distinct from the *cæcum* (*D*). The cæcum makes a sharp U-shaped bend with the colon proper at ten weeks, and this flexure is responsible for the *colic valve*. The *transverse colon* courses ventral to the duodenum. The *descending colon*, like the ascending limb, is applied against the body wall and each loses its free mesentery in a way to be explained on p. 251 (Fig. 215). The terminal portion of the intestine (the *rectum*) is derived by the subdivision of the cloaca; Figs. 248 and 249 illustrate the process of separation, which is described in full on p. 279. After the anal membrane ruptures at the end of the eighth week, a short ectodermal proctodeum is added to the entodermal rectum. This *anal canal* results from the encircling growth of certain anal hillocks (Figs. 247 and 273).[1] The entire large intestine is originally slenderer than the small intestine; it is not until the fifth month that it becomes greater in diameter.

Proliferation of the epithelial lining of the duodenum leads to its occlusion in the sixth and seventh weeks (Fig. 190 *A*), but vacuolation soon restores a continuous lumen. All of the small and large intestine shows a similar phenomenon, but in lesser degree; the entire intestinal tract is finally clothed with a single-layered epithelium. *Villi* begin to appear at eight weeks as independent, rounded elevations of the epithelium (Fig. 190 B).[43] *Intestinal glands* (of Lieberkühn) arise as tubular ingrowths of the epithelium about the bases of the villi; they first appear toward the end of the third month and are closely followed by the compound *duodenal glands* (of Brunner). Both villi and glands increase greatly in number during childhood. *Lymph nodules* and *Peyer's patches* are present at five months. The colon in early fetal life bears villi; the *teniæ* are linear thickenings of the

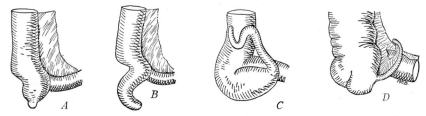

FIG. 189.—Development of the cæcum and vermiform process (after Kollmann and Patterson). *A*, At two months; *B*, at three months; *C*, in the newborn; *D*, at five years.

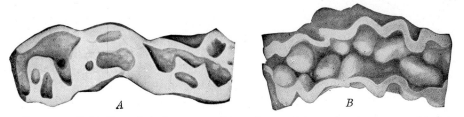

FIG. 190.—Epithelium of the human small intestine, at eight weeks, shown as models (after Johnson). × 70. *A*, Duodenum, cut lengthwise to illustrate the temporary occlusion and vacuolation of the lumen. *B*, Jejunum, opened to show the early villi.

longitudinal muscle layer. A spiral structure has been claimed for the digestive tube, and the mechanics of its histogenesis analyzed.[39]

Meconium begins to collect in the intestine after the third month. This mass is a pasty mixture of mucus, bile, cast-off epithelial cells, and lanugo hairs and vernix caseosa swallowed with amniotic fluid. It is greenish in color and is wholly voided by the third or fourth day after birth—a fact of medicolegal value. At birth the intestine and its contents are perfectly sterile, but a bacterial flora is acquired promptly.

Anomalies.—The intestine may show stenosis or atresia; this occurs most often in the duodenum as a partial or complete retention of the temporary fetal occlusion (Fig. 190 *A*). The failure of the cloacal membrane to rupture results in an *imperforate anus* (Fig. 191 *A*); it may be combined with atresia of the rectum. More or less of a permanent cloaca follows the incomplete separation of rectum from urogenital sinus (Fig. 251 *A, B*). Two per cent.

of all adults show a persistence of the proximal end of the yolk stalk which forms a pouch, Meckel's *diverticulum of the ileum* (Fig. 191 *B; cf.* p. 108); this may extend as a patent tube even to the umbilicus and thus constitute a fecal *umbilical fistula* (*C*). 'True diverticula' of the intestine are local sacculations that develop synchronously with the gut as a whole. 'False diverticula' are acquired evaginations due to weakness of the intestinal wall. Remnants of the tail-gut are held responsible for some coccygeal cysts and tumors.

Congenital *umbilical hernia* is due either to the perpetuation of the transitory fetal condition or to a secondary protrusion of the viscera after primary withdrawal (*D*); the wall of the sac is commonly thin. Other hernias of the bowel are explained on pp. 264 and 303. Rarely there is *non-rotation* of the returning intestine; the jejuno-ileum then lies on the right side, the colon on the left (*E*). Reversed torsion of the colon, after re-entry, can result in the transverse colon passing behind the duodenum without any other relations being disturbed. The cæcum may have a high position because it does not become fixed but ascends with the liver. Transposition of the digestive tract right for left, as in a mirror image, is one feature of the more general conditions known as *situs inversus* (p. 242); the participation of the intestine in this process is characterized by a complete reversal of the normal course of rotation (Fig. 206 *B*).

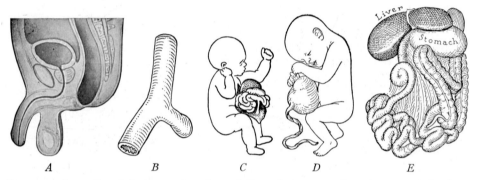

| *A* | *B* | *C* | *D* | *E* |

FIG. 191.—Anomalies of the human intestine. *A*, Imperforate anus; *B*, ordinary Meckel's diverticulum; *C*, umbilical fistula; *D*, congenital umbilical hernia; *E*, non-rotation of the intestine.

THE LIVER

The liver is a ventral outgrowth from the gut entoderm in the region of the anterior intestinal portal. Its primordium lies between the pericardial cavity and the attaching yolk stalk. Here, in embryos with 17 somites (about 3 mm.), the floor of the future duodenum gives rise to a sacculation named the *hepatic diverticulum* (Fig. 192 *A*). This consists of a cranial portion that will differentiate into the glandular tissue and its bile ducts, and a caudal portion that becomes the gall bladder and cystic duct (*C*). The hepatic diverticulum forces its way ventrad into a mass of splanchnic mesoderm that will furnish most of the substance of the diaphragm; at this stage the primitive diaphragm is named the septum transversum (*A*, *B*). A little later, the region of the septum occupied by the liver becomes drawn out as the ventral mesentery, and the final relation of the liver is then more intimately related to this mesentery than to the diaphragm proper (Fig. 207).

Straightway after its appearance, the cranial portion of the hepatic diverticulum buds off epithelial cords which invade the septum transversum farther and continue to proliferate there into a rapidly expanding spongework (Figs. 192 and 193 *A*). From the first the diverticulum lies close to the paired vitelline veins which flank the gut, and these veins send branches into the region of proliferation (Fig. 192 *B*). The result is a mutual and intimate intergrowth of tortuous liver cords and sinusoidal channels (*C*). Perhaps it is because of its rich blood supply that the hepatic mass enlarges so rapidly (Fig. 203). In any event, the liver of a 5 mm. embryo is a large crescentic mass with a wing extending upward on each side of the gut

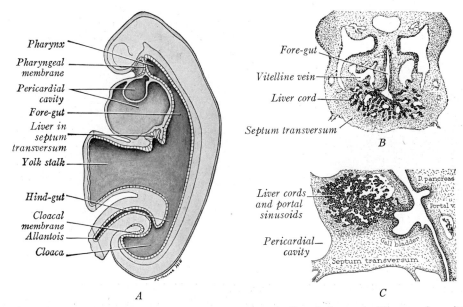

FIG. 192.—Origin and relations of the human hepatic diverticulum. *A*, At 3 mm., in sagittal section (Prentiss, after His; × 25). *B*, At 3.5 mm., in transverse section (× 60). *C*, At 5 mm., in sagittal section (× 60).

(Fig. 184 *A*). While these changes have progressed, the original diverticulum is elongating and differentiating into the duct system (Fig. 196).

The Parenchyma and Blood Vessels.—The early epithelial cords are the forerunners of the definitive *trabeculæ* around which the endothelium of the broad sinusoids becomes closely applied (Fig. 193 *A*). From the second to the seventh month of fetal life (and decreasingly until after birth) blood cells are actively differentiating between the hepatic cells and the covering endothelium (*B*).

In its early growth upward around the gut, the wings of the liver come to enclose and interrupt the nearby vitelline veins. After this occurs, only *sinusoids* interconnect the supplying (portal) and draining (hepatic) vessels

(Fig. 315). At first relatively far apart, these two venous trees grow steadily as the liver expands and thus progressively 'approach' each other in an alternating (or dovetailing) manner (Fig. 194 *A–C*). The regularity of the system of branching is responsible for the creation of the characteristic *hepatic lobules* from the parenchyma and sinusoids. In a 4 mm. embryo the whole liver is a single, complete lobule; at 7.5 mm. it is bilobed and has two lobules; at 11 mm. there are six lobules, while a late fetus has many thousands. Each lobule is surrounded by several terminal branches of the portal vein and is drained by a single hepatic vessel. Toward the end of the fetal period, but mostly after birth, these primary lobules subdivide into smaller, secondary units. A central (hepatic) vein bifurcates or gives off a side branch, and new lobules arise by the simple splitting (*i.e.*, through connective tissue invasion) of such a lobule which has thus acquired two central

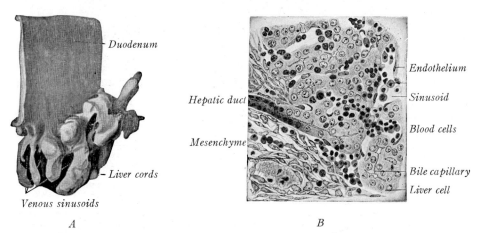

FIG. 193.—Differentiation of the human liver. *A*, Model of half of the duodenal wall and liver, at 4 mm. (Bremer; × 100). *B*, Section, at 16 mm. (Bloom; × 350).

veins (*D*).[44] The portal veins at the periphery branch correspondingly as they push in between the new lobules to keep the vascular relationship unchanged. A clear demarcation of the definitive lobules is not seen until early childhood.

The Ducts.—The main portion of the hepatic diverticulum elongates into the *ductus choledochus* (common bile duct) and *hepatic duct* (Fig. 196 *A, B*). The *bile ducts* within the liver, which are tributary to the hepatic duct, arise in a secondary manner beginning at eight weeks. Wherever the liver cords come under the influence of connective tissue that grows in with the branching portal vein, they transform into *interlobular ducts* (Fig. 193 *B*).[45, 46] The liver cords are presumably hollow at their earliest appearance and hence *bile capillaries* are primary lumina and not secondarily acquired.[46]

The *gall bladder* constitutes a separate, caudal region of the originally shallow hepatic diverticulum (Fig. 192 *C*). In a 5 mm. embryo it is a solid cylinder which is carried away from the duodenum by the elongating common duct (Fig. 196 *A*). A distinct stem, or *cystic duct*, is then recognizable (*B*, *C*), and in the seventh week a lumen has been established throughout most of the tract which then appears like an offshoot from the main biliary passage. Bile is secreted in fetuses about three months old.

Accessory Tissues.—The growing liver expands greatly that portion of the septum transversum (later ventral mesentery) within which it lies (Fig. 208 *B*). The surface of the mesentery furnishes a peritoneal covering to the liver, while the mesenchyme of the interior differentiates into the con-

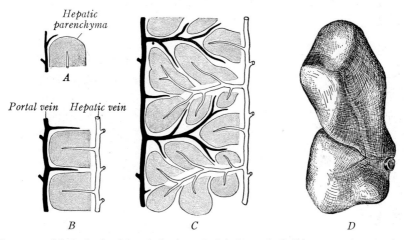

FIG. 194.—Method of origin of the hepatic lobules. *A–C*, Diagrams of successive stages of growth and subdivision (after Mall). *D*, Bifurcating lobule of the postnatal pig's liver (after Johnson; × 35).

nective-tissue framework of the liver and the muscular walls of the larger ducts and gall bladder.

The Liver as a Whole.—The primary attachment of the liver to the septum transversum causes it to 'descend' (*cf.* p. 219 and Fig. 222) with the latter organ from a cervical level of origin. The liver soon outgrows its original location in the septum transversum and at four weeks bulges caudad into the abdominal cavity (Fig. 210). The continued progressive separation of liver from septum occurs at the time when the gut is also drawing away from the septum to produce a definite ventral mesentery. This is the reason why the later liver is intimately associated with both the septum and ventral mesentery (Fig. 207). Such relations and the development of the *hepatic ligaments* will be described on p. 253. The history of the vitelline and umbilical veins with respect to the liver may be found on pp. 346 to 349.

The first hepatic swellings are the paired *right* and *left lobes* (Fig. 195 *A*). Originally these are of equal size, but the right lobe becomes larger after the third month.   In part this asymmetry is due to intrinsic growth factors, although the greater available space on that side plays a practical rôle while the vitelline and umbilical veins are usually credited with some influence as well.   At six weeks the *caudate lobe* is recognizable, bounded by the ventral mesentery and inferior vena cava (*B*).   The *quadrate lobe* originates later with the atrophy of the liver tissue overlying the intrahepatic portion of the umbilical vein; it lies between that vein and the gall bladder (*C*).

The developing liver is spongy and highly plastic, so that it tends to occupy the available space not used by firmer, neighboring organs; this accounts largely for its general final shape.   In certain regions the hepatic

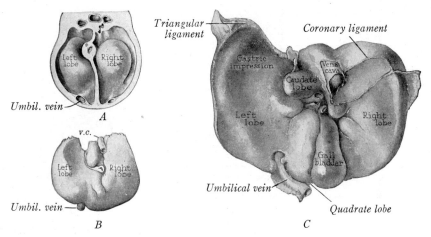

FIG. 195.—External form of the human liver, viewed from the dorsal surface. *A*, At 8 mm.; *B*, at 16 mm.; *C*, at birth ($\times \frac{2}{3}$).

tissue undergoes degeneration (due to pressure atrophy?) and especially is this true peripherally in the left lobe.   The liver attains its largest relative bulk at nine weeks when it is three times the final ratio with respect to body size.

Anomalies.—A reduction or an increase in the external lobation of the liver is a rare occurrence. An increase sometimes results in lobation resembling that in lower mammals. The main ducts and the gall bladder are subject to duplication as the result of early splitting, subdivision or sacculation. Absence of the gall bladder (as occurs normally in the horse and elephant) is well known. A congenitally narrowed or solid condition of the gall bladder or of the chief ducts is a retention of the temporary embryonic occlusion.

THE PANCREAS

Two outpocketings from the entodermal lining of the gut represent the earliest indications of the future pancreas.   These buds arise on opposite

sides of the duodenum in embryos of 3 to 4 mm. (Fig. 196 *A*).   One pushes
out from the dorsal wall, just cephalad of the level of the hepatic diverticulum; it is the *dorsal pancreas*.   The other, probably originally paired,[47]
appears ventrally in the caudal angle between gut and hepatic diverticulum,
and consequently is designated the *ventral pancreas*.   Of the two pancreases
the dorsal one grows more rapidly (*B*); in the sixth week it is an elongate,
nodular structure with a centrally coursing duct (*C*).   It extends into the
dorsal mesentery and, arising near the mouth of the developing omental
bursa, continues its growth within the dorsal layer of that sac (Fig. 212).

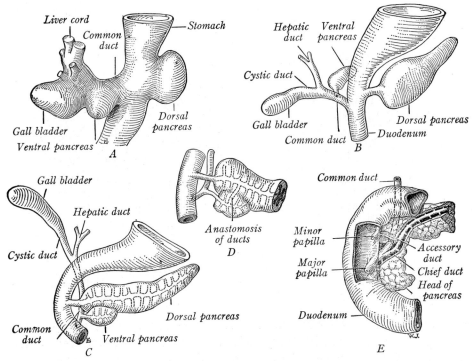

Fig. 196.—Development of the human pancreas, shown by models viewed from the left side.
A, At 6 mm. (× 83); *B–D*, at 8, 12 and 16 mm., respectively (× 42); *E*, at birth (× 1).

The ventral pancreatic bud remains smaller; its duct is promptly carried
away from the duodenum by the lengthening common bile duct and then
arises directly from the latter (Fig. 196 *B*).   Unequal growth of the duodenal wall shifts the bile duct dorsad and brings the ventral pancreas into
the dorsal mesentery, near the stem of the dorsal pancreas (*B*, *C*).   During
the seventh week the two interlock intimately (*D*) and no histological distinction exists between the derivatives of the two components.   Grossly, the
dorsal pancreas forms all of the adult gland except the head which comes
mostly from the ventral primordium (*E*).

The short ventral duct, fusing early with the dorsal duct, taps it (Fig. 196 *D*). Thereafter the long distal segment of the dorsal duct plus the entire ventral duct will serve as the chief line of drainage (*E*). This combined tube is known in adult anatomy as the *pancreatic duct* (of Wirsung). A common outlet into the duodenum for the bile and pancreatic ducts is a direct retention of the original relation between these parts. The proximal segment of the dorsal duct constitutes the so-called *accessory duct* (of Santorini); this becomes tributary to the ventral duct but commonly retains its duodenal outlet as well (*E*). A similar arrangement of ducts is found in the sheep, while in the pig and ox the relation is reversed and the dorsal duct acts as the chief stem; less specialization occurs in the horse and dog which retain both ducts as functional outlets into the intestine.

The *acini* begin to appear in the third month as terminal and side buds from the ducts (Fig. 197 *A*). *Pancreatic islands* (of Langerhans) also are

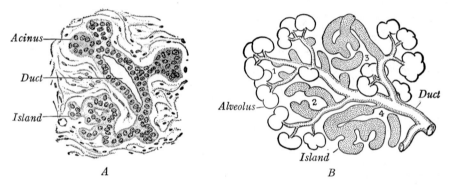

FIG. 197.—Differentiation of the human pancreas. *A*, Section, at fourteen weeks, demonstrating the origin of acini and islands from ducts (after Lewis; × 350). *B*, Diagram showing four stages (1–4) in the organization of islands.

differentiating from the ducts at about the same time. They are composed of distinctive cells[48, 49] which take the form of single sprouts but later through growth (and, it is claimed, through concrescence)[49] become complex island masses (*B*). In all, about a million islets are formed,[50] some of which retain their original (but soon impervious) connections with the parent ducts. Although acini and islands originate from the same source they take different lines of specialization and, once formed, do not normally reconvert.[51] The connective-tissue bed, in which the glands develop, subdivides the organ into *lobes* and *lobules*.

Anomalies.—Accessory pancreases are common. Many of these lie within the wall of the intestine and stomach; others are associated with the spleen and omentum. The development of supernumerary primordia and the displacement of parts of the diffuse, early pancreas are responsible for these several conditions. An annular pancreas encircling the intestine, bile duct or portal vein sometimes occurs. The ventral pancreas, and accordingly the main duct of the adult gland, may arise directly from the duodenum. Absence of that part of the gland derived from the dorsal primordium, failure of union between the dorsal and ventral pancreatic components, and completely independent ducts (regardless of the degree of glandular fusion) are all well known.

REFERENCES CITED

1. Politzer, G. 1931. Zeitschr. f. Anat. u. Entwickl., **95**, 734–768.
2. Chase, S. W. 1926. Anat. Rec., **33**, 357–376.
3. Glasstone, S. 1935. Jour. Anat., **70**, 260–266.
4. Thoma, K. H. 1919. Jour. Dent. Res., **1**, 95–143.
5. Sicher, H. 1915. Anat. Anz., **47**, 545–562.
6. Ashley-Montague, M. F. 1935. Quart. Rev. Biol., **10**, 32–59; 181–208.
7. Atwell, W. J. 1926. Am. Jour. Anat., **37**, 159–193.
8. Gilbert, M. S. 1935. Anat. Rec., **62**, 337–359.
9. Bailey, P. 1932. Sect. 20 in Cowdry's 'Special Cytology.' 2nd ed., Hoeber, N. Y.
10. Melchionna, R. H. and Moore, R. A. 1938. Am. Jour. Path., **14**, 763–771.
11. Guthzeit, O. 1921. Ueber die Bedeutung des Tuberculum impar. Inaug.-Diss. d. Univ. Leipzig, 45 pp.
12. Hammar, J. A. 1901. Anat. Anz., **19**, 570–575.
13. Frazer, J. E. 1926. Jour. Anat., **61**, 132–143.
14. Lewis, W. H. 1910. Chapter 12 in Keibel and Mall's 'Human Embryology,' Lippincott, Phila.
15. Hellman, T. J. 1921. Upsala läkaref. Förhandl., **26**, No. 11, 1–72.
16. Baumgartner, E. A. 1917. Am. Jour. Anat., **22**, 365–383.
17. Politzer, G. and Hann, F. 1935. Zeitschr. f. Anat. u. Entwickl., **104**, 670–708.
18. Frazer, J. E. 1914. Jour. Anat. and Physiol., **48**, 391–408.
19. Ramsay, A. J. 1935. Am. Jour. Anat., **57**, 171–203.
20. Minear, W. L., Arey, L. B. and Milton, J. T. 1937. Arch. Otolaryng., **25**, 487–519.
21. Norris, E. H. 1938. Carnegie Contrib. Embryol., **27**, No. 166, 191–208.
22. Dearth, O. A. 1928. Am. Jour. Anat., **41**, 321–352.
23. Kostowiecki, M. 1930. Bull. Internat. Acad. polon. de Sci. de Cracovie Sc. Nat. (Ser. B), 589–628.
24. Hammar, J. A. 1926. Zeitschr. f. mikr.-anat. Forsch., 6 (Ergänz.-bd.), 1–570.
25. Winiwarter, H. 1924. Bull. d'Histol., **1**, 11–25.
26. Badertscher, J. A. 1915. Am. Jour. Anat., **17**, 437–494.
27. Hammar, J. A. 1921. Endocrinology, **5**, 543–573.
28. Norris, E. H. 1937. Carnegie Contrib. Embryol., **26**, No. 159, 247–294.
29. Kingsbury, B. F. 1939. Am. Jour. Anat., **65**, 333–359.
30. Politzer, G. 1936. Zeitschr. f. Anat. u. Entwickl., **105**, 429–432.
31. Norris, E. H. 1916. Am. Jour. Anat., **20**, 411–448.
32. Norris, E. H. 1918. Am. Jour. Anat., **24**, 443–466.
33. Snook, T. 1934. Am. Jour. Anat., **55**, 323–341.
34. Snook, T. 1934. Anat. Rec., **58**, 303–319.
35. Pernkopf, E. 1922–26. Zeitschr. f. Anat. u. Entwickl., **64**, 96–275; **73**, 1–144; **77**, 1–143; **85**, 1–130.
36. Arey, L. B. 1938. Carnegie Contrib. Embryol., **27**, No. 168, 233–270.
37. Plenk, H. 1931. Zeitschr. f. mikr.-anat. Forsch., **26**, 547–645.
38. Scott, G. H. 1925. Am. Jour. Dis. Child., **30**, 147–173.
39. Carey, E. J. 1921. Anat. Rec., **21**, 189–215.
40. Dott, N. M. 1923. Brit. Jour. Surg., **11**, 251–286.
41. Frazer, J. E. and Robbins, R. H. 1916. Jour. Anat. and Physiol., **50**, 76–110.
42. Hunter, R. H. 1928. Jour. Anat., **62**, 297–300.
43. Johnson, F. P. 1913. Am. Jour. Anat., **14**, 187–233.

44. Johnson, F. P.   1919.   Am. Jour. Anat., **25**, 299–331.
45. Horstmann, E.   1939.   Arch. f. Entwickl.-mech. d. Organ., **139**, 363–392.
46. Bloom, W.   1926.   Am. Jour. Anat., **36**, 451–465.
47. Siwe, S. A.   1926.   Morph. Jahrb., **57**, 84–307.
48. Kardasewitch, B. I.   1927.   Zeitschr. f. Anat. u. Entwickl., **83**, 793–803.
49. Neubert, K.   1927.   Arch. f. Entwickl.-mech. d. Organ., **111**, 29–118.
50. Clark, E.   1913.   Anat. Anz., **43**, 81–94.
51. Woerner, C. A.   1938.   Anat. Rec., **71**, 33–57.
52. Van Dyke.   1941.   Anat. Rec., **79**, 179–209.
53. Sgalitzer, K. E.   1941.   Jour. Anat., **75**, 389–405.
54. Enbom, G.   1939.   Anat. Rec., **75**, 409–414.

CHAPTER XII

THE RESPIRATORY SYSTEM

The nose and naso-pharynx belong to the respiratory apparatus, but since this relation is a secondary adaptation their development is described in other chapters. As with all hollow viscera, the respiratory tree is lined with an epithelium (in this instance entoderm) which is strengthened and supported by other layers differentiated from the surrounding mesenchyme. In addition, the lungs expand into the cœlom (pleural cavities) and in so doing gain a covering of visceral pleura whose free surface is mesothelium.

The earliest indication of the future respiratory organs (embryos of 3 mm., with 20 somites) is the so-called *laryngo-tracheal groove* which runs lengthwise in the floor of the gut, just caudal to the pharyngeal pouches (Fig. 182).[1] In surface view the entoderm projects as a ventral ridge (Fig. 198 *A*). This primordium is destined to become in order the *larynx* and the

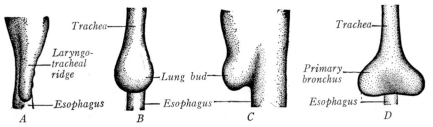

FIG. 198.—Early stages of the human respiratory primordium (after Grosser and Heiss). ×75. *A*, At 2.5 mm., in ventral view; *B*, *C*, at 3 mm., in ventral and lateral view; *D*, at 4 mm., in ventral view.

trachea, while its more rounded caudal end will give rise to the *lungs* (*B*). A lateral furrow appears on each side along the line of junction between ridge and esophagus (*C*); becoming progressively deeper and extending cephalad, they split off first the lung bud and then the trachea. At the upper end, the laryngeal portion of the ridge actually advances slightly cephalad until it lies between the fourth branchial arches. At the 4 mm. stage the lung bud begins to bifurcate and the respiratory organs are then represented by a laryngeal slit, the tubular trachea, and two primary bronchi (*D*). The latter buds are potentially more than bronchi, since by growth and branching they will ultimately produce all the sub-divisions of the respiratory tree.

The Larynx.—This organ develops somewhat differently in its upper

11

and lower halves.   The lower portion forms around the stem of the trachea, whereas the part above the vocal folds rises out of the pharyngeal floor in the region of the primitive glottis.

The *epiglottis* is peculiar to mammals.   Embryos of 5 mm. show a rounded prominence that elevates midventrally from the bases of the third and fourth arches (Fig. 199 *A*).   This soon alters its shape (*B–D*) and consolidates into the transverse flap that guards the entrance to the larynx during swallowing (*E*).   It becomes concave on its laryngeal surface and in the middle of fetal life differentiates cartilage internally (*F*).

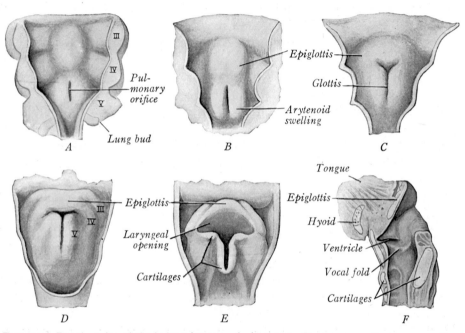

FIG 199.—Development of the human larynx.   *A*, At 5 mm.; *B*, at 9 mm.; *C*, at 12 mm.; *D*, at 16 mm.; *E*, at 40 mm. (× 7); *F*, sagittal hemisection, at birth (× 1.5).

The slit that opens from the floor of the pharynx into the trachea is the primitive *glottis* (Fig. 199 *A*).   Presently it is bounded on each side by a rounded eminence, of fourth and fifth arch origin, known as an *arytenoid swelling* (*B*).   These two swellings straightway begin to grow in a tongue-ward direction.   On meeting the primoridum of the epiglottis they arch upward and forward against its caudal surface (*C*).   In the seventh week this results in the original, sagittal slit adding a transverse groove to its upper end, so that the laryngeal orifice becomes T-shaped (*D*).   However, the entrance to the larynx ends blindly for some time because fusion of the epithelium in the upper larynx has obliterated the lumen.   When the epithelial union is dissolved (10 weeks) the entrance becomes more oval in contour (E) and a pair of lateral recesses (*laryngeal ventricles*) is evident in the restored cavity. Each is bounded cranially and caudally by a projecting, lateral shelf; the caudal pair is the *vocal folds* which later differentiate elastic tissue (F).

The epithelial larynx is supported by dense mesenchyme derived from the fourth and fifth branchial arches. Early in the seventh week this mass shows localized condensations that foretell the *laryngeal cartilages* (Fig. 199 D–F). These belong to the skeleton and will be described in a later chapter (p. 385). The *laryngeal muscles* also originate from the same branchial arches and consequently continue to be innervated by the vagus nerves which supply those arches.

The Trachea.—The tracheal tube elongates rapidly for a time (Figs. 184 to 186). In the course of development its point of bifurcation into chief bronchi 'descends' (like the lungs) a distance of eight segments. The epithelial lining changes but little from its early columnar form. Muscle fibers and cartilaginous rings differentiate from the surrounding condensed mesenchyme at the end of the seventh week. The glands develop as ingrowths from the epithelium after the fourth month of fetal life.

The Lungs.—Soon after the primary bronchi appear (4 mm.), the right one becomes larger and is directed more caudad (Fig. 200 A). At 7 mm. these bronchi give rise to two lateral bronchial buds on the right side and to one on the left (B); as a result, the plan of the future pulmonary lobes is indicated even at this stage (C, D). On the right side the upper bud is small and is called the *apical bronchus* since it presages the upper lobe; the other lateral bud is the axis for the middle lobe, whereas the termination of the stem bronchus will form the lower lobe. On the left side the single lateral bud identifies the future upper lobe and the stem bronchus the lower one.

The apical bronchus of the right upper lobe is also called the *eparterial bronchus* because it alone lies upon (*i.e.*, originally dorsal to, but later, as the hearts descends, cranial to) the pulmonary artery (Fig. 201). It is commonly stated that this bronchus was anciently a secondary branch in what was then the upper lobe of the lung; in the course of evolutionary advance it is supposed to have migrated upward onto the main stem and induced the formation of a new lobe about it.[2] Others view this bronchus as an entirely independent, replacing outgrowth, at a higher level, that became selected as the basis for a new lobe.[3]

The left upper lobe seems to contain a bronchial branch (Fig. 200 D, Ap) that is the equivalent of the entire apical bud on the right side. Since, however, this branch remains small and fails to induce the formation of a separate lobe, the upper lobe of the left lung is homologous to both the upper and middle lobes on the right side.[3] The suppression of the upper left lobe has been interpreted as an adaptation to facilitate the normal, caudal recession of the aortic arch (p. 338).[2] Such an explanation has been criticized and an alternative offered that stresses the lessened opportunity for pulmonary expansion on the left side consequent on the results of the rotation of heart and esophagus in opposite directions.[3] As a contributory factor the more caudal position of the left common cardinal vein is doubtless significant.[1, 4] Also on the left side an important branch is suppressed in the lower lobe, due to the position of the heart and pulmonary vein;[3] this, however, affords opportunity for an excessive development of the corre-

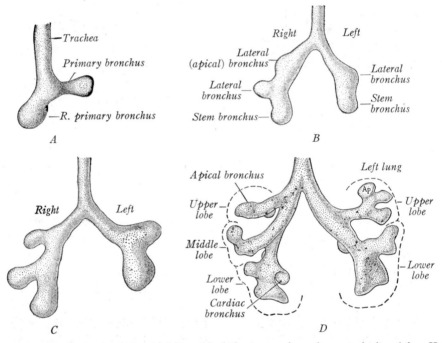

FIG. 200.—Development of the chief bronchi of the human lung, in ventral view (after Heiss and Merkel). × 50.   A, At 5 mm.; B, at 7 mm.; C, at 8.5 mm.; D, at 10 mm.

sponding right ramus which then projects into the space between the heart and diaphragm as the *cardiac bronchus* (Fig. 200 A).

The bronchial buds continue to grow and branch, so that the tubular system in each pulmonary lobe becomes increasingly bush-like with dorsal, ventral, lateral and medial rami (Fig. 201). It has been much discussed whether the primary method of branching is by simple forking of a growing tip,[5] by side-branching proximal to the nonbifurcating tip,[2] or by a combination of these two methods.[4] Both styles apparently occur, but not always typically enough to avoid differences in interpretation.

In the fifth fetal month the epithelial lining of the terminal buds of the respiratory tree is cuboidal (Fig. 202 *A*). Early in the sixth month the adjoining capillaries begin to push through the epithelium so that the lining soon becomes discontinuous[6] and the epithelium largely disappears (*B*).[7, 8] At this time seventeen generations of pulmonary branchings are present; these represent the full prenatal plan of the lung.[6] The terminal buds have the appearance of irregular spaces bordered by capillary networks. According to some investigators this is the permanent structure of the alveolar

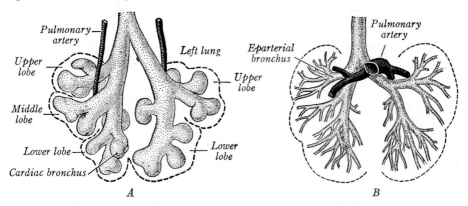

FIG. 201.—Developmental plan of the human lungs, in ventral view. *A*, At 14 mm. (after Ask; × 33); *B*, at birth (adapted; × 1).

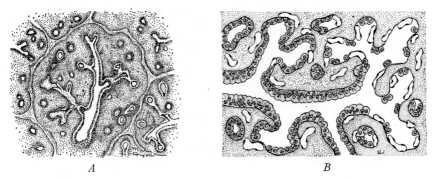

FIG. 202.—Sections of the human lung. *A*, Developing lobules, at four months (× 75). *B*, Loss of epithelium in the terminal air passages, at eight months (× 125).

sacs.[9] Such an interpretation contrasts sharply with the traditional description of a continuous epithelial lining which flattens in the later fetal months to assume the character of a thin but intact lining.[10]

After birth the branching of the pulmonary tree resumes, and it continues at least through middle childhood to produce the final number of about twenty-four generations.[11, 12] The method of this postnatal growth at the periphery of the pulmonary tree is disputed; a continuation of the prenatal type of new branching,[11] retrograde splitting of pre-existing air passages,[5] and a combination of both methods[12] have all been advocated. Nevertheless, the progressive budding-out of new alveolar sacs, with a corresponding transformation of the parent sacs into bronchioles, is now described for the postnatal lung of the opossum and man.[11, 13]   This explains the occurrence of permanent alveoli on the walls of the alveolar ducts and smaller bronchioles.

The entodermal lining of the early respiratory primordium develops within a median mass of mesenchyme, dorsal and cranial to the main peritoneal cavity.   This tissue resembles a broad mesentery; it is later named the *mediastinum* (Fig. 203).   The original right and left bronchial buds grow out laterally into their respective pleural cavities, carrying before

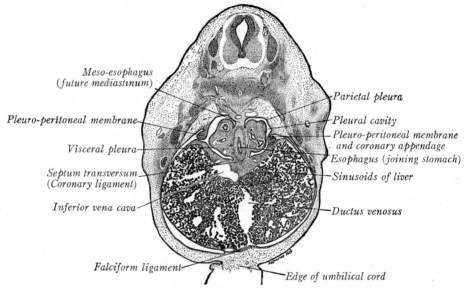

Fig. 203.—Mediastinum, lungs and pleural cavities of a 10 mm. human embryo, in transverse section (Prentiss).   × 23.

them dome-shaped investments of mesenchyme surfaced with mesothelium. The subsequent branching of the bronchial buds takes place within this simultaneously growing tissue-mass.   The mesoderm adapts itself to the shape of the two bronchial trees (Fig. 204) and gradually the external lobation of the lungs takes form (Fig. 205).   Internally each lobe becomes subdivided into lobules (Fig. 202 *A*).   The mesenchyme actually encasing the respiratory tree ultimately differentiates into the muscle, connective tissue and cartilage plates of the walls of the bronchi and bronchioles and the supporting tissue of the alveolar sacs.   Into it grow blood vessels and nerve fibers.

As the lungs enlarge, they make room at the expense of the spongy

tissue of the adjacent body wall (Fig. 230). This burrowing advance splits
off an increasingly extensive pericardium from the thoracic wall and allows
the lungs more and more to flank the heart on each side (Fig. 204). When
the pleural cavities are completed, the mesothelial and connective-tissue

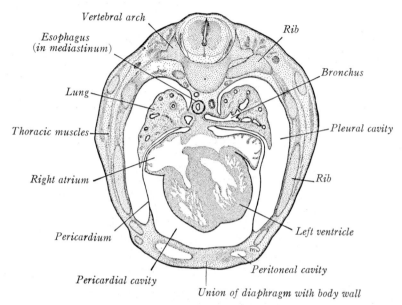

FIG. 204.—Growth of the human lungs and pleural cavities (and the consequent extension of the
pericardium), shown in a transverse section at nearly eight weeks. × 12.

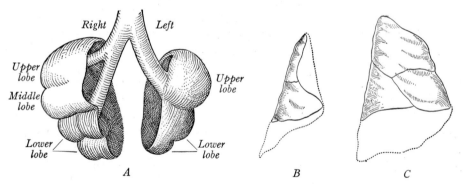

FIG. 205.—External form of the human lungs. *A*, At 13 mm., in ventral view (after Blis-
nianskaja; × 19). *B*, *C*, Right lung, at birth, in ventral and lateral views (× ⅔); broken lines
indicate the unfilled extent of the pleural cavity.

covering of the lungs becomes the permanent *visceral pleura*. The corresponding layers lining the thoracic wall constitute the *parietal pleura*. These
two pleural layers are derived respectively from the visceral (splanchnic)
and parietal (somatic) mesoderm of the embryo.

Respiratory-like movements of the chest sometimes occur in fetuses near term.[14] Nevertheless, until normal breathing distends the lungs with air, these organs are relatively small; in particular they leave unfilled the ventral and caudal portions of the pleural cavities (Fig. 205 *B, C*). With the onset of respiration after birth the lungs gradually expand and occupy fully the space allotted them. The pulmonary tissue, which was previously compact and resembled a gland in structure (Fig. 202), becomes light and spongy owing to a great increase in the size of its alveoli and blood vessels. The alveolar sacs then interlock and press against each other until their arrangement is highly intricate. Evidence of such expansion (the lungs float in water) has medicolegal value in determining whether respiration ever occurred. When inflation has been completed (three days after birth) the lungs are considerably larger in every diameter and have more rounded

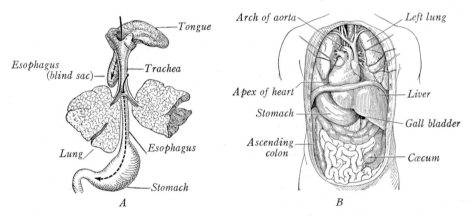

FIG. 206.—*A,* Atresia of the human esophagus, in a newborn, with a fistulous opening of its lower segment into the trachea. *B,* Complete transposition of the adult viscera.

margins. Because of the greater amount of blood admitted to the lungs after birth, their absolute weight increases somewhat.

Anomalies.—Variations occur in the size and the number of the major lobes of the lungs. Rarely there is an eparterial bronchus, or even a third lobe, on the left side. The right eparterial bronchus at times arises directly from the trachea, as in the sheep, pig and ox; contrariwise, it may imitate the relations on the left side. The presence of a distinct cardiac lobe of the lung, though infrequent, is interesting since it occurs regularly in some mammals, including certain primates. A serious anomaly is presented when there is a fistulous connection between the trachea and esophagus (Fig. 206 *A*); the esophagus usually is atretic and divided transversely, the trachea opening into its lower segment while the upper portion ends as a blind sac. The cause lies in an incomplete separation of the early laryngo-tracheal groove from the gut.[19]

A striking malformation of the viscera in general is *situs inversus*, in which the various organs are transposed in position, right for left and left for right, as in a mirror image (Fig. 206 *B*). This reversal may affect all the internal organs, or an independent transposition of the thoracic or abdominal viscera alone may occur. Positive knowledge of the cause is lacking, but there is reason to believe that the development of the embryonic organs occurs in definite, dependent sequences. If, therefore, for any reason the initial organ of such an interdependent system undergoes a reversal in position, all the succeeding stages are correspondingly affected; for example, rotation of the stomach to the right results automatically in transposition of the intestine. The left vitelline vein and the left umbilical vein are larger than their mates and have long been regarded as determining the early positions of the heart and liver which then act as such key organs. However, more recent studies of the problem of asymmetry in the viscera suggest that the controlling factors may lie in the gut and become operative even before the liver bud appears.[15] In continuance of this interpretation it has been urged that the prime determining factor is the normal spiral organization of the developing gut which when reversed in direction automatically leads to transposition;[16] some objections have been advanced against this view.[17]

Transposition of the viscera is an extreme type of symmetry reversal; left-handedness and counter-clockwise hair whorl on the crown are other more familiar but milder expressions of the same tendency. When, in the case of twins, the establishment of symmetry and asymmetry in the blastoderm precedes the twinning moment, there is a high degree of such symmetry reversal in one individual; a delay in the fixation of those relations until after twinning is accomplished results in both twins showing the same asymmetries.[18]

REFERENCES CITED

 1. Heiss, R. 1919. Arch. f. Anat. u. Physiol., Anat. Abt., Jahrg., 1–129.
 2. Flint, J. M. 1906. Am. Jour. Anat., **6**, 1–138.
 3. Huntington, G. S. 1920. Am. Jour. Anat., **27**, 99–201.
 4. Ekehorn, G. 1921. Zeitschr. f. Anat. u. Entwickl., **62**, 271–351.
 5. Bender, K. W. 1925. Zeitschr. f. Anat. u. Entwickl., **75**, 638–704.
 6. Palmer, D. 1936. Am. Jour. Anat., **58**, 59–72.
 7. Barnard, W. G. and Day, T. D. 1937. Jour. Path. and Bact., **45**, 67–73.
 8. Norris, R. F. *et al.* 1941. Am. Jour. Dis. Child., **61**, 933–950.
 9. Loosli, C. G. 1938. Am. Jour. Anat., **62**, 375–425.
10. Miller, W. S. 1937. The Lung. Thomas, Springfield.
11. Broman, I. 1923. Anat. Anz., **57** (Ergänz.-heft), 83–96.
12. Willson, H. G. 1928. Am. Jour. Anat., **41**, 97–122.
13. Bremer, J. L. 1935. Carnegie Contrib. Embryol., **25**, No. 147, 83–110.
14. Windle, W. F. *et al.* 1939. Surg., Gynec. and Obstet., **69**, 705–712.
15. Morrill, C. V. 1919. Anat. Rec., **16**, 265–292.
16. Carey, E. J. 1920. Jour. Gen. Physiol., **3**, 61–83.
17. Lewis, F. T. 1922. Science, **55**, 704–706.
18. Newman, H. H. 1928. Biol. Bull., **55**, 298–315.
19. Gruenwald, P. 1940. Anat. Rec., **78**, 293–302

MESODERMAL DERIVATIVES

CHAPTER XIII

THE MESENTERIES AND CŒLOM

THE MESENTERIES

The Primitive Mesentery.—The gut arises when the entoderm is folded into a tube (Fig. 146). The splanchnic mesoderm, which is associated with the entoderm, co-operates in this maneuver. It soon takes the form of a double-layered partition, extending from the roof of the cœlom to the mid-ventral body wall. This median partition is the *primitive mesentry;* it divides the cœlom into halves and contains the gut between its component sheets (Figs. 207 and 208). The early, straight gut naturally subdivides the mesentery into an upper and lower portion; for convenience they are designated the *dorsal* and *ventral mesentery.* At about the same time the heart and liver make their appearance and come to be enclosed similarly, but within the ventral mesentery. When the heart, lungs and abdominal viscera soon lie within separate cœlomic compartments, the linings of these cavities are named *pericardium, pleura* and *peritoneum,* respectively; collectively they comprise the serosa, which consists of a layer of connective tissue overlaid with simple, flat epithelium. The two splanchnic layers of the primitive mesentery constitute the visceral lamellæ of pericardium, pleura and peritoneum; the somatic mesoderm furnishes the parietal layer, next the body wall.

In addition to the mesenteries of the digestive tube and its associated organs there are special mesenterial supports for the urogenital organs; these will be described in the next chapter.

Specialization of the Dorsal Mesentery.—At first the gut is broadly attached dorsally, and its roof lies directly beneath the notochord and descending aorta. Presently this region of attachment becomes relatively narrower, and the gut is then suspended throughout most of its length by a definite *dorsal mesentery* that extends like a curtain in the midplane (Fig. 208). The pharynx and upper esophagus have no mesentery since they lie cephalad in regions where there is no permanent cœlom. The lower esophagus courses in a *meso-esophagus,* which also serves as a mesentery ('meso-pulmonum'; later, the pulmonary root) for each laterally expanding lung (Fig. 203). Ultimately the meso-esophagus furnishes the basis for a thick and specialized median partition that encloses all the thoracic viscera except the lungs (Fig. 204). In its altered, final state this is designated by a new name, the *mediastinum*. On the other hand, the remainder of the digestive canal, which extends throughout the peritoneal cavity, is suspended by a typical dorsal mesentery. Distinctive names are given to its several successive, but continuous, regions (Fig. 207): thus there is the *dorsal meso-*

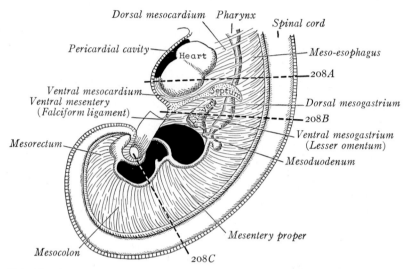

FIG. 207.—Primitive human mesenteries, shown as a diagram viewed from the left side (after Prentiss). The broken lines indicate the approximate levels of Fig. 208 *A–C*.

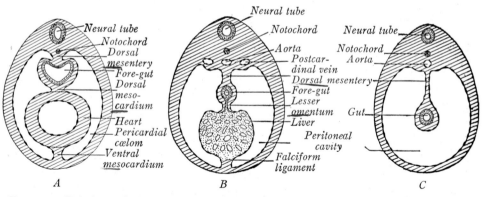

FIG. 208.—Relations of the human mesenteries, shown in diagrammatic transverse sections through the levels (*A–C*) indicated on Fig. 207 (after Prentiss).

gastrium (or *greater omentum*) of the stomach, the *mesoduodenum*, the *mesentery proper* of the jejunum and ileum, the *mesocolon* and the *mesorectum*.

The Omental Bursa.—The history of the dorsal mesogastrium is chiefly concerned with the development of a huge, secondary sacculation, known as the *omental bursa* or *lesser peritoneal sac*. Often described as a folding of the omentum, brought about by the rotation of the stomach, it actually arises as an independent invagination into the interior of the originally thick mesentery.

The earliest indication of the bursa is in 3 mm. embryos when a pocket appears on the right surface of the dorsal mesogastrium and straightway proceeds to burrow deeper inward (*i.e.*, to the left). One subdivision of this recess extends cephalad between the esophagus and the right lung bud (Fig. 209 *A*).[1,2] Such an extended passage is permanent in reptiles, but in human embryos it is soon interrupted by the developing diaphragm; the

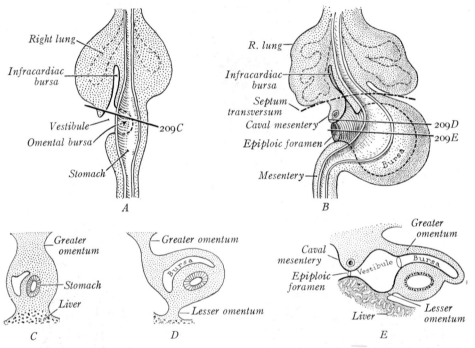

Fig. 209.—Early development of the omental bursa in human embryos (partly after Frazer). *A, B,* Ventral views, at four and six weeks. *C–E,* Transverse sections, at the levels indicated on *A, B.*

pinched-off apex then constitutes a small sac (*infracardiac bursa*) that frequently persists in the adult (*B*). The other subdivision of the original recess is located more caudally. It enlarges toward the left, dorsal to the stomach (*A*), and, as it advances, creates a blind pocket within the substance of the mesogastrium (*C*). This is the beginning *omental bursa*. After the stomach has rotated, the bursa lies dorsal to the stomach, whereas the stomach is then carried on the ventral bursal wall (*D*). The mouth of this bursal sac is relatively small; it opens into a common *vestibule* which also receives the mouth of the recess that extended lungward (*B, E*). The vestibule, in turn, communicates through a common aperture (*epiploic foramen*) with the general peritoneal cavity (Fig. 211).

It must be understood that the epiploic foramen is quite separate from the aperture into the omental bursa proper (Fig. 211). Sections passing through both foramina give the false appearance of a long mesogastrium,

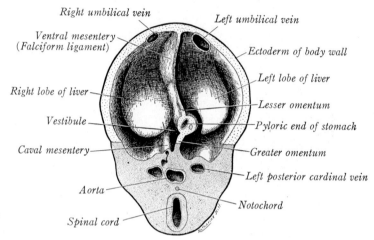

Right umbilical vein

Left umbilical vein

Ventral mesentery
(Falciform ligament)

Ectoderm of body wall

Right lobe of liver

Left lobe of liver

Lesser omentum

Vestibule

Pyloric end of stomach

Caval mesentery

Greater omentum

Left posterior cardinal vein

Aorta

Notochord

Spinal cord

FIG. 210.—Early relations of the human omental bursa, shown in a simplified model at 8 mm. (Prentiss). The observer looks cephalad.

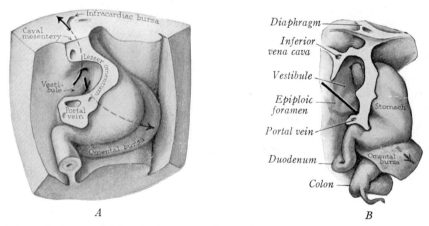

Infracardiac bursa

Caval mesentery

Lesser omentum

Vesti-bule

Portal vein

Omental bursa

Diaphragm

Inferior vena cava

Vestibule

Epiploic foramen

Portal vein

Duodenum

Stomach

Omental bursa

Colon

A   B

FIG. 211.—Early omental bursa of human embryos, in ventral view. *A*, At six weeks (after Frazer; × 25); *B*, at eight weeks (after Braus; × 5).

folded simply upon itself (Fig. 209 *E*); the true nature of a narrow-necked sacculation is not revealed by such a section. The omental bursa proper is a progressively growing sac whose expanding walls become thinner as it pushes to the left of the general, medially located mesogastrium (Fig. 211 *A*). Subsequent inclination of the stomach to a slantingly transverse position

changes the direction of growth of the sac so that it extends caudad (B).
This flattened, saccular portion of the bursa then overlies the intestines
ventrally (Fig. 213 B).

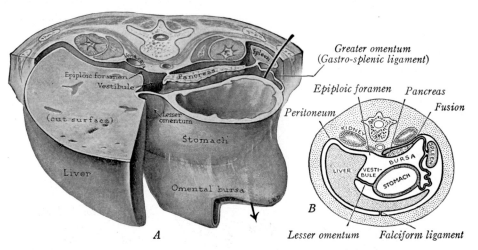

FIG. 212.—Relations of the human omenta and general peritoneum, at about four months.
A Model, cut transversely; *B*, transverse section.

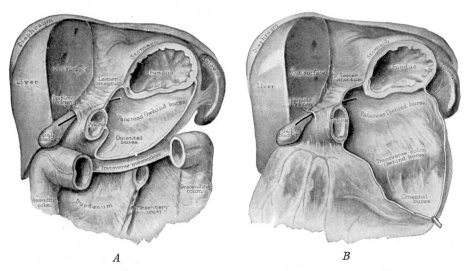

FIG. 213.—Dissections, showing the relations of the human omental bursa and lesser omentum.
A, Before union of the bursa and transverse mesocolon; *B*, after union.

The common vestibule, already mentioned, is bounded cranially and
laterally by a lip-like fold of the mesentery that continues caudad along the
dorsal body wall into the right mesonephric fold; this is the *caval mesentery*
in which the upper segment of the inferior vena cava develops (Fig. 211).

Moreover, as the liver comes to locate within the ventral mesentery its primitive right lobe both enters into relation with the caval mesentery and also grows caudad (Fig. 210). In this manner the cavity of the vestibule is extended caudad, to the level of the pyloric stomach, while the caval mesentery and right hepatic lobe form its lateral wall on the right side (Fig. 216.) The left wall of the vestibule is, of course, the stomach and mesogastrium.

When the stomach has changed form and rotated so that its midventral line becomes the lesser curvature and lies at the right, the position of the lesser omentum (*i.e.*, the ventral mesogastrium between stomach and liver) is also shifted from a sagittal to a frontal plane (Fig. 212). The epiploic foramen then presents a slit-like opening leading from the peritoneal cavity into the vestibule of the omental bursa (Fig. 213). The foramen is bounded

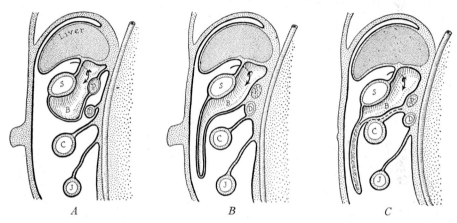

FIG. 214.—Secondary fusions of the omental bursa, shown by schematic longitudinal sections of the body (after Kollmann). *A*, At two months; *B*, at four months; *C*, adult.
B, Omental bursa; *C*, transverse colon; *D*, duodenum; *J*, jejunum; *P*, pancreas; *S*, stomach.

ventrally by the free border (originally caudal edge) of the lesser omentum, dorsally by the inferior vena cava, cranially by the caudate process of the liver and caudally by the wall of the upper (transversely directed) duodenum.

In the third month the omental bursa begins to make secondary attachments. Its flat, dorsal lamella, into which the pancreas has extended, is then fusing with the dorsal body wall, thereby fixing the tail of the pancreas and covering the left suprarenal and part of the left kidney (Fig. 212). This results in the mesogastrium acquiring a new line of origin at the left of the midplane (Fig. 217). When the adhesion of the dorsal bursal wall reaches the transverse mesocolon and colon, it likewise continues to fuse where it lies upon them (Figs. 213 and 214). This results in the transverse mesocolon becoming fundamentally a double structure (Fig. 217), but, as in all similar fusions, any evidence of compounding soon vanishes. The omental connection between stomach and colon is henceforth designated the *gastro-colic ligament*. Caudal to this attachment, the walls of the omental bursa unite and obliterate its cavity (Fig. 214 *C*); the cavity of the adult omental bursa thus may be limited chiefly to a space between the stomach and the dorsal lamella of the greater omentum, which latter layer is largely fused to the peritoneum of the dorsal body wall (Fig. 213 *B*). The spleen develops in the cranial portion of the greater omentum; that stretch of the omentum between stomach and spleen is known as the *gastro-splenic ligament*, while its continuation beyond the spleen is the *spleno-renal ligament* (Fig. 212 *B*).

The Intestinal Mesentery.—As long as the gut remains a straight tube, the dorsal mesentery is a simple sheet whose two attached edges are equal

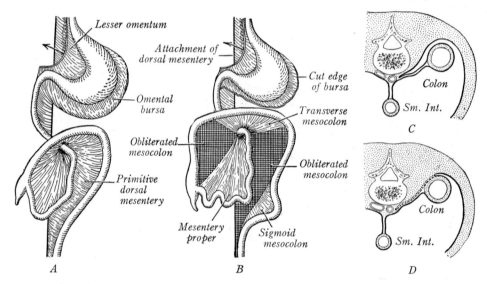

FIG. 215.—Secondary fusions of the mesocolon. *A*, At three months, before fusions begin. *B*, Later stage; fused surfaces indicated by cross hatching. *C*, *D*, Method of obliteration, shown in transverse section.

in length. But when the intestine begins to elongate faster than the body wall, the intestinal attachment of the mesentery grows correspondingly (Fig. 184 *B*, *C*). The result is an elongate, somewhat fan-shaped mesentery, and in this state it is carried out into the umbilical cord between loops of the gut. On the return of the now highly coiled intestine into the abdomen, the characteristic rotation, already begun at the time of herniation into the cord, is completed. It will be remembered that in this process the cæcal end of the colon is carried over to the right, whereby the future transverse colon crosses ventral to the duodenum (Fig. 215 *A*) and the small intestine lies caudally and at the left of the primitive ascending colon. There is thus accomplished a torsion of the mesentery (about the origin of the superior mesenteric artery as an axis) and this rotation is accentuated even more as the limb of the ascending colon elongates and its flexure beneath the liver gains prominence (p. 224; Fig. 188). From a focal point at the root of the artery the continuous mesentery of the entire intestine spreads out like a funnel (Fig. 215 *A*).

Previous to the middle of the fourth month the entire intestine is freely movable within the scope of its restraining mesentery, while the latter still retains its primitive line of origin along the mid-dorsal abdominal wall (Fig. 215 *A*). At this period, however, secondary fusions begin which affix certain portions of the gut and thereby produce new lines of attachment. Such fixation is apparently related to upright posture, since it especially characterizes the anthropoid apes and man. These mesenterial adhesions, a part of the normal developmental plan, have much in common with those occurring pathologically after inflammation of the peritoneum. It is interesting that the original left side of the dorsal mesentery alone effects fusions with the body wall. This is true of both the omentum and mesentery proper, except for the short mesoduodenum where the right side attaches.

The duodenum, which recurves from the pylorus to run transversely, is crossed by the transverse colon (Fig. 213 *A*). Its *mesoduodenum* is laid against the dorsal body wall, at the right of the midline, and mostly obliterates; this portion of the small intestine then becomes permanently fixed. The pancreas, growing dorsad into the mesoduodenum and greater omentum, necessarily shares the fates of these mesenteries and assumes a retroperitoneal position (*B*). The complete fixation of the duodenum and pancreas is limited to mammals with erect posture. The *mesentery proper* of the jejuno-ileum is thrown into numerous folds, corresponding to the loops of the intestine, but normally remains entirely free (Fig. 215 *A*, *B*). It does, however, acquire a secondary line of origin where it joins the fixed mesentery of the ascending colon (Figs. 215 *B* and 217).

The large intestine suffers extensive mesenterial loss. The *ascending* and *descending mesocolons* grow rapidly, carrying the corresponding segments of the colon, right and left respectively, far laterad in the abdomen. The mesocolons themselves become pressed against the dorsal body wall and their flat surfaces progressively fuse (mediolaterad) with the adjacent peritoneum (Fig. 215 *B–D*). In this manner these two limbs of the colon become permanently anchored by the end of the fifth month, usually attaching broadly to the general peritoneum (Fig. 217). The *transverse mesocolon* remains largely free (Fig. 215 *B*), although it does fuse with and cover the duodenum where the colon crosses it (Fig. 217); this aids the duodenum in becoming secondarily retroperitoneal in position. The line of junction of the free, transverse mesocolon with the neighboring, obliterated, mesocolic sheets gives a new (and transverse) line of origin to the former (Figs. 215

B and 217). The fusion between omental bursa and transverse colon has been described in an earlier paragraph (p. 249). The *sigmoid mesocolon* remains free (Fig. 215 *B*) but the primitive *mesorectum* obliterates (Fig. 217).

Specialization of the Ventral Mesentery.—The same splanchnic mesodermal layers that comprise the dorsal mesentery also continue around the gut and recombine beneath it as the ventral mesentery. This mesentery is associated intimately with two important organs, the heart and the liver. The primordial heart becomes an elongate, single tube by the progressive 'union' (*cf.* p. 321) of paired blood vessels, each coursing in a corresponding fold of splanchnic mesoderm (Fig. 287). Hence, through its very manner of formation, the heart lies beneath the fore-gut and is contained within a

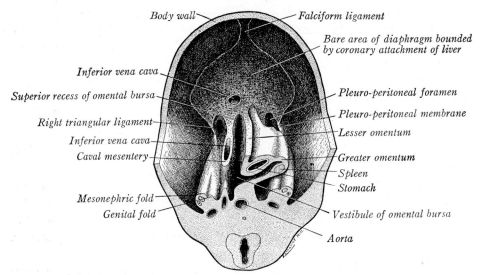

FIG. 216.—Mesenterial relations in the region of the diaphragm, shown in a simplified model of a 14 mm. human embryo (adapted by Prentiss). The liver has been cut away from its attachments to permit the observer to look cephalad toward the septum transversum.

specialized region of the ventral mesentery (Figs. 207 and 208 *A*). The dorsal portion of this mesentery constitutes the *dorsal mesocardium*. For a brief period it suspends the heart (Fig. 288 *B*), but soon disappears; thereafter the heart lacks any mesenterial support. The ventral portion, or *ventral mesocardium*, is at best transitory and in mammals is said to have no real existence as such.[3] Secondary shiftings and re-arrangements cause the heart and pericardium to occupy the ventral region of the permanent mediastinum (Fig. 230).

The septum transversum, and the liver which grows within its substance, are even more significantly related to the ventral mesentery of the lower esophagus, stomach and upper duodenum. At first these divisions of the fore-gut directly overlie the septum (Fig. 220 *A*). When, however, the fore-gut soon draws away, its region of attachment with the septum stretches and thins into the definitive ventral mesentery (mostly *ventral mesogastrium*) of this region. At the same period the rapidly enlarging liver begins to project from the surface of the septum and the relations come to be as in Figs. 207 and 208 *B*. Henceforth the liver can be said to lie within split halves of the ventral mesentery. Caudal to the septum transversum and liver, no ventral mesentery is recognizable even in young embryos (Figs. 207 and 208 *C*).

Ligaments of the Liver.—Since the ventral mesentery encloses the liver, it gives rise to its fibrous capsule and mesenterial supports; the latter are designated *ligaments*. Except where the liver impinges on the diaphragm, the enveloping hepatic capsule is covered by mesothelium that is continuous with the general peritoneum (Fig. 208 *B*). Along its mid-dorsal and mid-ventral lines the liver maintains permanent connections with the ventral mesentery. The portion of the mesentery that extends from the stomach and duodenum to the liver is the *lesser omentum* (Fig. 213); for convenience it is more specifically subdivided and given two regional designations, the *hepato-gastric* and *hepato-duodenal ligaments*. The mesenterial attachment of the liver to the ventral body wall is named the *falciform ligament* (Fig. 212 *B*) because it extends caudad, from diaphragm to umbilicus, in a sickle-shaped fold (Fig. 210).

The peritoneum does not invade the area of contact where the liver abuts against the septum transversum (later, the diaphragm). Instead it reflects from the diaphragm to the otherwise exposed surfaces of the liver, leaving a 'bare area' on the diaphragm. This area is continued dorsolaterad by prolongations of the lateral liver lobes known as the coronary appendages (Fig. 203). The attachment of the liver to the septum transversum then has the outline of a crown (Fig. 216) whose name, the *coronary ligament*, is more appropriate at this stage than later (Fig. 217). As these illustrations show, the dorsoventral extent of the coronary ligament is relatively reduced during later development and the shape becomes more crescentic. Nevertheless, the coronary ligament is extended caudad somewhat by an attachment established between the right lobe of the liver and the ridge ('caval mesentery') in which the inferior vena cava of this level is developing. The lateral extensions of the coronary appendages upon the diaphragm give rise to a *triangular ligament* on each side (Fig. 195 *C*).

The *ligamentum venosum* and *ligamentum teres* are not mesenteries but obliterated blood channels; they are described in Chapter XV.

In general, the several displacements and secondary fusions of the primitive mesentery, already recorded, cause its line of attachment with the body wall and diaphragm to depart markedly from the original midsagittal position. The final condition is illustrated in Fig. 217.

Anomalies.—The mesenteries show frequent variations of form and relations; these are commonly due to the persistence of simpler embryonic conditions and are then correlated with inhibited development of the intestinal canal. On the other hand, more extensive changes than normal occur; for example, the sigmoid mesocolon may be obliterated by adhesion. In about one-fourth of all cases the ascending or descending mesocolon is more or less free; faulty fusion with the dorsal peritoneum accounts for some of these conditions, while others appear to be secondarily acquired after childhood. If fixation of the intestine fails entirely, the bowel may twist about the root of its fan-shaped mesentery (*volvulus*) and give rise to obstruction. The primitive cavity of the omental bursa sometimes falls short of

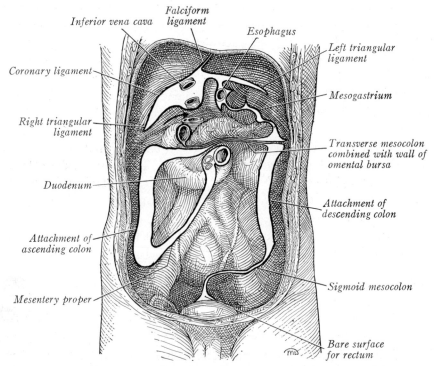

FIG. 217.—Final lines of attachment of the human mesenteries to the dorsal abdominal wall and diaphragm.

its normal degree of obliteration. In these instances the inferior recess may extend to the caudal end of the greater omentum, as is normal in many mammals.

THE CŒLOM

The Primitive Cœlom.—Originally the cœlom of animals was used as a temporary reservoir for excretory wastes, but this function has been superseded in vertebrates so that it now serves as a large bursa to permit frictionless movement of the heart, lungs and abdominal viscera. From the standpoint of development, the cœlom permits the visceral organs to grow and shift position without hindrance.

The first occurrence of a body cavity in early human stages is in the extra-embryonic mesoderm that lies between the embryo proper and the primitive chorionic capsule (Fig. 64 *A*). This cleft appears toward the end of the second week and divides the extra-embryonic mesoderm into a *somatic layer*, which lines the chorion, and a *splanchnic layer* which invests the yolk sac. The space itself is the *cœlom*, while the mesodermal cells that bound it flatten into a limiting membrane called *mesothelium*.

About one week later (at the beginning of somite formation) numerous horizontal clefts appear also in the unsegmented mesoderm of the embryo itself; these lie lateral to the mesodermal segments and begin to split the solid mesodermal sheet of each side into a somatic and a splanchnic layer (Fig. 218). Such isolated cœlomic spaces coalesce first in the head region where they form a canal on each side; these cavities do not communicate laterally with the extra-embryonic cœlom. The cranial ends of the two cœlomic channels are continuous with a space located ahead of the embryo (Fig. 219 *A*, *B*). Since this is the cardiac region, the pericardial cœlom

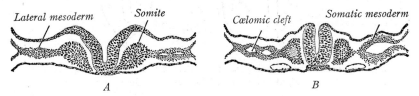

Lateral mesoderm   *Somite*   *Cœlomic cleft*   *Somatic mesoderm*

A   B

FIG. 218.—Origin of the human intra-embryonic cœlom, shown by transverse sections. × 65. The right half of each section is somewhat more advanced than the left. *A*, At two somites; *B*, at seven somites.

presently underlies the heart itself (*C*), due to the absence of any real ventral mesocardium in mammals (Fig. 287 *C*).[3]

Meanwhile new spaces have been appearing as fast as differentiation of the embryo in a tailward direction permits. These then link up progressively to extend the cœlomic cavities caudad. In the region where the lungs will develop, just caudal to the heart, the cœlom remains as two separate canals (Fig. 219 *C*). At this level the head-end of the embryo is separating from the underlying blastoderm, and the body cavity cannot connect laterally with the extra-embryonic cœlom. Caudal to each prospective lung-region a communication with the extra-embryonic cavity still exists in this specimen. Thus, in an embryo about 2.5 mm. long, the cœlom of the embryo comprises a ∩-shaped system; the thick bend of the ∩ corresponds to the *pericardial cavity*, whereas the right and left limbs may be called *pleural canals*. The peritoneal cavity, as such, has not differentiated at this stage, but the continuation of cœlomic development in a caudal direction, combined with the separation of embryonic from extra-embryonic regions, soon brings it into existence.

The earliest cœlom occupies a flat, horizontal plane (Fig. 219), but the forward growth of the head-end of the embryo and the accompanying reversal of the cardiac region presently swing the pericardial cavity to a more ventral position beneath the embryo (Fig. 70). This single, pericardial chamber still communicates with the paired pleural canals, which

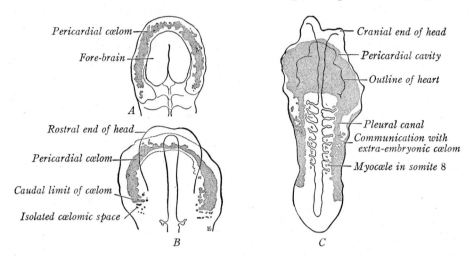

FIG. 219.—Early cœlom of human embryos, in dorsal view (adapted). × 25. *A*, At one somite; *B*, at two somites; *C*, at nine somites.

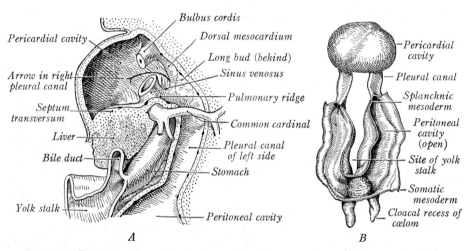

FIG. 220.—Reconstructions of the body cavities in human embryos of 3 mm. *A*, Section, at left of midplane, viewed from the left side (after Kollman; × 40). *B*, Cœlomic system, in ventral view (adapted after Davis; × 24).

now lie more dorsally (Fig. 220 *A*). Farther caudad the pleural canals, in turn, connect with the future *peritoneal cavity;* the latter (with the formation of the gut and the absence of most of the ventral mesentery) is and remains a single space, even though partially divided by the persistent dorsal mesentery and gut. At the end of this early period the cœlomic system thus consists of single pericardial and peritoneal cavities, interconnected by a pair of pleural canals (Fig. 220 *B*). As the embryo continues its folding and elongation, the peritoneal chamber is separated progressively from the extra-embryonic cœlom; the last region of closure is at the site of the developing umbilical cord.

Two specialized portions of the intra-embryonic cœlom will not be considered in the account that follows. One, the myocœles or tiny cavities of the mesodermal segments, disappears early and has only an historical significance (Fig. 219 *C*). The other, the vaginal sacs, extends from the inguinal region of the abdominal cavity into the scrotum (Fig. 270); their development will be described in Chapter XIV.

The division of the continuous, primitive cœlom into separate, permanent cavities is accomplished through the development of three sets of

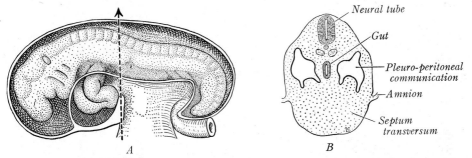

FIG. 221.—Relation of the septum transversum to the cœlom of a human embryo of four weeks. × 15. *A*, Opened cœlom, viewed from the left side. *B*, Diagrammatic section, in the plane indicated by the arrow in *A*, showing the position and relations of the septum.

partitions. They are: (1) the unpaired *septum transversum*, which serves as an early, but incomplete, diaphragm; (2) the paired *pleuro-pericardial membranes*, which join the septum and complete the division between pericardial and pleural cavities; and (3) the paired *pleuro-peritoneal membranes*, which also unite with the septum and complete the partition between each pleural cavity and the peritoneal cavity.

The Septum Transversum.—When the pericardial region undergoes the reversal of position that brings it beneath the embryo proper, the original cranial margin of the pericardium becomes its definitive caudal wall (Fig. 70). This unsplit mass of mesoderm then constitutes a transverse partition occupying the space between the gut, yolk stalk and ventral body wall (Fig. 221 *A*). Standing thus between the pericardial and abdominal cavities, it is called the *septum transversum*. It is, however, an imperfect septum since the paired pleural canals, which connect the pericardial and abdominal portions of the general cœlom, course dorsally above the septum on each side (Figs. 220 and 221 *B*). Such communicating pleural and abdominal cavities characterize amphibia, reptiles and birds. Sharply contrasted are the mammals, which supplement this partial septum with addi-

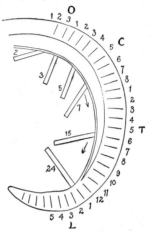

FIG. 222.—'Caudal migration' of the human septum transversum, shown in a composite diagram (after Mall). Numerals by the septa indicate the respective lengths of the embryos; letters and numbers, at the right, identify the occipital, cervical, thoracic and lumbar somites.

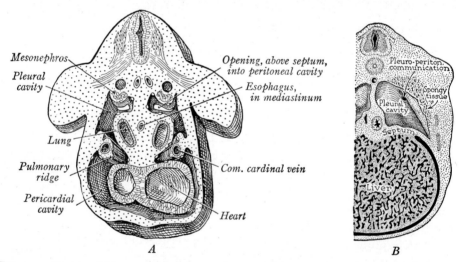

FIG. 223.—Models of human embryos, cut across the pleural cavities and viewed in a caudal direction. *A*, At 7.5 mm. (after Kollman; × 17); *B*, at 16 mm. (after Frazer; × 12).

tional membranes; these complete the isolation of the pericardial, pleural and peritoneal cavities and, in so doing, produce a true *diaphragm*.

Only the cranial part of the early septum transversum continues in its rôle as an actual partition (Fig. 220 *A*). The liver bud penetrates the more caudal portion of the septum and, as the liver increases in size, this

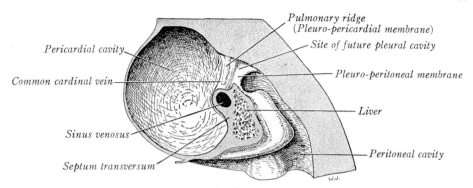

FIG. 224.—Model of a right portion of the human cœlom, at 5 mm. (adapted after Frazer). The model is cut longitudinally near the midplane.

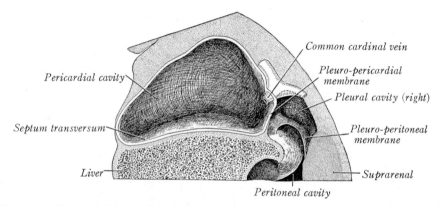

FIG. 225.—Model of right portion of the human cœlom at 13 mm. (adapted after Frazer). The model is cut longitudinally near the midplane.

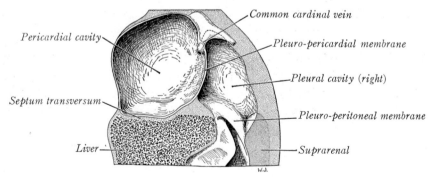

FIG. 226.—Model of a right portion of the human cœlom, at 16 mm. (adapted after Frazer). The model is cut longitudinally near the midplane.

caudal mass draws away, thus producing the ventral mesentery (containing the liver) as already described (p. 252; Fig. 207). Since both the primitive heart and liver abut against the septum, the stems of all the great veins (vitelline, umbilical and cardinal) course through its substance as they join the heart (Fig. 286 A).

The septum transversum of a 2 mm. embryo occupies a position opposite the highest occipital somite (Fig. 222). It then enters upon what is usually described as an extensive caudal migration; this displacement is, however, only relative and is caused chiefly by a faster forward growth of the dorsal body which leaves the more ventral structures behind. When opposite the fourth cervical segment the septum receives the phrenic nerve, by way of the pleuro-pericardial membrane, and carries it along (Fig. 229 A). The final location of the septum is at the level of the first lumbar segment; this position is attained in an embryo of two months (Figs. 222 and 229B).

The Pleuro-pericardial Membrane.[4]—In a 4 mm. embryo the lungs begin to develop within the mesial mass of mesenchyme that separates the

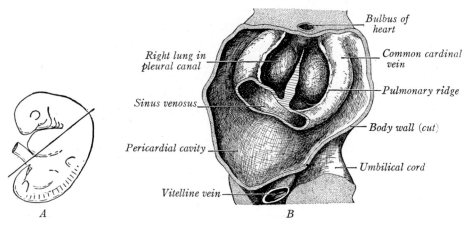

Right lung in
pleural canal

Sinus venosus

Pericardial cavity

Vitelline vein

Bulbus of
heart

Common cardinal
vein

Pulmonary ridge

Body wall (cut)

Umbilical cord

A   B

Fig. 227.—Model of the human pleuro-pericardial cavity, at 5 mm., opened ventrally (after Frazer). × 32. The plane of section is indicated on A.

two pleural canals, and soon bulge into them (Figs. 220 A and 223 A). The canals thereby become potential *pleural cavities*, and will be so termed hereafter. At this period the common cardinal veins (ducts of Cuvier), on their way to the heart, curve around the pleural cavities laterally in the somatic body wall (Fig. 220 A). Each vein courses in a mesodermal ridge that projects mesad into the adjacent pleural canal (Fig. 223 A). This major elevation ends in a projecting, irregular edge known as the *pulmonary ridge* (of Mall). When the ridge of each side presently grows into contact with the median mass of tissue (primitive mediastinum) and fuses with it, the separation of pericardial and pleural cavities is consummated.

The stages leading to this closure can be traced in Figs. 224 to 226, which represent dissections of the right body wall viewed from the inner side. The body cavities have been opened by a section cutting to the right

of the median plane, and the heart and lungs are removed. The free,
papillary border of the pulmonary ridge is apparent in Fig. 224, but in
embryos 11 mm. long it joins the median mass of mediastinal tissue.   Hence
Figs. 225 and 226 show the completed (and greatly expanded) membrane.
Other views of this closure are given in Figs. 227 and 228, which are also
dissections of the pericardial and pleural cavities.   Here one looks caudad,
after the head and part of the pericardium have been removed by a cut.
These stages illustrate the way in which the pulmonary ridge comes into
relation with the median mass between the lungs, thereby closing the communication between the pleural and pericardial cavities and masking the
lungs from view.   In Fig. 228 a mere slit still exists, somewhat like the
permanent condition in sharks, but this aperture closes in stages immediately
following.

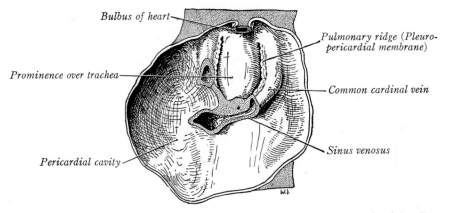

FIG. 228.—Model of the human pericardial cavity, at 10 mm., opened ventrally (after Frazer).
The plane of section is indicated on Fig 227 A.

The Pleuro-peritoneal Membrane.[5]—This pair of membranes is produced when the lungs can find room for lateral expansion only by invading
the adjoining body wall.   Representative stages are shown in Figs. 224 to
226.   At first there is merely a shallow and narrow space between the
common cardinal vein (and pulmonary ridge) cranially and a quite separate
fold now appearing caudally (Fig. 224).   The latter represents a dorsolateral extension of the caudalmost portion of the septum transversum.
Soon, however, growth of the lung and shiftings of the liver and common
cardinal vein create more room between these pleural boundaries.   In such
manner a definite pleuro-peritoneal membrane is brought into existence
(Fig. 225).   Continued expansion of the pleural cavity progressively increases the area of this membrane, and of the pleuro-pericardial membrane
as well (Fig. 226).   The opening between pleural and peritoneal cavities
becomes reduced during the seventh week (Fig. 223 B) and closes shortly

afterward (19 mm.).   Figure 229 illustrates the relations of the body cavities, at two important stages in their history, as revealed by lateral
dissections.

The Pericardium.—The primitive pleural cavities are small (Fig. 230
A).   To accommodate the rapidly expanding lungs huge extensions are

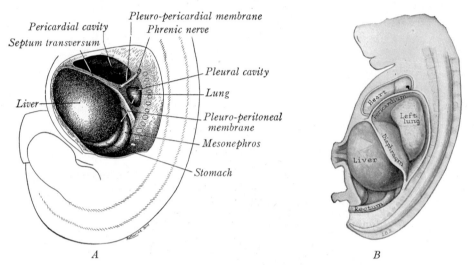

FIG. 229.—Human cœlomic cavities, viewed from the left side after removal of the lateral
body wall. *A*, At 11 mm., with incompletely partitioned cavities; note arrow (Prentiss, after Mall;
× 8).   *B*, At 28 mm., after separation is complete (after Frazer; × 3).

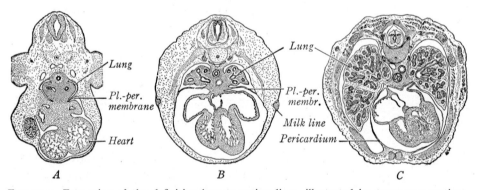

FIG. 230.—Formation of the definitive human pericardium, illustrated by transverse sections.
A, At 8.5 mm. (× 12); *B*, at 16 mm. (× 8); *C*, at 35 mm. (× 4).

added, so that almost all of the definitive pleural sacs are new formations
brought into existence in the following manner: Since enlargement of the
lungs is limited mesially by the mediastinal contents, they necessarily grow
in other directions.   Room is made for the lungs at the expense of the
adjacent body wall by the obliteration of its loose, spongy mesenchyme.

In this growth the lungs expand especially in lateral and ventral directions, splitting off additions to the pleuro-pericardial membranes as they advance (*B*, *C*). Thus the lungs more and more come to flank the heart. The membrane then separating heart from lungs represents not only the original pleuro-pericardial membranes but also the additions to them gained from the splitting of the body wall. The final partitioning membrane surrounds the heart like a sac and is named the *pericardium* (Fig. 301 *B*).

The Diaphragm.[6]—The complete separation of the pleural cavities from the abdomen by a diaphragm is a distinctive mammalian characteristic. It increases greatly the power of inspiration and, in its capacity as a septum, restricts to the thorax the negative pressure produced during inspiration.

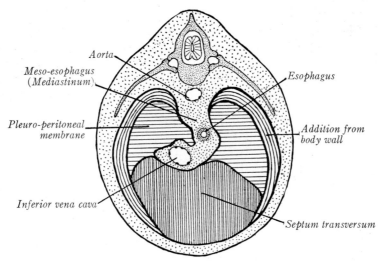

Fig. 231.—Diagram identifying the several contributions to the definitive diaphragm (Patten, after Broman).

The liver grows enormously during the second month, and on both sides some of the adjacent body wall is taken up into the septum transversum and pleuro-peritoneal membranes. The completed *diaphragm* is then derived from four sources (Fig. 231): (1) its ventral portion, from the septum transversum; (2) its lateral parts, from the pleuro-peritoneal membranes, plus (3) derivatives from the body wall; (4) lastly, a median dorsal portion is contributed by the dorsal mesentery. In addition to these components there is the striated muscle of the diaphragm, which traces origin to a pair of premuscle masses lying opposite the fourth cervical segments of 9 mm. embryos. This is the level at which the phrenic nerve enters the septum transversum. The exact origin of these muscle primordia is in doubt, but they probably represent portions of neighboring cervical myotomes. The muscle masses migrate caudad with the septum transversum and develop best in the dorsal portion of the diaphragm. The central, tendinous area apparently arises through muscle degeneration.

Anomalies.—The persistence of a dorsal opening in the diaphragm, usually on the left side, finds its explanation in the imperfect development of the pleuro-peritoneal membrane. Such a defect may lead to one type of *diaphragmatic hernia*, the abdominal viscera projecting to a greater or less extent into the corresponding pleural cavity (Fig. 232 *A*, *B*). An intact diaphragm, weakened by being locally deficient in muscle, can also herniate into a pleural cavity, but in this instance the abdominal viscera are contained in a sacculation of the diaphragm. Allied in nature is the faulty development of a pleuro-pericardial membrane which sometimes causes the cavities containing the heart and lung to communicate

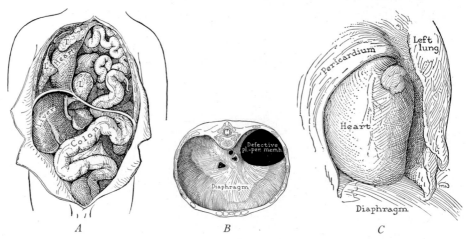

A   *B*   *C*

FIG. 232.—Anomalies of the human cœlom. *A*, Hernia of the intestine into the left pleural cavity. *B*, Cephalic surface of a diaphragm, with a defect like that in *A*. *C*, Incomplete pericardium, with the heart and left lung occupying a common cavity. *L*, Lung; *T*, thymus.

or even to occupy a common cavity (*C*). Congenital herniation of the abdominal cœlom into the umbilical cord has been described in an earlier chapter (Fig. 191 *D*). The normally temporary vaginal sac, which extends into the scrotum, may persist throughout adult life (Fig. 272).

REFERENCES CITED

1. Broman, I. 1905. Ergebn. d. Anat. u. Entwickl., **15**, 332–409.
2. Pernkopf, E. 1922. Zeitschr. f. Anat. u. Entwickl., **64**, 96–275.
3. Davis, C. L. 1927. Carnegie Contrib. Embryol., **19**, No. 107, 245–284
4. Elliott, R. 1933. Am. Jour. Anat., **48**, 355–390.
5. McGaw, W. H. 1924. Anat. Rec., **28**, 105–130.
6. Bremer, J. L. 1943. Arch. Path., **36**, 539–549.

CHAPTER XIV

THE UROGENITAL SYSTEM

The urinary and reproductive systems are intimately associated in origin, development and certain final relations. Both arise from the mesoderm as a common urogenital ridge; even though further growth soon brings about a subdivision into nephric and genital regions, the two systems develop from tissue in close approximation. Both drain into a common urogenital sinus; especially is this notable in the male where the urethra is utilized permanently as a common urinary and genital duct. Details of all these inter-relations will be made clear as the chapter progresses.

The history of each system is complicated. Some organs result from the association of structures originally separate and even remote. Other parts appear, only to disappear after a transitory existence during which they may never have functioned. Still other structures designed for one purpose abandon their original course and are turned to new uses. In this interwoven story it is far simpler to pursue separate narratives for the urinary and genital systems than to attempt a synchronized description.

As with other hollow viscera, it is the epithelial constituents that are primarily important and their development that will be chiefly discussed. The accessory, investing coats of muscle and connective tissue organize during the third month from condensed, neighboring mesenchyme.

THE URINARY ORGANS

Vertebrates have made three distinct experiments in the production of kidneys. Beginning with the simplest type in the lowest vertebrates two improved organs have appeared successively in higher forms. As might be anticipated, the embryos of the higher vertebrates indicate this progress by repeating the same kidney sequence during development; nowhere can be found a better illustration of the principle of recapitulation. The earliest and simplest excretory organ was the *pronephros*, functional today only in such adult forms as Amphioxus and certain lampreys. The pronephros, nevertheless, does serve as a provisional kidney in larval fishes and amphibians, but it is replaced by the *mesonephros* which remains as the permanent kidney of these animals. The embryos of reptiles, birds and mammals develop first a functionless pronephros and then a mesonephros (functional in some groups during fetal life), whereas the final kidney is a new organ, the *metanephros*. These three kidneys develop successively and over-

265

lappingly, one caudad of the other, in the time and place order named (Fig. 233).

All three kidney types are aggregates of uriniferous tubules, which have a common source of origin and exhibit somewhat the same structural plan. They arise from the mesoderm of the intermediate cell mass, or nephrotome; this tissue lies just lateral to the mesodermal segments and connects the latter with the somatic and splanchnic layers of mesoderm which enclose the cœlom (Figs. 234 A and 235 B). In conjunction with all three tubules there is a vascular tuft (glomerulus), specialized for separating urinary wastes from out the blood. The collected waste products are then conducted to the common excretory duct which discharges them from the body.

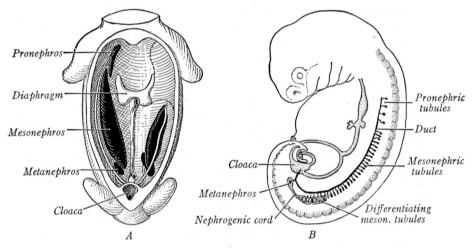

FIG. 233.—Locations and relations of the three kidney-types in mammals (semi-diagrammatic). A, Ventral dissection, the left side showing a later stage than the right. B, Lateral dissection.

The Pronephros.—The functional pronephros of lower vertebrates consists of paired *pronephric tubules*, arranged segmentally. One end of each tortuous tubule opens into the cœlom, the other into a longitudinal *excretory duct* which drains into the cloaca (Fig. 234 C). The ciliated, funnel-shaped communication with the body cavity is the *nephrostome*. Near by, but entirely separate from each tubule, an arterial tuft projects into the cœlom. These external *glomeruli*, covered only by thin splanchnopleure, filter wastes from the blood into the cœlom. The mixture of urine and cœlomic fluid is then taken up by the tubules and carried by ciliary currents into the main excretory duct. As implied by its name, the pronephros is located well cephalad in the body (Fig. 233); for this reason it has often been called the 'head kidney.'

Although the human pronephros is vestigial, it is as well developed as that of any reptile and better represented than in birds and other mammals.

It consists of about seven pairs of rudimentary pronephric tubules, formed as dorsolateral sprouts from the nephrotomes of the seventh to the fourteenth mesodermal segments, and sometimes from more cranial somites as well. The earliest tubules begin to degenerate before the last in the series appears. At their attached ends the originally solid nodules hollow out and open into the cœlom (Fig. 234); the distal, or free ends bend backward,

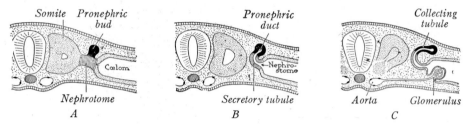

FIG. 234.—Development of the human pronephric tubule, illustrated by transverse sections of early embryos (semidiagrammatic). ✕ about 140.

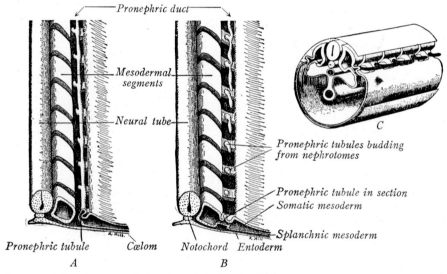

FIG. 235.—Development of the pronephric system, illustrated by models (after Felix and Burlend). A, Higher level of an embryo, with tubules and duct completed. B, Lower level, with tubules still forming and linking together. C, Relation of the pronephric system (in black) to the embryo as a whole.

canalize and unite into a longitudinal collecting duct (Fig. 235). Caudal to the fourteenth somite pronephric tubules do not develop. Nevertheless, the free end of the collecting duct, by a process of terminal growth, pushes caudad between the ectoderm and the nephrotomes until it reaches the lateral wall of the cloaca and perforates it. Thus are formed the paired primary excretory ducts, which at this period bear the name of *pronephric ducts*.

The pronephric tubules begin to appear in embryos with nine somites and, at the 23-somite stage, all have been formed. Soon afterward, in 4 mm. embryos, the two pronephric ducts reach the wall of the cloaca and promptly communicate with its lumen. The degeneration of tubules is concluded at about this time, but the pronephric ducts persist and serve as the main excretory ducts of the next set of kidneys, the mesonephroi.

The Mesonephros.—The mesonephros, or Wolffian body, is larger than the pronephros; not only does it contain more tubules, but also these are longer and more complicated. It is located farther caudad and is appropriately named the 'middle kidney' (Figs. 233 and 237 *A*). Unlike the pronephros, the primordium of the mesonephros differentiates into tubules only; these drain into the pronephric duct which is retained as an excretory canal and is henceforth known as the *mesonephric (Wolffian) duct*. Whereas the pronephros is entirely functionless in higher vertebrates, the mesonephros apparently serves the embryo as a temporary excretory organ.[1]

The mesonephros, like the pronephros, consists essentially of a series of tubules, each of which at one end becomes associated with a knot of blood vessels and at the other end opens into the mesonephric duct (Fig. 236). But the mesonephric tubule differs in two important respects: (1) the glomerulus is internal (*i.e.*, it indents the blind end of the tubule, and excreta from the blood pass directly into the tubule's lumen); and (2) the nephrostome is at best transitory and never serves as an actual mouth to the tubule proper.

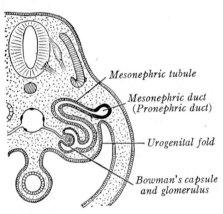

Mesonephric tubule

Mesonephric duct
(Pronephric duct)

Urogenital fold

Bowman's capsule
and glomerulus

FIG. 236.—Form and relations of a human mesonephric tubule, shown in a transverse section at 5 mm. (semidiagrammatic).

The mesonephric tubules arise just caudal to the pronephros and from the same general source, the nephrotome region. In man, however, only a few of the more cranial tubules trace origin to discrete nephrotomic masses, for caudal to the tenth pair of somites this bridge of mesoderm remains unsegmented. Nevertheless, it does retain the same potentialities, and, in preparation for tubule formation, separates into a continuous longitudinal bar; this so-called *nephrogenic cord* extends caudad as far as the twenty-eighth somite. As a whole, the mesonephric tubules bear no significant relation to the body segmentation, and commonly two or three (but even as many as nine) lie within the distance measured by a single somite. Their differentiation is induced by the nearby pronephric duct.[7]

Differentiation of the Mesonephros.—In embryos with about eighteen somites the nephrogenic cord begins to divide into spherical masses of cells which are destined to become mesonephric tubules. These appear first opposite the fourteenth somite, whereupon new primordia differentiate chiefly in a caudal direction although some are added above the initial level. Thus, in a 5 mm. embryo (with nearly all of its somites present) the cephalic limit is reached at the ninth somite (definitive sixth cervical), so that the highest tubules overlap those of the pronephros. At 7 mm. the caudal limit is reached at the twenty-sixth somite (third lumbar) (Fig. 237).

Immediately after their appearance, the originally spherical masses of mesonephrogenic tissue hollow into vesicles (Fig. 238 A, B). Each of these sends a solid extension to unite with the pronephric (now mesonephric) duct nearby (B). To complete a mesonephric tubule there is further canalization, growth with S-shaped bending, and association with a glomerulus (C, D).² The free end of the tubule enlarges and becomes thin-walled as a knot of blood vessels (the _glomerulus_) indents one side. The double-walled vesicle, thus invaginated like a simple gastrula, is _Bowman's capsule_; the capsule and glomerulus together comprise a unit known as the _mesonephric corpuscle_ (Fig. 239 A). Traced farther distad each tubule shows first a thicker, lighter-staining _secretory segment_ and then a thinner, darker-staining _collecting segment_ which, in turn, connects with the mesonephric duct (B).³ The glomeruli occupy a medial column in the gland; the duct is lateral in position and the tubules are largely dorsal. Lateral branches from the aorta supply the glomeruli, while the posterior cardinal veins, dorsally placed, break up into a network of sinusoids about the tubules; these latter channels are continuous in turn with the subcardinal veins and constitute a true renal-portal system, as in lower vertebrates.

When the developing mesonephric tubules begin to enlarge, there is not room for them in the dorsal body wall and they accordingly bulge ventrad into the cœlom. On each side of the dorsal mesentery there is thus produced a longitudinal _urogenital ridge_ which attains its greatest relative length at about 8 mm. by extending a distance of some fifteen somites (Fig. 252 A). Soon after its formation this common fold subdivides into a lateral _mesonephric ridge_ and a medial _genital ridge_ (B, C); both are suspended from the dorsal body wall by a narrower part of the original fold which serves as a mesentery. The mesonephros of man, along with that of the cat and guinea pig, is somewhat small (Fig. 252). By comparison, the mouse and rat have a tiny gland, while that of the sheep is medium-sized and the pig and rabbit have extremely large Wolffian bodies with more complexly coiled tubules (Fig. 239 C).⁴ In a general way, these varying degrees of size and differentiation are in inverse relation to the efficiency of the placenta as an excretory organ.

Embryos four to nine weeks old have a rather constant number of about thirty tubules in each mesonephros,[5] and within these time-limits the gland reaches the height of its development (Fig. 237). However, after the fourth week progressive degeneration of the more cranial tubules and continued new formation at the caudal end of the ridge effect a wavelike settling of the gland caudad. As a result of this, the upper five-sixths of

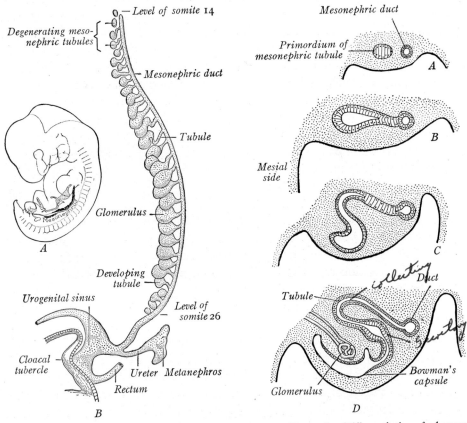

FIG. 237.—Location and composition of the human mesonephros. *A*, At 8 mm. (after Shikinami; × 45). *B*, At 10 mm., showing the mesonephric region in greater detail (after Felix; × 35).

FIG. 238.—Differentiation of a human mesonephric tubule, shown in simplified sections (adapted after Felix). × about 100.

its extent is lost by the end of the second month. The cranial remnant is reduced to a band known as the *diaphragmatic ligament* of the mesonephros. In the remaining one-sixth, new tubules seemingly arise partly by the budding and splitting of those already present. In all, a maximum number of about 80 pairs of tubules is possible, of which some 34 pairs persist at nine weeks.[4] Half of these are already nonfunctional, while within another week all become discontinuous;[5] yet degeneration is not complete until the end of the fourth month. How the male genital system salvages the mesonephric duct and the remnants of the tubules, and utilizes them for new purposes, will be traced later in the chapter (p. 294). Meanwhile it is necessary to describe the contribution of the mesonephric duct to the permanent urinary system.

The Metanephros.—The permanent kidney of amniotes arises far caudad in the body (Fig. 233). As in the case of the mesonephros, the essential parts of the permanent kidney are the renal corpuscles (glomeruli and Bowman's capsules), secretory tubules and collecting tubules. Also like the mesonephros, the metanephros is of double origin, but in this instance the duality extends even into the uriniferous tubules. The ureter, renal pelvis, calyces and collecting tubules are all derived from a bud growing off the

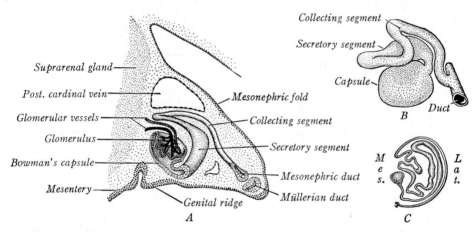

Collecting segment

Secretory segment

Capsule

Duct

B

Suprarenal gland

Post. cardinal vein

Glomerular vessels

Glomerulus

Bowman's capsule

Mesentery

Mesonephric fold

Collecting segment

Secretory segment

Mesonephric duct

Müllerian duct

Genital ridge

A

Mes.

M *L*
e *a*
s. *t.*

C

Fig. 239.—Models of mature mesonephric tubules. *A*, Human tubule, at 10 mm., partly opened and superimposed on a section of the left mesonephric ridge (× 95). *B*, Human tubule, at 13 mm. (× 75). *C*, Pig's tubule, at 80 mm. (after McCallum; × 3).

mesonephric duct (Fig. 240). On the other hand, the secretory tubules and Bowman's capsules differentiate from the caudal end of the nephrogenic cord and thus have an origin similar to that of entire mesonephric tubules, but at a lower level. Secretory and collecting portions then unite secondarily to complete the continuous *uriniferous tubules;* yet in structure and function these two components remain as different as was their origin.

In embryos of four weeks (4 mm.) the mesonephric duct makes a sharp bend just before joining the cloaca. It is at this angle (level of the twenty-eighth somite) that the 'ureteric' primordium appears, dorsal and somewhat medial in position (Fig. 240 *A*). The early primordium takes the form of a hollow bud which grows at first dorsad and then turns cephalad. The proximal, rapidly elongating portion of this evagination is the future *ureter*, while the distal, blind end expands at once into the primitive *renal pelvis*

(B).　On its first appearance (5 mm.) the ureteric bud pushes into a mass of condensed tissue which is the caudalmost portion of the nephrogenic cord (A).　This metanephrogenic mass separates from the more cranial mesonephrogenic tissue and surrounds the pelvic dilatation like a cap (B). Straightening of the body is the probable cause of a displacement by which the joint kidney primordium rises cephalad by the distance of four somites.[18] At six weeks the kidney has thus attained its definitive position; it lies in

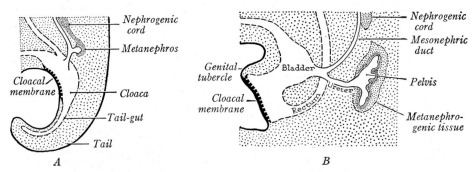

FIG. 240.—Origin and early relations of the human metanephros, illustrated by reconstructions viewed from the left side.　A, At 5 mm. (× 35); B, at 11 mm. (× 25).

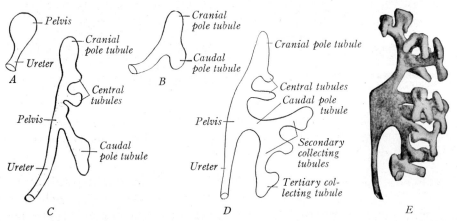

FIG. 241.—Development of the human ureteric bud illustrated, in side view, by diagrams and a reconstruction (after Felix and Huber).　× 50.　A, At 7 mm.; B, at 10 mm.; C, at 12 mm.; D, at 13 mm.; E, at about 20 mm.

a retroperitoneal position, dorsal to the mesonephros and at the level of the second lumbar segment.

　　Differentiation of the Ureteric Bud.—The primitive renal pelvis flattens from side to side, and toward the end of the sixth week (10 mm.) primary collecting tubules grow out from it (Fig. 241 A, B).　At first there are but two (cranial and caudal 'pole' tubules), but two less important 'central' tubules immediately follow them (C).　From the enlarged end of each primary tubule two or three secondary tubules sprout off (*D*). These in turn give rise to tertiary tubules (*D*, *E*) and the process is repeated into still higher orders. In the fifth month of fetal life twelve generations of tubules have been developed, while at the time of birth there is a maximum number of twenty branchings.

The renal pelvis and the primary and secondary tubules enlarge greatly during their early developmental period (Fig. 242 *A*, *B*). The cranial and caudal primary expansions (pole tubules) become the *major calyces* (*C*, 1) while the several secondary tubules form the *minor calyces* (*C*, 2). The tubules of the third and fourth orders are soon taken up into the walls of the enlarged secondary tubules, so that the tubules of the fifth order, 20 to

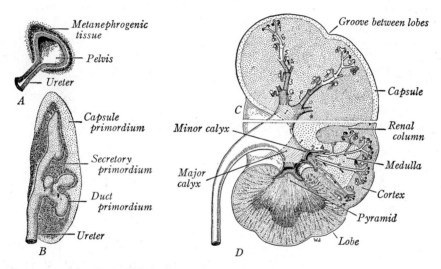

FIG. 242.—Organization of the human metanephros. *A*, Model, at 8 mm. (× 80). **B**, Model, at 12 mm. (× 65). *C*, Diagram of relations, at nine weeks (× 40). *D*, Frontal section, at birth (× 1.5).

30 in number, then open into the minor calyces as *papillary ducts* (*D*). The remaining, higher orders of diverging tubules constitute the permanent, straight *collecting tubules;* these make up a large part of the *medulla* of the definitive kidney and also project into the cortex as the cortical (sometimes called medullary) rays, or *pars radiata* of the cortex. The aggregate of all such tubular 'trees' that drain into any one, secondary calyx comprises a renal unit known as a *pyramid;* its base faces the periphery of the kidney and its apex, or *papilla,* projects into a calyx (*D*). Later these primary pyramids are subdivided into secondary and even tertiary pyramids, so that each calyx comes to receive more than one papilla.

The simple epithelium of the collecting tubules elevates to a distinctly columnar type. By contrast, the renal pelvis and ureter differentiate into a stratified 'transitional' epithelium; these parts of the urinary tract become invested with coats of smooth muscle and connective tissue.

Differentiation of the Metanephrogenic Tissue.—The encapsulating mass of early metanephrogenic tissue shows two layers (Fig. 242 A, B). The internal layer differentiates into the *secretory tubules*, whereas the external layer becomes the interstitial connective tissue and peripheral *capsule* of the kidney. This progressive organization will not take place in the absence of an ureteric bud.

When the four primary collecting tubules bud from the primitive renal pelvis, the enveloping metanephrogenic tissue is subdivided into an equal number of masses; one of these covers the end of each primary tubule (Fig. 242 B). As new orders of collecting tubules arise progressively, each mass of nephrogenic tissue not only increases steadily in amount but also subdivides in the same rhythm and is lifted to higher and higher levels. Since

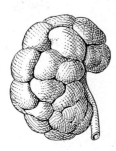

a small lump is left in association with each terminal collecting tubule, the metanephrogenic substance, as a whole, is responsible for the appearance of a definite *cortex* (C, D). This constitutes a thick shell of tissue over the base of each pyramid. As a further result of this type of growth, the boundaries of the several pyramids are indicated on the surface of the kidney by deep grooves (C). Later, subdivision of both pyramids and cortex produces smaller units (D).

FIG. 243.—External lobation of the kidney of the human newborn. × ⅔.

The human fetal kidney thus comes to be distinctly lobed (Fig. 243), this appearance decreasing progressively in infancy and early childhood as the grooves slowly fill in. On the other hand, lobation is permanent in reptiles, birds and some mammals (whale; bear; ox). The metanephrogenic tissue itself differentiates into the secretory tubules, which in the aggregate comprise the *pars convoluta*, or labyrinth of the cortex (Fig. 242 D). The rest of the cortex is the pars radiata, resulting from an invasion of radial bundles of collecting tubules, as already explained. In a reciprocal manner, the metanephrogenic tissue dips at intervals into the medulla, filling the spaces between pyramids, and is there designated the *renal columns* (of Bertin).

The details of tubule differentiation are as follows: During the seventh week some of the nephrogenic tissue about the ends of the collecting tubules condenses into spherical masses; these hang down in the angles between the end-buds of collecting tubules and their parent stems (Fig. 244 A). One such metanephric sphere is the forerunner of each secretory tubule. The formation of new spheres and their transformation into tubules continue at progressively higher levels as the cortex thickens throughout fetal life. The stage of a solid sphere is soon converted into a vesicle with an eccentrically placed cavity (*A, B*). The vesicle then elongates, thereby producing an S-shaped secretory tubule (*C*) which unites at one end with the adjacent terminal collecting tubule (*D*). The thinner-walled, blind end of the tubule becomes the capsule (Bowman's) of a renal corpuscle (*D, E*). The stage of the S-shaped tubule is followed by marked elongation and twisting (*E, F*).

The fully formed uriniferous tubule is arranged in a definite and orderly manner (Fig. 245 *C*). Beginning with *Bowman's capsule* each tubule con-

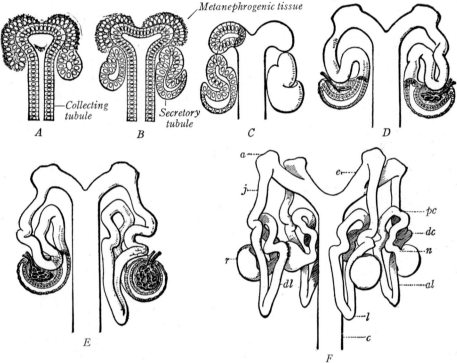

FIG. 244.—Semidiagrammatic stages of the differentiation of the mammalian uriniferous tubule (Huber). In *A–E* the left half of each figure shows an earlier condition than the right.

r, Renal corpuscle; *n*, its neck; *pc*, proximal convoluted tubule; *dl, al*, descending and ascending limbs of Henle's loop, *l*; *j*, junctional tubule; *a*, arch, and *e*, end-branch of collecting tubule, *c*.

sists of a *proximal convoluted* portion, a U-shaped *loop* (of Henle) with descending and ascending limbs, a *connecting piece* which lies close to the renal corpuscle, and a *distal convoluted* portion continuous over into the collecting tubule. These parts are derived from the S-shaped primordium in a manner more easily traced by the differential markings in Fig. 245 than through a written description. It should, however, be noted that the primitive loop (of Stoerck) includes not only the definitive Henle's loop but a portion of the proximal convoluted tubule as well. The concavity of

Bowman's capsule, into which grow the arterial loops of the glomerulus, is at first shallow (*A*); later, the walls of the capsule grow about and enclose the vascular knot except at the point where the arterioles enter and emerge (*B*).

The first few generations of secretory tubules are temporary, or provisional, and ultimately degenerate (Fig. 242 *C*).[6] The newer generations differentiate progressively in a capsular direction from the self-perpetuating, nephrogenic tissue; hence in the adult the oldest tubules are those nearest the medulla.   The development of young tubules terminates at birth when

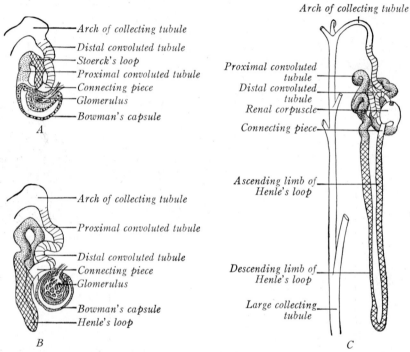

FIG. 245.—Reconstructions differentially marked to show the changing relations during the growth and specialization of a human uriniferous tubule (Prentiss, after Huber and Stoerck).

about a million have been produced in each kidney.   All later increase in kidney size results from the enlargement of tubules already present.   There is considerable specialization of the original epithelial lining of the secretory tubules to produce the characteristic modifications encountered at the various levels of a functional tubule.

The human kidney is capable of secretion early in the third fetal month.[1, 8] Since excretion is adequately performed by the placenta, renal function is not necessary before birth.   But even though the physiological conditions are unfavorable to efficient renal activity, urine is produced slowly.   Not only does the bladder fill in the early months, but also some urine voids into the amniotic sac; this, in turn, is drunk along with the amniotic fluid proper (p. 109). The full bladder of a newborn is emptied shortly after birth.

Anomalies.—A kidney may be lacking because of agenesis, or it may be present but dwarfed. Either an extra primordium or subdivision of the ordinary one is responsible for the rarely occurring supernumerary kidney. The two organs are sometimes united— most frequently by their lower ends ('*horse-shoe kidney*'; Fig. 246 *B*). Such unity could result either from secondary early fusion or from normal ureteric buds growing into a combined mass of metanephrogenic tissue. Double ureters and renal pelves also occur, apparently as the result of duplicated ureteric buds (*B*). A partially cleft pelvis and ureter trace origin to a branched ureteric bud (*B*).

A retention of various embryonic conditions explains other renal anomalies. At times one or both kidneys fail to ascend from the primary pelvic position (Fig. 246 *A*). Persistence of external lobation merely duplicates the normal adult condition in many animals (*B*).

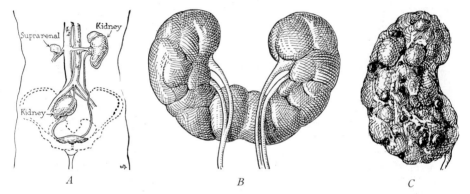

FIG. 246.—Anomalies of the human kidney and ureter. *A*, Unascended right kidney. *B*, Horse-shoe kidney, with fetal lobation retained ($\times \frac{1}{3}$); the right ureter is cleft, the left double. *C*, Congenital cystic kidney ($\times \frac{1}{4}$).

Congenital *cystic kidney* is characterized by the presence of blind secretory tubules that become dilated with retained fluid (*C*); the cause is attributed either to the primary non-union of secretory and collecting tubules or to the cystic degeneration of secondarily detached tubules.[9]

SUMMARY CONCERNING HUMAN EXCRETORY ORGANS

Organ	Source of Secretory Tubules	Source of Collecting Tubules	Origin of Excretory Duct	Somite Level of Origin	Stage of Earliest Appearance	Stage of Maximum Development
Pronephros	Nephrotomes. (Segmental.)	Nephrotomes. (Segmental.)	Tubule linkage and free growth.	2–14 (Mostly 9–13)	9 somites.	23 somites. (3 mm.)
Mesonephros	Nephrogenic cord.	Nephrogenic cord.	None; utilizes pronephric duct.	9–26	18 somites. (2.5 mm.)	4–9 weeks.
Metanephros	Nephrogenic cord.	Branches from ureteric bud.	Bud from pronephric (*i.e.*, mesonephric) duct.	26–28 (Ureter, 28)	5 mm. (4 weeks.)	After birth.

SUMMARY CONCERNING HUMAN EXCRETORY ORGANS—*Continued*

Organ	Period of Degeneration	Tubules in Each Kidney	Tubule Characteristics	Urinary Function	Permanent Features	Functional Derivatives
Pronephros	25–40 somites. (3.5–5 mm.)	7 ±	Segmental; short. Nephrostome. Ext. glomerulus.	None.	Duct.	Chief sex duct of male.
Mesonephros	7–110 mm. CR. (5–16 weeks.)	70 ±	Larger; nonsegmen. Int. glomerulus. Renal-portal blood system.	Transitory, in embryo.	Certain tubules.	Efferent ductules of male.
Metanephros	7–20 weeks. (Early orders of tubules.)	1,000,000 ±	Complex; long. Orderly arrangement.	Pre- and post-natal.	Entire organ and duct.	Permanent excretory system.

THE CLOACA

The Primitive Cloaca.—Vertebrates below the placental mammals retain a common entodermal chamber into which fecal, urinary and repro-

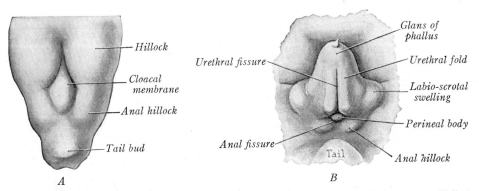

FIG. 247.—Region of the human cloacal membrane, in ventral view. *A*, At 3 mm. (after Keibel; × 60); *B*, at 21 mm. (after Otis; × 16).

ductive products all pass, and from which they are expelled to the exterior. Higher mammals have subdivided this *cloaca* into a dorsal rectum and a ventral bladder and urogenital sinus. In such manner two separate outlets are gained for fecal and urogenital discharge. These changes are consequent on the evolution of an external penis in higher mammals; cloacal subdivision has also brought into existence a *perineum,* separating the rectal orifice from the urogenital vent. The developmental course of the human cloaca, before complete division is attained, recapitulates several stages permanent in lower mammals.

In human embryos with six somites the future cloaca is merely a blind, caudal expansion of the hind-gut which already stands in contact ventrally with the ectoderm. This area of union between ectoderm and entoderm constitutes the *cloacal membrane* (Fig. 247 *A*), a region just caudal to the primitive streak that has been turned under by the tail fold (Fig. 70).[10] At first the cloacal membrane extends from the tail bud to the body stalk (Fig. 240 A), but later this expanse is diminished relatively by the ingrowth of mesoderm to produce the infra-umbilical belly wall (B).[11] At its cephalic end the cloaca gives off the ventrally directed allantoic stalk; laterally the cloaca receives the mesonephric ducts, while it is prolonged caudad as the transitory tail-gut (Fig. 248 A, B).

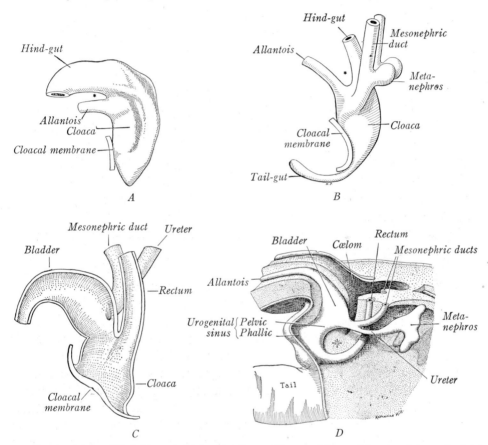

FIG. 248.—Partial division of the human cloaca, illustrated by models viewed from the left side. A, B, At 3.5 mm. and 4 mm., respectively (after Pohlman; × 50); C, at 8 mm. (× 50); D, at 11 mm. (after Keibel; × 25). An asterisk indicates the cloacal septum.

Subdivision of the Cloaca.—The facing walls of the hind-gut and allantois meet in a saddle-shaped notch, or fold, whose apex points caudad (Fig. 248,*). The wedge of mesenchyme filling this interval is the so-called _cloacal_ (or uro-rectal) _septum._ The mesenchymal mass pushes caudad as the fold advances, thereby dividing the cloaca into a dorsal _rectum_ and a ventral _bladder_ and _urogenital sinus_.[12] Division is completed during the seventh week (Fig. 249 C).

Even at the end of the sixth week (11 mm.), before the cloacal division is wholly finished, certain regions can be recognized in the ventral half (Fig. 248 *D*). The bladder is continuous with the allantois and receives the common stems of the mesonephric ducts and ureters at its caudal end. These stems also mark the upper end of the urogenital sinus, which shows two emerging regions. Proximally there is a *pelvic portion;* it connects the bladder with the *phallic portion*, which extends into the genital tubercle. Presently these two parts become clearly defined in both sexes (Fig. 249 *C*); their fates will be explained in a subsequent paragraph.

The Perineum.—When the cloacal septum extends to the level of the cloacal membrane, rupture of the entodermal-ectodermal plate follows promptly (7 weeks). This exposes the caudal edge of the septum, which is, naturally, surfaced with the entoderm of the advancing fold (Fig. 265).[13] This projecting wedge, interposed between anus and phallus, is the primitive *perineal body* (Fig. 247 *B*). The external fissure, resulting from the disappearance of the cloacal membrane, is closed again in its middle region by the merger of the perineal body with lateral folds flanking the fissure. The area so produced, covered finally by ectoderm and marked by a median raphé, is the *perineum* (Fig. 273 *B, D*). Hillocks, located behind the anus (Fig. 247 *B*), encircle its orifice and create a definite *anal canal* (proctodeum) lined with ectoderm (Fig. 273).[14]

The Bladder.—At the time of its emergence as such, the bladder still receives on each side the common stem of the mesonephric duct and ureter (Fig. 248 *D*). Growth processes quickly lead to the absorption of these stems, so that the four ducts acquire separate openings (Fig. 249 *A*). A somewhat complicated shifting then displaces the mesonephric ducts farther caudad (*B, C*).[12, 15] The two ureters come to lie well apart from each other, but the mesonephric ducts open close together at an elevation known as *Müller's tubercle* (Fig. 250 *A*). The germ-layer composition of the triangular area (the *trigone*) on the dorsal wall of the bladder and its continuation along the dorsal wall of the urethra to Müller's tubercle, marked off by these four ducts, is disputed. Theoretically it would seem to be a mesodermal island amid entoderm, because of the process of absorption already described.[16, 17] However, the actual events are perhaps deceptive and it is possible this area may be largely entodermal after all.[12, 15]

The bladder proper is originally tubular (Fig. 249 *C*), but after the second month it expands to an epithelial sac whose apex tapers into an elongate *urachus* (Fig. 271 *B*). The urachus, in turn, is continuous at the umbilicus with the remnant of the allantoic stalk, but it is believed that the latter contributes nothing to either urachus or bladder.[12] After birth the urachus may maintain its connection with the umbilicus and its communication with the bladder.[26] It persists throughout life as a more or less patent canal, about 5 cm. long, whose outer, fibrous coat may continue alone to the umbilicus. The whole complex is known after birth as the *middle umbilical ligament*. The general organization of the bladder, both as regards its stratified epithelial lining and muscular wall, is attained during the third month.

The Urethra.—The caudal region of the cloaca that separates away from the rectum becomes the primitive urogenital sinus; its pelvic and phallic segments have already been mentioned (Fig. 249 *C*). In the female the originally short neck between the bladder and the urogenital sinus elongates into the permanent *urethra* (Fig. 265). The pelvic and phallic portions of the sinus merge to create the shallow *vestibule* into which the urinary and

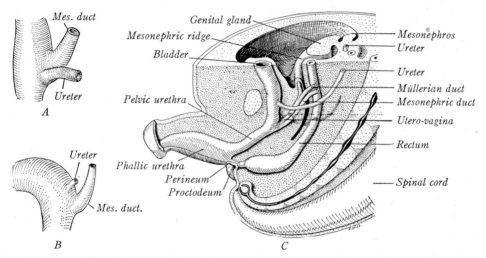

FIG. 249.—Completed division of the human cloaca, and associated changes, shown by models viewed from the left side. *A, B*, At six weeks (× 50) and seven weeks (× 35), respectively, illustrating the absorption of the left ureter and mesonephric duct into the wall of the bladder. *C*, At nine weeks (after Keibel; × 15).

genital tracts open separately. The female urethra does not extend into the clitoris, which is a partial homologue of the penis of the male.

The male urethra is more complicated. The counterpart of the entire female urethra is a short tube between the bladder and Müller's tubercle (the permanent seminal colliculus; Fig. 250 *A*). Below this level the pelvic portion of the urogenital sinus becomes the rest of the *prostatic* and all of the *membranous urethra*, whereas the phallic portion adds the *cavernous urethra* extending through the penis (*B*). Since the mesonephric ducts are utilized by the male as the chief genital ducts, all of the permanent urethra distal to their outlets serves as a true urogenital canal.

Accessory Genital Glands.—Several glands, associated with the genital system, trace origin to cloacal derivatives.

The Prostate Gland.—This organ develops as multiple outgrowths of the urethral epithelium, both above and below the entrance of the male ducts (Fig. 250 *B*). It is said that all of the prostate is entodermal in origin, no buds coming off the absorbed, possibly mesodermal, floor of the upper urethra.[12] The tubules arise at eleven weeks in five distinct groups and total an average number of 63. The surrounding mesenchyme differentiates both connective-tissue and smooth-muscle fibers, into which the prostatic buds grow. The prostate of the newborn shows evidence of activation (secretion) that is not resumed again until puberty. In the female the homologue is rudimentary; these isolated *para-urethral ducts* (of Skene) are but few in number.

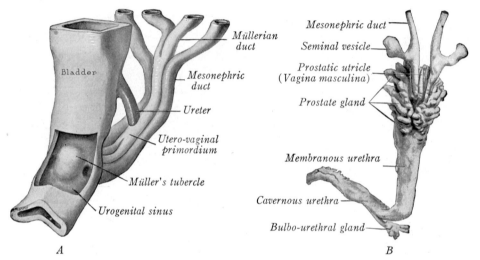

FIG. 250.—Differentiation of the human urogenital sinus, illustrated by models. *A*, Female fetus of nine weeks, in left front view (after Keibel; × 120); *B*, male fetus of four months, in left rear view (after Broman; × 13).

The Bulbo-urethral Glands.—These glands (of Cowper) arise in male embryos of nine weeks as a pair of solid buds that grow out from the ento-dermal epithelium of the cavernous urethra (Fig. 250 *B*). The outgrowths penetrate the investing mesenchyme of the primitive corpus cavernosum urethræ. At four months the epithelium becomes glandular. The *vestib-ular glands* (of Bartholin) are the female homologues. They appear at the same age as the male glands, grow through puberty and involute after the menopause.

The Seminal Vesicles.—Although of somewhat different origin, these saccular glands belong functionally in the present group. They are exclu-sively male organs which outpouch from the mesonephric (now deferent) ducts in fetuses of thirteen weeks and gain a muscular wall from the adjacent mesenchyme (Fig. 250 *B*).

Anomalies.—Imperforate anus results from a retention of the anal portion of the cloacal membrane (Fig. 191 *A*). A conspicuous malformation is a persistent cloaca, as in most vertebrates (Fig. 251 *A, B*); it is due to the failure of the rectum and urogenital sinus to separate normally. Only rarely is the bladder duplicated or divided into two chambers. It sometimes opens widely onto the ventral body wall and everts through the fissure (Fig. 251 *C*); failure of mesoderm to invade this region and reduce the expansive cranial extent of the early cloacal membrane would predispose to this condition (*cf.* Fig. 240). Due to the primary relation of the mesonephric ducts to the ureter, and their normal absorption into the differentiating cloaca, variations in the ureteric openings occur; they may terminate in the seminal vesicles, urethra, rectum, uterus or vagina. At times the urachus remains patent even to the umbilicus and establishes a fistula there through which urine escapes. Less complete remnants of the urachus are blind sinuses, leading from the bladder, or isolated epithelial cysts. Anomalies of the urethra and accessory genital glands are not common.

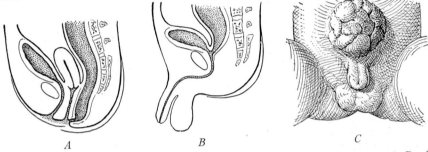

A   *B*   *C*

Fig. 251.—Anomalies resulting from faulty cloacal differentiation in man. *A*, Persistent cloaca in the female, shown in sagittal section. *B*, Similar condition in the male. *C*, Exstrophy of the bladder (ectopia vesicæ) in a newborn, combined with epispadias of the penis and undescended testes.

THE GENITAL ORGANS
INDIFFERENT STAGE

During the fifth and sixth weeks (5–12 mm.) the genital system makes its appearance. This has been named the 'indifferent period' because the sex of the embryo cannot be determined then, either by gross or microscopic inspection of the internal and external genitalia. In addition to a pair of generalized sex glands, all vertebrate embryos are equipped at an early stage with a double set of sex ducts (male and female). Both are held in readiness for the time when sexuality is declared, but only one set will advance significantly beyond its primitive state; the complementary set suffers regression.

Of course, the chromosomal, sex-determining mechanism is present from the moment of fertilization, but diagnosis of sex on this basis cannot be accomplished reliably as a routine procedure. Not until the seventh week, at the earliest, does sex recognition become practicable by simple inspection.

The Gonads.—As long as the prospective testis and ovary are structurally indistinguishable they are given the noncommittal name, *gonad*.

13

The primitive sex gland makes its appearance within a thickening that has already been described as the *urogenital ridge* (p. 269); this is appropriately named since it contains both the nephric and genital primordia (Fig. 252).

On the ventromedian surface of the urogenital ridge the peritoneal epithelium thickens (6 mm. embryos), rapidly becomes many-layered, and soon bulges into the cœlom to produce the *genital ridge* (Fig. 252). This thickened strip extends longitudinally and thus parallels the mesonephric ridge, but lies mesial to it. At six weeks the resulting, 'sexless' gonad con-

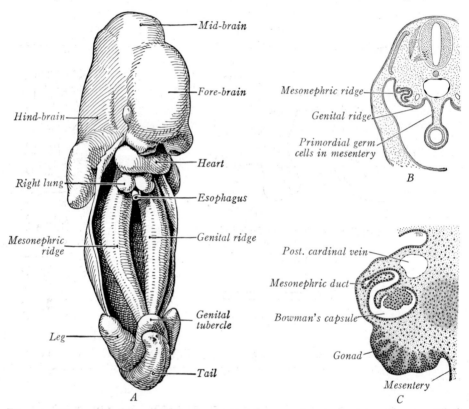

FIG. 252.—Urogenital ridge of the human embryo. *A*, Dissection, at 9 mm., in ventral view (Kollman; × 11). *B*, *C*, Transverse sections, at 7 mm. (× 35) and 10 mm. (× 75).

sists of a superficial *germinal epithelium* and an internal *epithelial mass*, somewhat loosely arranged, derived by proliferative ingrowth from the former (Fig. 253).[27] Longitudinal furrows separate the indifferent sex gland from the mesonephros laterally and from the gut mesentery medially. During the next two weeks the gonad begins to assume the characteristics of testis or ovary.

Even in presomite embryos certain large, distinctive cells can be recognized caudal to the embryonic disc in the yolk-sac entoderm. Soon afterward they lie in the cloacal entoderm, and in 4 mm. embryos they are migrating cephalad, by way of the entodermal gut and dorsal mesentery, into the epithelium of the genital ridge (Fig. 252 B).[19] Such cells are called *primordial germ cells* (Fig. 253 B); in embryos with 27 somites nearly 600 have been counted. Some claim that all definitive germ cells of the genital glands are descended from them. This contention has been challenged, as already discussed (p. 21), and it is uncertain whether these cells are the ones actually used or whether some or all of the definitive sex cells originate locally from the germinal epithelium.[20]

The Primitive Genital Ducts.—The male does not elaborate any ducts intended primarily for its own sexual purposes. Instead, with the degen-

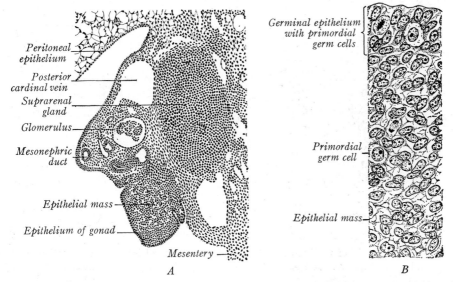

FIG. 253.—Indifferent stage of the human gonad, illustrated by transverse sections. *A*, At 12 mm., including associated regions (after Prentiss; × 82). *B*, At 12 mm., showing structural details (× 550)

eration of the mesonephros, it merely appropriates the mesonephric ducts and some of the mesonephric tubules and converts them into genital canals. The origin and early history of these parts have been adequately described in previous paragraphs (pp. 267 to 270).

Both sexes also develop somewhat more tardily a pair of female ducts (of Müller). In the sharks they arise from the direct longitudinal splitting of the mesonephric ducts, but in higher vertebrates their origin is otherwise. Human embryos of 10 mm. first indicate the future *Müllerian ducts* by a groove in the thickened epithelium of each urogenital ridge (Fig. 254 A); this furrow is located laterally on the mesonephros, near its cephalic pole. The extreme cranial end of the groove remains open like a flaring trumpet, while more caudally the lips of the groove close into a tube (B, C). Starting thus as an epithelial inrolling, the Müllerian duct continues to advance in a caudal direction by the progressive growth of its solid, blind end. The female duct courses just beneath the surface epithelium and lateral to the mesonephric (male) duct, with which its tip is intimately related.[28] It is generally held that the mesonephric duct does not contribute to the growth of the Müllerian duct, even though such growth is known to fail wherever the mesonephric duct is lacking.

Near the cloaca the two urogenital ridges have previously swung mesad to the midplane and fused into the so-called *genital cord* (Fig. 255 A). In this maneuver, the Müllerian ducts, originally lateral in position, necessarily are brought side-by-side in the midplane, whereas the mesonephric

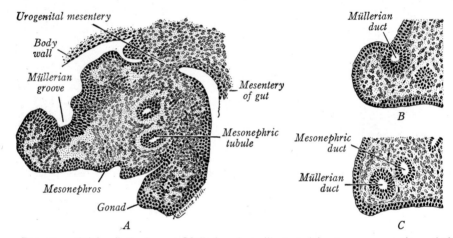

FIG. 254.—Origin of the human Müllerian duct, illustrated by transverse sections of the urogenital ridge at 12 mm. × 165. *A*, Through open groove. *B*, Slightly lower level, showing closure. *C*, Still lower level, showing free tube.

ducts assume a more lateral position $(B–D)$. Hence the progressively elongating Müllerian ducts, coursing through the genital cord, reach the dorsal wall of the urogenital sinus just mesial to the mesonephric ducts (A). In embryos of nine weeks the two Müllerian ducts have fused and end blindly at *Müller's tubercle*, a median projection demarcated by the earlier entrance of the mesonephric ducts into the dorsal wall of the cloaca (Fig. 250 A). This fused, common tube is the first indication of a uterus and vagina, whereas the more cranial portions of the ducts remain separate and will serve as the uterine tubes.

After the sex of the embryo is well established, the provisional ducts of the opposite sex regress and largely disappear (Fig. 262).

The External Genitalia.—Embryos at the start of the sixth week (8 mm.) show a conical *genital tubercle* in the midline of the ventral body, between the umbilical cord and tail (Fig. 252 *A*). Its caudal slope bears the shallow *urethral groove* which is flanked by slightly elevated *urethral folds*. During the seventh week the genital tubercle elongates into a somewhat cylindrical *phallus* whose tip is rounded into the *glans* (Fig. 247 *B*). Lateral to the base of the phallus, a rounded ridge then makes its appearance on each side; they are the *labio-scrotal swellings*. Rupture of the *urethral membrane* in the floor of the urethral groove provides an external opening for the urogenital sinus during the eighth week. From this generalized set of primordia, the external genital organs of the male or female will be modeled in an appropriate and distinctive manner during the ensuing weeks.

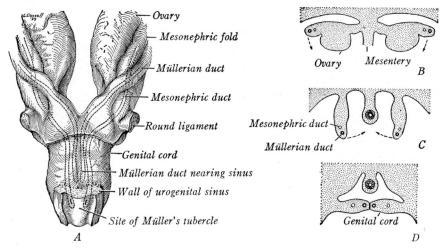

FIG. 255.—Course of the human urogenital ducts and formation of the genital cord. *A*, Model, at two months (× 25). *B–D*, Transverse sections, at three levels of the urogenital ridge.

INTERNAL SEXUAL TRANSFORMATIONS

Differentiation of the Testis.—As the male genital glands increase in size, they shorten relatively into more compact organs located farther caudad (*cf.* Fig. 267 *A*). At the same time the originally broad attachment to the mesonephros is converted into a gonadial mesentery known as the *mesorchium* (Figs. 256 *A* and 257 *A*). In embryos about 14 mm. long, destined to be males, the gonads begin to show two characteristics that mark them as testes (Fig. 256): (1) the appearance of branched and anastomosing strands of cells, the *testis cords;* and (2) the occurrence, between the covering (germinal) epithelium and the centrally located testis cords, of a layer of tissue that will become the *tunica albuginea*, or fibrous capsule of the gland.

The testis cords of most vertebrates arise as direct extensions from the germinal epithelium, but in man this relation is not plain;[16] instead, they seem to organize suddenly out of the diffuse epithelial mass already present at the stage of the indifferent gonad (Figs. 253 and 256). The radially arranged testis cords converge toward the mesorchium where another portion of the epithelial mass is emerging as the dense primordium of the *rete testis*. Soon the cell clusters of the rete primordium become a network of strands which unite with the testis cords (Fig. 257 *A*). Each of the latter splits into three to four daughter cords—the forerunners of the *seminiferous tubules*. Their peripheral portions join in looping arches (*B*), while the main extents of the tubules soon elongate into twisted *tubuli contorti*. Nearer the rete testis, however, they remain straight, as the *tubuli recti* (Fig. 258). The rete testis unites the tubuli recti with the rest of the duct system in a manner to be described presently (p. 294). Actually the testis

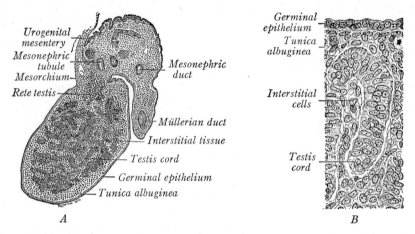

FIG. 256.—Early differentiation of the human testis, illustrated by transverse sections at nearly eight weeks. *A*, General organization and relations of the urogenital ridge (after Prentiss; × 70). *B*, Structural details of the testis (× 300).

cords do not canalize into tubules until the time of puberty (Fig. 17 *A*, *B*).[21] Their central cavities then unite with the cavities of the rete cords which were completed before birth. Thus the originally solid cords of both kinds end their development as a continuous system of tubules, lined with epithelium.

The early testis cords are composed chiefly of so-called indifferent cells, among which recognizable *primordial germ cells* are now lacking (Fig. 256). Some of the latter perhaps become early *spermatogonia*, but it is possible that the later generations of sex cells differentiate from certain of the small, 'indifferent' elements (p. 21; Fig. 257). Other indifferent cells of the cords transform into the *sustentacular cells* (of Sertoli). The full course of development of spermatogonia into spermatozoa, which first begins at puberty, has been described in an earlier chapter (pp. 32 to 35). The testis of a newborn shows definite evidence of a deleterious influence exerted by the maternal hormones during pregnancy.

The general bed of mesenchymal tissue, in which the tubules of the testis lie, organizes into the connective-tissue framework of the organ. Thus each *lobule* of the testis, containing the three or four seminiferous tubules

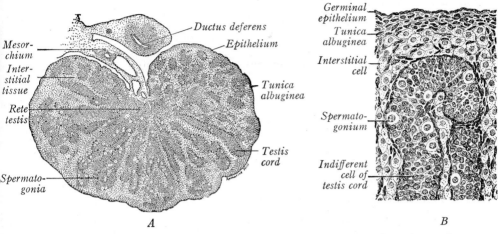

FIG. 257.—Later differentiation of the human testis, illustrated by transverse sections at fourteen weeks. *A*, General plan and relations (Prentiss; × 44). *B*, Structural details (× 150).

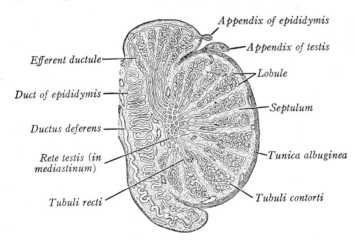

FIG. 258.—Plan of organization of the testis and its ducts in a newborn. × 4.

derived from a primitive testis cord, becomes isolated by partitions (Fig. 258). In one direction these *septula* converge to the *mediastinum testis* (where the rete tubules lie); in the opposite (peripheral) direction they extend to the encapsulating *tunica albuginea*. Certain cells of the mesenchymal stroma transform into large, pale elements which lie in the unspecialized connective-tissue between the seminiferous tubules and hence are designated *interstitial cells* (Fig. 257 *B*). They are very abundant in the fourth month and again increase in number after puberty.[22] They are generally believed to be responsible for the endocrine secretion of the testis. Following the early emergence of a tunica albuginea, the germinal epithelium reverts to an inert, peritoneal mesothelium which does not accompany the testis on its scrotal journey.

Differentiation of the Ovary.—Like the testis, the ovary gains a mesentery (*mesovarium*) and settles to a more caudal position (Fig. 268). Yet this gland does not exhibit any distinctive ovarian features until several weeks after the testis has declared itself in the male. However, gonads that do not differentiate epithelial cords during the seventh week can be diagnosed

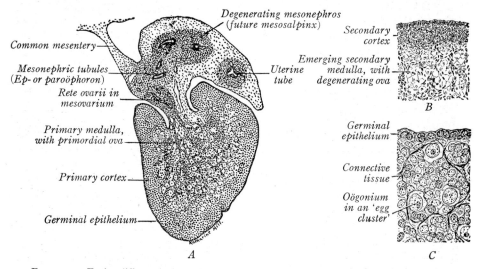

FIG. 259.—Early differentiation of the human ovary, illustrated by transverse sections. *A*, General organization and relations, at three months (after Prentiss; × 44). *B*, Structural details, at fourteen weeks (× 90). *C*, Secondary cortex, at four months (× 370).

negatively as ovaries. In the eighth week the internal epithelial mass of the indifferent period begins to show clusters composed of small, indifferent cells and one or more primordial germ cells. Soon there may be distinguished a denser *primary cortex* beneath the germinal epithelium and a looser *primary medulla* internally. In addition, a compact cellular mass bulges from the medulla into the mesovarium and establishes there the primitive *rete ovarii*, or homologue of the rete testis (Fig. 259 *A*). Neither epithelial cords nor tunica albuginea are developed at this stage, as in the testis.

In fetuses three to four months old three important changes are taking place (Fig. 259): (1) Most of the cells comprising the original internal cell mass transform into young ova, the conversion spreading from the region of the rete peripherad (*A*). (2) The ovary enlarges rapidly, due to the deposition of a new, definitive *cortex* upon the original internal cell mass (*B, C*). This secondary cortex arises partly by the division of cells of the internal cell mass, already present, and perhaps also through a renewal of proliferation by the germinal epithelium. In the human ovary this new stratum is said to be a homogeneous mass; distinct, cellular cords ('Pflüger's tubes') do not grow in from the germinal epithelium, as in other mammals.[16] (3) Ingrowth of connective tissue (accompanied by blood vessels) from the region of the rete ovarii produces supporting structures similar to the *mediastinum* and *septula* of the testis. At the periphery of the ovary the

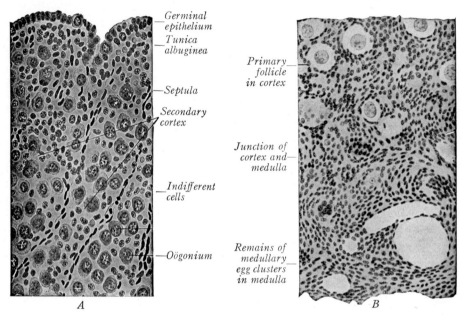

FIG. 260.—Later differentiation of the human ovary, shown in vertical sections. × 185. *A*, Cortex, at six months (after DeLee). *B*, Junction of cortex and medulla, at eight months (after Felix).

septula expand during the sixth month into a loose, connective-tissue layer known as the *tunica albuginea* (Fig 260 *A*); its appearance marks the end of the period of deposition of the new cortex.

Coincidental with the addition of new cells (secondary cortex) at the periphery of the ovary goes the decline of the earlier ova which were growing in the primary medulla and cortex (Fig. 259 *B*). Such clusters of germ cells, separated by invading connective tissue, regress and are replaced by a vascular, fibrous stroma; thus arises the permanent *medulla* (Fig. 260 *B*). In the secondary cortex single eggs and egg clusters are similarly isolated by connective tissue, but they do not succumb (Fig. 259 *C*). Instead, indifferent epithelial cells surround the young cortical ova in the later fetal months and thereby produce the *primary follicles* (Fig. 260). Although some of these advance further during fetal life and after birth, the development of *vesicular (Graafian) follicles* is mostly characteristic of the active sexual years (Fig. 11). The history of ova and follicles has been described in Chapter II; there also will be found a discussion as to whether the ripe ova, shed in the adult, represent grown primordial eggs or whether they are new cells proliferated month by month, as needed, from the cuboidal epithelium surfacing the ovary.

Bipotentiality of the Gonad.—The gonads of birds and mammals show a definite tendency toward bisexual organization. The first set of sex cords, which constitutes the primitive medulla of the ovary, is the equivalent of the definitive seminiferous tubules of the male; on the other hand, the functional cortex of the ovary is a distinctive, female characteristic.

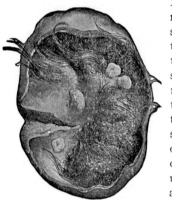

In a similar manner, the testes of some birds and mammals (including man)[23] exhibit for a short time the structural equivalent of an ovarian cortex in addition to the medullary, or male component. This double potentiality is the basis of sex reversal. That is, further stimulation of the germinal epithelium of a prospective male gonad adds an 'ovarian' cortex, while inhibition of the cortical addition to a prospective female gonad leads to testis formation. At the same time, the appropriate sex ducts undergo progressive development and those of the opposite sex are suppressed. These shifts in sex direction occur sometimes in nature and are producible under favorable conditions by experimental hormone administration.[24]

FIG. 261.—Teratoma of the human ovary, containing much hair, besides three teeth and a tiny tongue with papillæ. $\times \frac{2}{5}$.

According to the 'genic balance theory' of sex determination each individual possesses both male and female sex producers in its chromosome assortment; sex then turns on which outweighs the other.[25] In the early stages of male and female differentiation the genes are the effective agents that give direction to sex, and it is their quantitative unbalance that determines whether the male or female component of the bisexual gonad will dominate. From the physiological standpoint, what the genes actually control is the intensity of hormone (cortical or medullary) secretion; hence these endocrine substances are the active mediators of later sex differentiations in the reproductive tract and externally.

Anomalies.—Congenital absence or duplication of the testes and ovaries is very rare. Fused testes and lobed ovaries are recorded. A combined ovotestis is sometimes found as an accompaniment of hermaphroditism (p. 305).

Teratoma.—These peculiar tumor-like growths occur rather frequently in certain regions of the body, including the ovary, but less often in the testis. The simpler types, called *dermoid cysts*, contain such ectodermal derivatives as skin, hair, nails, teeth and sebaceous glands (Fig. 261). They grade into complexes consisting of misshapen, organ-like masses from all three germ layers, intermingled without order. Representatives of almost any tissue or organ may be present. The explanation of these chaotic assemblies seems to lie in an inductive influence which acts at an abnormal time and place on tissues that are somehow competent to respond. What is lacking is the capacity to organize as a whole; morphogenesis is faulty, while axiation and metamerism are lacking. Some experimental inductions performed on embryos offer interesting parallels.

Transformation of the Mesonephric Tubules and Ducts.—The meso-nephric system of amphibia performs a double function. Some of the more cranial tubules unite with the testis, while the caudal ones continue to excrete urine. Hence the mesonephric duct of the male amphibian conveys both urine and spermatozoa to the cloaca. In higher vertebrates the same potential arrangement is laid down, but the decline of the mesonephros as a urinary organ and the emergence of the permanent kidney to assume this function have resulted in individual ducts for the sexual and urinary prod-

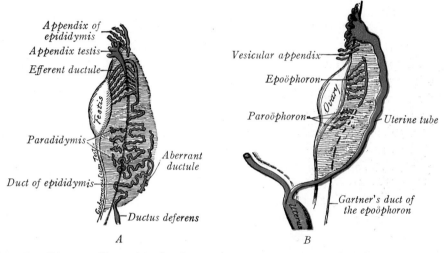

Fig. 262.—Diagrams illustrating the diverse fates of the mesonephric tubules and the meso-nephric and Müllerian ducts in the two sexes (after Heisler). *A*, Male; *B*, female.

ucts of the male. In the female the two kinds of ducts are separate from the start.

The growth of the gonad soon surpasses that of the mesonephros, which thereafter appears as an adjunct alongside (Fig. 259 *A*). Neverthe-less, both in male and female embryos of nine weeks there still remain some thirty mesonephric tubules; of these, half are intact and the rest more or less fragmented.[4, 5] During the tenth week the total number is reduced somewhat, while none then retains a continuous lumen. All the tubules that escape complete degeneration can be divided into a cranial and a caudal group on the basis of their subsequent history (Fig. 262). The cranial group soon consists of but 8 to 15 tubules; these project against the adjacent primordium of the rete testis or rete ovarii, as the case may be. Union of the rete cords and mesonephric tubules begins in fetuses of three or more months. The point of union has been described by some as occurring at Bowman's capsule and by others at the junction of secretory and collecting tubules; as a matter of fact, examples of both methods of union can be found.[4] The caudal group does not make such unions.

Male.—The fate of the mesonephric system can be followed in Figs. 258 and 262 *A*. The lumina of the rete tubules and cranial mesonephric tubules become continuous by the end of the sixth month, whereupon the mesonephric tubules are given a new name—the *efferent ductules* of the epididymis. Each coiled ductule makes a conical mass known as a *lobule of the epididymis*. A few mesonephric tubules of the cranial group comprise the cystic *appendix of the epididymis*. The entire caudal group of mesonephric tubules is vestigial, yet it persists as the blindly ending tubules called the *paradidymis* and *aberrant ductules*.

The efferent ductules are destined to convey spermatozoa from the rete testis into the mesonephric duct. The latter, accordingly, undergoes certain regional specializations which transform it into the chief genital duct. In completing these changes the upper end of the mesonephric duct becomes highly convoluted and is named the *duct of the epididymis;* the caudal portion remains straight and, as the *ductus deferens* and terminal *ejaculatory duct*, extends from epididymis to urethra. Near its opening into the latter canal the male duct dilates to form the *ampulla*, from the wall of which is evaginated the saccular *seminal vesicle* in fetuses of 13 weeks (Fig. 250 *B*).

Female.—Homologous fates in the female are illustrated in Fig. 262 *B*. The *rete ovarii* is vestigial, though retained in the adult.[29] Some time before birth it canalizes and often unites with the persisting cranial group of mesonephric collecting tubules, thus duplicating the functional connections in the male. Nevertheless, the cranial group of tubules always remains a functionless rudiment. Most of its components are blind canals attached to a short, persistent segment of the mesonephric duct. The whole complex is the *epoöphoron*. Certain other tubules of the cranial group locate in the fringes of the uterine tube or in the broad ligament nearby; they are the *vesicular appendices*. The caudal group of mesonephric tubules constitutes the smaller *paroöphoron;* it usually disappears before adult life is attained.

The greater part of each mesonephric duct atrophies in the female, the process beginning early in the third month; those portions that persist are the *ducts of the epoöphoron*. Such canals, also known as Gartner's ducts, may occur as vestigial structures at any level between the epoöphoron and hymen (Fig. 262 *B*). They are to be found, variably represented, in about one-fourth of all adult females, usually in or on the wall of the uterus or vagina.

Transformation of the Müllerian Ducts.—All vertebrates below marsupials retain separate Müllerian ducts which open into the permanent cloaca. In placental mammals, on the other hand, there is fusion to varying degrees at the caudal ends (*cf.* Fig. 266); in primates, complete caudal union of these ducts produces a common uterus and provisional vagina.

A previous page has described how the female ducts develop in the urogenital ridges, enter the genital cord, fuse there, and end at Müller's tubercle (Fig. 250 *A*). When the urogenital ridges are crowded laterad by the enlarging suprarenal glands and permanent kidneys, the Müllerian ducts naturally participate in this displacement (Fig. 263 *A*). As a result, each duct in its course makes two bends which roughly establish three regions, different in future potentialities: (1) a cranial, longitudinal portion

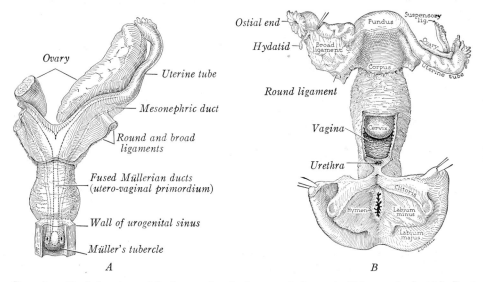

FIG. 263.—Genital system of the human female, in ventral view. *A*, At ten weeks (15×); *B*, at birth (× 1).

(uterine tube); (2) a middle, transverse portion (uterine fundus and corpus); and (3) a caudal, longitudinal portion (uterine cervix) which fuses with its fellow and perhaps becomes the upper vagina as well.

The young *uterine tubes* fail to match the elongation of the trunk as a whole, and their flaring ostial ends finally lie opposite the fourth lumbar vertebra, thirteen segments below their level of origin (Fig. 263). In the region of the transverse limbs of the Müllerian ducts the cranial walls of these tubes bulge in a cephalic direction, so that the original angle of their junction becomes convex (Fig. 264). In this manner a considerable extent is added to the *uterus;* it comprises the definitive fundus and corpus. The shorter, uterine cervix arises from the cranial portion of the original fusion of the Müllerian ducts. The *vagina* was formerly believed to represent the remainder of this fusion, but it is now known that the entodermal epithelium of the urogenital sinus invades this level of the genital cord and replaces the Müllerian epithelium wholly[30, 31, 32] or in part.[33] The *hymen* arises at the site of Müller's tubercle (Fig. 265 *A*) as a dorsal, semilunar fold between the future vagina and the urogenital sinus. Both of its surfaces come to be covered with sinus epithelium.[31] When the vagina acquires a lumen, the hymen serves as a perforate membrane guarding the entrance to the vagina (Fig. 263 *B*).

The uterine tube and uterus are lined with a simple epithelium. Only the uterus develops glands; these invaginate by the seventh month yet remain small until puberty. A distinction between uterus and vagina is not evident until the middle of the fourth month when the fornices appear (Fig. 265 *B*). For a time the vaginal epithelium is a solid column; when the lumen reappears as a central cleft in fetuses of about five months, the epithelium continues to be stratified. The muscular wall of the entire

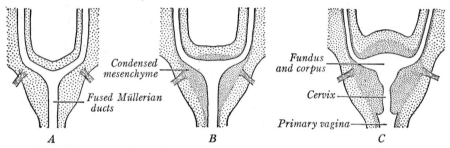

FIG. 264.—Diagrams illustrating the later history of the transverse limbs of the Müllerian ducts and their fused portions within the genital cord.

genital tract is foreshadowed in the third month by mesenchyme condensing about the epithelial lining. This investment is especially thick in the genital cord where the uterus develops (Fig. 264). The uterus grows rapidly in the last fetal months, loses one-third of its length shortly after birth, and does not recoup this loss until just before puberty.[35] This strong prenatal and pubertal growth is directed by the female hormone, estrogen, supplied first by the mother and later by the maturing girl.

The vagina is originally some distance above the outlet of the urogenital sinus (Fig. 265 *A*); the intervening stretch of sinus thereafter undergoes a great relative shortening to become the shallow vaginal *vestibule* into which both urethra and vagina open independently (*B*). From the standpoint of specialization of the primitive cloaca, this arrangement is an advance over the condition found in the male since a common urogenital sinus has been practically eliminated.

In the *male* these same primordia also develop but remain rudimentary (Fig. 276 *C*). Degeneration of the Müllerian ducts occurs in the third month and only the extreme cranial end is spared; this vestige is called the *appendix testis*. The vaginal primordium persists as a tiny pouch on the dorsal wall of the urethra to which has been given the name *prostatic utricle*, or *vagina masculina*. Like the vagina of the female, its original Müllerian epithelium is replaced by invading epithelium from the urogenital sinus.[36] The Müllerian tubercle is represented by the elevated *seminal colliculus*, from whose summit leads off the prostatic utricle.

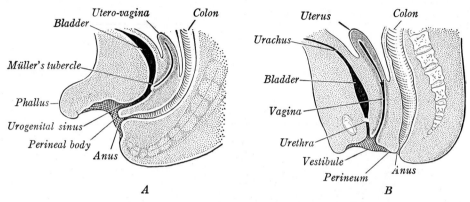

FIG. 265.—Sagittal sections of female fetuses, demonstrating the relative shortening of the urogenital sinus to a shallow vestibule. *A*, At ten weeks ($\times$ 4); *B*, at five months ($\times$ 1).

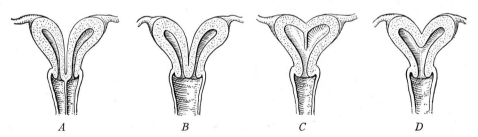

FIG. 266.—Anomalies of the human uterus. *A*, Duplex uterus and vagina; *B*, duplex uterus; *C*, bipartite uterus; *D*, bicornuate uterus.

The transformation of the Müllerian ducts is summarized in Fig. 276.

Anomalies.—The more common anomalous conditions include (Fig. 266): (1) Complete duplication of the uterus and vagina (as in monotremes and lower marsupials), due to the total failure of the Müllerian ducts to fuse (*A*). (2) Duplication of the uterus but not the vagina (as in most rodents), caused by an arrest of uterine fusion (*B*). (3) Bipartite uterus (as in carnivores and ruminants), resulting from uterine primordia which merge at their lower ends only and are more or less separated by a median partition (*C*). (4) Bicornuate uterus (as in the sheep), due to the imperfect absorption of the fundic segments which leaves paired pouches at the upper uterine ends (*D*). (5) Retention of the fetal or infantile condition. (6) Congenital absence of one or both uterine tubes, of one uterine horn, or of the uterus or vagina occurs rarely but may be associated with hermaphroditism of the external genitalia. (7) The vagina sometimes remains solid, and the hymen may retain its primary imperforate condition. (8) Stalked or sessile vesicles (hydatids) on or near the ostial end of the uterine tube are common (Fig. 263 *B*). Accessory Müllerian funnels, retained and become cystic, produce one sessile type of hydatid.

Ligaments of the Internal Genitalia.—At six weeks the urogenital ridge is attached broadly near the root of the gut mesentery (Fig. 253 *A*), but soon a common urogenital mesentery suspends the gonadic and mesonephric regions (Fig. 254 *A*). Toward the end of the second month there develop definite ligamentous supports for the internal genitalia. These are comparable in both sexes, but only in the female do they become structures of permanent importance.

Female.—The ovary is primarily suspended by a short mesentery, named the *mesovarium*, which comes into prominence as the gonad outgrows

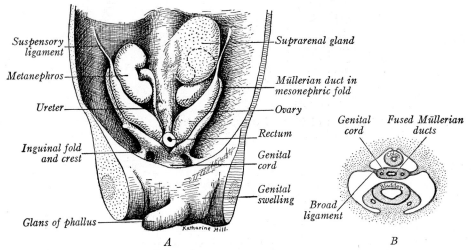

FIG. 267.—Urogenital organs of the female fetus, and especially the early genital ligaments. *A*, Ventral dissection, at two months (Prentiss). *B*, Transverse section through the lower trunk, at three months.

the mesonephros (Fig. 259 *A*). The remains of the primitive genital ridge at more cephalic levels persist as the *suspensory ligament* (Figs. 267 and 268). Similarly, the terminal portion of the genital ridge unites the caudal end of the ovary first to the transverse bend of the urogenital ridge and then to the uterus which develops in it. This connection becomes fibromuscular and is known as the *proper ligament of the ovary* (Fig. 268).

With the degeneration of the mesonephric system, the uterine tube lies in a mesenterial fold, the *mesosalpinx* (Figs. 259 *A* and 268). Somewhat earlier the mutual fusion of the caudal portions of the two urogenital ridges has produced the genital cord (Fig. 255 *B–D*). This is a mesenchymal shelf that bridges in the frontal plane between the two lateral body walls and contains the uterus in its center (Fig. 267 *B*). The shelf itself persists as the sheet-like *broad ligaments* on each side of the uterus. After the ovary and uterine tube 'descend' (*cf.* p. 300) to a lower position, the mesovarium and mesosalpinx are intimately associated with the broad ligament (Fig. 263 *B*).

During the seventh week another and more complicated ligament of the uterus is begun. At the level where each urogenital ridge bends horizontally toward the midplane in forming the genital cord, an outgrowth (*inguinal fold*) bridges across to a prominence (*inguinal crest*) on the adjoining abdominal wall (Fig. 267 *A*).[37] Within these parts is differentiated the *chorda gubernaculi*, which later becomes a fibro-muscular band. The abdom-

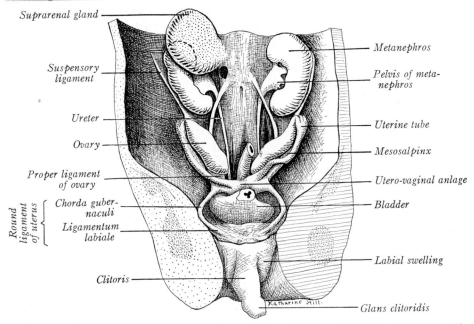

Suprarenal gland

Suspensory ligament

Ureter

Ovary

Proper ligament of ovary

Round ligament of uterus { Chorda guber- naculi

Ligamentum labiale

Clitoris

Metanephros

Pelvis of meta- nephros

Uterine tube

Mesosalpinx

Utero-vaginal anlage

Bladder

Labial swelling

Glans clitoridis

Katharine Hill.

FIG. 268.—Urogenital organs of a female fetus, at ten weeks (Prentiss). The ventral dissection displays especially the genital ligaments.

inal muscles develop around its caudal end in the form of a tubular *inguinal canal*. At the outer end of this canal the chorda connects with a second band that extends to the labial swelling of the external genitalia, and hence is designated the *ligamentum labiale*. By the beginning of the third month the chorda gubernaculi and the ligamentum labiale thus extend as a continuous, mesenchymal unit from the uterus to the labium majus; henceforth the combined cord is known as the *round ligament* of the uterus (Fig. 268).

Male.—The primitive mesentery of the testis is the *mesorchium* (Figs. 256 *A* and 257 *A*). It is represented in the adult merely by the fold between the epididymis and testis. The *ligamentum testis*, like the proper ligament of the ovary, develops in a caudal continuation of the genital ridge; it extends from the caudal pole of the testis to the transverse bend in the urogenital ridge. On the opposite side of the ridge a *chorda gubernaculi* soon bridges across to the adjacent body wall, as in the female (*cf.* Fig. 267 *A*). This in turn is continued by way of the *ligamentum scroti* into the scrotal swellings. At the beginning of the third month there thus exists a continuous, mesenchymal cable, the *gubernaculum testis*, extending from the caudal end of the testis through the inguinal canal to the scrotal swellings (*cf.* Fig. 268). The gubernaculum is composed of (Fig. 269): (1) the ligamentum testis; (2) a connecting cord in the region of the regressive mesonephros and uterine primordium; (3) the chorda gubernaculi; and (4) the ligamentum scroti. It is the homologue of the ovarian ligament plus

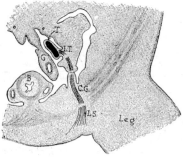

FIG. 269.—Components of the human gubernaculum testis, demonstrated by a schematic transverse section through a male embryo of two months (after Felix). × 10.

B, Bladder; G, gut; T, testis; L. T., ligamentum testis; C.G., chorda gubernaculi; L.S., ligamentum scroti.

the round ligament of the uterus, between which in the female the uterus intervenes.

Descent of the Testis and Ovary.—The original positions of the testis and ovary change during development. At first they are slender structures, extending caudad from the diaphragm (Fig. 252 *A*). A faster elongation of the trunk cephalad, in contrast to the slower growing gonad, produces a relative shift of the latter in a caudal direction until the sex gland lies ten segments below its level of origin (Figs. 267 and 268).[38] When this process of growth and shifting is complete (10 weeks), the caudal end of the gonad lies at the boundary between abdomen and pelvis.

Male.—In addion to its early 'migration' caudad (internal descent), just mentioned, the testis later leaves the abdominal cavity and descends bodily into the scrotum (external descent). At the beginning of the third month, while the testes are still fairly high in the abdomen, sac-like pockets appear in each side of the ventral abdominal wall. These are the beginnings of the vaginal sacs, and from the fourth to the end of the sixth fetal month the lower poles of the testes lie near them (at the site of the internal abdominal ring) without change of position (Fig. 271 *A*). Each *processus (saccus) vaginalis* evaginates through the ventral abdominal wall, by way of the slanting inguinal canal, then over the pubis, and so into the scrotum which it invades from the seventh month on.

During the seventh to ninth months the testes also descend along the same path (Figs. 270 and 271). The hypophysis activates this process, in which the gubernaculum testis plays an important, but disputed rôle. From the caudal pole of each testis the corresponding gubernaculum extends through the inguinal canal into the scrotum. During the seventh month the gubernaculum not only ceases growth but actually shortens one-half.[39] This shortening, both relative and actual, is commonly said to draw the testes into the scrotum where they are usually found by the eighth lunar month, or at least before birth. Others deny that the gubernaculum exerts any kind of traction; on the contrary, it is said to convert into mucoid tissue, to dilate the inguinal canal and to lose its sustaining power.[40, 41] As a result, the testis both sinks downward by a process of normal herniation and carries the processus vaginalis with it. It must be understood that the testis and gubernaculum are covered by peritoneum before the descent begins; consequently, the testis follows the gubernaculum along the inguinal canal dorsal to the peritoneum. On reaching the scrotum, the testis continues to be covered by a reflected fold of the processus vaginalis but lies entirely outside its cavity. The gubernaculum of a newborn is

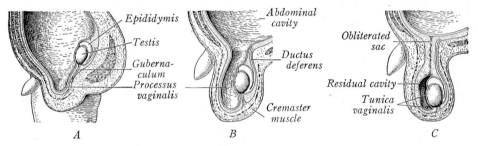

FIG. 270.—Descent of the human testis and its subsequent relations, shown in diagrammatic hemisections.

only one-fourth its length when descensus began;[39] after birth it atrophies almost completely. Sex hormones control the mechanism of descent.

Even before birth the narrow peritoneal canal, which connects the processus vaginalis with the abdominal cavity, frequently begins to become solid, and its epithelium eventually disappears.[34] The vaginal sac, now isolated, represents the *tunica vaginalis* of the testis (Fig. 270 *C*). Its visceral layer is closely wrapped about the protruding testis, whereas the parietal layer forms a lining to the scrotal sac. Thus the scrotum proves to be a specialized pouch of skin into which an extension of the body wall accompanies the evaginating sac of peritoneum. The ductus deferens and the spermatic vessels and nerves are carried down into the scrotum along with the testis and epididymis. They are embedded in connective tissue and constitute the *spermatic cord*. Owing to the path taken by the testis in the scrotal migration, the ductus deferens loops over the ureter (Fig. 276 *C*).

Female.—The ovary of the newborn female still lies at the pelvic brim. Afterwards the ovary and the uterus gradually attain their pelvic positions.

Each ovary rotates into a transverse position and also revolves about the uterine tube until it comes to rest dorsal to the tube (Fig. 263 *B*).

Shallow peritoneal pockets, frequently persistent as the *diverticula of Nuck*, correspond to the vaginal sacs of the male. Rarely, in cases of faulty

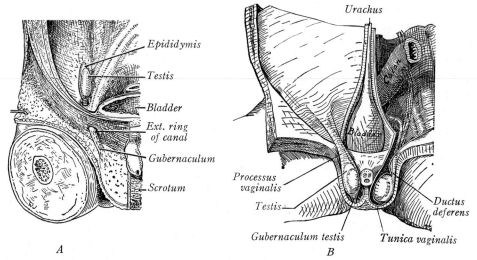

FIG. 271.—Relations before and after the descent of the human testis, shown by dissections. *A*, At six months. *B*, At birth; the left testis has been rotated 90° (partly after Corning).

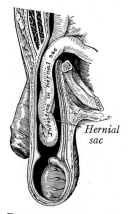

FIG. 272.—Congenital inguinal hernia, with its sac opened (Callander).

development of the internal genitalia, a more or less complete descent of the ovary into the labium majus occurs. The interposition of the uterus between the ovarian and round ligaments serves as a normal block to ovarian descent, and in this way is partly responsible for the retention of the ovaries in the abdomen (Fig. 268).

Anomalies.—Descent of the testis into an abnormal location (*e.g.*, pelvis or thigh) sometimes occurs. For primates and various other mammals a permanent scrotal location of the testes is normal. This is advantageous because of a lower temperature existing there, since spermatogenesis does not occur at the higher temperature of the abdomen.[42] If the testicular descent in these mammals is arrested at any point along its normal path, the condition is known as *cryptorchism* (*i.e.*, concealed testes; Fig. 251 *C*); an abdominal location is accompanied by sterility, for the reason already given. Cryptorchism is due to developmental anomalies, mechanical obstruction or hormone deficiency. Administration of the gonadotropic hormone of pregnancy urine is notably successful in inducing testicular descent in cryptorchid boys.[43]

In other mammals (whale; elephant) an abdominal position of the testes is normal, but the abdominal temperature in this group is well below that found in animals like primates with scrotal testes. Still other mammals (rodents; hedgehog; bats) maintain open inguinal canals; their testes remain in the abdomen except during the mating season when they experience a descensus to the cooler scrotum. Some hibernating animals have a periodic descent of the testes that follows the sharp rise in temperature on awakening.

When the inguinal canals of man do not obliterate, conditions are favorable for one type of *inguinal hernia* of the intestine into the scrotum (Fig. 272).

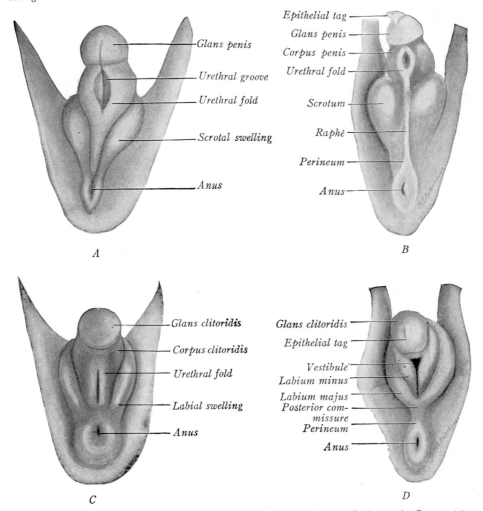

FIG. 273.—Differentiation of the human external genitalia (after Spaulding). × 8. Stages at ten and twelve weeks: *A*, *B*, male; *C*, *D*, female.

THE EXTERNAL GENITALIA

The phylogenetic acquisition of an external penis, with a penile urethra, in the male of higher mammals parallels the evolution of a vagina, uterus and the intra-uterine development of the young in the female. The relation of the external penis to the production of a perineum has been mentioned

(p. 278). Progressive stages in these several changes are illustrated in reptiles, monotremes and marsupials.

For a week or more after the external genitalia are first indicated, they are indifferent, or sexless, in appearance (Fig. 247 B). By the end of the seventh week sex begins to be distinguishable grossly through certain external characteristics, chief among which are the erectness of the phallus, the length of the urethral groove and the relations of the urethral folds to the labio-scrotal swellings (Fig. 273 A, C).[44, 45] Yet for a time these criteria are not perfectly reliable, as concomitant microscopical examinations of the sex glands prove. Especially is there liability to error in diagnosing retarded males for females.[46] Several additional weeks elapse before the distinctive modeling of the external genitalia begins. These changes progress rapidly and fetuses in the fourth month possess easily recognizable and fairly characteristic male or female genitalia.

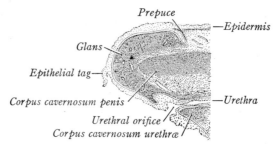

FIG. 274.—Tip of human penis, at four months, in longitudinal section. × 18.

Male.—Fetuses of ten weeks are at the beginning of the definitive stage. In the male the phallus becomes the *penis*. The edges of the urethral groove progressively fold together in a distal direction to transform an open urogenital sinus into the tubular *cavernous urethra* within the penis (Fig. 273 A, B). Their fused edges constitute a raphé. The scrotal swellings shift caudad until each becomes a half of the *scrotum*, separated from its mate by the *scrotal septum* and superficial *scrotal raphé* (B).[13] In the meantime the shaft of the penis elongates, and by the fourteenth week the urethra has closed as far as the glans (Fig. 274). The urethra is then continued along an epithelial plate, which represents a solid part of the original urethral primordium, now incompletely partitioning the glans. By splitting, the plate is first converted into a trough; this promptly recloses into a tube that continues the urethra to its permanent opening at the tip of the glans. During the third month a fold of skin at the base of the glans begins growing distad and two months later surrounds the naked, spheroidal glans.[47] This is the tubular *prepuce*, or fore-skin (Fig. 274). Fusion occurs between the epithelial lining of the prepuce and covering of the glans, but clefts appear later in this combined membrane and free the prepuce once more; this separation, however, is still incomplete at birth. A region of incomplete prepuce formation on the under surface of the glans produces the fold known as the *frenulum*. The *corpora cavernosa penis* are indicated in the seventh week as paired mesenchymal columns within the shaft of the penis. The unpaired *corpus cavernosum urethræ* results from the linking of similar mesenchymal masses, one in the glans and the other in the shaft.

Female.—Changes in the female are less profound, yet slower (Fig. 273 *C, D*). The phallus lags in development and becomes the *clitoris*, with its homologous *glans clitoridis* and *prepuce*. The shorter urethral groove never extends onto the glans, as in the male; it remains as the open *vestibule*. The urethral folds, which flank the original groove, constitute the *labia minora*.

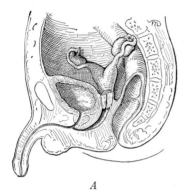
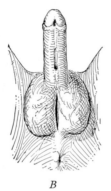
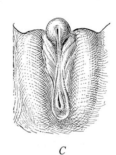

| A | B | C |

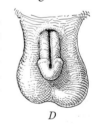

FIG. 275.—Anomalies of the human genitalia. *A*, True adult hermaphrodite, in sagittal section; the external genitalia are typically male, except for the empty scrotum; the internal genitalia are female and include a bicornuate uterus; an imperfect testis and ovary occur on each side. *B*, Hypospadias, showing in one drawing a composite of the common locations. *C*, Hypospadias, of a severe degree, in a false hermaphrodite. *D*, Epispadias.

D

The primitive labio-scrotal swellings grow caudad and fuse in front of the anus as the *posterior commissure*, while the original lateral portions enlarge into the *labia majora;* these parts now form a horse-shoe shaped rim, open toward the umbilicus. The cephalically located *mons pubis* arises later to complete the gap in the horse-shoe; it develops independently of the primitive swellings.[44]

Anomalies.—The name hermaphroditism (*i.e.*, Hermes plus Aphrodite) has been given to the condition that actually or apparently combines both sexes in one individual. *True hermaphroditism* consists in the presence of both testis and ovary in the same individual. It occurs rarely in birds and mammals, is not uncommon in the lower vertebrates, and is the normal condition in hag fishes and many invertebrates (worms; molluscs). In man there are authentic cases both with combined ovotestis[48] and with separate ovary and testis (Fig.

275 A);[49] however, functional competency of both kinds of sex glands does not exist. The internal genitalia are faultily bisexual, although female gonads and ducts may occur on one side and male gonads and ducts on the other. The external genitalia show mixed male and female characteristics. The secondary sexual characters (beard, mammæ, voice, etc.) are usually intermediate, tending now one way, now the other.

False hermaphroditism is characterized by the presence of the genital glands of one sex in an individual whose secondary sexual characters and external genitalia tend to resemble those of the opposite sex. The internal sexual tract can be that of either sex, or it may be double or mixed; it is commonly atrophic in some of its parts. In masculine hermaphroditism an individual possesses testes, often undescended, but the external genitals (by retarded development and severe hypospadias) and secondary sexual characters are like those of the female (Fig. 275 C). In the rarer feminine hermaphroditism ovaries are present and sometimes descended, but the other sexual characters, such as enlarged clitoris or fused labiæ, simulate the male.

No one theory accounts satisfactorily for all hermaphroditic conditions. In general, the relative activity of the cortical (female) and medullary (male) components of the primitive bisexual gonad is seemingly responsible for many of the conditions observed (p. 292). This would explain the separate testis and ovary or the combined ovotestis of a true hermaphrodite. Also, masculinized pseudo-hermaphrodites (with ovaries) have shown tumors of the ovarian medulla. On the other hand, the feminization of a male pseudo-hermaphrodite may well trace origin to undue influence of the maternal hormones during pregnancy.

Absence or doubling of the penis is very rare. Nevertheless, the penis may remain rudimentary or the clitoris may hypertrophy; both conditions are common in hermaphroditism. If the lips of the slit-like urogenital opening on the under surface of the penis fail to fuse anywhere along their extent, *hypospadias* results (Fig. 275 B); this is a common occurrence in false hermaphroditism simulating the female type (C). Rarely the urethra opens on the upper surface of the penis—*epispadias* (D). This defect commonly accompanies fissure of the abdominal wall (and exstrophy of the bladder) just above (Fig. 251 C); it seemingly could be due to a displacement of the cloacal membrane and the appearance of the phallus caudal to it.

HOMOLOGIES OF THE UROGENITAL SYSTEM

In the appended table are summarized the equivalent derivatives of the indifferent reproductive system; vestigial parts are printed in italics. Figure 276 sets forth the same facts in pictorial form.

TABULATION OF UROGENITAL HOMOLOGIES

MALE	INDIFFERENT STAGE	FEMALE
Testis (1) .... (2) Seminiferous tubules (3) Rete testis	Gonad	Ovary (1) Cortex (2) Medulla (primary) (3) *Rete ovarii*
(1) *Mesorchium* (2) .... (3) *Ligamentum testis* (4) *Gubernaculum testis* (in part) (5) *Gubernaculum testis* (as a whole) (6)	Genital ligaments	(1) Mesovarium (2) Suspensory ligament of ovary (3) Proper ovarian ligament (4) Round ligament of uterus (5) .... (6) Broad ligament of uterus
Efferent ductules and *appendix epididymidis*	Mesonephric collecting tubules Cranial group	*Epoöphoron* and *vesicular appendices*
Paradidymis and *aberrant ductules*	Caudal group	*Paroöphoron*
(1) Ductus epididymidis (2) Ductus deferens (3) Seminal vesicle (4) Ejaculatory duct	Mesonephric (Wolffian) duct	*Gartner's duct of the epoöphoron*
(1) *Appendix testis* (2) .... (3)	Müllerian duct	(1) Uterine tube (2) Uterus (3) Vagina (upper part?)
Seminal colliculus	Müller's tubercle	Hymen (site of)
(1) Bladder (except trigone?) (2) Upper prostatic urethra	Vesico-urethral primordium	(1) Bladder (except trigone?) (2) Urethra

(1) Lower prostatic urethra
   (a) *Prostatic utricle* (or
     vagina masculina)
   (b) Prostate gland
(2) Membranous urethra
 	
(3) Cavernous urethra
   Bulbo-urethral glands
	Urogenital sinus
	Pelvic portion
	
	Phallic portion
		(1) Vestibule (nearest vagina)
		   (a) Vagina (lower part, at least)
		
		   (b) *Para-urethral ducts*
		(2) Vestibule (middle part)
		
		(3) Vestibule (between labia minora)
		   Vestibular glands (of Bartholin)

(1) Penis
   (a) Glans penis
   (b) Urethral surface of penis
   (c) Corpora cavernosa penis
   (d) Corpus cavernosum urethræ
 	
(2) Scrotum
(3) Scrotal raphé
 	
(4) ....
	Phallus
	Glans
	Lips of urethral groove
	Shaft
	
	Labio-scrotal swellings
	
	Median swelling
		(1) Clitoris
		   (a) Glans clitoridis
		   (b) Labia minora
		   (c) Corpora cavernosa clitoridis
		   (d) Vestibular bulbs
		
		(2) Labia majora
		(3) Posterior commissure
		
		(4) Mons pubis

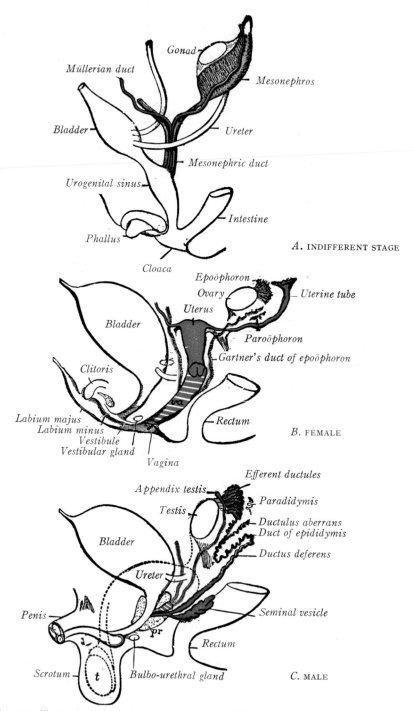

FIG. 276.—Diagrams illustrating the transformation of an indifferent, primitive genital system into the definitive male and female types (Thompson).

REFERENCES CITED

1. Gersch, I. 1937. Carnegie Contrib. Embryol., **26**, No. 157, 33–58.
2. Shikinami, J. 1926. Carnegie Contrib. Embryol., **18**, No. 93, 49–61.
3. Kozlik, F. and Erben, B. 1935. Zeitschr. f. mikr.-anat. Forsch., **38**, 483–502.
4. Bremer, J. L. 1916. Am. Jour. Anat., **19**, 179–210.
5. Altschuler, M. D. 1930. Anat. Rec., **46**, 81–91.
6. Kampmeier, O. F. 1926. Anat. Rec., **33**, 115–120.
7. Waddington, C. H. 1938. Jour. Exp. Biol., **15**, 371–376.
8. Chambers, R. and Cameron, G. 1938. Am. Jour. Physiol., **123**, 482–485.
9. Kampmeier, O. F. 1928. Surg., Gynec. and Obstet., **36**, 208–216.
10. Florian, J. 1933. Jour. Anat., **67**, 263–276.
11. Wyburn, G. M. 1937. Jour. Anat., **71**, 201–231.
12. Chwalla, R. 1927. Zeitschr. f. Anat. u. Entwickl., **83**, 615–733.
13. Politzer, G. 1931–32. Zeitschr. f. Anat. u. Entwickl., **95**, 734–768; **97**, 622–660
14. Tench, E. M. 1936. Am. Jour. Anat., **59**, 333–343.
15. Frazer, J. E. 1935. Jour. Anat., **69**, 455–468.
16. Felix, W. 1912. Chapter 19 in Keibel and Mall's 'Human Embryology.' Lippincott.
17. Wesson, M. B. 1920. Jour. Urol., **4**, 279–315.
18. Gruenwald, P. 1943. Anat. Rec., **85**, 163–176.
19. Politzer, G. 1928. Zeitschr. f. Anat. u. Entwickl., **87**, 766–780.
20. Everett, N. B. 1945. Biol. Rev., **20**, 45–55.
21. Stieve, H. 1930. Bd. 7, Teil 2 in Möllendorff's 'Handbuch der mikroskopischen Anatomie des Menschen.' Springer, Berlin.
22. Kitahara, Y. 1923. Arch. f. Entwickl.-mech. d. Organ., **52**, 550–615.
23. Grünwald, P. 1934. Zeitschr. f. Anat. u. Entwickl., **103**, 278–289.
24. Green, R. R. *et al.* 1939. Am. Jour. Anat., **65**, 415–469.
25. Bridges, C. B. 1939. Chapter 2 in Allen's 'Sex and Internal Secretions.' Williams and Wilkins, Baltimore.
26. Hammond, G. *et al.* 1941. Anat. Rec., **80**, 271–287.
27. Gruenwald, P. 1942. Am. Jour. Anat., **70**, 359–397.
28. Gruenwald, P. 1941. Anat. Rec., **81**, 1–20.
29. Wilkerson, W. V. 1923. Anat. Rec., **26**, 75–78.
30. Vilas, E. 1932. Zeitschr. f. Anat. u. Entwickl., **98**, 262–292.
31. v. Lippmann, R. 1940. Zeitschr. f. Anat. u. Entwickl., **110**, 264–300.
32. Kempermann, C. T. 1935. Morph. Jahrb., **75**, 151–179.
33. Koff, A. K. 1933. Carnegie Contrib. Embryol., **24**, No. 140, 59–90.
34. Mitchell, G. A. G. 1939. Jour. Anat., **73**, 658–661.
35. Scammon, R. E. 1926. Proc. Soc. Exp. Biol. & Med., **23**, 687–690.
36. Vilas, E. 1933. Zeitschr. f. Anat. u. Entwickl., **99**, 599–621.
37. Meyer, R. 1920. Arch. f. Gynäk., **113**, 441–445.
38. Higuchi, K. 1932. Arch. f. Gynäk., **149**, 144–172.
39. Broman, I. 1911. Normale und abnorme Entwicklung des Menschen. Bergmann, Wiesbaden.
40. Forssner, H. J. 1928. Acta Obstet. et Gynec. Scand., **7**, 379–406.
41. Moscowicz, L. 1935. Zeitschr. f. Anat. u. Entwickl., **105**, 37–71.
42. Moore, C. R. 1926. Quart. Rev. Biol., **1**, 4–50.
43. Cramer, A. J. 1937. Endocrin., **21**, 230–240.
44. Spaulding, M. H. 1921. Carnegie Contrib. Embryol., **13**, No. 61, 67–88.
45. Szenes, A. 1925. Morph. Jahrb., **54**, 65–135.
46. Wilson, K. M. 1926. Carnegie Contrib. Embryol., **18**, No. 91, 23–30.
47. Hunter, R. H. 1935. Jour. Anat., **70**, 68–75.
48. Kwartin, B. and Hyams, J. A. 1927. Jour. Urol. **18**, 363–383.
49. Young, H. H. 1926. Chapter 9 in 'Practice of Urology.' Saunders, Phila.

CHAPTER XV

THE VASCULAR SYSTEM

ANGIOGENESIS

Both the blood cells and blood vessels arise from mesenchyme. The earliest formative tissue of this kind has long been called *angioblast* (vessel former). Some trace its earliest origin to distinctive cells that separate away from the primary trophoblastic capsule (enclosing the embryo) at the

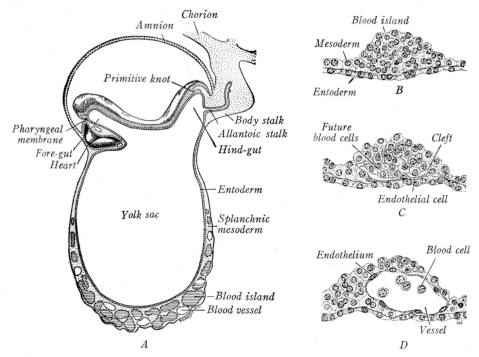

FIG. 277.—Differentiation of human blood vessels from blood islands. *A*, At seven somites (Prentiss, after Mall; × 23). *B–D*, At six somites, showing three progressive stages in detail (× 325).

same time the more generalized, extra-embryonic mesenchyme is similarly delaminating there.[1] Slightly later, angioblast appears (by spreading?) in the body stalk and the wall of the yolk sac. In the latter location the angioblast takes the form of isolated masses and cords termed *blood islands* (Fig. 277 *A*, *B*). Originally solid, they soon hollow out (*C*, *D*). In this process the peripheral cells become arranged as a flattened *endothelium*; the more central cells are the earliest *blood cells* and these float in the blood plasma. The latter appears as a clear fluid, apparently secreted by the cells of the blood island. The plasma first occupies discrete intercellular clefts, but these spaces soon coalesce and produce a common lumen. For a time, a cluster of primitive blood cells may adhere to the side of such an endothelial space; these cell groups are sometimes termed blood islands also. Such primitive blood cells soon separate, differentiate mostly into red blood cells, and are swept into the general circulation. However, the majority of blood cells, both red and white, do not trace origin to angioblastic elements on the yolk sac, but arise progressively from the mesenchyme of the embryo proper in a way to be described in the following section.

By growth and union the originally isolated vascular spaces, derived from solid angioblast, are converted into plexuses of blood vessels which are present on the yolk sac, body stalk and chorion of human embryos at the late head-process stage. In the wall of the yolk sac this network comprises the *area vasculosa* which eventually envelops the entire sac (Fig. 286 *A*). The first vessels within the embryo itself appear at the same time as the earliest somites. Many have held that they originate as direct extensions of the extra-embryonic vessels that progressively invade the embryo. However, it is now generally agreed that the fundamental origin of intra-embryonic vessels is from clefts differentiating locally in the mesenchyme wherever the need arises.[2] The specialization of mesenchymal cells into endothelium is not a single early act but is repeated at different times and places during early development.

Proliferative growth of the endothelium, thus primarily established, links the simple vascular spaces into continuous channels; the latter further expand their primitive network by independent sprouting (Fig. 282 *B–D*).[3] After a system of closed vessels (and a primitive blood circulation within them) has been established, new vessels arise only as outgrowths of pre-existing vessels.[4] The causative stimulus that induces budding is unknown.

HEMOPOIESIS

The development of blood cells (hemopoiesis) is similar in all embryonic sites. The parent tissue is the versatile mesenchyme which has many other derivatives (Fig. 280). Its cells round up, detach and become free, basophilic elements that are the progenitors of all types of blood cells.

As a preliminary to hemopoiesis the primitive mesenchyme of the embryo begins differentiating into three sorts of tissues: (1) blood islands on the yolk sac; (2) endothelium; and (3) fixed mesenchyme cells. Of these, the primitive blood cells of the yolk sac form mostly into early generations of nucleated red blood cells; these serve the embryo for a time and then die out.[55] The endothelium of early stages has capacities identical with the mesenchyme that gave it origin, but these powers are soon lost (Fig. 278). The mesenchyme is the chief blood-forming tissue of the embryo, while its successor, the fixed connective-tissue cells, serves the same function in the adult. In all the locations about to be mentioned, hemopoiesis is made possible by the detachment of mesenchymal cells which then serve as proliferative stem cells.

During the prenatal period several locations are utilized successively for the formation of red and white elements.[38] Their sequence and time of first appearance are as follows: (1) yolk sac (fourth week); (2) body mesenchyme and blood vessels (fifth week); (3) liver (sixth week); (4) spleen, thymus, and lymph glands (second to fourth month); and (5) bone marrow (third month). There is considerable overlap in the activities of these foci. For example, the yolk sac abandons hemopoiesis in the second month; by

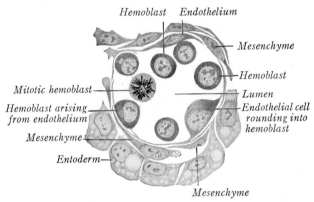

FIG. 278.—Section of a blood vessel on the yolk sac of a rabbit embryo, at five somites (Maximow). × 500.

contrast, the liver is the most active site until the middle of fetal life, when its activity decreases slowly and ceases at birth. One by one, these organs give up total blood formation until the red marrow alone remains as the single source from which all types of blood cells are recruited during postnatal life. This totipotent formative capacity of the bone marrow is supplemented by the lymphoid organs and fixed connective-tissue cells (other than fibroblasts); they are the principal sources of lymphocytes and monocytes.

Two sharply contrasted views are held as to the exact mode of origin (*hemopoiesis*) of the various blood elements. According to the *unitarian theory*, a common mother cell gives rise to all types of blood elements, both red and white (Fig. 280).[5] The *dualistic* and *trialistic theories*, on the contrary, respectively assert that the erythroplastids are derived from one mother cell, while the granular and non-granular leucocytes trace their ancestries to one, or to two, separate stem cells.[6] The total evidence seems to favor the unitarian view and the descriptions that follow will be based upon it, principally according to the specific interpretations of Maximow[5, 7] and Bloom.[8] Nevertheless, it should be recognized at the outset that hemopoiesis is a difficult and baffling study on which other opinions, divergent in certain respects from those set forth here, are held.[9]

The generalized mother cell from which the various blood elements are thought to differentiate may be called the *hemoblast* (Fig. 280). It has the typical appearance of a large lymphocyte, and accordingly is an ameboid cell with a large, open-structured nucleus and a relatively small amount of finely granular, basophilic cytoplasm. From such parent cells, according to the unitarian view, all blood elements arise. Specialization proceeds in divergent directions; one line leads to the red corpuscles, the other to the white series. The determining factor behind such diverse differentiation appears to be in part environmental and chemical. For example, in adult birds,[6] and possibly also in mammals,[9] red blood cells develop within blood channels and white cells outside them; there is reason to suspect that the

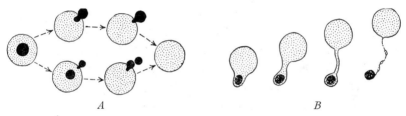

A   *B*

Fig. 279.—Methods by which the nucleus may be lost from mammalian normoblasts. *A*, Loss by extrusion, either as a whole (above) or in fragments (below). *B*, Loss by cytoplasmic constriction, as followed in blood cultures during a thirty-minute period (after Emmel).

real explanation for these differences lies in such factors as the degree of oxygen tension.[9]

Differentiation of Red Cells.—A generic name for the differentiating red cell is *erythroblast*. Springing from the totipotent hemoblasts of the blood islands, body mesenchyme, liver, lymphoid tissue and bone marrow, it undergoes in each location an identical transformation whereby the cytoplasm gains hemoglobin and the nucleus condenses and is lost. In this metamorphosis there are recognized three principal stages (Fig. 280):

1. *Megaloblasts* (once termed ichthyoid blood cells because of their resemblance to the typical red blood cell of fishes). They are characterized by checkered nuclei and the presence of some hemoglobin in the cytoplasm. For the first six weeks of development the megaloblast is the only red blood cell found; it multiplies within the blood vessels but after the third month practically disappears from the blood stream.

2. *Normoblasts* (once termed sauroid blood cells because they resemble the red blood cells of adult reptiles and birds). This stage first transforms

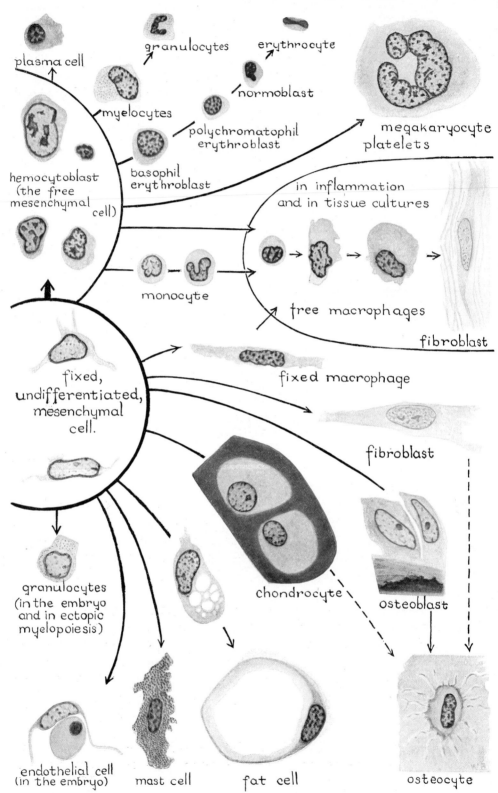

FIG. 280.—Derivatives of the primitive mesenchymal cells of mammals (Bloom). × 720. Human cells are shown; lymphocytes are included with the hemocytoblasts.

from megaloblasts in the liver, and is predominant in embryos of two months. Normoblasts are distinguished by their small, dense nuclei and richer hemoglobin, but in spite of this specialization they still undergo mitosis and so continue to aggregate in clusters. In the early months many normoblasts are present in the circulating blood.

3. *Erythroplastids* (red blood corpuscles). These elements, characteristic of mammals, originate from normoblasts through the loss of their nuclei. The way in which the nucleus disappears is disputed. It is usually said to be extruded as a whole or in fragments (Fig. 279 *A*),[7] but some claim that it is absorbed and others state that the cytoplasm buds away from the nucleated remnant (*B*).[10] The earliest red blood corpuscles are spherical elements; they are first formed during the second month, chiefly in the liver. During the third month the enucleated corpuscles first predominate.

Differentiation of Granulocytes.—In the locations already enumerated, the hemoblasts also serve as mother cells for differentiating granular leucocytes (Fig. 280). The young granulocytes, thus produced, elaborate within

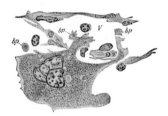

FIG. 281.—Origin of blood platelets (Wright). × 1000. A megakaryocyte extends processes into a blood vessel (*V*) and detaches platelets (*bp*).

their cytoplasm specific kinds of granules. While still immature, these cells continue to proliferate, yet they cannot transform into any other cell type beyond the one already begun. Ultimately the ability to divide is lost and differentiation into mature granulocytes proceeds to an end. In the marrow such developmental stages are designated *myelocytes*. Three types may be recognized:

1. *Neutrophils* have a finely granular and neutrally staining cytoplasm. The nucleus changes through crescentic to complex, lobate shapes.

2. *Eosinophils* develop coarse granulations and a bilobed nucleus. The granules stain intensely with acid dyes.

3. *Basophils* acquire an irregularly shaped nucleus and differentiate coarse cytoplasmic granules that stain heavily with basic dyes. These blood elements are a type entirely distinct from the tissue basophils, or mast cells.

Differentiation of Non-granular Leucocytes.—There is no essential difference between the hemoblast and the definitive large lymphocyte (Fig.

280). In fact, the latter must be considered as retaining its original toti-potent potentialities which may be exercised when needed. The large *lymphocytes* regularly give rise to the small type, and the latter in turn grow into large ones. From the primitive embryonic mesenchyme are differentiated the fixed tissue cells (*reticulo-endothelium*) of lymphoid, hepatic and marrow sinuses, as well as the freely wandering, highly phagocytic elements (*macrophages*) of close affinity. Both the macrophages and the hemoblastic lymphocytes, in turn, give rise to *monocytes* (large mononuclear leucocytes) with a characteristic, kidney-shaped nucleus, and to connective-tissue *mast cells* with basophilic cytoplasmic granules. Finally, some hemo-blastic lymphocytes specialize into *megakaryocytes*, which are the giant cells found typically in bone marrow.[11] From them *blood platelets* are commonly held to arise; some think they originate as detached cytoplasmic processes (Fig. 281).

THE PRIMITIVE VASCULAR SYSTEM

An earlier paragraph (p. 310) has described the formation of local mesenchymal clefts whose boundary cells flatten into endothelium. The linkage and subsequent growth of such vascular spaces into networks of vessels have also been mentioned. In accordance with this method the vascular system develops in all vertebrates. Its precocious differentiation in very young embryos of higher mammals is correlated with the absence of nutritive yolk and the consequent need of vessels that will extract nour-ishment and oxygen from the maternal circulation and distribute them to the tissues of the embryo. For a while the arteries and veins are not distinguishable structurally, yet even in young embryos they are named in anticipation of the vessels that are destined to arise from them. Around the endothelium, which is the primary tissue of the vascular system, the neighboring mesenchyme later adds accessory coats. These are: (1) the *tunica intima* (endothelial and fibrous); (2) the *tunica media* (muscular); and (3) the *tunica externa*, or adventitia (fibrous). Through folding, the tunica intima of veins gives rise to pocket-like valves.[12]

Delicate injections show that diffuse, capillary plexuses precede the formation of definite arterial and venous trunks in any region (Fig. 282). It is only through the selection, enlargement and differentiation of appro-priate paths in such networks that the definitive vessels arise;[13] those capil-laries from which the flow has been diverted, atrophy. The selection of appropriate channels from the diffuse capillary bed results both from the action of inherited patterns and from the hydrodynamic factors incident to the blood flow. What determines the differentiation of some channels into arteries and others into veins is unknown; presumably the mechanical conditions of the blood flow (speed, pressure and pulse) play a rôle.

The first paired vessels are represented in human embryos that stand at the beginning of somite formation (Fig. 283). There are two unfused heart tubes and paired *ventral* and *dorsal aortæ*. The latter connect on each side through a first *aortic arch*. The aortæ give off several *vitelline arteries* to the yolk sac and a pair of *umbilical arteries* which pass into the body stalk and branch in the wall of the chorion. A pair of *vitelline* and of *umbilical veins* provide for the venous return to the heart. Neither the vitelline nor umbilical vessels make a complete functional circuit at this time.

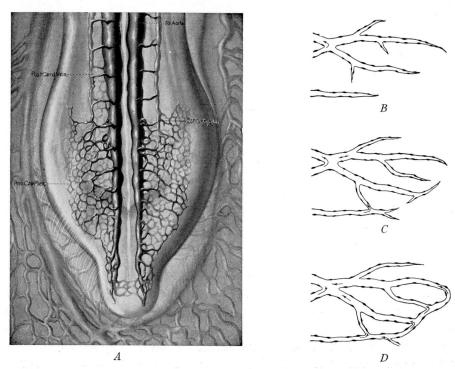

FIG. 282.—Growth of blood vessels. *A*, Primitive vascular plexus in the caudal end of a sixty-hour chick embryo (Evans; × 35). The sciatic artery will differentiate from the primary capillary plexus of each limb bud; aortæ have already formed from the mesial margins. *B–D*, Development of a capillary network, observed in the living rabbit (Clark; × 110).

Embryos with about 12 somites are characterized by a single *heart*, through the union of its component halves, and the establishment of vitelline and umbilical circulations (Fig. 284). Because of the early decline of the yolk sac, an actual vitelline circulation lasts but a short time. By contrast, the placental circuit remains functional until birth.

The next important advances are found in embryos about 3 mm. long that possess some 20 somites (Fig. 285). Two aortic arches are present and the dorsal aortæ begin to fuse into a single *descending aorta*. An out-

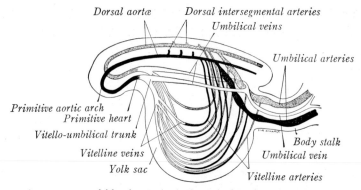

FIG. 283.—Arrangement of blood vessels, in lateral view, in a human embryo at the beginning of somite-formation (Prentiss, after Felix).

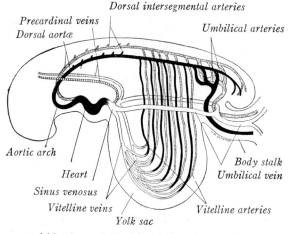

FIG. 284.—Arrangement of blood vessels, in lateral view, in a human embryo of twelve somites (Prentiss, after Felix).

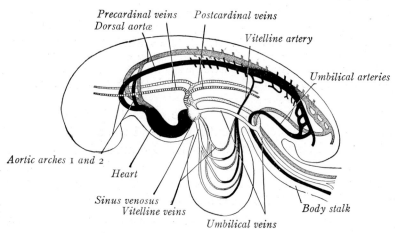

FIG. 285.—Arrangement of blood vessels, in lateral view, in a human embryo of twenty somites (Prentiss, after Felix).

standing feature is the appearance of paired veins to care for the drainage of blood from the embryo proper back to the heart. These vessels are the *precardinal veins* (already developing in the previous stage), which drain

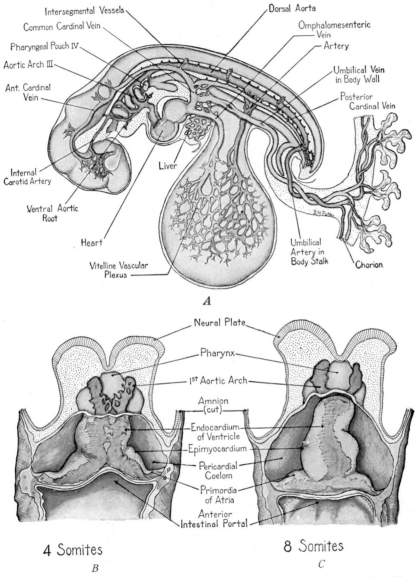

FIG. 286.—Heart and blood vessels of early human embryos (Patten and Davis). *A*, At four weeks, viewed from the left side (× 20). *B*, *C*, At four and eight somites, respectively, showing the exposed heart in ventral view (× 65).

blood from the head region, and *postcardinal veins*, which serve the lower levels of the body in a similar way. Before entering the heart the two sets of vessels on each side unite in a *common cardinal vein*.

In embryos about 5 mm. long (with the full number of 40 somites) five pairs of aortic arches (and a suggestion of another, rudimentary pair) have developed (Fig. 286 *A*). The single aorta bears numerous dorsal (intersegmental) and lateral branches; of the ventral, vitelline series, three are now prominent (Fig. 311): (1) the *cœliac artery* in the stomach-pancreas region; (2) the *superior mesenteric* in the small-intestine region; and (3) the *inferior mesenteric* in the large-intestine region.

The embryonic plan at the stage of paired symmetrical vessels is indicated in Fig. 286 *A*. Fusions, atrophy and rerouting lead to profound alterations and asymmetry in later stages. The descriptions that follow will treat these changes in their essential details.

DEVELOPMENT OF THE HEART

The heart is a blood vessel with a large lumen and especially thick muscular walls. In lower fishes and amphibians it seemingly develops in a simple, direct manner. A tubular cavity appears within the ventral mesentery of the fore-gut; about this cavity the mesenchymal cells straightway differentiate into endo-, myo- and epicardium. Nevertheless, the heart material is originally furnished by the merger of paired folds of the lateral mesoderm, each of which can, if kept separate, differentiate a separate heart.[54]

In bony fishes, reptiles and birds the early stages of cardiac development are more complicated. This is the result of a flattened blastoderm, due to excessive yolk, and the consequent necessity for the heart to develop as two lateral halves. At first well separated, the halves secondarily swing together and fuse in the midplane (Figs. 502 to 504).

The heart of mammals does not arise by pure fusion, like that of the bird.[14, 15] A cardiogenic plate is located in front of the head—in the splanchnic mesoderm and beneath the pericardial cœlom located there (Fig. 287 *A*). With the forward growth of the head (chiefly neural plate) there is a reversal of this portion of the blastoderm, as also described on p. 100 and illustrated in Fig. 70. The region thus turned under becomes the floor of the fore-gut (Fig. 287 *B*). In this process the heart primordium is necessarily reversed end-for-end with respect to its original orientation. It then lies above, instead of below, the pericardial cœlom, and in the splanchnic mesoderm that is situated beneath the fore-gut. The caudal end of the heart is continuous with the mass of mesoderm, just cephalad of the anterior intestinal portal, that forms the septum transversum. Here it receives the several veins that enter the septum to drain blood into the heart.

The earliest identifiable cardiac primordia are aggregates of splanchnic mesodermal cells that appear on the surface of the cardiogenic plate next the entoderm. They arrange themselves side-by-side as two longitudinal strands, each of which gains a cavity. These thin-walled, endothelial tubes lie within corresponding longitudinal folds of the splanchnic mesoderm. At the cranial end of the future heart the two tubes soon fuse into a single tube, whereupon their mesodermal folds become a single fold enclosing them ventrally and laterally (Figs. 286 *B* and 287 *C*). Traced caudad from the short, common pericardial cavity, where these events have occurred, separate tubes and folds are still seen. This is because they necessarily follow the course of the two lateral cœlomic canals which continue the mesial portion of the pericardial cavity caudad (Figs. 219 *A* and 287 *D*). As the anterior intestinal portal retreats in a caudal direction to elongate the fore-

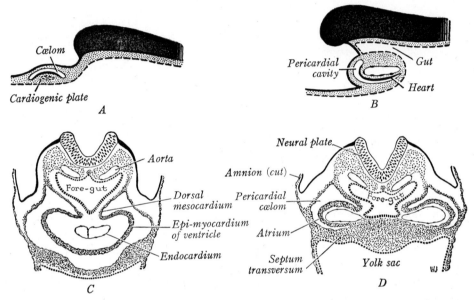

Fig. 287.—Development of the human heart. *A, B,* Diagrammatic sagittal sections, at a presomite stage and at seven somites, respectively, showing the reversal of the heart and pericardial cœlom. *C, D,* Transverse sections through the ventricle and paired atria, at seven somites (× 55).

gut, opportunity is offered for these paired cardiac primordia to unite with the median, unpaired portion, already formed. This they do, but not through side-by-side fusion with the subsequent absorption of their common mesial partition. Rather, the unpaired, mesial heart expands caudad in pace with the enlarging pericardial cavity which progressively incorporates the lateral cœlomic canals (Fig. 219). The paired cardiac primordia are likewise absorbed during this advance until the entire heart is a single organ (Fig. 286 *B, C*).

The internal, endothelial tube will become the essential component of the *endocardium;* the external, mesodermal layer gives rise to the *myocardium* and *epicardium* (Fig. 287 *C*). At this stage the unpaired heart is a double-walled tube, suspended by a mesenterial attachment where the lateral margins of the mesodermal folds are reflected upon the ventrolateral sides of the fore-gut. This mesentery, named the *dorsal mesocardium*, is only temporary; it is lost before the heart has advanced greatly (Fig. 288 *B* and 289 *B*). A peculiarity of the mammalian heart, in contrast to other vertebrates, is that there is no definite ventral mesocardium (Fig. 288 *B*).[14,15]

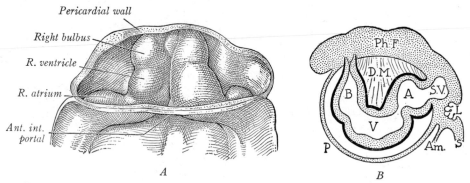

A   *B*

FIG. 288.—Human hearts in the simple tubular stage. *A*, Paired cardiac tubes, at six somites, within the ventrally opened pericardial cavity (after Davis; × 60). *B*, Sagittal section to show schematically the heart and its relations (after Frazer).

A. Atrium; *Am.*, amnion; *B.*, bulbus; *D.M.*, dorsal mesocardium; *L.*, liver; *P.*, pericardium; *Ph.F.*, pharyngeal floor; *S.*, septum transversum; *S.V.*, sinus venosus; *V.*, ventricle.

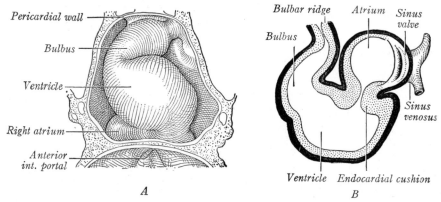

A   *B*

FIG. 289.—Human hearts in early flexion. *A*, Ventral view, at eleven somites, *in situ* (after Davis; × 50). *B*, Diagrammatic sagittal section of the heart (after Frazer).

This is because the cœlom arises very early from the coalescence of separate spaces and forms a complete cavity in the region of the heart before the head fold and heart, as such, begin to differentiate (Fig. 287 *A*, *B*).

Even before the bilateral cardiac halves merge, they each bear two constrictions which indicate the future regions marking off atrium, ventricle and bulbus (Fig. 288 *A*). The union of the bulbar and ventricular halves is complete in embryos with some nine somites, but the atria are still paired sacs. Such a heart shows at first three divisions (Fig. 289 A): (1) the *atrium*, which receives blood from the primitive veins; (2) the *ventricle*, or chief pumping region; and (3) the *bulbus*, continuous into short ventral aortæ. By the end of this period a fourth division, the *sinus venosus*, arises by constriction from the hind end of the atrium (Figs. 288 B and 290). It lies within the septum transversum and is a center of confluence for all the veins. Internally, a pair of sinus valves (right and left) guards the entrance into the atrium; swollen endocardial cushions (dorsal and ventral) narrow the heart locally into an atrio-ventricular canal, while elongate ridges (dorsal and ventral) course in the bulbus (Fig. 289 B).

EXTERNAL CHANGES IN THE HEART

Between the stages of 7 and 16 somites the dorsal mesocardium has arisen and disappeared, thereby leaving the heart unattached except at

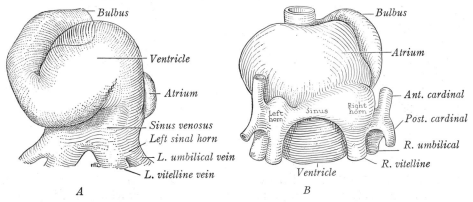

FIG. 290.—Human hearts in advanced flexion. *A*, Ventral view, at sixteen somites (× 60).
B, Dorsal view, at twenty-two somites (× 45).

its two ends (Fig. 289). Extending through and beyond this same period the cardiac tube grows faster than the pericardial cavity in which it lies, and as a result the heart is compelled to bend. The method of asymmetrical growth is such that the entire tube is thrown into a simple, spiralled S; the chief primary flexure is to the right, and by means of it the bulbus and ventricle become a U-shaped loop (Fig. 289). A continuation of this growth process drops the bulbo-ventricular loop still farther caudad and ventrad (Fig. 290). At the same time the sinus venosus is drawn out of the septum transversum, whence it follows the atrium until they both lie dorsal and cranial to the rest of the heart (Fig. 291). This shift is due to a more oblique position taken by the septum transversum.

These changes thus result in an essential reversal of the original cephalo-caudal relations of the primitive parts of the heart; in addition, the venous and arterial ends are brought close together as in the adult. The growing atrium is now constricted dorsally by the gut and ventrally by the bulbus. For this reason it can enlarge rapidly only in a lateral direction, and in so doing forms a sacculation on each side which becomes the future right or left atrium, respectively (Fig. 291); the location of the internal partition separating the two is marked superficially by the *interatrial sulcus*.   Meanwhile the right horn of the sinus venosus enlarges more rapidly than the left (Figs. 290 *B* and 296 *A*), due to an important shift in the blood flow from the left side of the body across the liver (Fig. 316).

As the bulbo-ventricular loop increases in size, the duplication of the wall between its two limbs lags in development (perhaps hastened by actual atrophy)[16] and disappears during the sixth week (Fig. 291).   The result is the merging of the two into a single chamber, the primitive ventricle

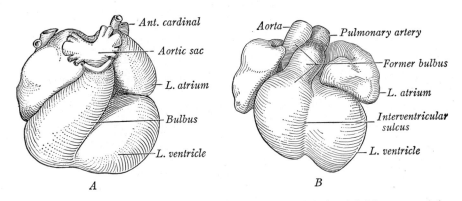

FIG. 291.—Human hearts, in ventral view, progressing toward the definitive external form. *A*, At 5 mm. (partly after Ingalls; × 33); *B*, at 12 mm. (after Wirtinger; × 15).

(Fig. 298), which is separated from the atria by a deep *coronary sulcus*. Soon the ventricle shows a median longitudinal groove that indicates the position of an internal septum already partitioning the unpaired chamber into two (Fig. 291 *B*); this external groove is the *interventricular sulcus*.

Thus in an embryo of six weeks (about 12 mm. long), the heart exhibits the general external shape and markings that characterize it permanently (Fig. 291 *B*).   At this period its relative size is about nine times that in the adult.   At first the heart lies high in the cervical region, but lengthening of the pharynx and the structures dorsal to it causes a relative recession toward the definitive position in the thorax.   This caudal 'migration' is attested permanently by the downwardly displaced courses of the recurrent and cardiac nerves.   After the diaphragm reaches its final location, the heart rotates so that the ventricles, which previously were ventral to the atria, henceforth become more caudal.

Experiments on amphibia show that a young heart, removed and grown in culture medium, develops normally. It is, therefore, self-differentiating. Moreover, isolated pieces of the young heart are totipotent and can develop into whole organs. Nevertheless, that the heart is also subject to environmental influences is proved by the abnormal development which follows its transplantation to a strange region of the body, and by the normal development of a heart removed and replaced after being turned end-for-end. This latter dependence is, however, not due to the flow of the blood stream; a normally located heart differentiates and beats normally even when the flow is lacking.

INTERNAL CHANGES IN THE HEART

In an embryo of 5 mm., the heart contains three as yet undivided chambers: (1) the *sinus venosus*, opening dorsally into the right dilatation of the atrium; (2) the bilaterally dilated *atrium*, communicating, in turn, by a common canal with (3) the primitive *ventricle*, which is already incorporating the bulbus into itself. This is the type of heart found in adult

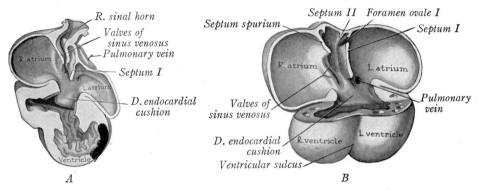

FIG. 292.—Human hearts, hemisected to show the internal structure and dorsal wall (after Tandler). × 40. *A*, At 6.5 mm.; *B*, at 9 mm.

fishes, where it pumps venous blood to the gills for oxygenation. But the replacement of gills by lungs in higher vertebrates has been accompanied by a partitioning of the heart into a venous and an arterial half, each with its own entrance and exit. Thus birds and mammals have a four-chambered heart, as the result of septa which arise independently in the atrium, ventricle and bulbus; in it venous blood circulates on the right side and arterial blood on the left. Amphibians and reptiles have intermediate types, with partially separated atria and ventricles.

Important changes, chiefly concerned with the elaboration of septa and valves, next follow; they lead to the formation of the four-chambered, human heart. These developments include: (1) the partitioning of the common atrium into separate right and left chambers; (2) the absorption of the sinus venosus into the wall of the right atrium and of the pulmonary veins into the left atrium; (3) the division of the atrio-ventricular canal

into two canals; (4) the merging of the bulbus into the prospective right
ventricle; (5) the partitioning of the single ventricle into right and left
chambers; (6) the longitudinal division of the bulbus into the aorta and
pulmonary artery; and (7) the histogenetic differentiation of the cardiac
wall, including the development of valves. Although most of these processes go on simultaneously it is more convenient to describe them separately; this will be done in the topics that follow. When practically
completed, as happens in an embryo of two months, the fetal heart has
attained the general structural features that will characterize it permanently.

Development of the Atria.—In human embryos of 6 mm. a thin, sickle-
shaped membrane grows down from the mid-dorsal wall of the atrium
(Fig. 292 *A*). This is called the *septum primum*, for it grows toward the

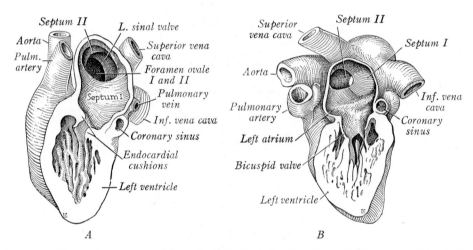

FIG. 293.—Human hearts, opened from the left side (after Prentiss). *A*, At 12 mm. (× 40); *B*,
at three months (× 4.5).

ventricle as a partition whose free edge soon fuses with the so-called *endocardial cushions*, thereby obliterating the previous interatrial communication. The two cushions are endocardial thickenings; one bulges from the
dorsal, the other from the ventral wall of the common canal which originally
connected atrium with ventricle (*B*). By the time the septum primum
arrives, these thickenings have already fused midway, figure-of-eight fashion, and so divide the single canal into a right and a left *atrio-ventricular
canal* (Fig. 297). It is on the merged tissue between these canals that the
septum primum attaches (Fig. 293 *A*). Meanwhile the septum primum
has thinned and become perforate in a previously intact region, thereby
forming secondarily the *foramen ovale I* (Fig. 292 *B*). So it is, that (except
for this foramen) there is already at the end of the sixth week (12 mm.) a
separate right and left atrial chamber; each connects through its respective

atrio-ventricular canal with the right or left ventricle, also incompletely partitioned at this time.

In the seventh week the *septum secundum* makes an appearance just at the right of the septum primum (Fig. 292 *B*). Its origin is somewhat obscure but seems to be related to the left sinus valve and the fused region of the two endocardial cushions.[17] The septum secundum is incomplete, its prominent foramen being known as the *foramen ovale II* (Fig. 293). The growth of these two partial atrial septa proceeds in such a manner that the main expanse of the septum primum overlaps the foramen ovale II; it serves as a flap-like valve which permits blood to pass from the right

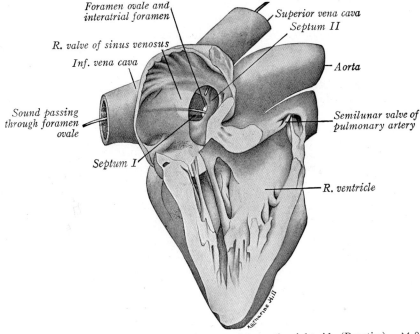

FIG. 294.—Human heart, at three months, opened from the right side (Prentiss).   × 8.

to the left atrium, but not in the reverse direction (Figs. 294 and 295); this condition maintains until after birth when the two combine as the permanent *atrial septum*, as will be described on p. 329.

Fate of the Sinus Venosus.—In embryos of about seven weeks the superior vena cava has been formed to return blood from the head end of the embryo, and the inferior vena cava to serve similarly for lower levels of the body. Both vessels drain into the right horn of the sinus venosus (Fig. 296 *A*). In embryos of six to eight weeks the atria increase rapidly in size and the right horn of the sinus venosus, relatively laggard in growth, is taken up into the wall of the right atrium. By this absorption the superior vena cava of necessity drains directly into the cephalic wall of the atrium, the inferior vena cava into its caudal wall (*B*). The main cavity of the right atrium, between these vessels, is bounded by the absorbed sinal wall (Fig. 295). It is distinguished permanently by a smooth, internal surface. The primitive atrium, with a thick and uneven muscular wall, becomes merely the *right auricle*. The transverse portion of the sinus venosus likewise opens into the dorsal wall of the right atrium (Fig. 296 *A*); it is destined to receive the veins of the heart itself, and in this capacity persists as the *coronary sinus*. The left sinal horn dwindles and disappears except for its tip which becomes the stem of the *oblique vein of the left atrium* (*B*).

The opening of the sinus venosus into the dorsal wall of the right atrium is guarded on each side (right and left) by a valvular fold (Fig. 292 *A*). Along the dorsal and cephalic wall of the atrium these two folds unite into the so-called *septum spurium*, which has no significance beyond that of

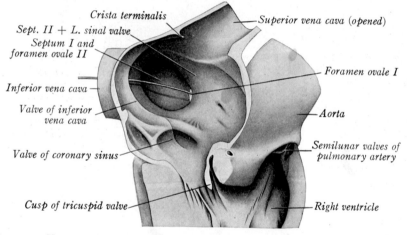

FIG. 295.—Human heart, at four months, opened from the right side (Prentiss). × 5.5.

keeping the two valves tense (*B*). Caudally the valves flatten out on the floor of the atrium. Through the slower growth of the intervening space, the *left valve* of the sinus venosus approaches and fuses with portions of both the septum primum and secundum. The *right valve* of the sinus venosus is broad until the end of the third month and nearly divides the atrium into two chambers (Fig. 294), but later it diminishes greatly in relative size. Its cephalic portion becomes a rudimentary crest on the wall of the right atrium; it is known as the *crista terminalis* (Fig. 295). The remainder of the valve is subdivided by a ridge into two parts; of these, the larger, cephalic division persists as the *valve of the inferior vena cava* (Eustachian valve), located at the right of the opening of that vein, while the smaller, caudal portion becomes the *valve of the coronary sinus* (Thebesian valve).

The Pulmonary Veins.—The final relation of the pulmonary veins to the heart is the result of an absorptive process which may be appropriately introduced at this time since the left atrium is thereby enlarged; the process and its general result are roughly comparable to the absorption of the sinus by the right atrium, already described. In embryos of about 6 mm., a single pulmonary vein drains into the caudal wall of the left atrium at the left of the septum primum (Fig. 296 *A*). This vessel bifurcates into right and left veins which in turn divide again, so that two branches extend to each lung. As the atrium grows, these pulmonary vessels are progressively drawn into the atrial wall. As a result, at first one, then two, and finally four pulmonary veins open into the left atrium (*B*). The absorbed stems of the veins are permanently recognizable as the smooth portion of the

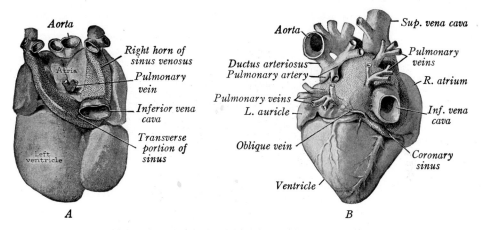

FIG. 296.—Human hearts, in dorsal view, showing the absorption of the sinus venosus (dark stippling) and pulmonary veins (pale stippling). *A*, At 7 mm. (after Braus; × 28); *B*, in newborn (× ⅔).

atrial wall. The primitive atrium thereby becomes restricted to the definitive *left auricle*.

Closure of the Foramen Ovale.—During fetal life the two atrial septa remain separate and serve as hemipartitions. Each is incomplete, but each is so shaped as to cover the defect in the other (Figs. 293 *B* and 295). A large volume of blood, both from the superior and the inferior vena cava, enters the right atrium of the fetus. Consequently, when the atria are filling, blood passes across, by way of the foramen ovale, into the left atrium. It is not necessary to assume, as usually is done, that when the atria contract to force blood into the ventricles, the two septa are pressed together to prevent backflow. After birth the pressure declines in the right atrium.[18] This permits the two septa to lie in constant apposition and to unite slowly into a joint *atrial septum* (p. 357). The depression where the single layer of septum primum covers the defect in the septum secundum is the *fossa ovalis;* the rim of septum-secundum tissue bounding the fossa is the *limbus ovalis.*

Development of the Ventricles.—At the end of the fourth week (5 mm.) a median partition projects inward from the base of the common ventricle to the ventral endocardial cushion (Fig. 297 *A*).   This *ventricular septum* is brought into existence by the enlargement of the future halves of the ventricle on each side of it, and increases in height proportionately as the ventricular sacs grow deeper.   For a short time the septum makes an incomplete partition which partially divides the ventricle into right and left chambers; throughout this stage the communication between the two ventricles is known as the *interventricular foramen (B).*   This foramen in embryos of nearly seven weeks is bounded by: (1) the ventricular septum; (2) the proximal bulbar septum, continued downward from the longitudi-

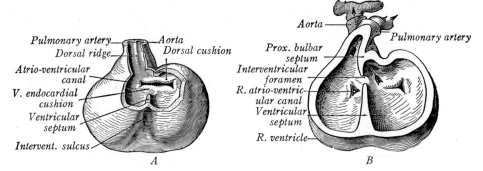

Fig. 297.—Subdivision of the bulbus, atrio-ventricular canal and common ventricle, shown in schematic ventral views (after Kollmann).   *A*, At 5 mm.; *B*, at 8 mm.

nally dividing bulbus; and (3) the fused portion of the endocardial cushions. A day or two later the foramen is being closed by tissue proliferated from the endocardial cushions.[19]   The resulting, thin membrane, which completes the partition, is the *septum membranaceum.*[56]

In the description of the external development of the heart, mention was made of the incorporation of the proximal part of the bulbus into the ventricle.   This absorption occurs through the laggard growth (and, perhaps, atrophy)[16] of the bulbo-ventricular fold (Fig. 298).   As a result, the bulbus loses its separate identity and the cavities of the bulbar and adjoining ventricular segments are merged into what is thereafter known as the right ventricle.

Origin of the Aorta and Pulmonary Artery.—Also in embryos of 5 mm. there arise in the aortic bulb two prominent longitudinal thickenings of the endocardial lining (Fig. 297 *A*).[56]   These ridges meet and fuse, thereby creating a septum which divides the unabsorbed portion of the bulbus into an aortic and a pulmonary trunk (Fig. 299 *A–C*). Proximally the two thickenings so pursue spiral courses that the *ascending aorta* and *pulmonary artery* slightly intertwine, the latter crossing ventral to the aorta (Fig. 297 *B*). Still more proximally the spiral division of the bulbus is continued toward the ventricular septum in such a way that the base of the pulmonary trunk (now to the right and somewhat ventral) opens into the right ventricle, while the base of the aorta (now lying on the left and somewhat dorsal) opens into the left ventricle.

In addition to the longitudinal thickenings of the endocardium that split the bulbus lengthwise, there are two narrower thickenings (Fig. 299 *A*). After the division of the bulbus occurs, both the aorta and the pulmonary artery contain one of the smaller ridges and a half of each of the larger ridges (*B, C*). Distally, the three plump thickenings, then present in each

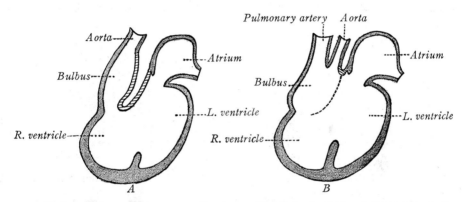

FIG. 298.—Diagrams of the mammalian heart to explain the incorporation of the bulbus into the right ventricle through the slower growth and atrophy of the bulbo-ventricular fold (hatched). Stage *B* is older and should be drawn much larger than *A*; the broken line marks the former extent of the fold (modified after Keith).

vessel, disappear. Proximally, at the level of the aortic and pulmonary roots, they enlarge and hollow out on their distal surfaces (*D*). Each set of three thin-walled pockets, formed in this manner, henceforth serves as *semilunar valves* (Fig. 294).

Differentiation of the Heart Wall.—An identical type of tissue differentiation and organization occurs throughout the whole heart, but it attains its highest expression in the ventricles which become thick and highly trabeculate. The internal endothelial tube of the primitive heart continues as the principal constituent of the *endocardium*. The investing folds of splanchnic mesoderm transform into both the massive *myocardium*, with its specialized type of muscle, and the serous coat known as the *epicardium*.

At first the endothelial cardiac tube is widely separated from the thick, outer coat, not yet differentiated beyond the stage of a common epi-myo-

16

cardium.   The intervening space is filled with a fluid jelly which later is
invaded by cells and comes to resemble mucous tissue (Fig. 300 A);[15] the
space is finally reduced as the jelly transforms into the connective tissue
of the endocardium (B).   The endocardial cushions and the bulbar thickenings are prominent because of a retention and exaggeration of this otherwise temporary condition.

The myocardial coat differentiates into a thin, cortical layer of dense
muscle and a thick, spongy layer whose loosely arranged trabeculæ project
into the heart cavity (Fig. 300 B, C).   As the muscular trabeculæ increase,
the originally simple sac of endocardium dips into their interspaces and
wraps around them.   Before long there is a condensation of the spongy
myocardial tissue, and especially is this marked at the periphery.   As a
result, the superficial muscle becomes increasingly compact, whereas the
trabeculæ nearer the lumen retain an open arrangement for a longer period
(D).   Such a condition is permanent for lower vertebrates, but in mammals

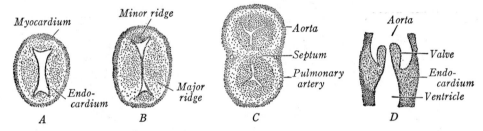

FIG. 299.—Subdivision of the human bulbus and the origin of the semilunar valves.   A–C,
Transverse sections, at five to seven weeks (× 27).   D, Longitudinal section, at seven weeks
(× 45).

the entire cardiac wall finally becomes compact.   The irregular muscle
bundles that persist next the ventricular cavities make up the *trabeculæ
carneæ*.   The musculature of the ventricles is far better developed than
that of the atria.   However, the thicker wall of the left ventricle is largely
acquired after birth as the result of harder work performed.

The myocardium, at first continuous throughout the whole heart, becomes divided by connective tissue at the atrio-ventricular canal and leaves
only a small bridge there.   This connecting strand of modified muscle
(continued from the sino-atrial node in the sinus venosus) is located behind
the dorsal endocardial cushion.   It is called the *atrio-ventricular bundle* (of
His).   The first heart beats are spasmodic twitchings that soon gain in force
and regularity.   By analogy with other vertebrates it is supposed that the
human heart begins to set the blood in motion during the fourth week when
the embryo has 7 to 17 somites.   At that time the rhythmic contractions
are purely muscular phenomena, since the nerves first invade the heart
several weeks later.   The rate of the heart beat is 65 pulsations a minute

in 15 mm. embryos, but this is increased to 130 to 145 in older fetuses. The pulse of the female is faster than that of the male.

The surface of the original epi-myocardial coat flattens into mesothelium; combined with a substratum of connective tissue it constitutes the *epicardium* (Fig. 300 *B*).

Cardiac Valves.—The blood is kept in its proper course through the heart by means of valves which prevent backflow. A previous paragraph (p. 328) has described how the right valve of the sinus venosus adapts itself as the *valve of the inferior vena cava* and of the *coronary sinus*.

An important valve occurs on each side between the respective atrial and ventricular chambers.[57] Their development is bound up with that of the endocardial cushions (p. 326) which by fusion, figure-of-eight fashion, convert the single atrio-ventricular canal into two canals (Fig. 297). Ele-

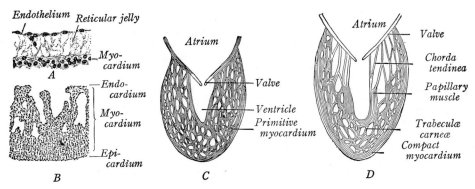

Fig. 300.—Differentiation of the human ventricular wall and the atrio-ventricular valves. *A*, *B*, Vertical sections, at 2 mm. (× 115) and 7 mm. (× 55), respectively. *C*, *D*, Diagrammatic longitudinal sections (after Gegenbauer).

vated folds of the endocardium appear at the margins of these canals, and each set of thickenings becomes both invaded by muscle and attached to the muscular trabeculæ of the ventricular wall. Three such flaps, or valvular cusps, are formed about the right atrio-ventricular canal, two around the left. The size of the primitive cusps is presently increased by an undermining process in which the attached muscular cords, beneath, become less numerous and more widely spaced (Fig. 300 *C*, *D*). Degeneration ensues both in the muscle tissue of the valves and in that of the subjacent muscular cords. As a result, the valvular cusps turn fibrous and connect with *chordæ tendineae* similarly transformed from the muscular cords; the latter, in turn, continue into unaffected *papillary muscles*. Thus there are developed the three cusps of the *tricuspid valve* between the right chambers of the heart, and the two flaps of the *bicuspid (mitral) valve* between the left chambers (Fig. 293 *B*).

The Pericardium.—The parietal layer of the pericardium (somatic mesoderm) and the visceral (or epicardial) layer (splanchnic mesoderm) are originally in broad continuity through the presence of a dorsal mesocardium (Figs. 287 *C* and 288 *B*). Since this mesentery disappears promptly and the ventral mesocardium is lacking from the first, it soon happens that the only region of continuity is then at the two ends where veins enter and arteries leave (Fig. 301 *A*). Flexion of the tubular heart brings these ends close together, so that the regions of continuity are separated from each other only by a space, the *transverse sinus* of the pericardium (*B*).

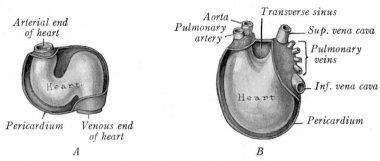

FIG. 301.—Diagrams of the changing relations of the heart and pericardium (after Braus). *A*, At period of early flexion; *B*, at definitive stage.

SUMMARY OF CERTAIN RELATIONS IN CARDIAC DEVELOPMENT

Primary Division	Permanent Representative	Primitive Septa	Fate of Primitive Septa	Primitive Valves	Fate of Primitive Valves
Right sinal horn Trans. portion Left sinal horn	Right atrium (except auricle) Coronary sinus Oblique vein (stem)			Right sinal Left sinal	Crista terminalis Valve of inf. v. cava Valve of cor. sinus Contributes to atrial septum
Atrium	Right auricle Left auricle	Septum I Septum II	Atrial septum	Endocardial cushions	Bicuspid valve Triscuspid valve Septum II Septum membranaceum
Ventricle	Right ventricle Left ventricle	Ventricular	Ventricular septum (larger part)		
Proximal bulbus	Absorbed into right ventricle	Prox. bulbar	Ventricular septum (in part)		
Distal bulbus	Aorta and pulmonary artery	Dist. bulbar	Splits bulbus (see column 2)	Bulbar ridges	Semilunar valves

Anomalies.—Among the rare anomalies of the heart is a tendency toward doubling due to incomplete fusion of the paired primordia. Also rare is *ectopia cordis* which is characterized by the heart protruding through a fissure in the ventral thoracic wall (Fig. 302 *A*); its mode of origin is obscure. *Dextrocardia* represents a condition of transposition by which the heart and its vessels are reversed in position (*B*); it is usually associated with general inversion of the viscera (p. 242; Fig. 206 *B*). The aorta and pulmonary artery may also be transposed in the absence of dextrocardia; in this instance they connect with the wrong ventricles and impure blood fails to be oxygenated.

An incomplete ventricular septum is a common anomaly which usually rests upon faulty development of the septum membranaceum (Fig. 302 *C*). Most common of all cardiac defects is a persistence of the foramen ovale, due to improper fusion of the septum primum and secundum (*D*). Incomplete closure occurs in nearly one out of four individuals; in spite of this high percentage, actual mingling of the blood or inconvenience to the individual is unusual because either the interatrial communication is small or the overlapping septal folds are pressed together during atrial contraction, thus serving as an effective valve. In a small number of cases the passage of impure blood into the left atrium is sufficient to produce a purplish hue in the child, which is known popularly as a '*blue baby.*' This condition may persist into adult life, but when very severe it sometimes leads to early death.

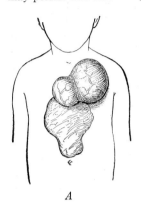

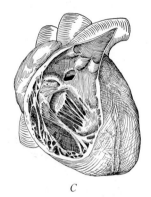

A   *B*   *C*

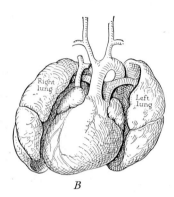

FIG. 302.—Anomalies of the human heart. *A*, Ectopia of a heart, which also shows a bifid ventricle; more caudad the thoraco-abdominal wall is poorly closed by a membranous layer. *B*, Dextrocardia, unaccompanied by transposition of either its great vessels or the lungs. *C*, Incomplete ventricular septum, the oval defect lying just below the three-cusped semilunar valve. *D*, Persistent foramen ovale combined with a multiply perforate valve.

D

Valvular anomalies occur in both atrio-ventricular and semilunar valves. Such variations may involve either the size or the number of cusps; the latter condition is caused by an atypical division of the bulbus or from irregularities in the arrangement, division and fusion of the pad-like primordia about the primitive atrio-ventricular canal.

DEVELOPMENT OF THE ARTERIES

Toward the end of the fourth week (5 mm.) the primitively paired set of arteries is giving way to the partly unpaired system that characterizes later stages. The dorsal aortæ combine into a common trunk, the *descending aorta*, which bears dorsal, lateral and ventral branches. It terminates in the so-called *middle sacral artery*, whose dorsal position as an apparent aortic branch is the result of secondary shifting through growth. Except at the earliest stage, when dorsal and ventral aortic vessels connect by a single arch, there is little in a human embryo that can definitely be called ventral aortæ; almost from the start the bulbus of the heart continues into

an enlargement which has received the name *aortic sac* (Fig. 303 *B*).[20]   From
this sac the several *aortic arches* radiate and curve upward around the
pharynx to reach the dorsal aortæ.

The chief changes leading toward the definitive arterial system include:
(1) the transformation of the aortic arches; (2) the specialization of certain
branches of the aorta; and (3) the development of arteries in the extremities.

Transformation of the Aortic Arches.[20]—The aortic arches of the human
embryo have great significance when viewed comparatively.   Five or more
pairs of arches are provided in connection with the functional gills of fishes,
and either three or four pairs serve the same purpose in tailed amphibia.
In higher vertebrates there is both a reduction in number and an extensive
transformation into vessels more appropriate to air-breathing animals.

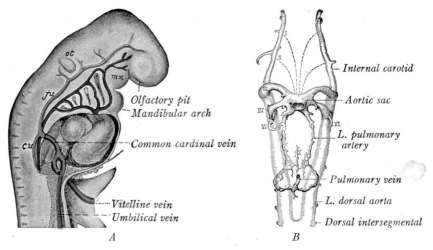

A   *B*

Fig. 303.—Aortic arches of human embryos.   *A*, At 4 mm., viewed from the right side (His;
× 20).   *B*, At 5 mm., in ventral view (after Congdon; × 25).

Some reptiles retain two pairs of arches while tailless amphibia have a complete, single arch on each side; of the remaining vertebrate groups, birds
use the right half of the fourth pair and mammals the left half as the sole
typical arch.

In the embryos of man and other mammals six pairs of aortic arches
develop, but all are not present at any one time.   Figures 303 *A* and 304 *A*
are inaccurate in this respect.   This total includes a rudimentary and
inconstant pair (number five of the series) whose status as true arches has
not escaped challenge (Fig. 304 *B*).[20, 21]   It is largely for this reason that
some prefer to call the arch which follows the suppositious fifth, not the
sixth arch but merely the pulmonary arch since its history is bound up with
the formation of arteries to the lungs.   The period of development of the
aortic arches extends throughout the fourth week, and their transformation

mainly occupies the fifth to seventh weeks. The characteristic changes of this region are brought about by the loss or interruption of some arches and portions of the aortæ, correlated with a reduction or stagnation of the blood flow, and by the enlargement of certain vessels and the new formation of others.

The first and second pairs of aortic arches drop out early (Fig. 303 *B*) and are replaced, respectively, by new mandibular and stapedial vessels which do not connect with the aortic sac. The dorsal aortæ at the level of these arches persist, but between the third and fourth arches both vessels atrophy (Fig. 305 *A*). The outcome on each side is a continuous vessel, beginning with the third arch and continued by way of the dorsal aorta to the head region. These vessels are the primitive *internal carotid* arteries, which not only branch in the head to supply the brain, eyes and ears but also connect with the basilar artery in a way to be described later

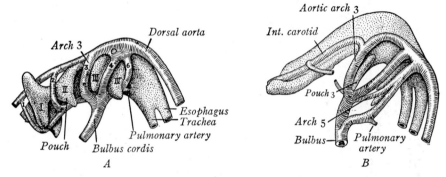

FIG. 304.—Reconstructions of the human aortic arches and pharyngeal pouches, viewed from the left side (after Tandler). × 38. *A*, At 3–5 mm. (composite); *B*, at 9 mm.

(p. 340). The *external carotid* arteries are new, direct outgrowths of the aortic sac which move their bases up onto the third arches and for a time supply merely the territory of the first and second branchial arches. Henceforth the common stem of the third aortic arch, proximal to the origin of the external carotid is known as the *common carotid*.

Both fourth arches persist, but their histories differ (Fig. 305 *A*). On the left side the arch is commonly said to represent the permanent *arch of the aorta*. This is in large measure true, but to the primitive arch is added proximally the left half of the aortic sac and distally that segment of the left dorsal aorta next caudad. On the right side the right half of the aortic sac elongates into the *innominate* artery, which then serves as the main stem for both the common carotid and subclavian vessels of that side. The right *subclavian* itself begins with the right fourth arch and then continues caudad to include practically all of the right dorsal aorta down to the level of union with its mate; the continuation of the right subclavian into the arm bud is a branch off the primitive aorta, and this part alone corresponds to the entire subclavian on the left.

The so-called fifth aortic arches have been mentioned. They are inconstant, incomplete and transitory. Shortly after the 7 mm. stage they disappear without trace.

The pulmonary (sixth) arches come into being when a sprout from each dorsal aorta bridges across to the primitive *pulmonary arteries* which are already growing caudad from the aortic sac to the lung buds (Fig. 305 *B*). The distal portion of each pulmonary vessel, so tapped, then appears as a mere offshoot set at right angles to the composite arch; the latter soon shows no sign of its double nature (*C*). On the right side the pulmonary

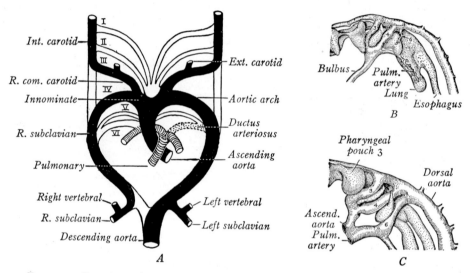

FIG. 305.—Transformation of the human aortic arches. *A*, Scheme, in ventral view, with all vessels spread to the same plane. *B*, *C*, Development of the pulmonary arch, at 5 mm. (✕ 20) and 11 mm. (✕ 17), respectively (adapted after Congdon).

arch loses connection with the right dorsal aorta, but on the left the corresponding distal segment remains as an important channel (the *ductus arteriosus* of Botallo) until birth (Figs 305 *A*, *C* and 306).

Meanwhile, when the arches are transforming, the aortic sac and the primitive bulbus have been splitting into aortic and pulmonary stems. This division proceeds in such a manner that the aortic trunk is continuous with the third and fourth arches, while the pulmonary trunk opens into the left sixth arch (Fig. 305 *C*). The final relations of the heart, aorta and aortic-arch derivatives result from so-called caudal displacements and readjustments. Nevertheless, any 'caudal migration' is relative rather than actual; it is due to a failure to keep pace with the growth cephalad of adjacent structures like the neural tube and pharynx. The innominate and common carotid arteries elongate in step with this upward growth (and the appearance of a neck), while the left subclavian shifts considerably higher on the permanent aortic arch (Fig. 306).

The different courses of the recurrent laryngeal nerves find an explanation in various facts already cited. The primitive vagus nerves give off branches which reach the larynx directly by passing caudal to the sixth aortic arches, but when the arches are left behind in the growth cephalad, both nerves become looped around them. As a result of the arch-transformations the left recurrent nerve remains hooked around the ligamentum arteriosum, while the right nerve, released by the degeneration of the fifth and sixth arches on that side, bears a similar looped relation to the right subclavian (*cf.* Figs. 306 and 444).

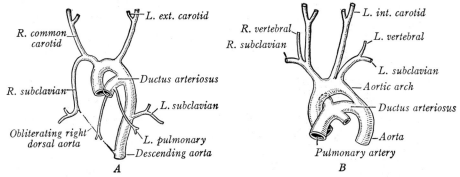

FIG. 306.—Changing relations in the human arteries near the heart, shown in ventral view. *A*, At 17 mm.; *B*, at birth.

Branches of the Dorsal Aorta.—Previous to the fusion of the dorsal aortæ during the fourth week, each vessel bears dorsal, lateral and ventral branches. These are repeated serially and each set is arranged in a longitudinal row (*cf.* Fig. 285). After aortic fusion has occurred, the relations are as shown in Fig. 307. It is with the transformation of these paired arteries into more specialized vessels that the following paragraphs deal; the period involved is mainly that of the fifth to seventh weeks of embryonic life.

1. The *dorsal branches* total some thirty pairs. Since they are regularly arranged between successive body segments, it is appropriate to designate them as intersegmental rather than segmental vessels. The dorsal branches supply primarily the spinal cord, but this is soon overshadowed by a later distribution to the body wall so that the original arteries appear as minor offshoots. In accomplishing this reversal of importance the primary vessel comes to look deceptively like a mere dorsal ramus, whereas it is in fact the larger, ventral ramus that is secondarily developed (Fig. 307).

From the *dorsal rami* of the dorsal intersegmentals are given off neural branches, which bifurcate into dorsal and ventral *spinal* arteries and supply the spinal cord.   An important secondary vessel on each side is the *vertebral* artery which arises by a longitudinal linkage of the first six dorsal rami, just dorsal to the ribs (Fig. 307; 'postcostal anastomosis').[22]   Their original stalks, one to five, then atrophy so that the permanent vertebral artery

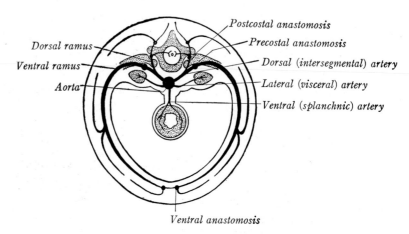

FIG. 307.—Arrangement of the primitive aortic branches, shown in a schematic transverse section of the trunk.   Longitudinal anastomoses are shown as bead-like enlargements.

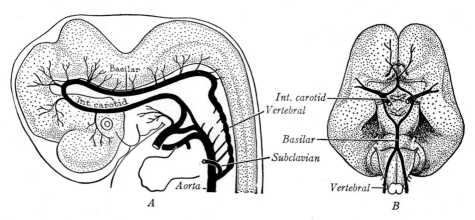

FIG. 308.—Human arteries of the head and neck regions.   *A*, At 12 mm., viewed from left side (× 6).   *B*, At fourteen weeks, showing the arteries of the brain in ventral view (× 1).

takes origin from number six (sixth cervical) in the series (Fig. 308 *A*). The vertebral arteries establish functional communications in the head with certain branches of the internal carotids.   The intermediary vessel, responsible for this linkage, is the *basilar* artery.   It arises quite independently of the others through the consolidation of two longitudinal channels beneath the brain.[20, 22]   Anastomotic unions on the part of the basilar and internal carotids at the base of the brain produce the *circulus arteriosus* of Willis (Fig. 308 *B*).

The *ventral rami* of the dorsal intersegmental arteries become especially prominent in the thoracic and lumbar body wall where they persist as the serially arranged *intercostal* and *lumbar* arteries (Fig. 309 *A, C*). Longitudinal ventral anastomoses between the tips of these rami (Fig. 307) com-

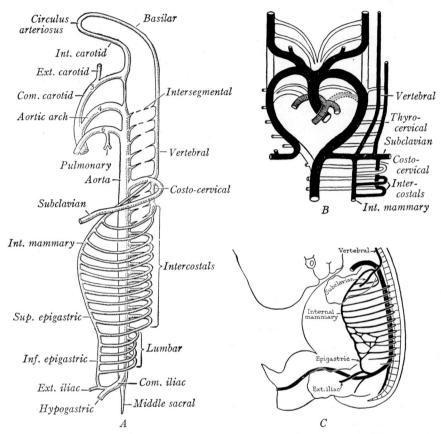

FIG. 309.—Derivatives of the human dorsal intersegmental arteries. *A*, Diagram, viewed from the left side. *B*, Scheme, in ventral view, explaining origins in the vicinity of the subclavian artery. *C*, Origin and relations of the internal mammary and epigastric arteries, at 16 mm., viewed from the left side (after Mall).

plete a vascular chain known as the *internal mammary* and the *superior* and *inferior epigastrics* (Fig. 309 *A, C*). The root of the internal mammary and the important *subclavian* (all of the left and the tip of the right) represent the enlarged main stem and ventral ramus of the sixth cervical in this dorsal series (Fig. 309).[22] Also connected with the subclavian are the *thyrocervical* and *costo-cervical* trunks. The former comes from longitudinal precostal anastomoses (*i.e.*, ventral to the ribs) of more cephalic ventral rami whose stems drop out (Fig. 307). The costo-cervical trunk arises in a similar fashion from the three ventral rami next caudal to the subclavian, but the distal segments of the second and third vessels survive as intercostal arteries (Fig. 309 *A*, *B*).

2. The *lateral branches* of the descending aorta are not arranged segmentally (Fig. 307). They supply structures arising from the nephrotome region (mesonephros, sex glands, metanephros and suprarenal glands). (Fig. 310). The original number is reduced, and from them emerge the *renal*,[23] *suprarenal*, *inferior phrenic*, and *internal spermatic* or *ovarian arteries*.

3. The *ventral branches* are imperfectly segmental. Primitively they constitute the paired vitelline arteries to the yolk sac (Fig. 284). As the dorsal aortæ combine, single ventral vessels appear—apparently by fusion (Fig. 307). The total number persisting is progressively reduced until, at 8 mm., they occur at three levels only. These three vessels, remaining,

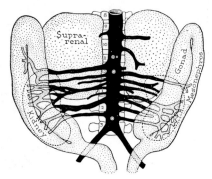

FIG. 310.—Lateral branches of the human aorta, at seven weeks, in ventral view (after Felix)˙
× 20.

pass by way of the mesentery to the gut; they are converted into the *cœliac* artery of the stomach-pancreas region, the *superior mesenteric* of the small-intestine region, and the *inferior mesenteric* of the large-intestine region, (Fig. 311 *A*, *C*).

Another set of ventral branches is established in very young embryos as the arteries that accompany the allantois and continue through the body stalk into the chorion. They are known as *umbilical* arteries (Fig. 283). By the end of the fourth week the umbilical arteries acquire secondary lateral connections with the aorta (Fig. 311 *A*), and the earlier ventral stem promptly disappears. The new replacing stem (from the aorta to the level of the *external iliac* which buds from this new trunk) becomes the *common iliac* (*B*). The remainder of the original umbilical trunk (located distad, but annexed by the replacing stem) makes up the *hypogastric* artery (*C*). When the placental circulation ceases at birth, the distal portions of both hypogastric arteries, from bladder to umbilicus, collapse; they revert to the solid cords which persist as the *lateral umbilical ligaments* of adult anatomy (Fig. 324).

All the ventral aortic vessels undergo caudal displacement from the levels where they first appear; in this descent the cœliac wanders 13 segments, the superior mesenteric 11 and the inferior mesenteric 3. To explain this migration two views have been advanced: one emphasizes the attachment to new, caudal roots and the simultaneous atrophy of old, higher roots;[24, 25] the other refers the cause to the unequal growth of the dorsal and ventral walls of the aorta.[25, 26]

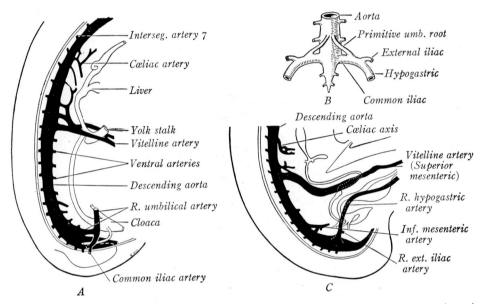

FIG. 311.—Derivatives of the ventral branches of the human aorta. *A, C,* At 5 mm. (× 23) and 9 mm. (× 12), respectively, viewed from the right side (after Tandler). *B,* Lower aorta at 5 mm., in ventral view, showing the replacement of the umbilical root by the common iliac.

The Glomus Coccygeum.—The *coccygeal body* is an arterio-venous anastomosis developed in connection with the midsacral artery. Appearing in the third month, it becomes a channelled mass whose polyhedral cells are interpreted as highly modified, smooth-muscle elements[27] or as postembryonal angioblasts.[28]

Arteries of the Extremities.—Several lateral aortic branches grow into the early limb bud. These unite there in a capillary plexus to constitute the earliest vessels of the limbs (Fig. 321).[29]

Arm.—In human embryos of 5 mm., only one arterial stem remains. This has joined the primitive subclavian artery and now appears as a direct extension from it (Fig. 321). The expansion into the future free arm is plexiform at first, but later a single axis is selected which differentiates successively into the *brachial* artery of the upper arm and the *interosseus* artery of the forearm and hand (Fig. 312 *A*). The *median* artery soon branches off the brachial and annexes the vessels of the hand (*A, B*). Following this, first the *ulnar* (*B*) and then the *radial* (*C*) arise as brachial branches. They become the most prominent vessels of the forearm and take over the vessels of the hand (*D*). Before the end of the second month these rearrangements are complete (*E*).

Leg.[30]—A branch known as the axial, or *sciatic* artery is given off from the umbilical (future hypogastric) artery, and in embryos of 9 mm. it is

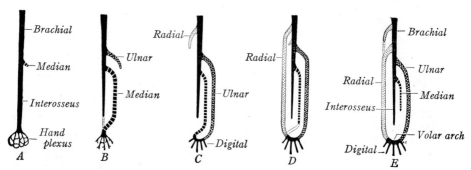

FIG. 312.—Development of the arteries of the human arm.

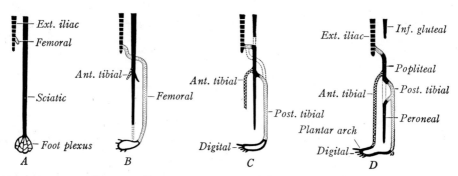

FIG. 313.—Development of the arteries of the human leg.

the chief arterial stem of the lower extremity (Fig. 313 *A*). A little later the sciatic is being superseded by the *femoral* which is a continuation of the *external iliac* (*A, B*); the latter vessel, as a secondary branch, buds off from a replacing stem of the umbilical, the latter thereafter to be called the *common iliac* (Fig. 311 *B*). The femoral artery annexes the sciatic and its branches distal to the middle of the thigh (Fig. 313 *C*). The sciatic then persists proximally only as the *inferior gluteal* artery; its original, distal course is marked by the *popliteal* and *peroneal* vessels (*D*). The *anterior tibial* artery is a branch from the popliteal (*C*). The *posterior tibial* arises by union of the lower femoral with the popliteal (*C*). These two tibial vessels take over the arteries of the foot (*D*). All these alterations are completed in the third month.

Anomalies.—Anomalous blood vessels are of common occurrence. They may be due: (1) to the choice of unusual paths in the primitive vascular plexuses; (2) to the persistence of vessels normally obliterated; (3) to the disappearance of vessels normally retained; (4) to incomplete development; and (5) to fusions and absorptions of parts usually distinct.

Outstanding anomalies specific to arteries include the following: The aorta and pulmonary artery are transposed in position when the spiral septum which divides the bulbus proceeds in the reverse direction from normal (*cf.* Fig. 297 *B*). The aortic arch may turn to the right (Fig. 206 *B*), as in birds, or be duplicated as is normal for reptiles (Fig. 314 *A*). Persistence of a patent ductus arteriosus may produce a 'blue baby.' Variations in the origins, positions and relations of the carotids, subclavians and vertebrals are common (*B, C*); some combinations atypical for man occur regularly in lower mammals; all result from the variable selection of definitive vessels from the primitive aortic-arch pattern. The originally paired dorsal aortæ may fuse imperfectly and so produce more or less of a double aorta. Variations in the number and relations of the renal arteries are frequent.

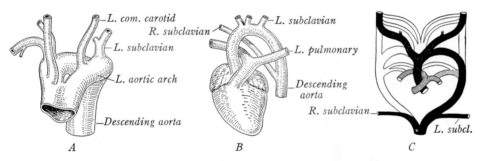

FIG. 314.—Anomalies of the human aortic arches, in ventral view. *A*, Double arch. *B*, Anomalous right subclavian. *C*, Diagram, at an earlier stage, explaining *B*.

DEVELOPMENT OF THE VEINS

Three systems of paired veins are present in embryos with 20 somites and about 3 mm. long (Fig. 286 *A*): (1) the *umbilical veins* from the chorion; (2) the *vitelline veins* from the yolk sac; and (3) the *cardinal veins* from the body of the embryo itself. The latter are really in two sets: the precardinals which drain blood from the head region, and the postcardinals which return blood from levels caudal to the heart; both pairs unite at the heart into short *common cardinal veins* (ducts of Cuvier). At this stage it thus happens that three venous stems open into the right horn of the sinus venosus and three into the left. Somewhat later two other pairs of veins, the *subcardinals* and the *supracardinals*, successively replace and supplement the postcardinals.

The subsequent history of venous development is a recital of the changes that these primitive symmetrical vessels undergo. Such alterations are more extensive than those occurring among arteries. The factors responsible for the final, poorly bilateral venous plan are: (1) shifts of position and direction; (2) anastomoses; (3) local transformations and readjustments; (4) loss by atrophy; and (5) secondary replacements.

Transformation of the Vitelline Veins.—The developing liver exerts a profound influence in modifying the primitive vitelline and umbilical veins. The paired vitelline vessels follow the yolk stalk into the body. They then turn cephalad, continue alongside the short fore-gut to the septum transversum and enter the sinus venosus (Fig. 303 A). Also into the septum

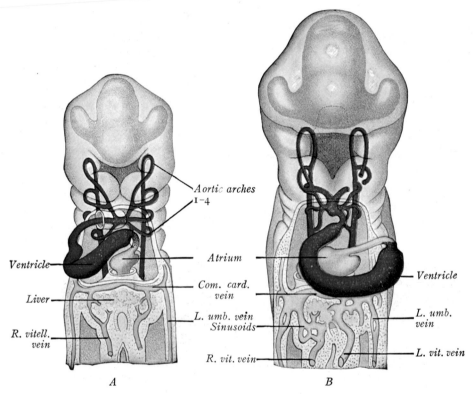

FIG. 315.—Veins in the vicinity of the heart, in ventral view (His). A, At 3 mm.; B, at 4 mm.

transversum grows the liver bud, already proliferating into cords. It will be remembered that there is a mutual intergrowth between hepatic cords and vitelline endothelium (Fig. 192). As a result, the vitelline vessels at the level of the liver resolve during the fourth week into networks of sinusoids that are incorporated into the expanding right and left hepatic lobes (Fig. 315).

Each vein, thus interrupted by a sinusoidal labyrinth, is effectively divided into a distal segment, which follows the gut from yolk sac to liver, and a short, proximal segment, which returns blood to the corresponding horn of the sinus venosus (Figs. 315 and 316 *A–C*). In anticipation of descriptions to follow it can be stated here that the distal portions are converted into the portal vein, the intermediate sinusoids mostly remain as such but in part expand into the ductus venosus, while the right proximal stem represents the hepatic vein (*D*).

The early symmetrical relations, still essentially present in Fig. 316 *A*, are promptly disturbed by further changes that lead quickly to the final arrangement of vessels. Even at the 5 mm. stage the distal segments of

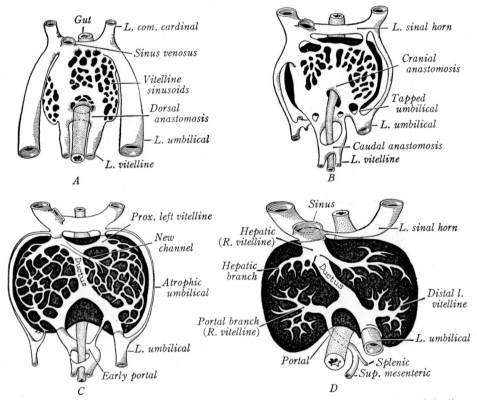

Fig. 316.—Transformation of the human, vitelline and umbilical veins in the region of the liver, seen in ventral view (adapted). *A*, At 4.5 mm.; *B*, at 5 mm.; *C*, at 6 mm.; *D*, at 9 mm.

the paired vitelline veins communicate by three cross anastomoses (*A, B*). There are: (1) a cranial connection in the liver (and, necessarily, ventral to the duodenum); (2) a middle bridge, dorsal to the duodenum; and (3) a caudal anastomosis, ventral to the duodenum. In this manner, two venous rings are created through which the gut weaves. The left limb of the cranial ring and the right limb of the caudal ring next atrophy and disappear; neither does the caudal anastomosis have any permanent representative (*C, D*). The *portal vein*, surviving these changes, is a composite, S-shaped vessel consisting of: (1) the right limb of the cranial ring; and (2) the middle transverse anastomosis. Its caudal limit is established by the union of the *splenic* vein with the *superior mesenteric* vein (*D*), just caudal to the transverse anastomosis. Nevertheless, the superior mesenteric is not the distal portion of the left vitelline, as might be supposed, but a new, replacing vessel arising in the dorsal mesentery of the intestinal loop; it supersedes the vitelline veins in this region as the latter disappear with the decline of the yolk sac. Within the liver some distal remnants of the right and left vitelline veins persist (*D*). On the right there is a branch, directly continuous with the portal. A left branch connects with the umbilical, but after that channel becomes functionless at birth, it is attached to the portal.

The proximal segments of the early vitelline veins drain blood from the sinusoids into the respective horns of the sinus venosus (Fig. 316 *A*, *B*). When the right horn soon is favored as the drainage outlet, the left vitelline and left horn cannot compete and both decline and disappear (*C*, *D*). The

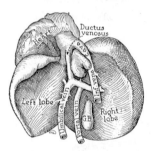

FIG. 317.—Relations of veins to the human liver, at the time of birth. × ½.

blood from the sinusoids on the left side is then rerouted across to the right sinal horn, and a new drainage channel arises to take care of this territory (*C*, *D*).[31] The surviving stems of the right vitelline vein are the *hepatic veins* which subsequently become tributaries of the later-formed inferior vena cava.

Transformation of the Umbilical Veins.— Coincidental with the vitelline alterations go certain related changes in the umbilical veins. The primitive right and left lobes of the liver expand laterally and soon come in contact with the umbilical veins coursing in the body wall (Fig. 315). Both of the latter are tapped and their blood, so diverted, finds a more direct route to the heart by way of the hepatic sinusoids (Fig. 316 *A*, *B*). When all of the umbilical blood enters the liver, as happens in embryos of 6 mm., the entire right umbilical and the proximal segment of the left atrophy (*C*) and soon disappear (*D*). At 7 mm. the distal remainder of the left umbilical is already large; it continues to maintain itself throughout fetal life, shifting to the midplane and occupying the free edge of the falciform ligament (Fig. 317).

As the channel of the early right vitelline vein within the liver is larger than the left, the blood from the tapped left umbilical vein first takes that route to reach the right horn of the sinus venosus (Fig. 316 *A*, *B*). But with the progressive growth of the right lobe of the liver, this pathway becomes increasingly circuitous. A more direct course is, therefore, created through the enlargement of a diagonal passage out of the hepatic sinusoids (*C*). This is the *ductus venosus* (*D*). It continues in direct line with the left umbilical vein and empties into the inferior vena cava. Consequently, the purer blood from the placenta avoids the general system of hepatic sinusoids to a large extent; yet the umbilical vein does give off branches to the liver and makes an anastomotic connection with the portal vein (Fig. 316 D).

After birth the ductus venosus is no longer of use. However, it persists as the solid, fibrous *ligamentum venosum*. Similarly the lumen of the left umbilical vein obliterates, and from umbilicus to liver its fibrous remnant constitutes the *ligamentum teres* (Fig. 324 A).

Transformation of the Precardinal Veins.—Each precardinal (anterior cardinal) vein consists of two parts (Fig. 318 A): (1) the *primary head*

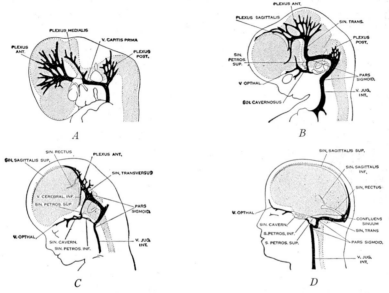

FIG. 318.—Transformation of the primary head vein into dural sinuses (Streeter). *A,* At six weeks; *B,* at eight weeks; *C,* at eleven weeks; *D,* at birth.

vein, which courses ventrolateral to the brain wall throughout all but the caudal end of the head; and (2) the true *precardinal,* located laterally in the segmented portion of the head and in the neck, and emptying into the common cardinal vein.

The primary head veins drain three pairs of tributary plexuses that extend dorsad over the brain (Fig. 318 A).[32] Coincidentally with the growth of the internal ear, the segment of head vein just ventral to it disappears and a new channel, connecting the middle and posterior plexuses, develops dorsal to the ear (B). The rostral portion of the head vein is spared; it receives the ophthalmic vein and constitutes the *cavernous sinus* (B–D). The original stem of the middle plexus, retained as the *superior petrosal sinus*, interconnects the cavernous sinus with the new dorsal channel (*B*). The *transverse sinus* is a main line of drainage. It arises from portions of the middle and posterior plexuses that are linked by the new dorsal vessel; part of its extent is the so-called sigmoid portion (*B, C*). The *inferior petrosal sinus* results from the re-establishment of a channel along the course of the degenerated segment of the head vein (*C*). The *superior sagittal sinus* develops in the midplane from portions of the anterior plexus (*B, C*). The *inferior sagittal* and *straight sinuses* arise from a part of the plexus that extends downward between the cerebral hemispheres (*C, D*). The enormous growth of the two hemispheres is chiefly responsible for the definitive positions and relations of the several dural sinuses (*D*).

The true precardinals begin near the base of the head and run caudad into the heart (Fig. 319 *A*). They communicate during the eighth week by an oblique cross-channel which shunts blood from the left vein across

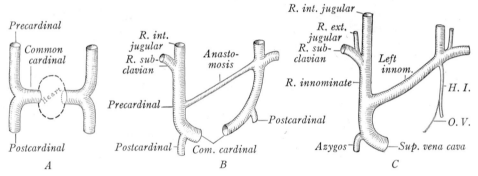

Fig. 319.—Transformation of the cardinal veins of human embryos, shown by diagrams in ventral view. *A*, At six weeks; *B*, at eight weeks; *C*, adult.
H.I., Highest intercostal; *O.V.*, oblique vein of the left atrium.

to the right one (*B*). As a result of this diversion, the stem portion of the left precardinal, just caudad, soon loses its communication with the common cardinal on the same side and survives merely as part of the highest intercostal vein (*C*). The left common cardinal comprises most of the inconstant *oblique vein of the left atrium* (*cf.* p. 328). The right common cardinal and the right precardinal, as far up as the intercardinal anastomosis, become the *superior vena cava*. The anastomosis itself forms the *left innominate* vein, while the portion of the right precardinal next cephalad (between the anastomosis and the right subclavian vein) is known as the *right innominate*. Still more cephalad, the precardinals continue as *internal jugular* veins. The *external jugular* and *subclavian* veins are both extraneous vessels that develop independently and attach secondarily.

Transformation of the Post-, Sub- and Supracardinal Veins.—Caudal to the heart there appear in succession three pairs of veins, whose histories both overlap and interweave. These vessels care for the venous drainage from the legs, body wall and viscera (Fig. 320). The first is the *postcardinals*, which are developed primarily as the vessels of the mesonephroi (*A*); they run dorsal to the mesonephroi and also receive tributaries from the legs and body wall. Next to appear are the *subcardinal* veins, which lie ventromesial to the mesonephros; they connect not only with each other but also, through the mesonephric sinusoids, with the postcardinals (*A*). Finally the *supracardinals* make their appearance (*B*); they course dorsomesial to the postcardinals and in a sense replace them. The fates of these three vessels vary somewhat in different animals, depending on the size of the mesonephroi and the duration of their functional activity.[33] The present account refers especially to man,[34] although except for details it is equally applicable to animals like the pig, sheep and cat in which the activity of the mesonephroi also persists over a comparatively long period.[33, 35] In man the transformations are largely accomplished during the sixth, seventh and eighth weeks.

The postcardinals appear with the mesonephroi and disappear as that organ wanes. An early anastomosis where the caudal and leg veins are received unites the two postcardinal trunks (*A*); this connection is destined to persist as the longer and more oblique left common iliac vein. The only permanent representatives of the postcardinal system are (*D*): (1) the root of the *azygos*, where it joins the superior vena cava on the right; and (2) the *common iliacs* (which are later annexed by the inferior vena cava); the veins of the legs are tributary to them.

The subcardinals follow closely on the appearance of the postcardinals. Their original cranial connections, permitting drainage into the respective postcardinals, are soon lost (*A, B*). Anastomoses with the latter veins also disappear, but a prominent set of connections between the two subcardinals, midway in their course, is destined to serve as the stem uniting the left renal vein to the vena cava (*A–D*). The only further subcardinal contributions to the permanent system of veins are the paired suprarenal and sex veins, and a segment of the vena cava formed from the right subcardinal (*D*).

The supracardinals become broken in the region of the kidneys (*C*). Above this level they unite by a cross anastomosis and become the *azygos* and *hemiazygos* vessels (*D*). Below the kidneys the right supracardinal alone is taken over as the caudalmost section of the inferior vena cava (*D*), whereas the left vein drops out without trace. Some criticisms have been directed against this interpretation of the relations and fate of the supracardinals; the interested reader must weigh the evidence for himself.[36, 37]

The Inferior Vena Cava.—The unpaired inferior vena cava is complex and requires some additional description. Its history involves the several

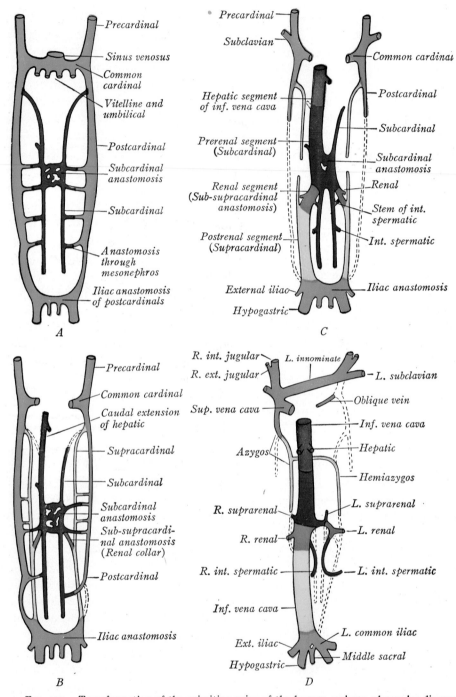

Fig. 320.—Transformation of the primitive veins of the human embryo, shown by diagrams in ventral view (adapted after McClure and Butler). *A*, At six weeks; *B*, at seven weeks; *C*, at eight weeks; *D*, adult.

changes through which blood returning from the lower body is progressively shifted from the left side to the right. This is accomplished by anastomoses between some vessels, by the enlargement and consolidation of others, and by the regression and replacement of still others. The outcome is a new, compound path to the heart which rapidly straightens and consolidates into what looks thereafter like a simple, homogeneous vein.

The inferior vena cava is composed, in order, of the following veins: (1) an hepatic segment; (2) a prerenal segment, formed from the right subcardinal; (3) a renal segment, comprising an anastomosis ('renal collar') between the right subcardinal and right supracardinal veins; and (4) a postrenal segment, from the lumbar portion of the right supracardinal vein.

(1) The hepatic segment is derived from the hepatic vein (proximal right vitelline) and the hepatic sinusoids. It connects with the right subcardinal through a vein in the caval mesentery (Fig. 320 B). The latter structure is a ridge which extends caudad from the attachment of the right lobe of the liver to the dorsal body wall (Fig. 210). Capillaries invade this mesentery from the liver and meet and fuse with similar capillaries growing cephalad from the right subcardinal. (2) The prerenal segment begins at the junction (through the vein of the caval mesentery) of the hepatic segment with the right subcardinal and continues to the level of the kidneys (Fig. 320 B). (3) The renal segment represents an important anastomosis that unites the right sub- and supracardinals (B, C). (4) The postrenal segment is a continuation of the right supracardinal down to the level of the iliacs (C, D). These latter vessels are annexed when the degeneration of the postcardinals would otherwise leave them without central connections.

Caval Tributaries.—Accompanying these complex changes there emerge tributary vessels to the vena cava, some of whose origins and relations are correspondingly intricate. As the permanent kidneys assume their final positions, a *renal* vein appears on each side and drains into the anastomosis developed between the sub- and supracardinals (C). Since on the right this anastomosis is incorporated into the vena cava as its renal segment, the corresponding renal vein empties directly into the vena cava. On the left the situation is more complicated because the primitive renal vein opens into the sub-supracardinal anastomosis which, in turn, must find its way to the vena cava through the great anastomosis between the subcardinals. For this reason the adult left renal vein is longer and more complex than its mate (D).

The two suprarenal veins likewise are not wholly homologous vessels. The *right suprarenal* is a simple branch off the subcardinal at a level where this vessel becomes a part of the inferior vena cava (C, D). On the other hand, the *left suprarenal* is a prerenal portion of the subcardinal itself; it corresponds to the right subcardinal contribution to the inferior vena cava

(*C, D*). The prospective left suprarenal first communicates with the right subcardinal through the great anastomosis, but after this anastomosis becomes the stem of the left renal, it naturally is tributary to the latter vessel.

The *spermatic* or *ovarian* veins are the remnants of the paired subcardinals below the kidneys (*C*). The right opens into that portion of the right subcardinal that is incorporated into the inferior vena cava. The left early drains into the left caudal border of the great subcardinal anastomosis which, as already described, becomes the stem of the left renal vein (*A–C*). Soon secondary roots arise from new anastomoses (*C*) and both sex veins shift their origins onto the sub-supracardinal anastomoses (*D*). The final

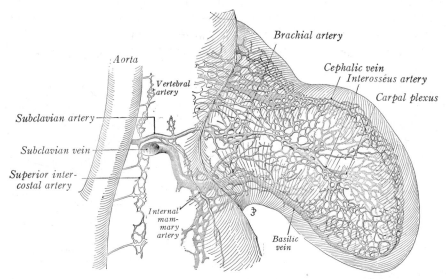

FIG. 321.—Primitive blood vessels in the left fore-limb of a 12 mm. pig embryo, seen in ventral view (Woollard). × 30.

attachments are still to the inferior vena cava and left renal vein, respectively, but to segments of different origin than originally was the case.

The *posterior intercostal* and *lumbar* veins are at first tributaries of the postcardinals. As the latter vessels degenerate, these veins connect secondarily with the replacing supracardinal veins. Later they of necessity drain into the azygos veins and inferior vena cava, respectively.

Veins of the Extremities.—The primitive capillary plexus of the flattened limb buds gives rise to a peripheral *border vein* (Fig. 321) which serves as an early drainage channel. Along the cranial margin this vein is smaller and mostly disappears, but on the caudal margin it transforms into permanent vessels. The border vein appears in the arm and leg in the sixth and eighth weeks, respectively; the general venous plan becomes outlined within the next two weeks.

Arm.—The radial extension of the border vein atrophies but the ulnar portion persists, forming at different levels the *subclavian, axillary* and *basilic* veins. The border vein originally opens into the dorsal wall of the postcardinal, but, as the heart shifts caudad, it ultimately drains by a ventral connection into the precardinal (internal jugular) vein. The *cephalic* vein develops secondarily in connection with the radial border vein; later it anastomoses with the external jugular, but finally opens into the axillary vein, as in the adult.

Leg.—Homologous with conditions in the arm, the tibial continuation of the primitive border vein disappears, while the fibular part persists to a large degree. The *great saphenous* vein arises separately from the postcardinal, gives off the *femoral* and *posterior tibial* veins, and then annexes the fibular border vein at the level of the knee. Distal to this junction, the border vein develops into the *anterior tibial* and, probably, the *small*

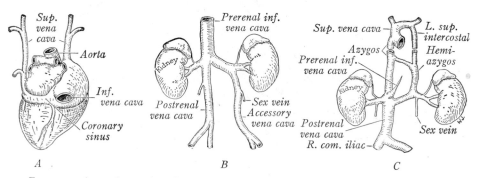

FIG. 322.—Anomalous veins of man. *A*, Double superior vena cava. *B*, Accessory postrenal vena cava on left side. *C*, Rudimentary prerenal vena cava and compensatory development of the azygos system of vessels.

saphenous; proximally, it becomes greatly reduced, forming the *inferior gluteal.*

Pulmonary Veins.—The primitive vessel derives from the pulmonary plexus (Fig. 303 *B*).[58] It joins the heart and its main stems are absorbed into the left atrium (Fig. 296).

Anomalies.—Among the anomalous veins produced through the operation of the general factors already cited (p. 345) are found such conspicuous specimens as the following (Fig. 322): paired superior (*A*) or inferior venæ cavæ (*B*); unpaired, left superior or inferior vena cava; azygos vessels serving as a main venous pathway (*C*); hemiazygos vein opening into the coronary sinus (*i.e.*, into the primitive left sinal horn); retention of the original, single trunk of the pulmonary vein (*cf.* Fig. 296).

FETAL CIRCULATION AND THE CHANGES AT BIRTH

Fetal Circulation.—During fetal life oxygenated blood, returning from the placenta, enters the embryo by way of the large umbilical vein and is conveyed to the liver (Fig. 323).   Thence it flows to the inferior vena cava, in part directly through the ductus venosus but to a much larger extent indirectly through the liver sinusoids and hepatic veins.   The impure blood of the portal vein and inferior vena cava contaminates only partially the large volume of placental blood.   Accordingly, the mixture entering the right atrium from the lower body is relatively well oxygenated.   By contrast

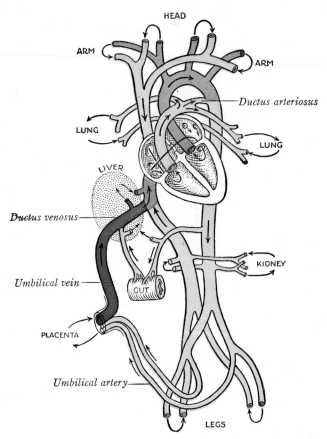

FIG. 323.—Plan of the human circulation before birth (partly after Dodds).   Colors show the quality of the blood and arrows indicate its direction of flow.

the superior vena cava carries oxygen-poor blood returning from the upper body; it also enters the right atrium.

   The course of blood through the heart is no longer in doubt (Fig. 323).[39, 40] The less pure (superior caval) blood is directed into the right ventricle, whence it leaves the heart through the pulmonary artery.   Some of this blood reaches the lungs, while the remainder continues through the ductus arteriosus to the descending aorta.   Here it is distributed to the trunk, abdominal viscera, legs and placenta.   On the other hand, the purer (inferior caval) blood takes a double course through the heart. A smaller amount goes directly to the right ventricle and then follows the course already described. The main volume, however, crosses through the foramen ovale into the left atrium and thus reaches the left ventricle. From here it is pumped into the ascending aorta and thence to the coronary arteries, head and arms. In this manner the heart and brain, in particular, would be given preferential treatment with respect to oxygenated blood from the placenta.

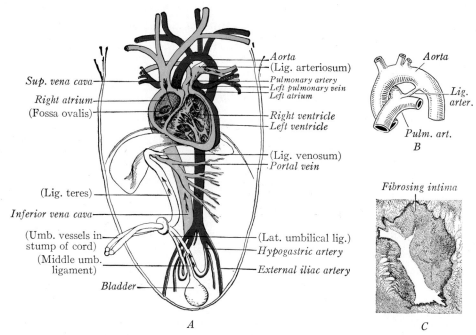

FIG. 324.—Changes in the human circulation after birth. *A*, Plan of circulation, in ventral view; obliterated fetal passages are designated by Roman type within parentheses (Heisler). *B*, Ligamentum arteriosum, at three months. *C*, Transverse section of the interior of the obliterating ductus arteriosus, at one month (after Schaeffer).

Changes at Birth.—When the lungs become functional, the placental circulation ceases quickly. This transfer of the seat of oxygenation not only changes the character of the blood in many vessels but throws some important fetal vessels and passages into disuse (Fig. 324 *A*).[39] As a group these latter channels abandon their functional rôles suddenly and completely, whereas anatomical obliteration is a gradual process of fibrosis which proceeds slowly in the postnatal months.[41]

The septum primum, which serves as the valve of the foramen ovale, fuses with the margin of the foramen ovale. This union is completed after about one year, but more than 20 per cent. of all individuals never obtain perfect closure.   The site of the previous aperture in the septum secundum is marked permanently by the depressed *fossa ovalis* (Fig. 324 *A*).

When breathing begins, muscular contraction closes the ductus arteriosus.   Its anatomical obliteration is caused by the internal coat proliferating pads of fibrous tissue into the lumen (Fig. 324 *C*).[42]   After one month it has usually become impervious, at least in part of its length.

The empty umbilical vessels contract and gradually lose their lumina by fibrous invasion; this extends through the first two or three months of postnatal life.   Distally the arteries obliterate into the *lateral umbilical ligaments*; proximally they continue as functional hypogastric arteries (Fig. 324 *A*).   The vein becomes cord-like and persists as the unpaired *ligamentum teres* of the liver.   The ductus venosus likewise atrophies; within two months it transforms into the fibrous *ligamentum venosum*, superficially embedded in the wall of the liver (Fig. 317).

THE LYMPHATIC SYSTEM

The lymphatics develop quite independently of blood vessels and any temporary venous connections which they may show are acquired secondarily.   They originate as discrete spaces in the mesenchyme;[43] the mesenchymal cells bordering each space flatten into an endothelial lining.   By progressive fusion such locally formed clefts link into continuous channels[44] which also grow, branch and extend the system further (Fig. 325 *B–F*).[3,4] Through the combination of both processes the lymphatic system attains its final form.

The first plexus of lymphatic capillaries is distributed along the primitive, main venous trunks.   The dilatation and coalescence of this network at definite regions gives rise to five lymph sacs (Fig. 325 *A*): (1, 2) Paired *jugular sacs* appear at seven weeks, lateral to the internal jugular veins. (3) In embryos of two months the unpaired *retroperitoneal sac* develops at the root of the mesentery, adjacent to the suprarenal glands, and at this stage the *cisterna chyli* also differentiates.   (4, 5) Likewise at the end of the second month paired *posterior sacs* arise in relation to the sciatic veins.

All these sacs at first contain blood which they soon discharge into neighboring veins and thereupon lose their venous connections.   With relation to the lymph sacs as centers, the *thoracic duct* and the *peripheral lymphatics* develop rapidly.   Thus lymphatic vessels grow to the head, neck and arm from the jugular sacs; to the hip, back and leg from the posterior sacs; and to the mesentery from the retroperitoneal sac.   The jugular sacs are the only ones to acquire permanent connections with the venous system. They drain into the internal jugular veins by openings which are utilized later by the thoracic and right lymphatic ducts, respectively.   The various sacs themselves are eventually replaced by chains of lymph glands.   Lymphatic vessels differentiate like thin-walled veins, and at intervals develop valves.[45]

Lymph Glands.[46]—The earliest, or primary lymph glands appear during the third month as the lymph sacs begin to break down into plexuses of lymphatic vessels (Fig. 325 *A*). Secondary lymph glands develop later along the course of the peripheral lymphatics which spread from these centers. The first stage of development is marked by a lymphatic plexus which lies in association with strands of mesenchymal tissue. Continued

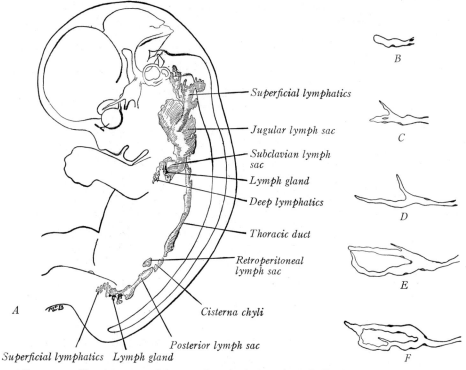

Superficial lymphatics

Jugular lymph sac

Subclavian lymph sac

Lymph gland

Deep lymphatics

Thoracic duct

Retroperitoneal lymph sac

Cisterna chyli

Posterior lymph sac

Superficial lymphatics   Lymph gland

B

C

D

E

F

A

FIG. 325.—Development of human lymphatic vessels. *A*, Profile reconstruction of the primitive lymphatic system in an embryo of two months (after Sabin; × 3). *B–F*, Growth of a capillary, observed in a living rabbit (after Clark; × 90).

proliferation and differentiation enlarge these strands into nodular lymphoid masses, and the vessels are crowded to the periphery where the *peripheral sinus* then makes its appearance (Fig. 326 *A*, *B*). About the whole a connective-tissue *capsule* condenses, while the *trabeculæ* and *central sinuses* spread inward from the *hilus* (*B*, *C*).[47] Ordinarily it has been believed that the sinuses of lymph glands represent primary lymphatic plexuses, but an alternative interpretation is that they are independent channels in the lymphoid reticulum, arising as clefts in the mesenchyme and acquiring lymphatic connections secondarily.[48] Blood vessels, which even at an early

17

period supply the lymphoid masses, also enter and leave at the hilus. *Medullary cords* differentiate from the common lymphoid primordium, but a true cortex appears much later since definite *cortical nodules*, with germinal centers, are completed mostly after birth.

Hemal (Hemolymph) Glands.—The development of a hemal gland is much like that of lymph glands, but its origin is traced to a condensation of mesenchyme that develops in relation to blood vessels, not lymphatics.[49] The peripheral sinus arises independently; its vascular connections are secondary.

The Spleen.—Embryos of 8 mm. exhibit a swelling on the left side of the dorsal mesogastrium (Fig. 327 *A*). This bulge is due to an accumulation of mesenchymal cells, just beneath the surface (peritoneal) epithelium. That some of these elements come from the simultaneously organizing epi-

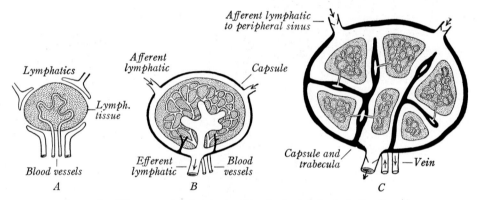

FIG. 326.—Diagrams of a developing lymph gland (adapted after Braus).

Lymph sinuses are shown as broad channels and the smaller blood vessels as fine plexuses connecting with trabecular vessels.

thelium is both asserted and denied.[50, 51] However, this controversy loses force when it is understood that epithelium and mesenchyme both trace origin to the generalized splanchnic mesoderm and are in the act of diverging on separate paths of specialization. As the mass increases in size, it projects above the omental surface, usually as several hillocks which slowly merge (*A*). The region of union of the spleen with the dorsal mesogastrium, or greater omentum, (*B*) fails to keep pace with the general enlargement and is reduced to a narrow band, the gastro-splenic ligament (*C*). At three months the spleen acquires its characteristic form.

The mass of splenic mesenchyme is well vascularized, and from it differentiate the *capsule, trabeculæ* and *pulp cords*. The specialization into red and white pulp seems to be dependent upon the development and distribution of the vascular channels, but there is no agreement as to which type is primary. The *sinuses*, which at first have no connection with the blood vessels, are said to originate as separate cavities in the mesenchyme.[52] For a time the circulation is within a closed system of vessels; the peculiar 'open-walled' sinuses are acquired by the middle of fetal life.[53] Lymphoid tissue appears early, but it is not until six months that the *splenic corpuscles* form ovoid nodules about arteries. From the fifth to eighth months of fetal life the formation of white blood cells is supplemented by red corpuscles which develop actively within the splenic mass.

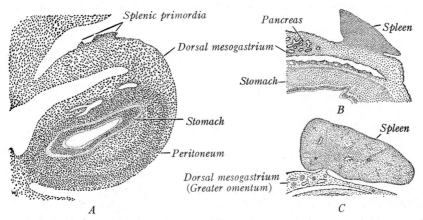

FIG. 327.—Development of the spleen, shown by transverse sections through human embryos. *A*, At 12 mm. (× 65); *B*, at two months (× 40); *C*, at four months (× 18).

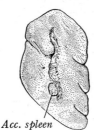

FIG. 328.—Spleen of a newborn, showing partial subdivision and an accessory spleen. × **1.**

Anomalies.—The spleen is sometimes partially subdivided (Fig. 328), or even multiple. Smaller, accessory spleens are common in the newborn (Fig. 328). These types result either from the continuance of the early, multiple hillocks or from an exaggeration of temporary incisures that appear in the third and fourth months.

The Tonsils and Thymus.—For their development see pp. 212 to 214.

REFERENCES CITED

1. Hertig, A. T. 1935. Carnegie Contrib. Embryol., **25,** No. 146, 37–82.
2. McClure, C. F. W. 1921. Anat. Rec., **22,** 219–237.
3. Clark, E. R. 1909. Anat. Rec., **3,** 183–198.
4. Clark, E. R. and E. L. 1932. Am. Jour. Anat., **51,** 49–87.
5. Maximow, A. 1924. Physiol. Rev., **4,** 533–563.
6. Sabin, F. L. 1922. Physiol. Rev., **2,** 38–69.

7. Maximow, A.   1927.   Bd. 2, Teil 1 in Möllendorff's 'Handbuch der mikroskopischen Anatomie des Menschen.'   Springer, Berlin.
8. Bloom, W.   1938.   Sect. 13 in Downey's 'Handbook of Hematology.'   Hoeber, N. Y.
9. Sabin, F. L.   1928.   Physiol. Rev., **8**, 191–244.
10. Emmel, V. E.   1914.   Am. Jour. Anat., **16**, 127–206.
11. Kingsley, D. M.   1937.   Anat. Rec., **67** (Suppl.), 30.
12. Kampmeier, O. F. and Birch, C. L.   1927.   Am. Jour. Anat., **38**, 451–499.
13. Streeter, G. L.   1918.   Carnegie Contrib. Embryol., **8**, No. 24, 5–38.
14. Yoshinaga, T.   1921.   Anat. Rec., **21**, 239–308.
15. Davis, C. L.   1927.   Carnegie Contrib. Embryol., **19**, No. 107, 245–284.
16. Frazer, J. E.   1917.   Jour. Anat. and Physiol., **51**, 19–29.
17. Odgers, P. N. B.   1935.   Jour. Anat., **69**, 412–422.
18. Hamilton, W. F. *et al.*   1937.   Am. Jour. Physiol., **119**, 206–212.
19. Odgers, P. N. B.   1938.   Jour. Anat., **72**, 247–259.
20. Congdon, E. D.   1922.   Carnegie Contrib. Embryol., **14**, No. 68, 47–110.
21. Heuser, C. H.   1923.   Carnegie Contrib. Embryol., **15**, No. 77, 121–139.
22. Schmeidel, G.   1932.   Morph. Jahrb., **71**, 315–435.
23. Bremer, J. L.   1915.   Am. Jour. Anat., **18**, 179–200.
24. Broman, I.   1908.   Anat. Hefte, **36**, 405–549.
25. Pernkopf, E.   1922.   Zeitschr. f. Anat. u. Entwickl., **64**, 94–275.
26. Evans, H. M.   1912.   Chapter 18 in Keibel and Mall's 'Human Embryology.'   Lippincott, Phila.
27. Schumaker, S.   1907.   Arch. f. mikr. Anat. u. Entwickl., **71**, 58–115.
28. Krompecher, S.   1940.   Zeitschr. f. Anat. u. Entwickl., **110**, 423–442.
29. Woollard, H. H.   1922.   Carnegie Contrib. Embryol., **22**, No. 70, 139–154.
30. Senior, H. D.   1919–20.   Am. Jour. Anat., **25**, 55–95.   Anat. Rec., **17**, 271–279.
31. Schneider, H.   1937.   Zeitschr. f. Anat. u. Entwickl., **107**, 326–352.
32. Streeter, G. L.   1915.   Am. Jour. Anat., **18**, 145–178.
33. Butler, E. G.   1927.   Am. Jour. Anat., **39**, 267–363.
34. McClure, C. F. W. and Butler, E. G.   1925.   Am. Jour. Anat., **35**, 331–383.
35. Huntington, G. S. and McClure, C. F. W.   1920.   Anat. Rec., **20**, 1–30.
36. Reagan, F. P.   1927.   Anat. Rec., **35**, 129–148.
37. Grünwald, P.   1938.   Zeitschr. f. mikr.-anat. Forsch., **43**, 275–331.
38. Gilmour, J. R.   1941.   Jour. Path. and Bact., **52**, 25–45.
39. Barron, D. H.   1944.   Physiol. Rev., **24**, 277–295.
40. Barclay, A. E. *et al.*   1939.   Brit. Jour. Radiol., **12**, 505–515.
41. Scammon, R. E. and Norris, E. H.   1918.   Anat. Rec., **15**, 165–180.
42. Jager, B. V. and Wollenman, O. J.   1942.   Am. Jour. Path., **18**, 595–613.
43. Huntington, G. S.   1914.   Am. Jour. Anat., **16**, 259–316.
44. McClure, C. F. W.   1915.   Anat. Rec., **9**, 563–579.
45. Kampmeier, O. F.   1928.   Am. Jour. Anat., **40**, 413–457.
46. Hellman, T.   1930.   Bd. 6, Teil 1 in Möllendorff's 'Handbuch der mikroskopischen Anatomie des Menschen.'   Springer, Berlin.
47. Heudorfer, K.   1921.   Zeitschr. f. Anat. u. Entwickl., **61**, 365–401.
48. Downey, H.   1922.   Hæmatologia, **3**, 431–468.
49. Meyer, A. W.   1917.   Am. Jour. Anat., **21**, 375–495.
50. Holyoke, E. A.   1936.   Anat. Rec., **65**, 333–349.
51. Bergel, A. and Gut, A.   1934.   Zeitschr. f. Anat. u. Entwickl., **103**, 20–29.
52. Thiele, G. A. and Downey, H.   1921.   Am. Jour. Anat., **28**, 279–339.
53. Barta, E.   1926.   Compt. rend. Soc. biol., **94**, 1122–1124.
54. Ekman, G.   1925.   Arch. f. Entwickl.-mech. d. Organ., **106**, 320–352.
55. Bloom, W. and Bartelmez, G. W.   1940.   Am. Jour. Anat., **67**, 21–53.
56. Kramer, T. C.   1942.   Am. Jour. Anat., **71**, 343–370.
57. Odgers, P. N. B.   1939.   Jour. Anat., **73**, 643–657.
58. Davies, F. and MacConaill, M. A.   1937.   Jour. Anat., **81**, 437–446.

CHAPTER XVI

THE SKELETAL SYSTEM

HISTOGENESIS OF THE SUPPORTING TISSUES

Connective tissue, cartilage and bone all differentiate from that type of diffuse mesoderm known as *mesenchyme* (Fig. 7 *A*). Mesenchyme arises primarily from the primitive streak and secondarily from mesodermal somites and the lateral somatic and splanchnic layers (Fig. 337). It is a spongy meshwork composed of branching cells whose processes perhaps touch rather than actually anastomose;[1] between the cells occur open, labyrinthine spaces which are filled with a ground-substance of coagulable fluid. In early embryos the mesenchyme acts as an unspecialized packing material between the external and internal epithelia, but it soon enters on various lines of differentiation (Fig. 280). Of these, the inert supporting tissues are peculiar in that a ground-substance, or matrix, appears which usually becomes bulkier than the cellular elements themselves. The matrix may be fibrous, cartilaginous or bony in nature; in each instance it is a matter of controversy whether the matrix originates within the substance of the mesenchymal cells or is merely organized and laid down in the spaces between them.

CONNECTIVE TISSUE

The old idea that connective-tissue fibrils are transformed directly within typical cytoplasm is no longer tenable as an inclusive theory. In most instances the fibrils seem to develop in a gelatinous ground-substance that lies between the cells. The chief question today concerns the nature and origin of this ground-substance. Some, modifying the intracellular view, claim it to be a syncytial ectoplasm derived from the mesenchyme.[2,3] Others interpret the ground-mass as a lifeless matrix secreted by the cells.[4,5,6] Observations on living connective tissue indicate that fiber differentiation occurs in relation to, and apparently at the expense of, cytoplasmic material projected from the surface of *fibroblast cells*.[7]

Reticular Tissue.—Except for the jelly-like mucous tissue of the umbilical cord, reticular tissue departs least from the embryonal type (Fig. 329, at top). Its stellate cells are usually described as maintaining a clasping relation, wrapped about the reticular fibrils. The latter are fine filaments, staining electively with silver. They can develop into white fibers and are, in this sense, an immature stage of these elements.[5,6]

White Fibrous Tissue.—The differentiation of this tissue may be divided into two phases: first, there is a prefibrous stage marked by the appearance of fibrils resembling those of reticular tissue (Fig. 329, at top); next, the parallel fibrils aggregate into bundles and are converted through a chemical change into typical white fibers (Fig. 329, at middle). The early, mesenchymal cells specialize into *fibroblasts* and other free types. In *areolar tissue* and fibro-elastic sheets of denser weave, the white fibers predominate in an irregular meshwork; in *tendons* and *ligaments* they are arranged in compact parallel fascicles.

Elastic Tissue.—Yellow elastic fibers differentiate later than the white variety, but probably in the same general manner (Fig. 330).[8] Typically they remain single, coarse fibers which both branch and anastomose. They may group into *elastic ligaments* or form fenestrated plates.[9]

Adipose Tissue.—Certain of the mesenchymal cells give rise to *lipoblasts*, which are the forerunners of fat cells. It is not surely known whether

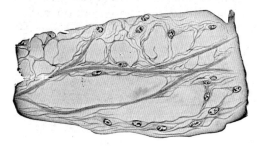

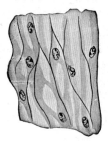

FIG. 329.—Differentiation of white fibers in the skin of a 5 cm. pig fetus (after Mall). × 270. At top, reticular tissue.

FIG. 330.—Differentiation of elastic fibers in the umbilical cord of a 7 cm. pig fetus (after Mall). × 270.

cells once differentiated as fibroblasts can later transform into fat cells. Perhaps the new adipose cells of the adult come from undifferentiated mesenchymal cells. A lipoblast elaborates within its cytoplasm droplets of fat which increase in size and become confluent (Fig. 331); in one carefully studied animal the future droplets begin as nucleolar buds and undergo a complicated history before reaching the actual droplet condition.[10] As the amount of fat increases, the cell body becomes rounded. When at last a huge globule distends the cell, the nucleus is pressed to the periphery. Fat cells arise in close association with developing blood vessels in areolar tissue and appear first during the fourth month. The primitive clusters are foci for the later lobules; it has been urged that these constitute specific organs.[11]

At various locations in the fetus there are groups of distinctive granular lipoblasts that are set apart as so-called *adipose glands*. Fat cells derived from them are peculiar in containing multiple fat droplets which for a time do not coalesce; yet in early infancy they become indistinguishable from the ordinary type.[12] In the cat this specific tissue continues until maturity,[13] and in rodents it constitutes the permanent 'hibernating gland.'[14] Pigment gives the tissue a brownish color.

CARTILAGE

A preliminary stage in the development of cartilage begins in the fifth week with the enlargement and differentiation of mesenchyme into a compact, cellular *precartilage* (Fig. 332). The cells become definitive cartilage cells. The origin of matrix is interpreted variously. Many claim that it appears as a formed deposit between the cells (*A*). According to a second theory, mesenchymal cells produce an ectoplasmic syncytium which develops fibrillæ and then converts into the matrix peculiar to cartilage (*B*); meanwhile the cells proper separate away and fill the intercellular spaces.

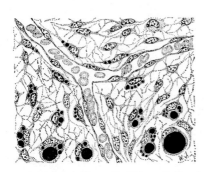

FIG. 331.—Fat cells differentiating in the fifth month from the connective tissue near a capillary. × 250.

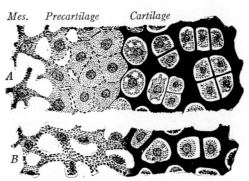

Mes.   Precartilage   Cartilage

FIG. 332.—The origin of cartilage matrix, as interpreted by rival theories (Lewis).

The firm matrix of *hyaline cartilage* contains a feltwork of masked fibrils. In *fibrocartilage*, heavier white fibers also are deposited within the matrix; in *elastic cartilage*, yellow elastic fibers. Cartilage grows internally and also at its periphery. Internal, or interstitial growth results both from the division of cartilage cells and from the production of new matrix by them. Peripheral, or appositional growth takes place through the mitotic activity of the connective-tissue sheath, the *perichondrium*. Its inner cells transform into young cartilage cells; these deposit matrix and become buried by their own activities.

BONE

Bone begins to appear after the seventh week. There are two types: the *membrane bones* of the face and cranium, which develop directly within blastemal (*i.e.*, mesenchymal) sheets, and the *cartilage bones* which replace the earlier cartilaginous skeleton. The actual mode of histogenesis, however, is identical in each instance. Bone matrix is deposited through the activity of specialized connective-tissue cells, named *osteoblasts* (bone-formers). A soft preosseus tissue, made up of fibrillæ, first differentiates, but this becomes impregnated with lime salts almost as fast as it appears (Fig. 333 *B, C*).[31] To what extent bone matrix is transformed ectoplasm or an intercullular secreted deposit, is debated.

Development of Membrane Bone.—The flat bones of the face and cranial vault are preceded by a primitive, connective-tissue membrane. At one or more internal points *intramembranous ossification* begins. Such

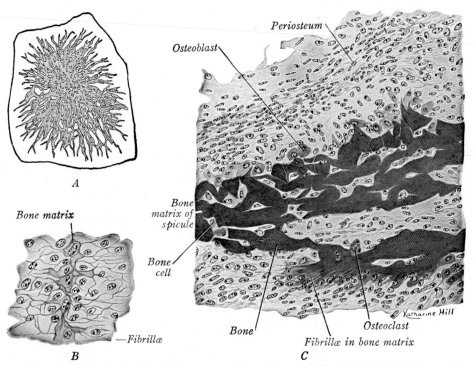

FIG. 333.—The development of human membrane bone. *A*, Parietal bone, at three months, in surface view to illustrate the spread of ossification (× 4). *B*, Growing tip of a spicule, at two months (after Mall; × 270). *C*, Vertical section of the surface of the mandible, at three months (Prentiss; × 325).

centers of ossification are characterized by the appearance of osteoblasts which promptly deposit bone matrix in the form of spicules (Fig. 333 *B*). These unite into a meshwork of trabeculæ that spreads radially in all directions (*A*). Since the osteoblasts are arranged in an epithelioid layer upon the surface of a spicule, the latter grows both in thickness and at its tip. As the matrix is progressively laid down, some osteoblasts become trapped and remain imprisoned as *bone cells* (*C*); these are lodged in spaces termed *lacunæ*.

After these primary internal centers are well under way, the entire primordium becomes enclosed within a *periosteum* (Fig. 333 *C*). This is a fibrous membrane condensed from the local mesenchyme. Osteoblasts differentiate on its inner surface and deposit parallel plates (lamellæ) of compact bone. This process is known as periosteal ossification. In such manner are developed the dense inner and outer *tables* of the cranium. The mass of spongy bone joining the two tables is the *diploë.*

Much bone that is first formed is provisional, and so is resorbed and replaced in varying degrees as the bone grows and assumes its final modeling. During resorption large mutlinucleate cells appear upon the surface of the bone matrix (Fig. 333 *C*). To these phagocytic giant cells has been given the name *osteoclasts* (*i.e.*, bone destroyers). There is, however, no positive evidence that the osteoclasts are actually responsible for bone dissolution; to a certain extent, at least, they are composed of fused osteoblasts and freed bone cells.[15, 32] The plates and trabeculæ of any bone are arranged spatially in conformity with the stresses encountered; in all instances maximum strength is gained from a minimum of material.[16] The open spaces of spongy bone are filled with cellular and fibrous derivatives of the mesenchyme. Such reticular tissue, fat cells, sinusoids and developing blood cells constitute the *red bone marrow.*

Development of Cartilage Bone.—Most bones of the body are preceded by a temporary cartilaginous model of the same shape as the definitive bone (Fig. 335). The chief peculiarity of this method of bone formation is the preliminary destruction of the cartilage, which is provisional and must be got rid of before ossification can proceed. For this reason these skeletal elements are often designated replacement, or substitution bones. When the cartilage is once removed from an area, the course of events is essentially as in the development of a membrane bone. Ossification occurs both within the eroded cartilage and peripherally beneath its perichondrium (Fig. 334 *A*). In the first case the process is *intracartilaginous,* or *endochondral;* in the second instance, *perichondral* or, better, *periosteal.*

Endochondral Bone Formation.—In the center of the cartilage the cells enlarge, become arranged in characteristic radial rows, and some lime is deposited in their matrix (*cf.* Fig. 334 *A*). The cartilage cells and part of the calcified matrix then disintegrate and disappear, thereby bringing into existence primordial marrow cavities. This destruction apparently is caused by the vascular *primary marrow tissue* which simultaneously invades the cartilage; some multinuclear giant cells, the so-called *chondroclasts,* also are in evidence. The early marrow tissue arises from the inner, cellular layer of the perichondrium and burrows into the cartilage in bud-like masses. Such eruptive tissue gives rise both to osteoblasts and to the vascular marrow which occupies the early marrow cavities. The osteoblasts deposit matrix at many points, and at first directly upon spicules of cartilage which

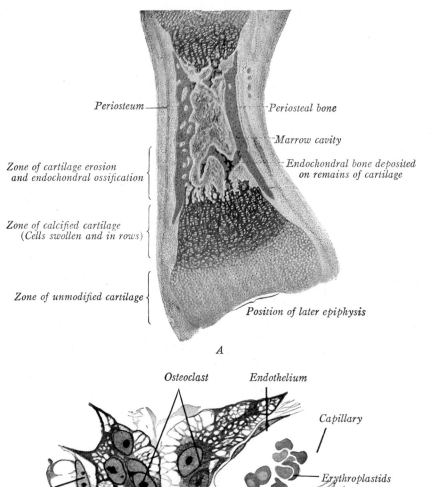

Periosteum

Periosteal bone

Marrow cavity

Zone of cartilage erosion and endochondral ossification

Endochondral bone deposited on remains of cartilage

Zone of calcified cartilage (Cells swollen and in rows)

Zone of unmodified cartilage

Position of later epiphysis

A

Osteoclast   Endothelium

Capillary

Erythroplastids

Mesenchyme

Osteoblast

Bone matrix

Calcified cartilage

Osteoblast   B   Calcified cartilage

FIG. 334.—Cartilage bone development in human fetuses. *A*, Longitudinal section through a finger at five months (after Sobotta; × 15). *B*, Detail of spongy bone from the humerus at three months (Maximow; × 700).

have escaped destruction; hence endochondral bone is characteristically spongy (Fig. 334 *B*). In a progressive manner the hitherto intact regions of cartilage also undergo similar invasion, destruction and replacement until eventually the entire cartilage is superseded by spongy (cancellous) bone.

Periosteal Bone Formation.—While the foregoing changes are occurring within the cartilage, compact bone develops around it (Figs. 334 *A* and 335). This process is identical with the formation of the tables of the flat bones, and is due to a corresponding activity of the inner osteogenetic layer of the perichondrium which henceforth is called more appropriately the *periosteum*. During the waves of destruction that accompany the modeling of bone wherever found, grooves and tubular channels become hollowed out.[17] Penetrating buds of osteogenetic tissue then lay down secondary deposits of bone as concentric cylinders whose central axis is a tube containing blood vessels; the whole is known as an *Haversian system* (Fig. 334½).

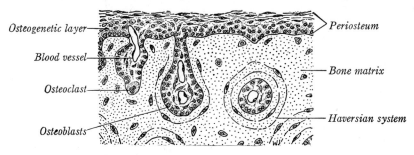

FIG. 334½.—Three stages illustrating the origin of Haversian systems. × 250.

Growth of Bones.—Flat membrane bones increase in lateral extent by continued marginal ossification from osteoblast-rich connective tissue at the site of the later sutures. Both cartilage and membrane bones grow in thickness through the further deposition of periosteally-formed matrix at their peripheral surfaces. In a long bone this superficial accretion is accompanied by a central resorption which destroys not only the endochondral osseous tissue but also the earlier periosteal layers (Fig. 335 *E, F*). As a result, the main shaft becomes a hollow cylinder, whereas spongy bone persists only at the ends. Red bone marrow fills all these cavities; its replacement by *yellow bone marrow* begins before puberty and is completed at about the twenty-fifth year.[36]

Many cartilage bones (especially long bones and vetrebræ) increase in length by an interesting method. While still in the fetal condition, the cartilage at each end of such a bone continues to grow rapidly and ossify in the same manner that was used from the start (Fig. 335 *A–C*). However, at some time between birth and puberty, or even later, osteogenetic tissue invades these terminal cartilages and secondary ossification centers, the *epiphyses*, are established there (*D*).   Both surfaces of the cartilaginous plate, left between the original bone and its epiphysis, continue to develop new cartilage as long as the bone lengthens, and this in turn is steadily replaced by bone matrix (*E*).[18]   However, such growth is chiefly on the diaphyseal side.   Finally, when the adult length is attained, the cartilage ceases proliferation, submits to ossification and the epiphyses are firmly united to the rest of the bone (*F*).   The adult *epiphyseal lines* mark this union.   If the free end of an epiphysis is to become an articulation, it remains cartilaginous permanently.   Short tubular bones, such as those of the fingers, have an epiphysis at one end only.

Epiphyses are of three sorts:[19] (1) pressure epiphyses, developed at the ends of long bones; (2) traction epiphyses, affording processes for the

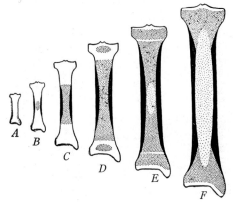

FIG. 335.—Ossification and growth in a long bone. *A*, Cartilaginous stage. *B*, *C*, Deposit of spongy, endochondral bone (stipple) and compact, perichondral bone (black). *D*, Appearance of an epiphysis at each end. *E*, Appearance of the marrow cavity (sparse stipple) by resorption of endochondral bone. *F*, Union of epiphyses, leaving articular cartilage at free ends; enlargement of marrow cavity by the resorption of periosteal bone, centrally, as deposition continues peripherally.

attachment of muscles (*e.g.*, the trochanters of the femur); and (3) atavistic epiphyses, representing a formerly separate bone (*e.g.*, the coracoid process of the scapula).

Most bones have more than one center of ossification (Fig. 335 *D*).   In all there are over 800 such centers, but half of them do not arise until after birth.   On the average, therefore, there are four centers for each mature bone.   All of these appear earlier in females than do the centers of corresponding bones in males.   The epiphyses of females also unite sooner with the diaphyses, so that growth in length ceases earlier by some three years.   But even in the male most of the fusions are ending at about the twentieth year.

Joints.—The joints, or *articulations*, occur at regions where bones meet.

These include two general groups: (1) *synarthroses*, in which little or no movement is allowed; and (2) *diarthroses*, or freely movable joints.

In joints of the synarthrodial type, the intervening mesenchyme differentiates into a uniting layer of connective tissue (*syndesmosis; e.g.,* suture of cranium), cartilage (*synchondrosis; e.g.,* pubic symphysis), or bone (*synostosis; e.g.,* epiphyseal union).

Diarthrodial joints are characterized both by a prominent *joint cavity*, between the movable skeletal parts, and by a ligamentous *capsule* at the periphery.[33] The joint cavity arises in the third month from clefts in the dense mesenchyme, located between the prospective bones; the capsule is derived from the denser external tissue continuous with the periosteum (Fig. 336 *A*). The cells of the inner layers of the capsule become a lubricative sheet called the *synovial membrane* (*B*). Ligaments or tendons that

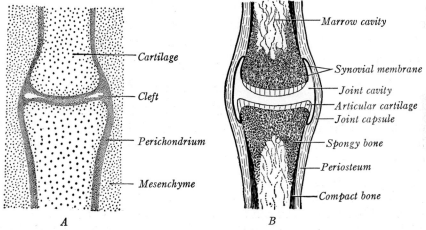

FIG. 336.—Stages in the development of a diarthrodial joint.

apparently course through the adult joint cavities actually represent secondary invasions, covered with synovial membrane reflected about them, and hence are really external to the cavity. A joint cavity may be divided by an *articular disc*, which is merely a fibro-cartilaginous plate fashioned midway in the mesenchyme between the two compartments. *Sesamoid bones* (*e.g.,* the patella) develop in relation both to tendons and to joints; they commonly arise in the substance of the primitive joint capsule and sometimes exhibit a cartilaginous stage. *Bursæ* (*i.e.,* fluid-filled sacs at regions of frictional play) are present in the later fetal months.

MORPHOGENESIS OF THE SKELETON

The skeleton includes both the axial skeleton (skull, vertebræ, ribs and sternum) and the appendicular skeleton (pectoral and pelvic girdles and the limb bones). Except for the flat bones of the face and cranial vault, the bones of the mammalian skeleton exhibit first a blastemal (*i.e.*, mesenchymal or membranous) stage, next a cartilaginous phase, and finally a permanent, osseous condition. A comparable ascending series occurs among the adult chordates of the present day. In explanation of this, it is held that those bones of higher vertebrates that are inherited directly from the cartilaginous skeleton of lower forms are obliged to pass through a reminiscent, cartilaginous stage. On the other hand, those bones made necessary by the acquisition of such newer features as a large brain, prominent nose and palate are not ancestrally bound, and hence develop directly in membrane.

The human body contains about 270 bones at birth (Fig. 353 *B*). Fusion of some of these in infancy reduces this number slightly, but from then until puberty there is a steady increase, due to the appearance of the epiphyses and the bones of the carpus and tarsus. At puberty there are 350 separate bony masses, and this number is increased still further during adolescence. Thereafter, fusions again bring about a reduction to the final quota of 206, yet this reduction often is not completed until middle life. Age is determinable from the progress of ossification.[34, 35]

The Axial Skeleton

The primitive axial support of all vertebrates is the *notochord*, or chorda dorsalis, the origin of which has been traced on pp. 68 to 73. The cellular notochord constitutes the only skeleton of Amphioxus and its allies, but in higher animals it is increasingly replaced by a stiffer axial skeleton composed mainly of jointed vertebræ. Among mammals a supporting notochordal rod is transient except at the intervertebral discs, within which it persists as the swollen, mucoid *nuclei pulposi* (Fig. 339 *B*).

The axial skeleton differentiates from mesenchyme that traces origin to the serially-arranged pairs of mesodermal segments. During the fourth week the ventromesial wall of the somite breaks down as it proliferates a mass of diffuse cells (Fig. 337, left). This aggregate of mesenchyme, designated a *sclerotome*, migrates toward the notochord (Fig. 337, right). The sclerotomes are destined to form vertebræ and ribs.

The Vertebræ.—The sclerotomic mesenchyme comes to lie in paired segmental masses alongside the notochord, separated from similar masses before and behind by the intersegmental arteries. In embryos of about 4 mm. each sclerotome proliferates in its caudal half so that this region is denser (Fig. 338 *A*). A fissure next separates these parts and the component halves reunite in new combinations. That is, the denser, caudal part of each original sclerotome joins the looser, cranial half of the sclerotome next caudad (*B*). These recombinations, and not the primitive sclerotomes, are the primordia of the definitive vertebræ.

From each bilateral pair of primordia, growth takes place in three principal directions (Fig. 337, right): (1) mesad, to surround the notochord and establish the *vertebral body;* (2) dorsad, flanking the neural tube, to constitute the neural, or *vertebral arch;* and (3) ventrolaterad, to provide the *costal processes*, or primordia of the ribs. The denser portion, almost unaided, gives rise to the processes that become the vertebral arch and ribs.

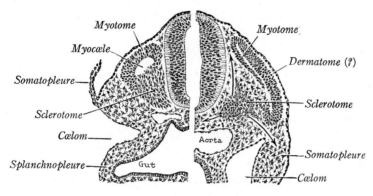

Fig. 337.—Growth and separation of the human sclerotome, shown in transverse sections. On left, beginning migration toward notochord (at seventeen somites; × 140). On right, separate sclerotomic mass; arrows indicate the directions of further spread which will produce the body, arch and costal process of a vertebra (at twenty-five somites; × 115).

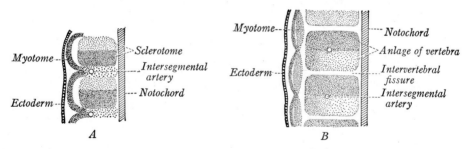

Fig. 338.—Early stages in the differentiation of human vertebræ, illustrated by frontal sections through the left somites. × about 75. *A,* At about 4 mm., showing the differentiation of each sclerotome into a less dense and denser region. *B,* At about 5 mm., illustrating the union of the halves of successive sclerotomes into definitive vertebral primordia.

At this stage the mesenchymal vertebræ have somewhat the proportions modeled in Fig. 339 *A*.

The recombination of sclerotomic masses, just mentioned, establishes intervertebral fissures between the organizing vertebræ (Fig. 338 *B*). Mesenchymal tissue, derived from the ends of two abutting vertebræ, condenses into an *intervertebral disc* within each interspace. It is at these intervals that remnants of the notochord, incorporated in the discs, persist as the pulpy nuclei (Fig. 339 *B*). Since a vertebra develops from parts of two adjacent sclerotomes, it is also evident from this diagram that the inter-segmental artery not only comes to pass midway over the body of a vertebra, but also that the myotomes and definitive vertebræ alternate in position. This alternation is a fundamentally necessary arrangement in order that the myotomic muscles may move the spine.

Following this blastemal stage, centers of *chondrification* begin to appear in the seventh week and quickly follow at successively lower levels.   There are two centers in the vertebral body and one in each half of the still incom-

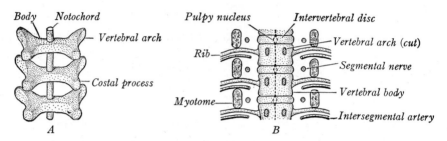

FIG. 339.—Form and relations of early human vertebræ, seen in dorsal view. *A*, Models of mesenchymal vertebræ, at 7 mm. (after Bardeen; × 30).   *B*, Diagram of vertebral relations.

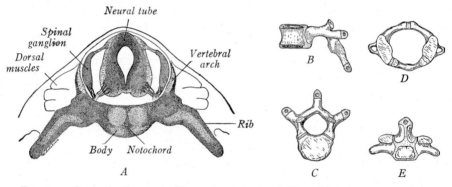

FIG. 340.—Later development of human vertebræ. *A*, Chondrification centers, shown in a transverse section at 13 mm. (after Bardeen; × 18).   *B, C*, Ossification of a thoracic vertebra (side and front views); composites up to seventeen years.   *D*, Atlas, at three years, in cephalic view. *E*, Epistropheus, in third year, in dorsal view.

plete vertebral arch (Fig. 340 *A*).   The four centers enlarge and merge into a solid, cartilaginous vertebra.   The vertebral arches do not unite and enclose the spinal cord until well into the third month; from them grow out the transverse and spinous processes (Fig. 204).

Finally, in the tenth week, the stage of vertebral *ossification* sets in (Fig. 353 *A*).   Each lateral half of the arch has a single center.   Whereas the vertebral body appears to have but one, there are often transient indi-cations of doubleness and even separate centers.   In the fifth month centers are present in all but the sacral vertebræ. The full union of these primary bony components is not completed until several years after birth. At about the seventeenth year secondary centers arise in the cartilage still covering the cranial and caudal ends of the vertebral body and resolve it into disc-like bony *epiphyses* (*B*). These plates, peculiar to mammals, unite with the rest of the vertebra at about the twentieth year. Still other secondary centers appear during adolescence and fuse equally late. The various *ligaments* of the vertebral column differentiate from mesenchyme in proximity to the vertebræ.

While the foregoing account holds for vertebræ in general, a few marked deviations occur. When the *atlas* is forming, its body differentiates typically but is soon taken over by the body of the *epistropheus* (axis). It thereafter serves as the peg-like extension (the *dens*) of the latter (Fig. 340 *E*). The vertebral arch of the atlas, remaining, is closed-in ventrally, so that it takes the shape of a ring (*D*). The sacral and coccygeal vertebræ represent types with reduced vertebral arches. Between puberty and about the twenty-fifth year the sacral vertebræ progressively unite into a single bony mass; a similar fusion occurs between the rudimentary coccygeal vertebræ (Fig. 342 *B*).

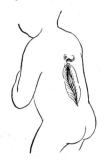

The vertebral column and its associated muscles served primitively as a flexible locomotor apparatus for propelling vertebrate animals through the water. Terrestrial life introduced many functional changes, and man has altered conditions still further by adopting an erect posture; this position, and the modified locomotion

FIG. 341.—Rachischisis, or cleft spine, exposing a flat spinal cord. Above is an adventitious tuft of hair and a separate opening.

that accompanies it, has made necessary certain peculiar adaptations. A narrowing of the spine in the upper thoracic region and toward its lower end is correlated with the presence of ribs and sternum, which help relieve the spine at the former level, and with the transference of weight to the pelvis at the latter. The curves in the vertebral column, which appear when the child learns to walk, have been mentioned in an earlier chapter (p. 183).

Anomalies.—With the exception of the cervical region, numerical variations above or below the normal number of vertebræ are not infrequent (Fig. 342 *B*). Most vertebral defects are due either to the absence of certain cartilages or bony centers, or to the imperfect fusion of otherwise well-formed components. The non-union of the paired vertebral arches is *rachischisis*, or cleft spine; it is variable in extent and exposes a corresponding length of the spinal cord (Figs. 341 and 401 *B*). When combined with a comparable defect of the brain case the condition is designated *cranio-rachischisis* (Fig. 357 *B*).

The Ribs.—The history of the ribs begins with the costal processes which grow out from the primitive vertebral mass, as already described. Only in the thoracic region do they become long bars, following the curvature of the body wall (Fig. 342 *A*). The mesenchymal rib-tissue acquires a single center of chondrification and transforms into cartilage (Fig. 340 *A*). The original union of costal process with vertebra is replaced by a joint in which a concavity on the vertebra receives the *head* of the rib; at the same time, a prominent transverse process of the vertebra extends outward and makes an articulation with a growing *tubercle* of the rib (Fig. 342 *D*).

A center of ossification appears near the future angle of each rib even before any centers occur in the corresponding vertebra. The cartilaginous rib progressively converts into bone, but the distal ends of the thoracic ribs

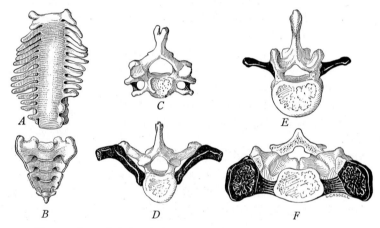

FIG. 342.—Human ribs and their relations to vertebræ. *A*, Growing thoracic ribs, in ventral view, at 13 mm. (after Müller). *B–F*, Types of vertebræ, and ribs (*C–F*, in black); *B*, anomalous sacrum composed of four (instead of five) vertebræ; *C*, cervical; *D*, thoracic; *E*, lumbar; *F*, sacral.

always remain cartilaginous. At about the time of puberty two epiphyseal centers appear in the tubercle and one in the head. The highest development of ribs is realized in the thoracic region where they maintain movable articulations with the vertebræ and follow the curving body wall to join the sternum in the midventral line (Fig. 343). In the neck they are short, and unite with the cervical vertebræ; their tubercles fuse with the transverse processes and their heads with the vertebral bodies, thus leaving an interval, the *transverse foramen*, through which the vertebral arteries course (Fig. 342 *C*). In the lumbar region the ribs are again diminutive and fused to the transverse processes (*E*). The modified ribs of the sacral vertebræ are represented by prominent, flat plates which unite on each side as a pars lateralis of the common sacrum (*B*, *F*). Only in the first of the coccygeal vertebræ do traces of ribs remain (*B*).

Anomalies.—Overdevelopment of costal processes may lead to a supernumerary rib in connection with the lowest cervical or highest lumbar vertebra (Fig. 343). The former is important practically, since it may injure the brachial plexus or subclavian artery nearby. Bifurcation of ribs sometimes occurs at their ventral ends (Fig. 343).

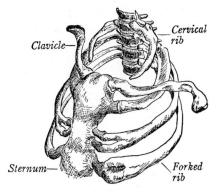

FIG. 343.—Cervical ribs and bifurcated ribs in an adult.

The Sternum.—Modern studies agree that the sternum originates from a pair of mesenchymal bands that can be identified in human embryos of

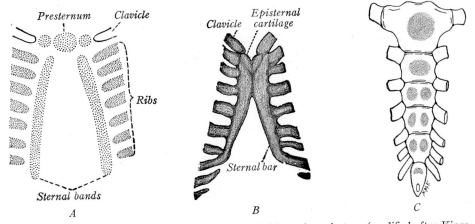

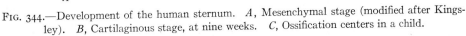

FIG. 344.—Development of the human sternum. *A*, Mesenchymal stage (modified after Kingsley). *B*, Cartilaginous stage, at nine weeks. *C*, Ossification centers in a child.

six weeks.[20] These lie ventrolaterally in the body wall and at first have no connection either with the ribs or with each other (Fig. 344 *A*). Following the prompt attachment of the ribs the paired sternal bars unite progressively in a cephalocaudal direction, at the same time incorporating cranially a smaller mesial mass which corresponds to the presternum of lower animals (*A*, *B*). At nine weeks the union of the cartilaginous bars is complete. The cranial end of the developing sternum bears two imperfectly separated episternal cartilages with which the clavicles articulate (*B*).   They usually join the manubrium of the sternum and lose their identity.

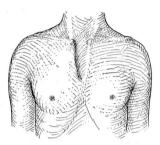

Ossification begins at about five months, but all the centers are not present until childhood. Variations in the ossification centers are not uncommon, although a bilateral tendency is evident (*C*). The segmentation of the sternum into sternebræ is acquired secondarily and has no phylogenetic significance.

FIG. 345.—Adult with a cleft sternum.

Anomalies.—Cases of cleft sternum, perforated sternum and notched xiphoid process all reflect the bilateral origin of this organ (Fig. 345). 'Suprasternal bones' are merely ossified episternal cartilages that fail to attach to the manubrium sterni (*cf.* Fig. 344 *B*); in many lower mammals such bones occur normally.

The Skull.—The head skeleton includes three primary components: (1) the brain case; (2) capsular investments of the sense organs; and (3) a branchial-arch skeleton, derived from the embryonic counterparts of the peculiar arches that support the mouth and pharynx of adult fishes and tailed amphibia (*cf.* p. 176 and Fig. 74).   Apart from some exceptions in the third group, these several elements unite intimately into a composite mammalian skull.   The branchial-arch components originally subserved the functions of respiration and mastication, and this morphological relationship has been largely maintained.   The perfecting of a palate in mammals is an innovation which makes it possible for the young to suck (and the adult to chew) and breathe at the same time.

The early notochord extends into the head as far as the pharyngeal membrane, but its termination is identified later by the caudal border of the fossa for the hypophysis located in the sphenoid bone.   In replacing the notochord of the head region, early vertebrates evolved a cartilaginous cranium that is still used by sharks, but is represented in mammals only by the floor of the cartilaginous, and later osseous, cranium.   The chordal part of this ancient cranium exists in shark embryos as two *parachordal cartilages* which accompany the notochord into the head (Fig. 346 *A*).   In man they are united as a single *basal plate* from their first appearance; this is the forerunner of the occipital bone.   Farther rostrad the prechordal part of a shark's cranium is represented by two *trabecular cartilages* (the future sphenoid bone), which flank the pituitary gland, and their fused extensions (the nasal septum of the ethmoid).   A slight trace of this doubleness can be seen in human embryos.

Alongside the parachordals, cartilaginous capsules were primitively built around the otocysts, only to fuse later with the parachordals (Fig. 346).   Their counterparts in mammals give rise to the petrous and mastoid portions of the temporal bone.   The eyes have remained independent, movable bulbs.   On the other hand, the capsules surrounding the olfactory organs joined with the trabecular cartilages and gave rise to the lateral ethmoids.

The hind- and mid-brains were primitively supported by the parachordal cartilages. However, the functional relation of the ears (both auditory and equilibratory) with the hind-brain led to the development of a prominent cerebellum, and this became housed by newer bones. These bones originated in the skin covering the brain of fishes, and they continue to differentiate similarly as membrane bones in man. The prechordal part of the skull was a primitive support for the fore-brain which expanded greatly as the result of its relation with the eyes and nose. In consequence of this, a capacious dome of dermal bone was added secondarily, and mammals similarly build a cranial vault of intramembranous origin.

Mesodermal segments do not occur rostral to the otocysts (Fig. 346 *A*). Accordingly, except in the occipital region where there are indications of the incorporation of three or four vertebræ into the skull (*B*), this part of the skeleton lacks any direct evidence of segmentation (*cf.* p. 398). The line of union of the several cartilaginous components of the primitive skull is indicated by various foramina through which nerves and blood vessels find their outlets (*B*).

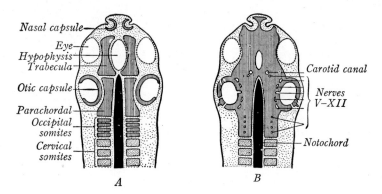

FIG. 346.—Development of the chondrocranium, somewhat schematized (after Clara).

The Desmocranium.—The earliest indication of the skull is a mass of dense mesenchyme which, during the fifth and sixth weeks, envelops the cranial end of the notochord and extends cephalad into the nasal region (Fig. 347 *A*). Laterally it expands into wings which are continuous with the general head mesoderm that houses the brain. Ventrally it communicates with the mesodermal cores of the branchial arches.

The Chondrocranium.—During the seventh week chondrification begins mesially in the future occipital and sphenoidal regions; from here it spreads laterad and to a slight extent dorsad, and also extends into the nose (Fig. 348 *A*).[21] At the same time, the internal ears become invested with cartilaginous otic capsules which eventually unite with the occipital and sphenoidal cartilages. The *chondrocranium*, as it is termed, is thus confined chiefly to the base of the skull, whereas the rest of the sides and roof is at this period a connective-tissue membrane. Chondrification also occurs more or less extensively in the branchial arches. The process as a whole is at its height by the middle of the third month and the chondrocranium is then a unified cartilaginous mass (Figs. 347 *B* and 348 *B*).[22]

The Osteocranium.—In the period of ossification which now ensues, it becomes evident that most bones develop from two or more formative centers.   To a large extent these multiple origins betray ancestral histories, since it is definitely known that certain bones, separate in lower animals, have thus combined into the compound bones of the human skull.   As such

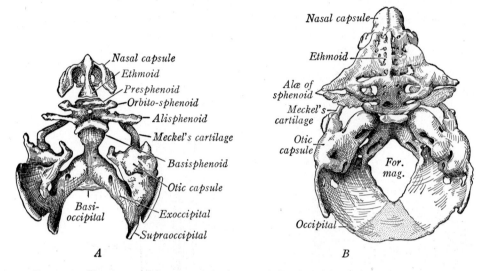

FIG. 347.—Developmental stages of the human skull, viewed from above.   *A*, Mesenchymal and cartilaginous skull, at about seven weeks (adapted; × 5).   *B*, Cartilaginous skull, at three months (after Hertwig; × 3).

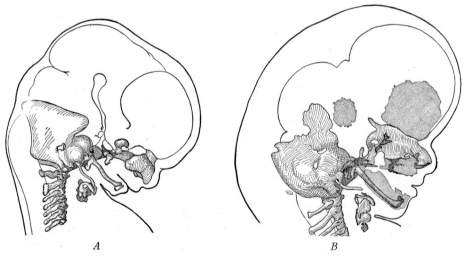

FIG. 348.—Chondrocranium of the human fetus.   *A*, During the eighth week (adapted after Lewis; × 5).   *B*, At ten weeks (after Macklin; × 3).   Membrane bones are in stipple.

components may arise either in membrane or in cartilage, the mixed nature of various adult bones is also explained.   Ossification of the chondrocranium begins early in the third month, but some membrane bones are even more precocious (Figs. 348 *B* and 353 *A*). The union of the several components of compound bones is not completed until after birth; in certain ones many years elapse before final fusion is accomplished. A striking feature of the fetal skull is the great relative size of the neural portion (Fig. 134); the ratio of cranial to facial volume decreases from 8:1 at birth to 2.5:1 in the adult.

The Occipital Bone.—Four centers appear in the cartilage about the foramen magnum (Fig. 349). From the ventral center comes the basilar part (*basioccipital*) of the future bone; from the lateral centers, the lateral portions (*exoccipitals*) which bear the condyles; from the dorsal center, the squamous part (*supraoccipital*) below the superior nuchal line. The squamous area (*interparietal*) above that line is a double-centered addition of intramembranous origin.

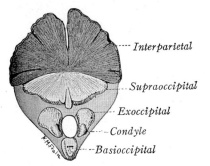

- ····*Interparietal*
- ···*Supraoccipital*
- ··*Exoccipital*
- ···*Condyle*
- ···*Basioccipital*

FIG. 349.—Human occipital bone, at four months. × 1.5. Unossified cartilage is shown as a homogeneous background.

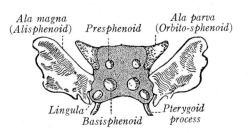

Ala magna (*Alisphenoid*)   *Presphenoid*   *Ala parva* (*Orbito-sphenoid*)

Lingula   *Basisphenoid*   *Pterygoid process*

FIG. 350.—Human sphenoid bone, at nearly four months. × 2. Parts still cartilaginous are represented in stipple.

The Sphenoid Bone.—Ten principal centers arise in the cartilage that corresponds to this bone[23] (Fig. 350): (1, 2) in each ala parva (*orbito-sphenoid*); (3, 4) in each ala magna (*alisphenoid*); (5, 6) in the corpus between the alæ parvæ (*presphenoid*); (7, 8) in the corpus between the alæ magnæ (*basisphenoid*); and (9, 10) in each *lingula*. Intramembranous bone also enters into its composition, one center forming the orbital and temporal portion of each ala magna and another center the mesial lamina of each *pterygoid process* (except the hamulus).

The Ethmoid Bone.—The ethmoidal cartilage consists both of a mesial mass, which extends from the sphenoid to the tip of the nasal process, and of a pair of masses lateral to the olfactory sacs (Fig. 351). The terminal part of the mesial mass persists as the cartilaginous *nasal septum*, but ossification of the upper portion produces the *perpendicular plate* and the *crista galli* which complete the septum. The lateral masses ossify at first into the spongy bone of the *ethmoidal labyrinths*. From these, the definitive honeycomb structure (*ethmoidal cells*) and the *conchæ* differentiate through invaginations of the nasal mucous membrane and the simultaneous resorption of bone. (In other regions of the cranium a similar invasion of the mucous membrane and a corresponding dissolution of bone produce the

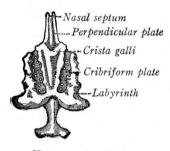

FIG. 351.—Human ethmoid bone, at four months. × 1.5.

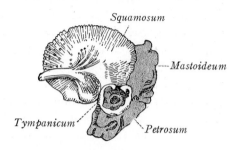

FIG. 352.—Human left temporal bone, at birth. × 1. The portion of intracartilaginous origin is represented in stipple.

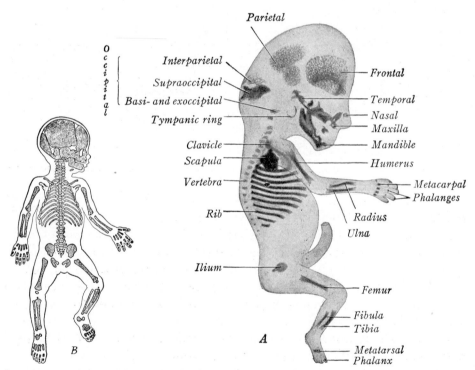

FIG. 353.—Extent of ossification in human fetuses. *A*, At eleven weeks (after Broman; × 1.5). *B*, At birth (Scammon, after Hess; × ⅛).

frontal, sphenoidal and maxillary *sinuses;* p. 485.) Fibers of each olfactory nerve at first pass between the unjoined mesial mass and its respective lateral mass. Later on, cartilaginous trabeculæ surround these bundles of nerve fibers and interconnect the three masses; upon ossifying, the perforated parts of the completed ethmoid are designated *cribriform plates*.

The Temporal Bone.—Multiple centers of ossification in the periotic cartilage produce a composite, bony capsule about the inner ear.[24] This constitutes the *petrous* and *mastoid* portions of the temporal bone (Fig. 352). However, a definite *mastoid process* first develops after birth by an outward bulging of the petrous bone. Its internal cavities, the mastoid cells, result from a postnatal invagination of the epithelial lining of the middle ear which first induces erosions and then lines the spaces thus excavated. The *squamosal* and *tympanic* portions of the temporal bone are of intramembranous origin, while the *styloid process* originates from the dorsal end of the second (hyoid) branchial arch.

Membrane Bones of the Skull.—From the preceding account it is evident that although the bones of the base of the skull arise chiefly in cartilage they receive substantial contributions from membrane. The remainder of the sides and the entire roof of the skull are wholly of intramembranous origin (Fig. 354), each of the *parietals* developing from a double center, the *frontal* from paired centers (Fig. 353 *A*). At the incomplete angles between the parietals and their adjacent bones, union is delayed for months after birth. These membrane-covered spaces constitute the *fontanelles*, or 'soft spots' (Fig. 354). Inconstant 'Wormian bones' appear frequently in such locations.

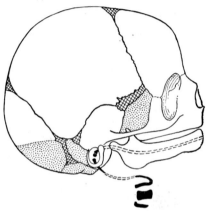

FIG. 354.—Components of the human skull, at birth. White areas represent membrane bone; stippled areas, cartilage bone; black areas, branchial-arch derivatives; cross-hatched areas, fontanelles.

The *vomer* forms from two centers in the connective tissue that flanks the lower border of the perpendicular plate of the ethmoid. The cartilage of the ethmoid, thus invested, undergoes resorption. Single centers of ossification in the mesenchyme of the facial region give rise to the *nasal, lacrimal* and *zygomatic*, all pure membrane bones. The mandible, maxilla and the palate bones are described in the next paragraphs.

Branchial Arch Derivatives.—The total contributions of the cartilaginous branchial arches to the skull are shown in black in Fig. 354. They also are illustrated more in detail in Fig. 356 and are tabulated on p. 178. The *first branchial arch* on each side forks into a rostral maxillary and a caudal mandibular process (Fig. 75). Although the jaws have a cartilaginous ancestry, no trace of this tissue appears in the developing upper jaw of mammals; on the contrary, the *maxilla* and the *palate* bones arise directly in membrane, and (like the mandible) are held to be substitutions acquired later in phylogeny (Fig. 353). Each palate bone develops from a single center of ossification. Two centers contribute to the formation of each maxilla; one gives rise to the portion bearing the incisor teeth, the other to the entire remainder.[25, 26] This agrees with the double origin from pre-maxillary and maxillary regions that is observed in the gross formation of the upper jaw (Fig. 163).

The mesenchymal core of the mandibular process transforms into a cartilaginous bar, *Meckel's cartilage*, which extends dorsad into the tympanic cavity of the ear and is there encased by the future temporal bone (Fig. 348). Despite the presence of this ancestral jaw material, which constitutes the whole lower jaw of sharks, it does not ossify into the definitive *mandible*. Instead, membrane bone has been substituted, originally for the

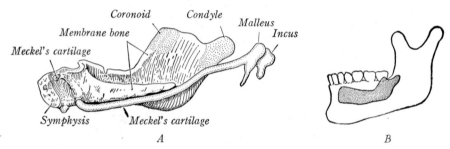

FIG. 355.—Ossification and growth of the human mandible. *A*, Relation of Meckel's cartilage to the mandible at two months (after Low; × 8); the right half of the mandible is viewed from the mesial side. *B*, Mandible of the newborn (stippled) superimposed on the adult mandible to show their relative size and shape ($\times \frac{1}{3}$).

purpose of strengthening the primitive mandible and providing supports for the teeth. Such replacing bone develops ventrally in the body of the future lower jaw and encloses both Meckel's cartilage and the inferior alveolar nerve, whereas more dorsally, in the ramus, it takes the form of a plate that merely lies lateral to these structures (Fig. 355 A). This relation explains the position of the adult mandibular foramen, where the nerve enters the jaw bone. The portion of Meckel's cartilage invested by bone disappears and contributes nothing to the permanent jaw; the latter results from the fusion of the two substitute halves, each with a single center.[27] Traced dorsad of the mandibular foramen the cartilage becomes in order: the *spheno-mandibular ligament;* the *malleus;* and the *incus* (Fig. 355 A and 356).[28] The mandible changes greatly in shape as the result of growth and the acquisition of permanent teeth (Fig. 355 B).

Each *second branchial arch* (Reichert's cartilage) also enters into relation dorsally with the otic capsule. This segment resolves into the separate *stapes,* as well as into the *styloid process* which combines with the temporal bone (Figs. 356 and 480).[26]   The succeeding portion of the arch is converted into the *stylo-hyoid ligament;* it connects the styloid process with the ventral end of the arch which, like its mate, also undergoes intracartilaginous ossification to form a lesser horn of the *hyoid* bone (Fig. 356).

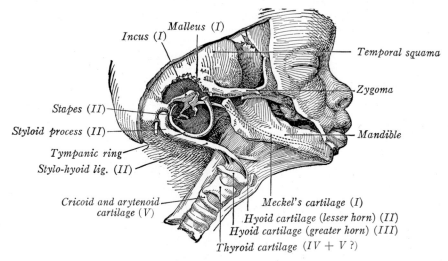

FIG. 356.—Derivatives of the human branchial arches, demonstrated in a lateral dissection of the head (after Kollmann).

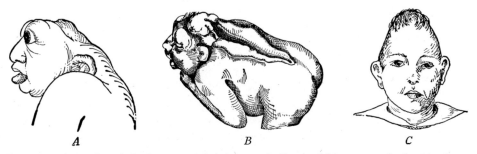

FIG. 357.—Anomalies of the human axial skeleton.   *A,* Cranioschisis, or acrania, in a newborn. *B,* Cranio-rachischisis in a newborn.   *C,* Scaphocephaly.

Cartilage occurs only in the ventral portions of the *third branchial arches.* These ossify and refashion into the paired greater horns of the *hyoid* bone, while the extreme ventral ends unite as its body (Fig. 356).

The *fourth branchial arches* differentiate in their more ventral regions into the *cuneiform* and *thyroid* cartilages (Fig. 356).[29]

The *fifth branchial arches* transform similarly into the *corniculate, arytenoid* and *cricoid* cartilages (Fig. 356).[28]   It is possible that a contribution is made to the thyroid cartilage, as well.

Anomalies.—An unclosed roof to the skull is designated *cranioschisis;* severe examples are given the names *hemicrania* and *acrania*, and in such specimens the head is set on the shoulders, without a neck (Fig. 357 *A*). The brain, thus exposed, may be either reduced in size or herniated to the outside. Sometimes combined with these defects is a similar open condition of the vertebral column, *cranio-rachischisis* (*B*). Premature closure of certain sutures, while growth continues along other margins, can result in distortions known as *scaphocephaly* (wedge-shaped cranium, *C*), *acrocephaly* (pointed top to head), or *plagio-cephaly* (asymmetrical or twisted skull). Cleft palate (p. 204), hare lip and allied conditions (p. 182) have been discussed previously.

THE APPENDICULAR SKELETON

The appendicular skeleton consists of a cranial and a caudal internal support, or girdle, and the skeleton of the free appendages attached to them. Fundamentally the two sets of girdles and limbs are comparable,

but especially in the highest vertebrates and man has specialization complicated some of the existing homologies. Torsion in opposite directions also adds to the superficial differences between the limbs (p. 185). The appendicular skeleton seems to be derived directly from the unsegmented somatic mesenchyme and not from the sclerotomes. In embryos of 10 mm. mesenchymal condensations have formed definite blastemal masses both at the sites of the future pectoral and pelvic girdles and within the primitive limb buds (Figs. 358 and 366 *A*). Following this condition, the various primordia pass through a cartilaginous stage (Fig. 368) and then transform into bone.

FIG. 358.—Mesenchymal primordium of the arm bones in a 12 mm. human embryo. × 30.

The appendicular skeleton of the newborn is incompletely ossified; some elements, like those of the wrist, are still wholly cartilaginous (Fig. 360 *A*). Secondary centers organize epiphyses between birth and the twentieth year (*B, C*). Fusions occur mostly in late adolescence.

The Upper Limb.—The *clavicle* is very large in man and some other mammals that enjoy great freedom of motion of the fore limb. It is the first bone of the skeleton to ossify, two primary centers appearing for the shaft in embryos 15 mm. long (Fig. 359). Prior to ossification it is composed of a peculiar tissue which has made it difficult to decide whether the bone is intracartilaginous or intramembranous in origin; there are some considerations in favor of the latter method.[30]

The *scapula* arises as a single plate with two chief centers of ossification and several later epiphyseal centers (Fig. 359). An early primary center forms the body, including the spine and acromion. The other, after birth, gives rise to the rudimentary *coracoid process;* in lower vertebrates this is a separate bone extending from scapula to sternum, but in man it unites with the body of the scapula and persists merely as a small projection.

The *humerus, radius* and *ulna* ossify each from a single primary center in the diaphysis and an epiphyseal center at each end (Figs. 335 and 359). Additional epiphyseal centers are typical for the humerus and may occur on the radius and ulna.

In the cartilaginous *carpus* there is a proximal row of three, and a distal row of four elements (Fig. 359 *B*). Other inconstant cartilages (like the centrale and pisiforme) may appear and subsequently disappear, or

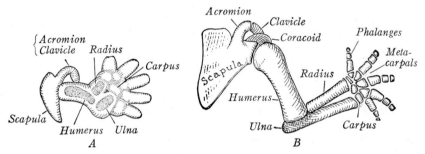

FIG. 359.—Cartilaginous skeleton of the human upper limb (adapted after Lewis). × 9. *A*, At 11 mm., with chondrification beginning. *B*, At 20 mm., with advanced chondrification.

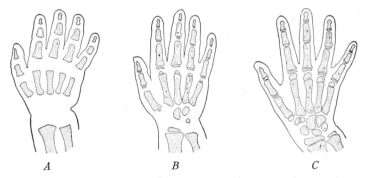

FIG. 360.—Postnatal ossification in the human wrist and hand. *A*, At birth; *B*, at three years; *C*, at seven years.

they may become incorporated into the carpal bones. Each element corresponding to an adult carpal bone ossifies after birth from a single center (Fig. 360). Each *metacarpal* and *phalanx* likewise develops from a single primary center, but there is also an epiphyseal center at one end (*B*, *C*).

The Lower Limb.—The cartilaginous plate of the coxal, or *hip bone*, is at first so placed that its long axis is perpendicular to the vertebral column (Fig. 366 *A*). Later it rotates to a position parallel with the vertebral column and then shifts slightly caudad; this brings it into relation with the first three sacral vertebræ (Fig. 361 *A*). A retention of the blastemal condition in the lower half of each primitive, cartilaginous coxal plate accounts for the *obturator membrane* which closes the foramen of the same name (*C*). Three main centers of ossification appear and gradually shape into the primitively dorsal *ilium*, ventral *ischium* and caudal *pubis* (*D*). Where the three elements join there is a cup-shaped depression, the *acetabulum*, which receives the head of the femur. The two pubic bones unite in the symphysis pubis along their midventral lengths, while the ilia articulate with the sacrum.

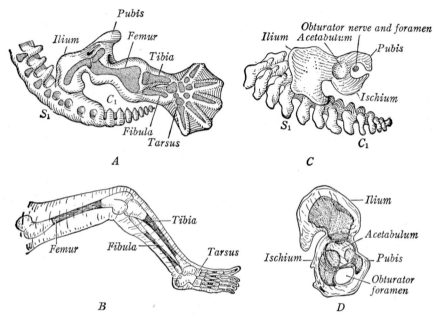

Fig. 361.—Developmental stages of the human lower limb. *A*, Early chondrification, at 14 mm. (after Bardeen; × 20). *B*, Ossification in cleared leg, at three months (× 2). *C*, Cartilaginous primordium of hip bone, at two months (after Bardeen; × 15). *D*, Ossifying hip bone, at birth (× ½).

The general development of the *femur, tibia, fibula, tarsus, metatarsus* and *phalanges* is similar to that of the corresponding bones of the upper extremity (Fig. 361 *A*, *B*). The *patella* is regarded as a sesamoid bone which develops within the tendon of the quadriceps femoris muscle.

Anomalies.—See p. 186 where malformed appendages are described, and also p. 13 for a discussion of giant and dwarf conditions.

REFERENCES CITED

1. Lewis, W. H. 1922. Anat. Rec., 23, 177–184.
2. Lewis, M. R. 1917. Carnegie Contrib. Embryol., 6, No. 17, 45–60.
3. Jordan, H. E. 1939. Am. Jour. Anat., 65, 229–251.
4. Baitsell, G. A. 1921. Am. Jour. Anat., 28, 447–475.

5. Wolbach, S. B.   1933.   Am. Jour. Pathol., **9** (Suppl.), 689–699.
6. Maximow, A.   1929.   Zeitschr. f. mikr.-anat. Forsch., **17**, 625–660.
7. Stearns, M. L.   1940.   Am. Jour. Anat., **67**, 55–97.
8. Hueck, W.   1920.   Beitr. z. pathol. Anat., **66**, 330–376.
9. Ranke, O.   1915.   Zeitschr. f. ges. Neurol. u. Psychiat., **27**, 221–245.
10. Schreiner, K. E.   1915.   Anat. Anz., **48**, 145–171.
11. Wassermann, F.   1926.   Zeitschr. f. Zellforsch. u. mikr. Anat., **3**, 235–328.
12. Shaw, H. B.   1901.   Jour. Anat. and Physiol., **36**, 1–13.
13. Sheldon, E. F.   1924.   Anat. Rec., **28**, 331–347.
14. Rasmussen, A. T.   1923.   Jour. Morph., **38**, 147–205.
15. Arey, L. B.   1920.   Am. Jour. Anat., **26**, 315–345.
16. Koch, J. C.   1917.   Am. Jour. Anat., **21**, 177–298.
17. Arey, L. B.   1919.   Anat. Rec., **17**, 59–61.
18. Digby, K. H.   1916.   Jour. Anat. and Physiol., **50**, 187–188.
19. Parsons, F. G.   1908.   Jour. Anat. and Physiol., **42**, 388–396.
20. Hanson, F. B.   1919.   Am. Jour. Anat., **26**, 41–115.
21. Lewis, W. H.   1920.   Carnegie Contrib. Embryol., **9**, No. 39, 299–324.
22. Macklin, C. C.   1921.   Carnegie Contrib. Embryol., **10**, No. 48, 57–103.
23. Fawcett, E.   1910.   Jour. Anat. and Physiol., **44**, 109–110; 207–222.
24. Bast, T. H.   1930.   Carnegie Contrib. Embryol., **21**, No. 121, 53–82.
25. Felber, P.   1919.   Morph. Jahrb., **50**, 451–499.
26. Vallois, H. V. and Cadenat, E.   1926.   Arch. de Biol., **36**, 361–425.
27. Low, A.   1910.   Jour. Anat. and Physiol., **44**, 83–95.
28. Jenkinson, J. W.   1911.   Jour. Anat. and Physiol., **45**, 305–318.
29. Frazer, J. E.   1910.   Jour. Anat. and Physiol., **44**, 156–191.
30. Hanson, F. B.   1920.   Anat. Rec., **19**, 309–325.
31. Bloom, W. and Bloom, M. A.   1940.   Anat. Rec., **78**, 497–523.
32. Bloom, W. *et al.*   1941.   Anat. Rec., **81**, 443–475.
33. Whillis, J.   1940.   Jour. Anat., **74**, 277–283.
34. Noback, C. R.   1944.   Anat. Rec., **88**, 91–125.
35. Flecker, H.   1942.   Am. Jour. Roent. and Rad. Ther., **47**, 95–159.
36. Piney, A.   1922.   Brit. Med. Jour., **2**, 792–795.

CHAPTER XVII

THE MUSCULAR SYSTEM

THE HISTOGENESIS OF MUSCLE

The muscular system is composed of specialized cells, called *muscle fibers*, whose specific contractile elements are assumed to be the component *myofibrils*. These cells constitute a distinctive tissue in which contractility has become the predominant function. The fibers are of three sorts: (1) *smooth*, found principally in the walls of the hollow viscera, glandular ducts and blood vessels; (2) *cardiac*, localized in the myocardium of the heart; and (3) *skeletal*, chiefly attached to the skeleton. Of these, cardiac and skeletal muscle are banded with cross stripes, but only skeletal fibers are under voluntary control. All three differentiate from formative *myoblasts*, originating in the middle germ layer; the only exceptions are the smooth muscles of the iris and, apparently, of the sweat and mammary glands, which are ectodermal.

Terminal, naked branches of nerve fibers end in intimate contact with muscle fibers. In smooth and cardiac muscle the endings are simply knobbed branches, but in skeletal muscle flattened terminal discs are developed which rest on a specialized 'sole plate' of muscle protoplasm.[1] The skeletal type is called a *motor end plate* (Fig. 365 E).

Myogenesis.—Cells become myoblasts by differentiating out of: (1) unspecialized mesenchyme (smooth muscle; Fig. 362); (2) splanchnic mesoderm of the myocardium (cardiac muscle; Fig. 363); and (3) myotomes and branchial arches (skeletal muscle; Fig. 365). In their early state they seem to interconnect in a syncytial manner. It may be, however, that the alleged cytoplasmic bridges represent detachable processes rather than actual anastomoses.[2, 3] Fibrillæ, coursing lengthwise in the elongating myoblasts, soon make an appearance. They are commonly described as differentiating through the linear arrangement and union of cytoplasmic granules,[4, 5] but other interpretations of fibril formation have been advanced (Fig. 363).[6, 7] The primitive fibrils multiply rapidly by splitting and thus tend to group in bundles. The fibrillæ of cardiac and skeletal muscle acquire alternate dark and light bands, the former being thickened regions (Fig. 365 C).

It is important to emphasize that myofibrillæ have never been observed in living, undisturbed muscle.[2, 3, 8] Our entire information concerning fibrils, including their development, has been obtained on dead cells after chemical or other treatment. Yet this does not necessarily imply that the fibrils are artefacts, since they may be invisible in living cells because of their optical qualities. It is wholly possible that closer study of favorable, living material may reveal them, as some think has been done in cultures of embryonic heart muscle.[25]

Smooth Muscle.—Certain stellate cells of the mesenchyme enlarge and elongate wherever smooth muscle is to appear (Fig. 362 *A*). Some of the fibrillæ of such spindle-shaped myoblasts associate in compound bundles

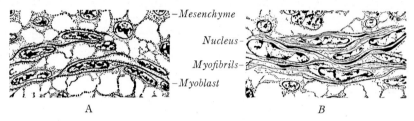

A   B

FIG. 362.—Stages in the histogenesis of smooth muscle (adapted after McGill.) *A*, 13 mm. pig embryo (× 550). *B*, 27 mm. pig embryo (× 850).

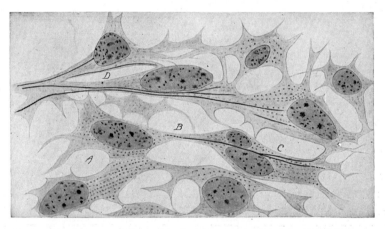

FIG. 363.—Stages in the histogenesis of cardiac muscle from a 9 mm. rabbit embryo (adapted after Godlewski). *A*, Linear arrangement of granules; *B*, coalescence of granules into a fibril; *C*, fibril splitting; *D*, long fibrils extending through syncytium.

(*B*).[6] Perhaps these correspond to the coarser border fibrils that sometimes have been interpreted as inert supporting elements.[9] Part, at least, of the reticular fibrils that surround smooth muscle fibers seem to develop within the myoblasts.[6] The nucleus retains a central position and elongates to adapt itself better to the general shape of the cell. In older fetuses new muscle elements arise not only by the transformation of interstitial cells between fibers and the specialization of mesenchyme at the surface of the muscle mass, but also by the mitotic division of fibers already present.

Cardiac Muscle.—The cardiac type of involuntary muscle develops from the splanchnic mesoderm investing the primitive heart tubes (Fig. 363). Myofibrils arise first at the periphery of the strands of cytoplasm and soon extend long distances through the 'syncytium.' The nuclei remain centrally placed; they divide mitotically at first, but perhaps amitotically later on. The characteristic *intercalated discs* appear in the later fetal stages of man and some other mammals;[10] they are still sparse in the early years but increase with age.[7, 11] The common opinion that cardiac muscle retains permanently its syncytial character has been challenged by one authority.[3]

The *Purkinje fibers* of the impulse-conducting system, located directly under the endocardium, take a different line of specialization from ordinary cardiac fibers. They are thick elements, swollen about the nuclei; their few myofibrils are located peripherally in the fiber.

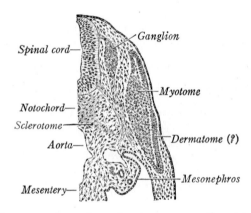

Fig. 364.—Human myotome, shown in a transverse section at 7 mm. × 48.

Skeletal Muscle.—All striated voluntary muscle is derived either from the myotomes of somites (muscles of the neck, trunk and, possibly, limbs) or from mesenchyme of the branchial arches (muscles of the head and, in part, neck).

The portion of the somite left after the emigration of the sclerotome mass is the *myotome*, or muscle plate (Fig. 337). Whether or not the lateral wall of the remaining somite becomes a *dermatome*, which furnishes connective tissue for the skin, is debated.[12, 13] In any event, the mesial wall thickens, and its cells differentiate into myoblasts (Fig. 364). These spindle-shaped elements arrange themselves parallel with the long axis of the body and transform into skeletal muscle fibers. Certain mesenchymal cells of the branchial arches undergo a similar metamorphosis.

The most controverted topic of muscle histogenesis is how these early fibers acquire their elongate and multinucleate characteristics. One interpretation views a completed fiber as a greatly drawn-out myoblast whose nucleus has undergone repeated division,[13, 14] first by mitosis and later, perhaps, by amitosis.[5] Other investigators, however, maintain that the same end is accomplished by the union of separate myoblasts into a composite fiber.[15, 16] It is possible that both methods occur. At the beginning of differentiation the nuclei lie centrally, surrounded by a granular cytoplasm (Fig. 365 A). The latter gives rise to the myofibrillæ (B, D). In the third month the light and dark markings on the fibrils come to coincide in alignment and thereafter appear as continuous bands across the fiber (C). During development the nuclei are crowded to the surface by the unequal distribution of newly forming fibrils. *Krause's membranes* consist of bridging discs of the ground cytoplasm (*sarcoplasm*); these unite the fibrils at regular intervals and produce continuous plates that are inserted peripherally into the cell membrane, or *sarcolemma*. The distinctive motor nerve endings differentiate in the fourth month (E).[17]

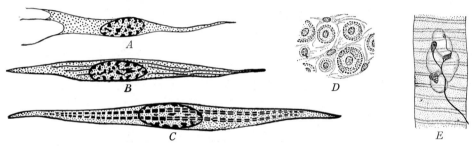

FIG. 365.—Histogenesis of skeletal muscle. *A–C*, Myoblast stages, showing fibril formation, splitting and striation (after Godlewski). *D*, Transverse sections of fibers, at different stages of differentiation ($\times$ 400). *E*, Motor end plate, at birth (after Tello; $\times$ 1000).

For a time new muscle fibers arise by the continued differentiation of myoblasts and the longitudinal splitting of fibers already present.[1] When this proliferation ceases, all further enlargement of a muscle is by the relatively enormous increase in the size of individual fibers. During myogenesis there is also a variable destruction of partly developed fibers to make room for blood vessels and connective-tissue stroma; it is possible, however, that this degenerative phase is less widespread than has commonly been credited.[1, 16]

MORPHOGENESIS OF THE MUSCLES

The muscles of the body are distributed in two systems; these are the visceral musculature and the skeletal musculature.

The Visceral Musculature.—This group, of splanchnic mesodermal origin, is associated chiefly with the hollow viscera and is under the invol-

18

untary control of the sympathetic nervous system.   Except for the striated cardiac muscle in the wall of the heart, the visceral muscles are smooth. Their commonest arrangement is in orderly sheets or interlacing bundles.

The Skeletal Musculature.—As the name indicates, these striated voluntary muscles are attached primarily to the skeleton.   With the exception of those muscles of the head and neck that differentiate out of the branchial arches, the skeletal muscles originate from myotomes.   Mesodermal segments first appear in the future occipital region of embryos about 1.5 mm. long (Fig. 71) and the full number of about forty is acquired at 6 mm. (Fig. 74).   At the latter stage (early fifth week), the older myotomes enter upon the differentiation of muscles; within the remarkably short space of the next three weeks the definitive muscles of the fetus become well fashioned and begin to be capable of correlated movements (Fig. 366 B).[18]   In this process of morphogenesis, the muscle fibers aggregate in groups that constitute the individual muscles.   These are true organs, supported and enclosed by connective tissue differentiating from out the local mesenchyme.

Fundamental Processes.—Although the primitive segmental arrangement of myotomes is for the most part soon lost, their original innervation by the segmental spinal nerves is retained throughout life.   For this reason the history of adult muscles formed by fusion, splitting, migration or other modifications may be traced with considerable certainty.   A nerve enters its muscle at or near the midpoint.   Although this innervation is acquired early, an innate capacity for contractility already resides in the muscle fibers.   Nor is the development of a muscle or a muscle group dependent on the presence of nerve.

An analysis of how muscles develop grossly shows that there are several basic principles operating, and that these are utilized again and again by different muscles throughout the body.   Since this is true, it is easier and more instructive to state the general principles involved rather than to describe in detail the histories of individual muscles, or even minor muscle groups.   Some six developmental factors can be recognized and listed, as follows:

1. A *change in direction* of muscle fibers from the original cranio-caudal orientation in the myotome.   The fibers of but few muscles retain their initial orientation parallel to the long axis of the body.

2. A *migration* of muscle primordia, wholly or in part, to more or less remote regions.   Thus the latissimus dorsi originates from cervical myotomes but finally attaches to the lower thoracic and lumbar vertebræ and to the crest of the ilium.   A shift in the opposite direction is shown by the facial musculature of expression which takes origin in the second branchial arches.   The muscles of the ventral trunk illustrate ventral growth from the dorsally placed myotomes.

3. A *fusion* of portions of successive myotomes into a composite muscle. Both the rectus abdominis and the sacro-spinalis illustrate this process.

4. A *longitudinal splitting* of myotomes or branchial-arch muscle primordia into subdivisions. One example is found in the sterno- and omohyoid, another in the trapezius and sterno-mastoid.

5. A *tangential splitting* into two or more layers. The oblique and the transverse muscles of the abdomen are formed in this common way.

6. A *degeneration* of myotomes or parts of myotomes. By this method fascias, ligaments and aponeuroses are produced.

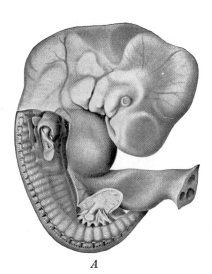
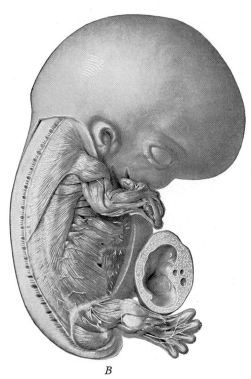

A   B

FIG. 366.—Muscles of the trunk and limbs in human embryos (after Bardeen and Lewis). *A*, At 9 mm., showing the partially fused myotomes and the premuscle masses of the limbs ($\times$ 7); distally, in the upper limb, the radius, ulna and hand plate are disclosed; in the lower limb the primordial hip bone and the border vein show. *B*, At 20 mm. ($\times$ 4.5).

Muscles of the Neck and Trunk.—The previous chapter has explained how the myotomes come to alternate with the permanent vertebræ (Figs. 338 and 339 *B*). From them arise not only the dorsal musculature, but also the lateral and ventral muscles of the thoracic and abdominal walls. In embryos 10 mm. long, all the myotomes have fused superficially, while ventral extensions have also grown out from those of the cervical and thoracic regions (Fig. 366 *A*). In this manner segmentation invades the somatopleure as a secondary phenomenon; in fishes the original myotomic segments remain distinct throughout the trunk. Nevertheless, at the 10 mm.

stage a dorsal longitudinal column of fused myotomes on each side can still be distinguished from the sheets produced from their combined ventral prolongations (Fig. 366 *A*).

From the superficial portions of the two dorsal myotomic columns there arise, by longitudinal and tangential splitting, the various *long muscles of the back and neck* innervated by the dorsal rami of the spinal nerves (Fig. 366 *B*). The deepest portions of the myotomes do not fuse but give rise to the several *intervertebral muscles* which thus retain their primitive segmental arrangement. This spinal musculature was primitively a powerful sculling mechanism—the first locomotor apparatus of vertebrates.

The *muscles of the neck*, other than those innervated by the dorsal rami just mentioned and those arising from the branchial arches, differentiate from ventral extensions of the cervical myotomes. The muscles of the

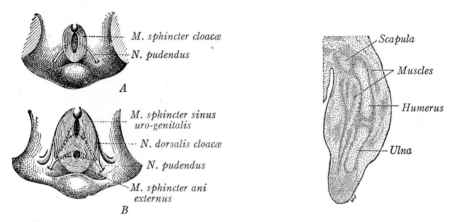

FIG. 367.—Early development of the human perineal muscles (Lewis, after Popowsky). *A*, At two months; *B*, at three months.

FIG. 368.—Muscle primordia of the human arm, at 16 mm. ($\times$ 18).

diaphragm, which in early stages lies at this high level, appear to have a like origin. In similar manner the *thoraco-abdominal muscles* arise from expansive ventral prolongations of the thoracic myotomes which grow into the body wall along with the ribs (Figs. 204 and 366). The ventral extensions of the lumbar myotomes (except the first) and of the first two sacral myotomes do not participate in the formation of the body wall. If they persist at all, it is possible that they contribute to the formation of the lower limbs. The ventral portions of the third and fourth sacral myotomes are represented, however, by the levator ani and coccygeus muscles.

The *perineal muscles* develop somewhat tardily, apparently from ventral portions of the third and fourth sacral myotomes. Temporarily there is a common cloacal sphincter (Fig. 367 *A*), but this undergoes subdivision in conformity with the partitioning of the cloaca into rectal and urogenital canals. The more dorsal of the secondary sphincters persists as the external anal sphincter, while the ventral sphincter differentiates into the various muscles of the urogenital region (B).

Muscles of the Limbs.—In sharks and rays it is clear that buds from the myotomes grow into the embryonic fins and there break down into mesenchyme that is the source of the fin muscles. With higher vertebrates this is not so clearly the case, and in birds and mammals a direct myotomic origin of the muscles of the appendages is usually denied. In this connection it should be emphasized that the segmental nerve supply of the limb muscles of higher animals is merely suggestive, not proof, of a myotomic origin. Nevertheless, a diffuse migration of cells from the ventral edges of human cervical myotomes has been claimed by several investigators,[19] and even myotomic extensions toward the limbs are now on record.[20] These cells soon lose their epithelioid character and blend with the undifferentiated mesenchyme of the limb buds. The limb tissue, of seemingly mixed origin, condenses into premuscle masses at about the 9 mm. stage (Figs. 366 A and 368). From them the girdle- and limb muscles differentiate; the proximal ones are the first to appear and, at any level, the extensors sooner than the flexors. The progressive modeling of distinct muscles reaches the level of the hand and foot in embryos of seven weeks (Fig. 366 B). The upper limbs naturally maintain an advance over the lower throughout development. Due to the opposite rotations of the arms and legs in reaching their definitive positions (p. 185), the muscles on the inner side of one set of limbs are homologous to those on the outer side of the other.

Muscles of the Head.—Except at the base, definite somites do not occur in the head region. It is possible, however, that a distinct mass of compact mesenchyme, from which the eye muscles of man are developed, is comparable to three specialized myotomic segments (so-called *head-cavities*) having a similar fate in the shark (Fig. 369 A). Of interest in this regard is the fact that the muscles of the eyeballs are activated by the third, fourth and sixth pairs of cranial nerves; all of these nerves are somatic motor in nature and thus are of the same type as those innervating other muscles derived from typical myotomes.

The remaining muscles of the head differ from all other skeletal muscles in that they arise from the lateral, uncleft mesoderm of the branchial arches and are innervated by nerves (visceral) of a different category from those (somatic) that supply myotomic muscles (p. 459). The muscles derived from the several arches retain their primitive branchial-arch innervation (Fig. 369 A and table, p. 178). Hence it follows that the mesoderm of the *first branchial arch* not only gives rise to the muscles of mastication but also that these are associated with the trigeminal (fifth) nerve. Similarly, the muscles of expression, and all other muscles supplied by the facial (seventh) nerve, originate from the *second* (or hyoid) *arch* (*B*). The *third arch* appears to be the source of muscles, like the pharyngeal constrictors, that receive branches of the glossopharyngeal (ninth) nerve. The *fourth* and *fifth arches* share the vagus (tenth) nerve; it innervates their derivatives, such as the laryngeal muscles and part of the pharyngeal and palate group. The accessory (eleventh) nerve, really a part of the vagus complex, innervates the sterno-mastoid and trapezius muscles which are usually regarded as of branchial-arch origin.

The *muscles of the tongue* are supplied by the hypoglossal (twelfth) nerve, originally a member of the spinal series. For this reason it is suspected that these muscles are derived from myotomes of the occipital region. Historically this assumption is undoubtedly true, and a continuation of the

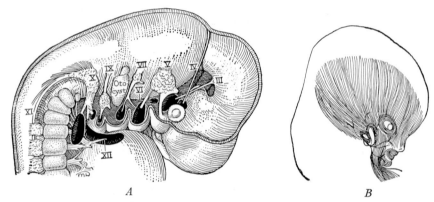

A *B*

FIG. 369.—Development of the muscles of the human head. *A*, Premuscle masses, at 8 mm. (× 10). The following muscles are identified by their numbered cranial nerves: ocular (III, IV, VI); masticatory (V); facial (VII); pharyngeal (IX); laryngeal and palatine (X); sterno-mastoid and trapezius (XI); lingual (XII). *B*, Superficial muscles of the head, at seven weeks (after Futamura; × 4); the distribution of the facial nerve is also shown.

same method of origin in present-day embryos is held by some authorities as highly probable even though not yet demonstrated.[21] A more objective interpretation, in the absence of any direct proof of migration, favors an *in situ* development from the mesoderm of the floor of the mouth.[22]

Segmentation of the Vertebrate Head.—The vertebrate head consists of fused segments. This was suggested to the earlier workers by the arrangement of the branchial arches (*branchiomerism*), by the presence of supposedly significant 'neuromeres' in the brain wall (p. 435), and by the discovery, in the embryos of lower vertebrates, of specialized somites (the so-called *head-cavities*).[23]

Only the first three head-cavities persist; they resolve into the eye muscles. All the remaining muscles of the head are derived from branchiomeres. Even assuming that the branchiomeres represent portions of the primary head somites—and there are sufficient observations which tend to disprove this—their segmentation still is not comparable to that of the trunk; this is because the branchial arches originate through the serial division of lateral mesoderm, tissue which in the trunk never segments. The branchial arches, therefore, represent a different sort of metamerism.[24] From what has been said it is evident that one cannot compare the relation of the cranial nerves to the branchiomeric muscles with the relation of a spinal nerve to its myotomic muscles. Because of this, the cranial nerves furnish unreliable evidence as to the primitive number of cephalic segments. Various investigators have set this hypothetical number between eight and nineteen.

Anomalies.—Sometimes a whole muscle or a part of a compound muscle is lacking because of agenesis. Some muscles, not normally found, are occasionally represented, while other constant components may have abnormal relations or attachments; since both conditions simulate features found regularly in lower primates, these occurrences are viewed as an expression of atavism. Numerous vestigial muscles are represented regularly (*e.g.*, ear; scalp) or occasionally (*e.g.*, elevator of clavicle; sternalis; tail muscles). Variations in the form, position and attachments of the muscles are common. Most muscular anomalies are referable to an over- or underexpression of particular developmental factors, as listed on p. 394.

REFERENCES CITED

1. Tello, J. F. 1922. Zeitschr. f. Anat. u. Entwickl., **64,** 348–440.
2. Lewis, M. R. 1922. Carnegie Contrib. Embryol., **9,** No. 35, 191–212.
3. Lewis, W. H. 1926. Carnegie Contrib. Embryol., **18,** No. 90, 1–21.
4. Godlewski, E. 1902. Arch. f. mikr. Anat. u. Entwickl., **60,** 111–156.
5. Weed, I. G. 1937. Zeitschr. f. Zellforsch. u. mikr. Anat., **25,** 516–540.
6. Haggquist, G. 1931. Bd. 2, Teil 3 in Möllendorff's 'Handbuch der mikroskopischen Anatomie des Menschen.' Springer, Berlin.
7. Cohn, A. E. 1932. Sect. 28 in Cowdry's 'Special Cytology.' Hoeber, N. Y.
8. Meigs, E. B. 1932. Sect. 27 in Cowdry's 'Special Cytology.' Hoeber, N. Y.
9. McGill, C. 1907. Internat. Monatschr. f. Anat. u. Physiol., **24,** 209–245.
10. Bruno, G. 1923. Arch. ital. di Anat., **20,** 1–22.
11. Zschiesche, E. S. and Stillwell, E. F. 1934. Anat. Rec., **60,** 477–486.
12. Williams, L. W. 1910. Am. Jour. Anat., **11,** 55–100.
13. Bardeen, C. R. 1900. Johns Hopkins Hosp. Rep., **9,** 367–400.
14. Iwanga, I. 1925. Mitt. ü. allg. Path. u. path. Anat., **2,** 395–406.
15. Meves, F. 1909. Anat. Anz., **34,** 161–165.
16. Asai, T. 1914. Arch. f. mikr. Anat., **86,** 8–68.
17. Cuajunco, F. 1942. Carnegie Contrib. Embryol., **30,** No. 195, 127–152.
18. Coghill, G. E. 1929. Arch. Neurol. and Psychiat., **29,** 989–1009.
19. Ingalls, N. W. 1907. Arch. f. mikr. Anat. u. Entwickl., **70,** 506–576.
20. Zechel, G. 1924. Zeitschr. f. Anat. u. Entwickl., **74,** 593–607.
21. Kingsbury, B. F. 1915. Am. Jour. Anat., **18,** 329–397.
22. Lewis, W. H. 1910. Chapter 12 in Keibel and Mall's 'Human Embryology.' Lippincott, Phila.
23. Neal, H. V. 1918. Jour. Morph., **30,** 433–453.
24. Kingsbury, B. F. 1926. Jour. Morph. and Physiol., **42,** 83–109.
25. Hogue, M. J. 1937. Anat. Rec., **67,** 521–535.

ECTODERMAL DERIVATIVES

CHAPTER XVIII

THE INTEGUMENTARY SYSTEM

The contributions of ectoderm to the oral, nasal and anal cavities, and specifically to the development of teeth, tongue, palate and salivary glands, are described in earlier chapters. Here will be presented the histogenesis of the skin and the development of its specialized derivatives.

THE SKIN

The integument is an organ of double origin. Its superficial component is a stratified epithelium called the *epidermis*, specialized from the ectoderm. The epidermis lies upon a fibrous *corium* of mesodermal origin.

The Epidermis.—The embryonic ectoderm is originally a single sheet of cuboidal cells (Fig. 370 *A*), but in the fifth week it begins to add a second layer (*B*). The outer cells make up a distinct, transient layer named the *periderm*. Its cells flatten and later spread to several times the diameter of the deeper cells. The basal cells, of cuboidal shape, are the reproducing elements that gradually give rise to new layers above them. During the third and fourth months the epidermis is typically three-layered, an intermediate stratum being gradually interposed between the basal and periderm cells (*C, D*).

After the fourth month the epidermis becomes highly stratified and specialized (Fig. 370 *E, F*). The deepest layer (basal cells) and its immediate descendants in the layers next above (prickle cells) constitute the definitive *stratum germinativum*. It contains the actively dividing cells of the epidermis. Daughter cells of this layer are crowded upward by still newer ones, and these outer layers undergo progressive cornification as they approach the free surface. Thus, directly above the germinative cells is the thin *stratum granulosum*, containing keratohyalin granules. Next higher lies the thin and clear *stratum lucidum* whose content is a fluid eleidin, supposed to represent softened and fused keratohyalin granules. Still nearer the surface, the epidermal cells flatten steadily and comprise the many-layered *stratum corneum*. The thickened ectoplasm becomes cornified in a way not well understood, and the epidermis thereby loses its primitive transparency. More centrally in the cytoplasm of these cells a fatty substance collects that is considered to be transformed eleidin (para-eleidin).

Nevertheless, it is only in the thickened epidermis of the palm and sole that all the layers just mentioned are distinguishable; over the general body surface the granular and lucid strata are not clearly represented. In a few regions, like the margin of the lip, cornification is slight. Pigment granules appear soon after birth in the cells of the stratum germinativum; these granules are probably elaborated by the cytoplasm of the epidermal cells themselves.[1] Negro infants are quite light in color at birth, but begin to darken within a few days; at six weeks their integument approaches the final degree of pigmentation.

When the hairs emerge, at about the sixth fetal month, they do not penetrate the toughened periderm of the epidermis but loosen or break it. Hence in mammals this layer is known also by another name, the *epitrich-*

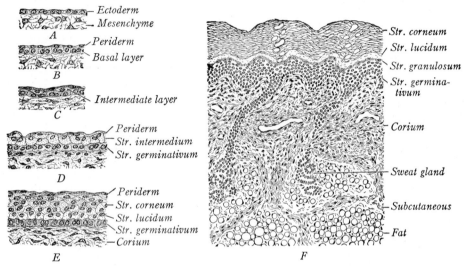

FIG. 370.—Development of the human skin, shown in vertical sections. × 160. *A*, At 4 mm.; *B*, at 12 mm.; *C*, at two months; *D*, at three months; *E*, at five months; *F*, at birth (× 100).

ium (*i.e.*, upon the hair). Desquamated epitrichial and epidermal cells mingle with cast-off lanugo hairs and sebaceous secretions to form the pasty *vernix caseosa* that smears the fetal skin. This material is alleged to protect the epidermis against a macerating influence which otherwise would be exerted by the amniotic fluid.

The plane of union between epidermis and corium is smooth until early in the fourth month when epidermal thickenings grow down into the corium of the palm and sole. About two months later corresponding elevations first appear on the skin surface (Fig. 370 *F*). These epidermal ridges complete their permanent patterns in the second half of fetal life.

The Derma or Corium.—The fibrous layer of the integument in the region of the somites is usually traced to cells proliferated from the lateral walls of these segmental elements. In consequence, the lateral wall of a somite has received the name *dermatome*, or cutis plate (Fig. 364).[2] Evidence in support of this claim is not plain in mammals and it has been urged that the so-called dermatome really belongs to the myotome.[3] In this event, the corium must differentiate from non-specific mesenchyme subjacent to the epidermis, most of which comes from the lateral sheets of somatic mesoderm.

Collagenous fibers differentiate in the third month and elastic fibers considerably later. Only gradually does a distinction between the compact corium proper and the looser, subcutaneous tissue become recognizable

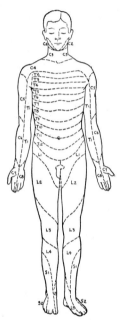

(Fig. 370 *F*). Later, fat develops abundantly in the subcutaneous layer, while some of the corial cells acquire pigment granules. Certain areas in the sacral region tend to be heavily pigmented; they are named 'Mongolian spots' since they occur regularly in children of the yellow

FIG. 371.—Diagram of the distribution of the segmental spinal nerves to 'dermatomic' cutaneous areas.

FIG. 372.—Severe ichythyosis in a human newborn.

race. Columnar papillæ project upward from the corium into the germinative stratum; the dermal papillæ are of two kinds, depending on whether they contain blood vessels or nerve endings. The skin is innervated by segmental spinal nerves that supply successive, ring-like bands or zones of the integument (Fig. 371). These are the so-called dermatomic areas.

Anomalies.—The deposition of pigment in the epidermis and elsewhere may fail (*albinism*) or be over-abundant (*melanism*). Such defective pigmentation sometimes affects local areas only. *Nævi* are either pigmented spots ('moles') or purple discolorations caused by cavernous vascular plexuses in the corium ('birth-marks'). *Ichthyosis* designates an excessive thickening of the stratum corneum. In severe cases there are horny plates separated by deep cracks, like the skin of reptiles (Fig. 372). *Dermoid cysts* (p. 292), resulting

from epidermal inclusions, are not infrequent along the lines of fusion of embryonic structures (*e.g.*, branchial grooves; mid-dorsal and midventral body wall).

THE NAILS

Nails are modifications of the epidermis that correspond to the claws
and hoofs of lower mammals.   The first indication of a nail is foreshadowed
at ten weeks by a thickened area of epidermis (*nail field*) on the dorsum of
each digit (Fig. 373 *A*).   This becomes bounded by an elevated wall under
which it soon grows in a proximal direction almost to the articulation of the
terminal phalanx (*B*).   Splitting of this plate gives origin to the *proximal
nail fold*, continuous laterally on each side with a shallow *lateral nail fold*.

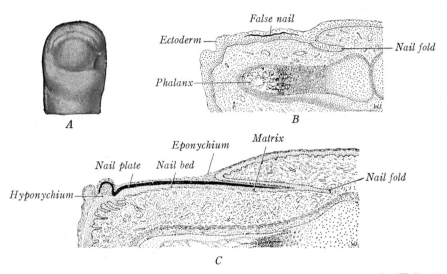

FIG. 373.—Development of the human nail.   *A*, Dorsum of finger, at ten weeks (Kollmann;
× 10).   *B*, Longitudinal section, at fourteen weeks (× 33).   *C*, Longitudinal section, at birth
(× 15).

Although the primitive nail field undergoes some local cornification
('false nail'; Fig. 373 *B*), the material of the true nail is developed within
the under layer of the proximal nail fold.   This layer is accordingly named
the *matrix* (*C*).   During the fifth month specialized keratin fibrils differentiate in the matrix layer, without having passed through a keratohyalin or
eleidin stage as in the ordinary method of cornification.[1]   The keratinized
cells flatten and consolidate into the compact tissue of which the *nail plate*
is composed.   In this manner the nail substance differentiates in the proximal nail fold as far distad as the outer edge of the *lunula* (the whitish
crescent at the base of the exposed nail), but not beyond it.   The nail plate
merely shifts progressively over the *nail bed* and reaches the tip of the finger
one month before birth.   As might be expected, the nails of the toes are

completed slightly later than the finger nails. The corium beneath the nail is thrown into parallel longitudinal folds which are said to produce the characteristic ridging and grooves.

The stratum corneum and periderm of the epidermis for a time cover completely the free nail and are jointly termed the *eponychium* (*i.e.*, upon the nail; Fig. 373 *C*). In late fetuses this is lost, but portions of the horny layer continue to adhere to the nail plate along the curved rim of the nail fold. Underneath the free end of the nail the epidermal cells also accumulate to constitute a piled-up epidermal mass known as the *hyponychium*, or substance beneath the nail; this region is much more important in a claw, and still more so in a hoof where it forms the 'sole.' The opacity of the lunula has been interpreted variously.

Anomalies.—Absence of nails (*anonychia*) is recorded.

THE HAIR

Hairs are specialized epidermal threads produced only by mammals. The comparative hairlessness of man today is a character acquired within

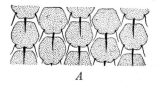 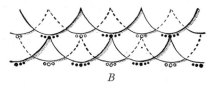

A   *B*

FIG. 374.—Relation of hair groups to scales. *A*, Arrangement on the opossum's tail (after Danforth and de Meijere). *B*, Arrangement in the human fetus, with hypothetical dermal scales drawn in (after Stöhr).

relatively recent times. Since it is similar to the condition found in late fetuses of anthropoid apes, this reduced hairiness is regarded as an example of arrested development. Hairs tend to be grouped in threes or fives, with the central one larger, and also to be arranged in lines. These relations are interpreted as the survival of a primitive mammalian condition in which the hairs stood in definite relation to scales which covered the skin, after the manner still seen in certain living forms (Fig. 374).

Hairs begin to develop early in the third month on the eyebrows, upper lip and chin; those of the general integument originate one month later. The first evidence of a future hair is the crowding and elongation of a cluster of germinative cells in the epidermis (Fig. 375 *A*). Their bases sink root-like into the corium, and active proliferation soon produces a cylindrical, epithelial peg (*B*). At this stage the hair follicle consists of an outer wall of columnar cells, continuous with the basal layer of the epidermis, and an internal mass of polyhedral cells. About the whole is a mesenchymal investment (the later *connective-tissue sheath*), and at the clubbed base the mesenchyme condenses into a mound-like *papilla*.

As development proceeds and the hair peg pushes deeper into the corium, its base enlarges into the *bulb* which becomes molded over the papilla (Fig. 375 *C*).   The actual hair substance is a proliferation from the basal epidermal cells lying next the papilla (Fig. 376).   These cells give rise to an axial core, destined to become the *inner epithelial sheath* and *shaft*, which grows upward toward the surface.   Quite distinct are the peripheral cells on the sides of the original downgrowth, which comprise the *outer epithelial sheath.*

The young hair shaft grows by the steady addition of new cells in the bulb.   In this manner it is pushed up through the central cells of the solid, primordial follicle and is molded into shape by the organizing inner sheath. The shaft finally reaches the epidermis, follows along a *hair canal* in it

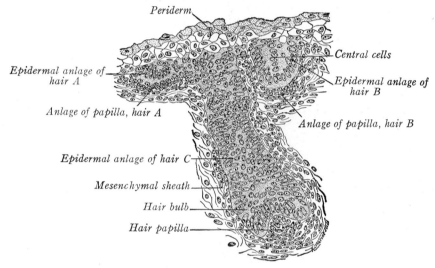

FIG. 375.—Human hair follicles, at three months, shown in longitudinal section (Prentiss). × 330. Three stages (*A*, *B* and *C*) are included.

(Fig. 378 *A*), and erupts at the surface.   Above the level of the bulb, the cells of the hair shaft cornify and differentiate into an outer *cuticle*, middle *cortex*, and central (inconstant) *medulla*.   Two swellings of the outer epidermal sheath appear on the lower side of the obliquely directed follicle (Fig. 376).   The upper of these becomes the *sebaceous gland*, which will remain permanently associated with the hair; the deeper swelling is the *epithelial bed*, a region of rapid mitosis that contributes to the growth of the periodically regenerating hair follicle.   Mesenchymal tissue near the epithelial bed transforms into the smooth fibers of the *arrector pili* muscle, which attaches to the side of the follicle.   Pigment granules develop early in the basal cells of the hair; such cells are carried upward along with other hair cells and cause the characteristic coloration.

The first generation of fetal hairs is a downy coat termed *lanugo*. It constitutes a dense covering to the body, prominent by the seventh month. Lanugo hairs are short-lived, all being cast off either before birth or soon afterward. The replacing hairs develop, at least in part, from new follicles. Thereafter hair is shed and formed anew periodically throughout life. At the termination of any growth cycle the hair is carried upward by its short-

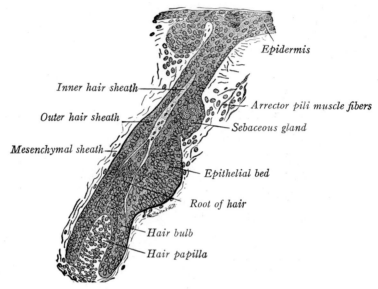

FIG. 376.—Human hair follicle, at six months, shown in longitudinal section (after Stöhr). × 220.

FIG. 377.—Hypertrichosis of the forehead and nose.

ening, regressive follicle. After a time the follicle reorganizes and begins to elaborate a new hair in the manner already described (Fig. 378 *B*).

Some hairs remain permanently of the lanugo type: in the female such occur on the face, neck and trunk; in the male, on the face (except beard), the flexor surface of the upper arms and various regions of the trunk. The replacing hairs of the brows, eyelashes and scalp of children are progressively larger and coarser than the first set. Under the influence of hormones, and especially those of the gonads, coarser and darker hairs appear at puberty on the pubis and axilla of both sexes and on the face and trunk of the male. The hair coat shows definite, directional patterns (streams; whorls). These are established by similar angular slants of the hair follicles at their first development in any local region.

Anomalies.—*Hypertrichosis* refers to excessive hairiness which may be localized (Fig. 341) or general, as in exhibited 'hairy monsters' (Fig. 377). It is undecided whether this is due to an augmented development of the later hair follicles or to a persistent overgrowth of lanugo. In the rare *hypotrichosis* the congenital absence of hair may be complete (*atrichia*); it is usually associated with defective teeth and nails.

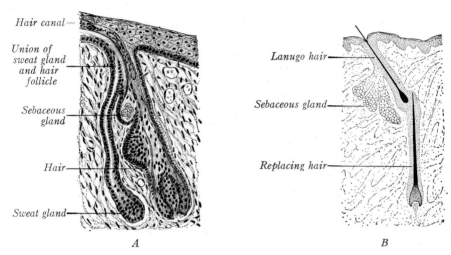

Hair canal —

Union of sweat gland and hair follicle

Sebaceous gland

Hair —

Sweat gland —

Lanugo hair —

Sebaceous gland —

Replacing hair —

A   B

FIG. 378.—Human cutaneous glands. *A*, Early stage in the development of a sebaceous gland and a sweat gland, both in association with a hair follicle (after Pinkus; × 125). *B*, Later sebaceous gland, connected to the follicle of a lanugo hair which is being replaced by a coarser hair (× 80).

SEBACEOUS GLANDS

Most of the sebaceous glands accompany hairs. However, some independent ones, such as those on the genitalia, anus, nostrils and upper eyelids develop from the general epidermis. Many of these do not organize until after birth.

Gland primordia appear first in the fifth month as swellings on the outer epithelial sheaths of the hair follicles (Fig. 376 *C*). The swelling becomes a lobulated, flask-shaped sac whose lumen arises by the fatty degeneration of the central cells (Fig. 378). The resultant oily secretion is an important constituent of vernix caseosa (p. 401); it is usually credited with helping to preserve the fetal skin from maceration. Cells in the neck of a sac are the reproducing elements. Throughout life they supply new cells, which are forced centrad and disintegrate in the process of oil elaboration. Such a gland is *holocrine* (*i.e.*, the secretion consists of altered gland cells themselves).

Anomalies.—Congenital occlusion of the ducts of sebaceous glands can lead to the formation of sebaceous cysts, such as the 'wens' located on the scalp. It is possible that some cysts arise through the displacement and growth of epithelial remnants of other kinds.

SWEAT GLANDS

Sudoriferous glands first begin to develop in the fourth month from the deep epidermal ridges of the finger tips, palms of the hands, and soles of the feet. They are formed as solid, cylindrical ingrowths, but differ from hair primordia in being more compact and in lacking the mesenchymal papillæ at their bases (Fig. 379 *A, B*). During the sixth month the simple

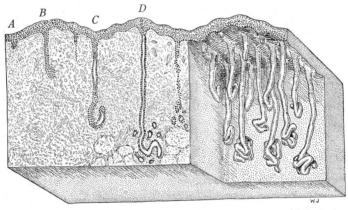

FIG. 379.—Development of human sweat glands, shown in a model of the skin. × 40. Left half, gland stages (*A–D;* four to seven months) in longitudinal section. Right half, epidermis and glands isolated from the corium.

cords coil, and in the seventh month their lumina arise by a hollowing process (*C, D*). An inner layer of cells about the lumen constitutes the gland cells. By contrast, the outer cells transform into flattened elements that are usually considered to be smooth muscle fibers; this interpretation is of special interest since such muscular elements would then be ectodermal. The duct portion of the gland at first ends blindly at the epidermis, but later, as cells are replaced during the course of growth in the stratified epithelium, a canal is left which continues the duct lumen to the surface.

In certain regions of the body supplied with coarse hairs (pubis; axilla; areola; eyelids) there are large, specialized sweat glands. These develop on the sides of the hair follicles and move upward until they acquire separate openings on the epidermis (Fig. 378 *A*).[4] An association with hair follicles is characteristic for sweat glands in general in most mammals.

Human glands of this type are *apocrine* (*i.e.*, the tops of their secretory cells break away along with the secretion).

MAMMARY GLANDS

Mammary glands are peculiar to mammals. It is remarkable that they appear so early in development, not only since they are of use to adults alone but also because they are a late acquisition among vertebrate organs.

Early in the sixth week of human development an ectodermal thickening extends on each side as a longitudinal band between the bases of the limb buds. At about 9 mm. it makes a distinct linear elevation that

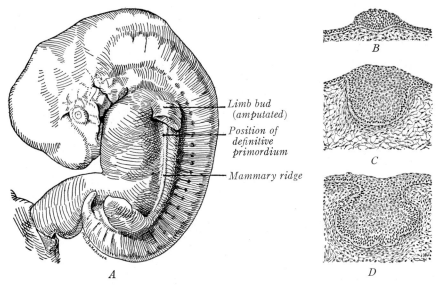

Limb bud
(*amputated*)

Position of
definitive
primordium

Mammary ridge

A   D

FIG. 380.—Early development of the human mammary gland. *A*, Unusually prominent mammary ridge, at 13 mm. (after Kollmann; × 5). *B–D*, Vertical sections of gland primordia, at six weeks, nine weeks and four months, respectively (× 80).

has been called the *mammary ridge*, or *milk line* (Fig. 380 *A*). In man this usually is inconspicuous except in the pectoral region, and in any event all but the cranial third normally vanishes quickly.[5] By contrast, lower mammals with serially repeated glands, like the pig, have a prominent milk line extending from axilla to groin (Fig. 548).

Each human mammary gland begins as one of several localized thickenings on the corresponding epidermal milk line in the region of the future breast. At first lens-shaped (Fig. 380 *B*), the primordium gradually becomes globular (*C*), and then bulbous and lobed (*D*). During the fifth month from 15 to 20 solid cords bud inward into the corial connective tissue (Fig. 381). These primary *milk ducts* branch, but *acini* are a very late feature. Two or three months later lumina appear by hollowing. Meanwhile the free surface of the primordium flattens and deepens into a pit into which the ducts open (Fig. 382).   About the time of birth this sunken area elevates into the *nipple*.   The *areola* is first recognizable as a circular area, free of hair primordia but acquiring branched *areolar glands* (of Montgomery) in the fifth month (Fig. 382).

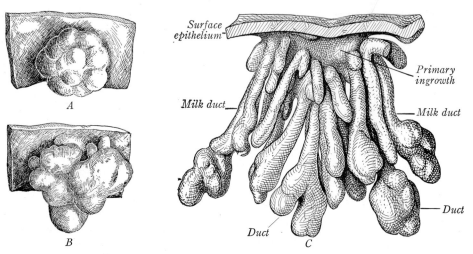

FIG. 381.—Later development of the human mammary gland, shown by models (after Broman and Lustig).   *A*, At fourteen weeks (× 45); *B*, at five months (× 45); *C*, at six months (× 30).

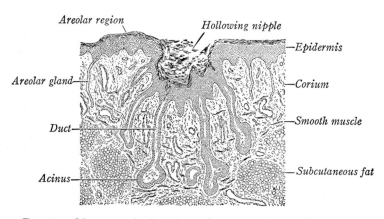

FIG. 382.—Mammary gland of the newborn, in vertical section.   × 24.

The male glands do not advance much beyond the infantile condition. In the female the areolar region becomes elevated before puberty, where-upon this stage is followed by a rapid enlargement (through fat deposition about the growing ducts) until the breast is a hemisphere bearing the areola and nipple at its apex (Fig. 383).   The mammæ are further augmented during pregnancy, the epithelial elements advancing greatly both in bulk and structural differentiation. Two or three days after parturition the glands become functionally active. This culmination of development is a response to hormonal stimulation. In this process, the ovarian secretions excite the preliminary changes, whereas the anterior lobe of the hypophysis is the final activator responsible for actual lactation. The mammary glands of the newborn of both sexes also yield a little secretion ('witch milk') within a few days after birth. Their activity at this time depends upon the presence in the blood of the same hormones, as the result of placental permeability, that bring about lactation in the mother.[6]

The mammary glands are regarded by most authorities as modified sweat glands of the apocrine type. This homology is made because their development is similar and because in the lowest mammals their structure

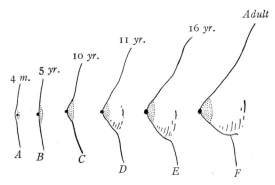

FIG. 383.—Profiles of the female breast after birth.

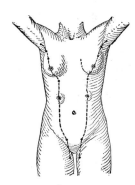

FIG. 384.—Accessory mammæ on the adult abdomen. The courses of the embryonic milk lines are also indicated, and the commonest locations of mammary rudiments are marked by dots.

is the same. Moreover, rudimentary mammary glands (the areolar glands), which also resemble sweat glands, occur about the nipple. In many mammals several pairs of mammary glands are developed along the milk line (pig; dog); in some a single pair occupies the pectoral region (primates; elephant); in others they are confined to the inguinal region (sheep; cow; horse).

Anomalies.—Absence of the mammary glands (*amastia*), retention of the prepubertal condition (*micromastia*) and the attainment of abnormal size (*macromastia*) are all known. In some instances the male develops a breast, more or less of the female type (*gynecomastia*). This condition has a tendency to be associated with hermaphroditism or other abnormalities of the sexual organs. Two examples of actual milk secretion by an adult male have been recorded.[7] Supernumerary mammary glands (*hypermastia*) are quite rare, but accessory nipples (*hyperthelia*) are fairly common in both sexes. It is said that at least 1 per cent. of large populations may show traces of them.[8] They occur chiefly between the axilla and groin and represent independent differentiations along the primitive milk line, such as occur normally in some mammals (Fig. 384).

REFERENCES CITED

1. Hoepke, H.   1927.   Bd. 3, Teil I in Möllendorff's 'Handbuch der mikroskopischen Anatomie des Menschen.'   Springer, Berlin.
2. Williams, L. W.   1910.   Am. Jour. Anat., 11, 55–100.
3. Bardeen, C. R.   1900.   Johns Hopkins Hosp. Rep., 9, 367–400.
4. Steiner, K.   1926.   Zeitschr. f. Anat. u. Entwickl., 78, 83–97.
5. Lustig, H.   1915.   Arch. f. mikr. Anat., 87, 38–59.
6. Lyons, W. R.   1937.   Proc. Soc. Exp. Biol. and Med., 37, 207–209.
7. Haenel, H.   1928.   Münch. med. Wochenschr., 75, 261–263.
8. Speert, H.   1942.   Quart. Rev. Biol., 17, 59–68.

CHAPTER XIX

THE CENTRAL NERVOUS SYSTEM

HISTOGENESIS OF THE NERVOUS TISSUES

Both the nervous system and the sensory epithelia are derived from portions of the primitive integument. The basis of most of the nervous system is a thickened band of ectoderm (*neural plate*) along the mid-dorsal line of the embryo (Fig. 393). This tissue is determined neurally by induction; in amphibians it occurs at the gastrula stage. At first the neural plate is flat and but a single layer of cells thick. However, it rapidly becomes stratified and the growth rate differs at the margins and in the midplane (Fig. 385 A).[1] As a result of such unequal growth the plate is folded into

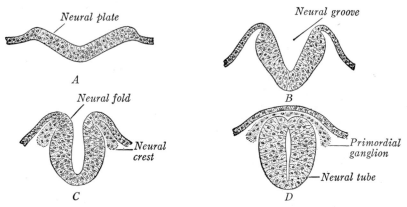

FIG. 385.—Origin of the neural tube and neural crest, illustrated by transverse sections from early human embryos. × 125.

a *neural groove* by the time somites are appearing; the groove itself is bounded on each side by an elevated *neural fold* (B, C). The groove continues to deepen and the thickened neural folds presently meet and fuse dorsally, thereby rolling the original plate into a *neural tube* (D). At the completion of this process the tube lies below the surface of the ectoderm and is detached from it.

Along the line of junction of the neural plate with the general ectoderm a longitudinal band of cells appears on each side (Fig. 389). [This is the *neural (ganglionic) crest*, from which are derived the ganglion cells of both the cranial and spinal ganglia, and, perhaps, of the sympathetic ganglia as well] The neural-tube substance gives rise to the remaining nervous elements with two exceptions: these are the nerve cells and fibers of the olfactory epithelium and certain cranial ganglia that receive contributions from special epidermal thickenings called *placodes*.[2] [3]

At the beginning of its development, the neural tube is composed of undifferentiated, proliferative epithelium. Its daughter cells adopt two lines of specialization (Fig. 387). One leads toward *nerve cells*, in which irritability and conductivity have become predominant functions; the other course is toward *ependymal* and *neuroglia cells*, which constitute the distinctive supporting tissue of the nervous system.

The formative nerve cell is a *neuroblast;* it passes through a bipolar stage, with a process at each end, to a multipolar stage or immediate precursor of the typical *neuron* of the central nervous system. The *spongio-*

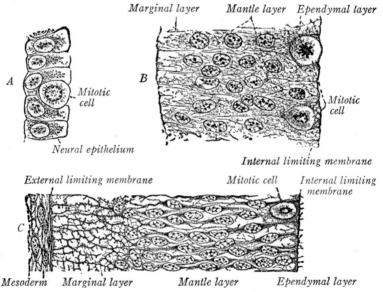

FIG. 386.—Differentiation of the wall of the neural tube (Hardesty). × 690. *A*, Stage of the neural plate; *B*, at 5 mm.; *C*, at 10 mm.

blast is the forerunner both of the *ependymal cells* and of neuroglia cells known as *astrocytes*. Some spongioblasts are migratory in nature; these differentiate into *oligodendroglia* and into astrocytes, as well. It has been claimed that migratory spongioblasts can also convert into neuroblasts,[4] but this interpretation is open to grave doubt.[5]

The wall of the neural tube, derived from an earlier single layer of columnar cells (Fig. 386 *A*), rapidly becomes many-layered (*B*); in doing this the component cells lose their sharp outlines and seemingly resolve into a compact syncytium, which is bounded on its outer and inner surfaces by an *external* and *internal limiting membrane*, respectively (*C*).[6] Some, however, maintain that the resemblance to a syncytium is an artefact and

the constituent cells are always distinct.[7,8]   In 10 mm. embryos the elements
of such a system are arranged radially and nearly parallel (C).   At this
stage the neural tube is sufficiently organized so that three layers may be
distinguished: (1) an inner *ependymal zone*, with its cell bodies abutting on
the internal limiting membrane and their processes extending peripherally;
(2) a middle, nucleated *mantle zone*, derived by proliferation of the innermost cells; and (3) an outer, noncellular *marginal zone*, into which the nerve
processes (nerve fibers) grow.

The ependymal zone, originally the uppermost stratum of the neural-
plate stage, not only contains the inertly supporting ependymal cells but
also mitotic stem cells.   The mantle layer makes up the future gray substance of the central nervous system; it is predominantly cellular in structure and contains the cell bodies of the neurons and many neuroglia cells.

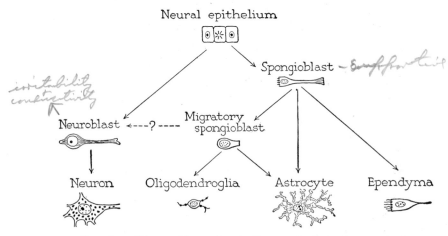

FIG. 387.—Diagram illustrating the lineage of cells in the neural tube.

The marginal layer is a fibrous mesh that provides a basis into which the
processes of nerve cells grow and reach their destinations; thereby neuron
is linked with neuron and center with center.   It becomes the white substance of both the brain and spinal cord.   The details of the transformation
of neuroblasts into neurons and spongioblasts into ependyma and neuroglia
will occupy the descriptions that follow.

The Differentiation of Neuroblasts.—The neuroblasts are embryonic
nerve cells which finally lose the power of division, develop cell processes
and convert into definitive *neurons*. [A neuron is the structural and functional unit of nervous tissue] it consists of a nerve cell with all its processes.
Mitosis among neuroblasts ceases during the first year of postnatal life,
although many have completed their proliferative course long before birth.
Thereafter the nervous system matures and enlarges, but the capacity of

cell division is forever lost. The total number of neurons contained in the nervous system is remarkably constant, and this regardless of the size of the individual.

The origin of the nerve fibers as extensions from the neuroblasts is easiest understood in the development of the root fibers of the spinal nerves.

The Development of Efferent Neurons.—Toward the end of the first month neuroblasts separate from the general 'syncytium' in the mantle layer of the neural tube. The young, bipolar neuroblasts become pear-shaped, and from the small end of the cell a slender primary process grows out (Fig. 388). This process is the *axon*, or axis cylinder. Such primary processes may course in the marginal layer of the neural tube, or penetrate

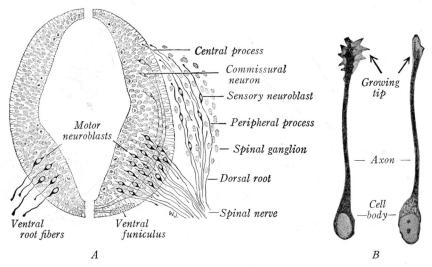

Central process

Commissural neuron

Sensory neuroblast

Peripheral process

Spinal ganglion

Dorsal root

Spinal nerve

Motor neuroblasts

Ventral root fibers

Ventral funiculus

A

Growing tip

Axon

Cell body

B

FIG. 388.—Differentiation and growth of human neuroblasts. *A*, Spinal cord, in transverse section; left, at 4 mm. (× 225) and right, at 5 mm. (× 140). *B*, Two neuroblasts, demonstrating neurofibrils and the enlarged, growing tip (Cajal; × 500).

the marginal layer ventrolaterally to emerge as a *ventral root* of a spinal nerve (Fig. 388 *A*). In a similar manner the efferent fibers of the cranial nerves grow out from neuroblasts of the brain wall. Within the cytoplasm of even young nerve cells and their primary processes, fine *neurofibrillæ* can readily be demonstrated by selective staining methods as elements distinct from mitochondria, Nissl granules and other cytoplasmic constituents (Fig. 388 *B*). Their visibility in living cells has been asserted and denied in recent years.[9,10] There is no proof that neurofibrillæ are the conducting elements through which nervous impulses are transmitted, and their functions remain unknown. The cell bodies of the efferent neurons soon become multipolar by the development of branched secondary processes, the *dendrons* (or *dendrites*).

Development of the Ganglia and Afferent Neurons.—After the formation of the neural plate and groove, a longitudinal ridge of cells appears on each side where the ectoderm and neural plate join (Fig. 389 *A*). This ridge of ectodermal cells is called the *neural (ganglion) crest.* Some emphasize its origin from the lateral part of the neural plate,[3,11] while others find that the adjoining body ectoderm also contributes to its substance.[12] When the neural folds become a tube and the ectoderm separates from it, the cells of the ganglion crests overlie the neural tube like a wedge and complete its closure (*B*). As development continues they separate into right and left linear halves, distinct from the neural tube, and settle to a position between the tube and the myotomes (*C*). On its arrival in this location the ganglion crest is a cellular band extending the full length of the spinal cord and far

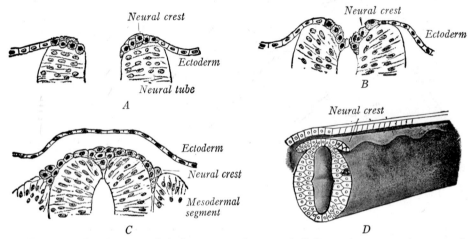

FIG. 389.—Development of the human neural crest. *A–C*, Successive stages, at 2.5 mm., in transverse section (Lenhossék; × 250). *D*, Model of the early spinal cord and beaded crest (Kingsley).

cephalad along the brain wall.[3] At regular intervals, agreeing with the position of mesodermal segments, the proliferating cells of the crest give rise to bead-like enlargements, the *spinal ganglia* (*D*). The serially repeated spinal ganglia of each side are interconnected for a short time by parts of the originally continuous crest substance (Fig. 437), but these bridges soon disappear (Fig. 438). In the hind-brain region, ganglia of the cranial nerves develop also from the crest but differ in not being segmentally arranged.

The cells of the ganglion primordia differentiate into *ganglion cells* and *supporting cells*, groups that are comparable to the neuroblasts and spongioblasts of the neural tube. The neuroblastic cells of the ganglia elongate into fusiform elements, and by developing a primary process at each end transform into neurons of the bipolar type (Fig. 388 *A*). The growing processes that are directed toward the neural tube converge into distinct bundles that represent the *dorsal roots*. These penetrate the dorsolateral walls of the neural tube; here their fibers bifurcate and course cephalad and caudad in the marginal layer of the spinal cord. By means of branched end-processes they come in contact with the neurons of the mantle layer. The peripheral processes of the ganglion cells complete the dorsal spinal roots by passing outward and joining the ventral roots; the common bundles, thus formed, constitute the trunks of the *spinal nerves* (Fig. 390 *A*). Although bipolar at first, most of the ganglion cells become unipolar in a way not surely understood. Presumably a part of the cell body draws out into

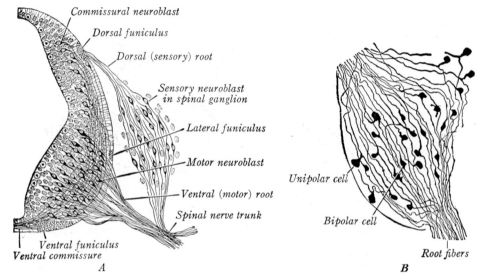

A   *B*

FIG. 390.—Development of a human peripheral nerve. *A*, Spinal cord and nerve, at 7 mm., in transverse section (× 120). *B*, Stages in the transformation of bipolar into unipolar nerve cells, shown in a longitudinal section of the spinal ganglion at ten weeks (Cajal).

a common stem that bears the two processes at its tip.[13] In Fig. 390 *B* there can be traced various stages between typical bipolar and unipolar cells. Rarely the bipolar ganglion cells persist in the adult, or develop secondary processes and thereby gain a multipolar shape.

In addition to forming the spinal and cerebral ganglion cells, certain neuroblasts of the ganglion crest are believed to migrate ventrally and differentiate into some of the cells of the sympathetic ganglia; the details of this process will be given in a later section. Other crest cells become encapsulating and sheath cells, while still others mingle with the general mesenchyme. The fate of the latter is not easy to follow, but in the amphibian head, at least, they can be shown to be responsible for the formation of certain cartilages of the branchial region.[14] In man a similar contribution to the first and second branchial arches is suspected,[3] but conditions observed in the rat throw some doubt on such interpretations.[11]

Differentiation of the Supporting Elements.—*Supporting Elements of the Neural Tube.*—The brain and spinal cord are given stability by ecto-dermal, interstitial tissue in the form of ependymal cells, which bound the spinal canal and extend outward toward the periphery, and by neuroglia cells which are more irregularly distributed. A preceding paragraph has described how the spongioblasts originate from the undifferentiated cells of the neural-plate tissue and become more or less altered. The degree and direction of this specialization determines whether they result in ependyma or neuroglia.

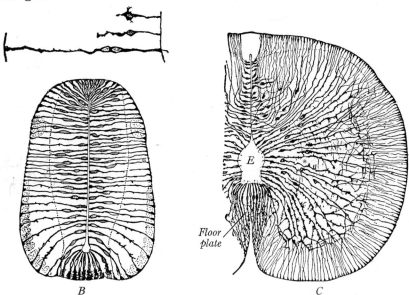

FIG. 391.—Differentiation of supporting tissue, demonstrated in transverse sections of the spinal cord (Cajal). *A*, Growth of ependymal cells in a chick embryo of one day (× 1000). *B*, Ependymal tissue in a chick embryo of three days (× 240). *C*, Human embryo of ten weeks (*E*, ependyma; *, neuroglia) (× 45).

For a while the spongioblastic elements are radially arranged like col-umnar epithelium. One end, which also contains the nucleus, projects cilia into the cavity of the neural canal; in the other direction the cell bodies extend even to the periphery of the neural tube (Fig. 391 *A*, *B*). Those spongioblasts that retain their primitive shape and position are known as *ependymal cells* (*C*, 'Floor plate'), but most spongioblasts differentiate further. These elements migrate outward and lose their connections with the neural canal (*C*, *); some cells, so displaced, retain a peripheral attach-ment, but most abandon both central and distal connections and convert into *neuroglia cells* (Fig. 392). It is of interest to note that the several developmental stages encountered in mammals merely recapitulate the progressive neuroglial conditions found within the chordate group.

In its final state the ependymal tissue consists of elements whose nuclei lie next the cavity of the brain or spinal cord, and whose cell bodies radiate outward like columnar epithelium. Primitive ependymal relations are clearly retained only at the midplane of the spinal cord and medulla (Fig. 391 *C*); in other regions the distal processes of ependymal cells extend only a short distance beyond the cell body. Elsewhere in the brain and spinal cord the supporting elements are neuroglia cells, distributed throughout the mantle and marginal layers. They are of two morphologic types: (1) *astrocytes*, stellate in shape and with long processes (Fig. 392 *A*, *B*); and (2) *oligodendroglia*, with a smaller cell body and fewer, finer processes (*C*). A third type, *microglia* (*D*), should be mentioned although it would appear that they do not belong developmentally, structurally or functionally with the true neuroglia. In spite of counterclaims,[15,16] these elements, which are

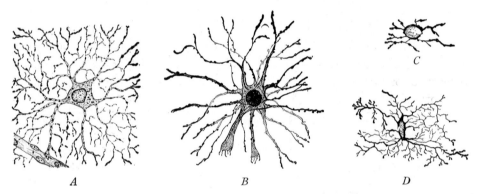

FIG. 392.—Types of neuroglia cells (after Penfield). × 650. *A*, Protoplasmic astrocyte; *B*, fibrous astrocyte; *C*, oligodendroglia cell; *D*, microglial cell.

ameboid phagocytes, probably originate from mesodermal cells.[17,18] They could, therefore, be appropriately named *mesoglia*.

The astrocytes are derived from full-length primitive spongioblasts, from spongioblasts that (due to the thickness of the tube) never connect with the periphery, and from wandering spongioblasts (Fig. 387). Astrocytes appear first in the third month. Those occupying the gray substance are named *protoplasmic astrocytes* (Fig. 392 *A*); another type, *fibrous astrocytes*, develop fibrils within their cytoplasm and are typical of the white substance (*B*). The oligodendroglia, derived solely from migratory spongioblasts, arise at a later period than astrocytes (*C*).

Supporting Elements of the Ganglia.—The supporting cells of the cerebrospinal ganglia at first make up an apparent syncytium, in the meshes of which are found the neuroblasts. The interstitial elements differentiate both into flattened *capsule cells*, which invest the ganglion cells, and into *sheath cells* which migrate peripherally along with the developing nerve fibers and envelop the axons (Fig. 447 *A, B*).

The Neurilemma Sheath.—Peripheral nerve fibers are enveloped by a cellular sheath (of Schwann). The component cells have two sources of origin. Some differentiate from the tissue of the early neural crest.[19] Slightly later many others emerge from the neural tube by way of the ventral roots.[20, 21] The young sheath cells are spindle-shaped and enclose bundles of nerve fibers. Multiplication on the part of the sheath cells then separates the bundles into single fibers, each with its own *neurilemma*.

The Myelin Sheath.—Between the fifth month and the weeks following birth a fatty *myelin* (medullary) *sheath* begins to appear about many nerve fibers.[22] It surrounds the chief process (axis cylinder) and, in turn, is enclosed by the neurilemma. The origin of the myelin is in doubt. By some it is believed to be a differentiation of the neurilemma, the myelin being deposited inside the nucleated sheath cell. Others regard the myelin as a direct product of the axis cylinder or as an intercullular substance precipitated through its influence. Still others refer to the co-operation of the neurilemma and axis cylinder.[23] The integrity of myelin is dependent, at least, upon the nerve cell and axis cylinder, for when a nerve is injured it promptly shows degenerative changes. In the central nervous system there are no distinct neurilemma sheaths investing the fibers. Nevertheless, scattered 'sheath cells' are said not only to be present but also most numerous during the period when myelin is differentiating. Some trace their origin to the spongioblastic supporting cells of the neural tube,[6] while others identify them with oligodendroglia.[5]

The *myelinated fibers* (*i.e.*, those with a myelin sheath) have a glistening, white appearance which gives the characteristic color to the white substance of the central nervous system and to the peripheral nerves. The process of myelin deposition is begun at the middle of fetal life, but is not completed until adolescence. Many of the fibers of the central nervous system remain *unmyelinated*. The same is true of many fibers in the peripheral nerves of the cerebro-spinal series and sympathetic nervous system, yet all these are supplied with a neurilemma sheath.

The Neuron Doctrine.—The neuron concept of the development and structure of nerve fibers has successfully withstood adverse criticism since its foundation by Kupffer (1857) and His (1886), and is generally accepted today. It repudiates the idea that nerve fibers develop from cell chains or a syncytium and holds: (1) that all axons and dendrites are true outgrowths from nerve cells; and (2) that each neuron remains throughout life a discrete structural and functional unit. The evidence for this conclusion, as seen in sectioned, developing embryos, has been corroborated by direct observation on axon growth day by day in living tadpoles[32] and by proving that nerve cells, isolated in clotted lymph, sprout out long processes.[24] Conversely it can be shown that the peripheral nerves of amphibian larvæ do not develop if the neural tube and crest are removed.[25] Critical cytological observations favor discontinuity where processes and cells of different neurons come into functional contact.[26] Collateral evidence is afforded by the behavior of neurons after severance or injury; the fibers distal to the point of section (and thus isolated from their cell bodies) degenerate, whereas the central stumps live and regenerate.[27]

MORPHOGENESIS OF THE CENTRAL NERVOUS SYSTEM

The primitive neural tube is fashioned by the folding of the neural plate into an epithelial tube, as described in the previous section. The groove begins to close about midway of its length in embryos with six somites and the closure advances progressively in both directions (Fig. 393). With continued growth of the embryo caudad, the neural groove extends steadily in that direction; at first an open trough, it folds into a tube as fast as is

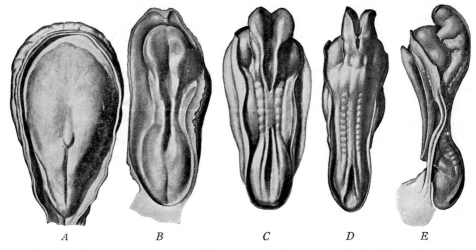

| A | B | C | D | E |

FIG. 393.—Developmental stages of the human neural groove and tube (Streeter). All but *E* are in dorsal view. *A*, Presomite embryo, with neural plate and primitive streak (× 40). *B*, At three somites, with deep neural groove (× 37). *C*, At seven somites, with closure beginning midway (× 31). *D*, At ten somites, with closure extending into brain region (× 31). *E*, At nineteen somites, with closure complete except for neuropores (× 20).

mechanically possible. The open caudal end of the neural tube is called the *posterior neuropore;* it closes off at about the 25-somite stage. Below this level the remainder of the neural tube cannot be added by folding. Instead, it differentiates progressively, along with the rest of the caudal trunk, out of the formative cell-mass that constitutes the 'end bud' (p. 99).[28]

In the meantime fusions at the rostral end of the groove have continued the neural tube into the future brain region. In embryos with 15 somites the tube is complete as far as the fore-brain, and shortly afterward (20 somites) the terminal aperture, known as the *anterior neuropore*, seals off (Fig. 394). This is not located at the original rostral end of the neural plate, since ventral fusions have advanced somewhat to meet the dorsal neural folds. The exact site in the brain of the end of the primitive neural plate is not known,[29] but is thought to be at the optic recess (Fig. 419).[30] But even in early stages of neural-tube formation, and before closure enters the future brain region, the rostral half of the neural tube has enlarged (and 'constricted' at two points) to indicate the three *primary brain vesicles* (Fig. 393). The rest of the neural tube, which remains smaller in diameter, is the *spinal cord*. Its elongation waits on the development of the caudal end of the body; in Fig. 393 *E* closure has progressed only to a low thoracic level.

Both the brain and spinal cord share in certain general histogenetic and morphogenetic processes; they are preliminary to the acquisition of those structural details that specifically characterize these organs. As a result of such differentiation the entire neural tube at an early period can be ana-lyzed both into concentric layers and into longitudinal strips. The concentric layer-ing is the outcome of the histogenetic differentiation already described. Viewed as a whole, the neural tube really consists of three concentric 'tubes,' which are in order (Fig. 395): (1) the inner *ependymal layer*, bounding the central canal; (2) the middle, cellular *mantle layer;* and (3) the outer, fibrous *marginal layer*. The neural tube also can be subdivided into six longitudinal strips or bands (Fig. 395). The primitive dorsal and ventral walls are primarily ependymal in structure and do not partic-ipate in the marked thickening that characterizes the lateral walls; these dorsal and ventral walls are named, respectively, (1) the *roof plate* and (2) the *floor plate*. Midway on the inner surface of each lateral wall is a groove, the *sulcus limitans*, which marks its subdivision into (3, 4) a more dorsal *alar plate* (sensory) and (5, 6) a more ventral *basal plate* (motor).

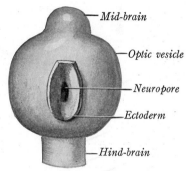

FIG. 394.—Anterior neuropore, shown in a front view of the brain of an eighteen-somite human embryo (after Sternberg). × 64.

The central nervous system is relatively large throughout the fetal period. Even at birth the brain constitutes 11 per cent. of the body weight, whereas in the adult it is but 2.5 per cent. The spinal cord relatively out-grows the brain during the postnatal years, increasing from 0.9 per cent. of the brain weight to 2 per cent.

The *meninges* serve as closed coverings to the brain and spinal cord. Next the neural tube is the delicate *pia-arachnoid*, which seems to be de-rived, at least chiefly, from migrant cells of the neural crest.[31, 32] More externally, *dura mater* organizes from the re-arrangement and condensation of the surrounding mesenchyme.[32, 33] It is a distinct membrane at eight weeks.

The remainder of the present chapter will be devoted to descriptions of how the spinal cord and the brain organize both in internal structure and external form.

THE SPINAL CORD

The wall of the spinal portion of the neural tube thickens so quickly that in the fourth week the typical three layers have already made their appearance (Fig. 395). Coincidental with this growth comes a relative narrowing of the internal cavity. For a time the neural canal is some-

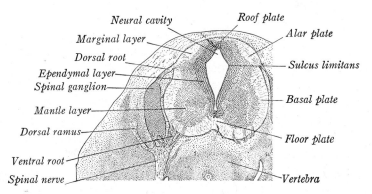

FIG. 395.—Human spinal cord, at six weeks, in transverse section (after Prentiss). × 30.

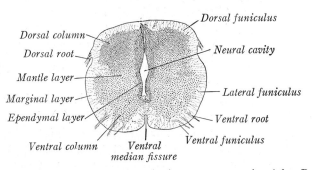

FIG. 396.—Human spinal cord, at nearly eight weeks, in transverse section (after Prentiss). × 30.

what diamond-shaped in transverse section, its lateral angle, as the sulcus limitans, subdividing the side wall into alar and basal plates. Later the side walls are approximated dorsally, and at about nine weeks fusion obliterates the dorsal part of the neural cavity (Figs. 396 and 397). In a fetus of three months the persisting ventral portion has rounded into the definitive *central canal* (Fig. 398).

The **Ependymal Layer** differentiates into a dorsal roof plate and a ventral floor plate (Fig. 395). Laterally its proliferating cells contribute neuroblasts and neuroglia cells to the mantle layer. This proliferation ceases first in the ventral floor which is thus narrower than the dorsal portion in 10 to 15 mm. embryos. When the ependymal layer ceases to contribute new cells to the mantle layer, its walls are approximated dorsally and fusion follows (Figs. 396 and 397). The cells lining the resulting central canal are ependymal cells proper (Fig. 398).

When the right and left walls of the central canal fuse dorsally, the bordering ependymal cells lose their radial direction and unite into a median seam (Fig. 391 *C*). Later, as the marginal layer of each side thickens and meets its mate, this septum is extended dorsally. In this manner the

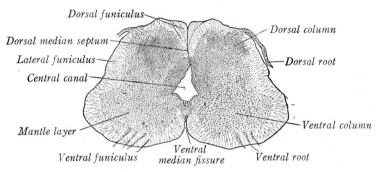

FIG. 397.—Human spinal cord, at nine weeks, in transverse section (after Prentiss). × 30.

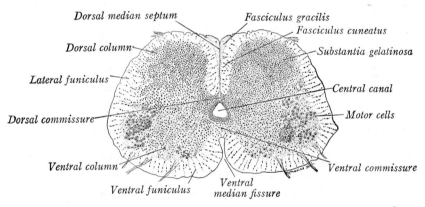

FIG. 398.—Human spinal cord, at three months, in transverse section (after Prentiss). × 30.

roof plate is obliterated as such, but is converted into part of the *dorsal median septum* of the definitive spinal cord (Fig. 398). On the ventral side the floor plate of ependymal tissue lags in development, and since it is interposed between the rapidly thickening right and left walls of the ventral marginal layer (ventral funiculi), these do not meet; instead there is produced a longitudinal furrow, known as the *ventral median fissure* of the spinal cord. The ependymal fibers of the persistent floor plate extend from central canal to the surface and thus retain their primitive relations (Fig. 391 *C*).

19

The **Mantle Layer** receives contributions from the proliferating cells of the ependymal layer in a manner already described (p. 415). In embryos of 10 to 15 mm. a thickening of this zone first becomes prominent ventro-laterally (Fig. 395). It constitutes the *ventral* (anterior) *gray column*, which in later stages supplies migrant cells that organize also a *lateral gray column*. Both are derivatives of the basal plate. In embryos of 20 mm. a tardier dorsolateral thickening of the mantle layer is likewise seen, the cells of which represent the *dorsal* (posterior) *gray column* (Figs. 396 to 398); about these cells the dorsal root fibers end. The cells of the dorsal gray column, deriv-atives of the alar plate of the cord, thus become terminal nuclei for the afferent spinal nerve fibers. Above and below the central canal, the mantle layer narrows into the *dorsal* and *ventral gray commissures*. Fetuses of three months have the *gray substance* arranged in what is essentially the per-manent form (Fig. 398). With respect to the functional specialization of neuroblasts it can be said that those concerned with the reception and transmission of sensory messages have their cell bodies situated in the cerebro-spinal ganglia; those that have to do with motor impulses are located in the ventral and lateral columns; all the remainder are concerned in linking up the sensory and motor systems.

The **Marginal Layer** is composed primarily of a framework made up of the processes from ependymal and neuroglia cells. Into this mesh grow the axons of nerve cells, so that the significant thickening of the marginal layer is due entirely to nerve fibers contributed by neuroblasts and ganglion cells located elsewhere. The development of myelin about many of the fibers in the marginal zone is responsible for the appearance of a definite, peripheral layer of *white substance* in the spinal cord.

The dorsal root fibers from the spinal ganglion cells, entering the cord dorsolaterally, subdivide the white substance in this region into *dorsal* and *lateral funiculi* (Fig. 397). The lateral funiculus, in turn, is marked off by the ventral root fibers from the *ventral funiculus*. In the ventral floor plate, nerve fibers cross over from both sides of the cord as the *ventral white commissure*. The white substance as a whole is arranged in bundles, or *tracts*, whose general relations and proportions are attained at the middle of the fetal period. The dorsal funiculus is formed chiefly by the dorsal root fibers of the ganglion cells, which enter and course cephalad and caudad in the marginal layer. It is subdivided into two distinct bundles, the *fasciculus gracilis*, median in position, and the *fasciculus cuneatus*, lateral (Fig. 398). The lateral and ventral funiculi are composed: (1) of *fasciculi proprii*, or ground bundles, originating in the spinal cord and intercon-necting adjacent regions; (2) of *ascending fiber tracts* from the cord to the brain; and (3) of *descending tracts* from the brain.

The activities of higher vertebrates are dominated by the brain to a much greater degree than is the case in lower forms. Stated differently, the nerve centers in the spinal cord of lower vertebrates are far more independent and automatous. With this in mind it is not astonishing to learn that the earliest tracts of nerve fibers to appear in the marginal zone of man differentiate early in the second month for the purpose of linking together the nerve centers of the spinal cord itself. In the third month long association tracts of two kinds come into existence. Some begin with cell bodies in the cord and ascend to the brain; these serve to relay to the fore-, mid- and hind-brains the sensory impulses that are arriving in the cord from without. Others originate in the mid-brain and hind-brain and descend, thereby making possible an influence of higher centers over lower ones. Finally, in the fifth month, the pyramidal tracts begin growing downward from the motor cells of the cerebral cortex; it is through these neurons that the brain controls the motor cells of the spinal cord. The pyramidal tracts of man are not only the largest in any animal but they also contain both crossed and uncrossed fiber bundles. The latter (direct tracts) are peculiar to man and anthropoid apes, and as late acquisitions are extremely variable in size.

The development of myelin in the nerve fibers of the cord begins in the middle of fetal life and is not completed in some fibers until between the fifteenth and twentieth years. The oldest tracts historically are myelinated earliest. Myelin appears first on the fibers of the motor roots of the spinal nerves. They are followed soon by the dorsal roots and certain tracts of the spinal cord and brain. Tardiest of all are the cortico-spinal (pyramidal) tracts; they myelinate largely during the first and second postnatal years. Since myelin is deposited in the various fiber tracts at different developmental periods, this condition has been utilized in tracing the origin and extent of the various fascicles of the central nervous system.

External Form of the Spinal Cord.—There is no special boundary between the brain and spinal cord; the latter can be considered as beginning at the level of the first pair of spinal nerves. For a time the spinal cord is a thick tube which tapers gradually to a caudal ending. In the fourth month it enlarges at the levels of the two nerve plexuses that supply the upper and lower extremities. As the additional fibers to the muscles of the arm and leg belong to nerve cells in the ventral gray column, the number of these cells (and hence the mass of the gray substance) is naturally increased at these levels. Since larger numbers of fibers from the integument of the limbs also enter the cord through the dorsal roots, there are likewise present more cells in the dorsal gray column about which sensory fibers terminate. These circumstances combine in producing the two swellings of the spinal cord; the *cervical enlargement* is located at the level of origin of the nerves of the brachial plexus to the arm, the *lumbo-sacral* *enlargement* opposite the origins of the nerves of the lumbo-sacral plexus to the leg (Fig. 399).

After the third month the vertebral column grows faster than the spinal cord. Since the cord is anchored to the brain, the vertebræ of necessity shift caudad along the spinal cord, thereby dragging down inside the vertebral canal the nerves that originally found exits between vertebræ that were located directly opposite (Fig. 400). For this reason the spinal cord appears to recede up the vertebral canal, until in the adult it ends in the small of the back at the level of the first lumbar vertebra. The roots of the sacral and coccygeal nerves leave the spinal cord in this region, while the nerves themselves course obliquely downward, nearly parallel with the spinal cord,

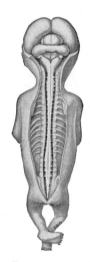

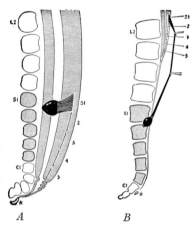

A   B

FIG. 400.—'Recession' of the human spinal cord, shown in simplified longitudinal sections (Streeter). The formation of the filum terminale and the drawing-out of a sample sacral nerve are illustrated. An asterisk indicates the coccygeal vestige. *A*, At nine weeks ($\times$ 6); *B*, at six months ($\times$ $\frac{4}{5}$).

FIG. 399.—Form and extent of the human spinal cord, at three months, exposed by a dorsal dissection. $\times$ 9.

to emerge at the sacrum some ten segments lower. As might be expected, the thoracic nerves are displaced to a less degree, while the cervical nerves incline but little in a caudal direction. The tip of the neural tube retains its terminal connections during this period of unequal growth; it becomes stretched and dedifferentiated into the slender, fibrous strand known as the *filum terminale* (Fig. 400).[34, 35] The obliquely coursing spinal nerves, together with the filum terminale, constitute the *cauda equina* which was so named from its fancied resemblance to a horse's tail. Traces of the original saccular termination of the neural tube in the integument are recognizable at birth (Fig. 400 *B*). It constitutes the *coccygeal vestige*, located near the tip of the coccyx; the site is frequently marked superficially by a dimple or pit in the skin (Fig. 129 *B*).[35, 36]

Anomalies.—Practical absence of the spinal cord is *amyelus*. This condition, an unclosed neural tube, and various herniations of the cord or its investing membranes often accompany *rachischisis* (cleft spine) (Fig. 401 *A*, *B*). However, it must be understood that the latter malformation is chiefly a skeletal defect, which is characterized by the vertebral column being more or less unclosed. When a sac, formed from the membranes about the neural tube, protrudes through such a cleft in the vertebræ the condition is referred to as *meningocœle;* if the neural canal alone sacculates, it is *myelocœle;* if, as is commonest, both are involved it is *meningo-myelocœle*. Such a herniation from the spinal cord is often designated by the term *spina bifida* (*C*). It is most frequent in the lumbo-sacral region where the sac is covered with skin and may become the size of an infant's head; yet in some instances neither cleft nor tumor is visible externally. Duplication of the central canal, especially toward its caudal end, sometimes occurs.

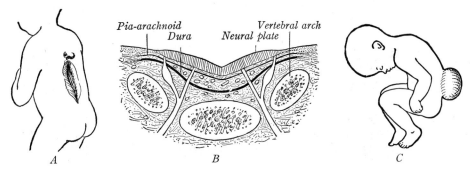

FIG. 401.—Anomalies of the spinal cord. *A*, Rachischisis, exposing a flat spinal cord. *B*, Section across a cleft spine and unclosed spinal cord, as in *A*. *C*, Spina bifida.

THE BRAIN

The general plan of the spinal cord is continued into the brain region, but the alar and basal plates undergo such a high degree of differentiation that much of the brain on casual inspection appears to have little in common with the cord. Two specific peculiarities in fundamental structure may be mentioned before passing to the detailed descriptions. Contrary to the teaching of His, the floor plate of the brain is now said to extend only as far as the caudal boundary of the mesencephalon, while the basal plate terminates at its rostral limit (Fig. 402).[30,37] The corollary of this conclusion is that both diencephalon and telencephalon are developed almost entirely out of alar-plate material.[38] A second peculiarity is found in the histological structure of certain regions of the brain, best illustrated by the cerebral hemispheres. Here the three primary layers are supplemented by a fourth, which is located superficially to the other three. The extra stratum is derived from neuroblasts that have migrated from the mantle layer through the marginal zone; at the surface they establish secondarily a thin, convoluted mantle of gray matter known as the *cerebral cortex* (Fig. 431).

Neurobiotaxis.—The proliferation of neuroblasts in localized regions leads to aggregations of cell bodies that are functionally alike. These are called *nuclei*. They may be subdivided by ingrowing nerve fibers into several parts, or they may invade the white substance and assume new locations there. This regional massing of nerve cells and fibers leads to relative thickenings and thinnings of the brain wall and is one of the chief agencies through which the brain takes form and acquires its internal organization.

In the various vertebrate groups the cerebral nuclei occupy quite different positions depending on the particular trends of brain specialization that have been followed. Such mass migrations to new locations not only can be noted from vertebrate group to group within the evolutionary series,[39]

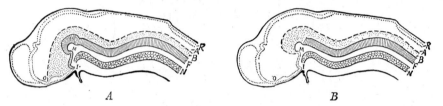

FIG. 402.—Diagrams of the vertebrate brain, in sagittal section, illustrating the forward extent of the roof-, alar-, basal-, and floor plates (after Kingsbury). *A*, According to His; *B*, according to Kingsbury.

A, Alar plate; *B*, basal plate; *F*, floor plate; *I*, infundibulum; *M*, mammillary recess; *N*, notochord; *O*, optic recess; *R*, roof plate. Broken line is the sulcus limitans.

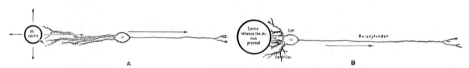

FIG. 403.—Diagrams illustrating the principle of neurobiotaxis (Kappers). Axons grow in the direction of the nervous current (indicated by arrow), while first the dendrites and then the cell body grow against the current toward the source of stimulation.

but also they are demonstrable in the development of individual embryos.[40] It is claimed that the shift is accomplished by the cell bodies moving closer to the source from which they receive most of their messages, that is to say, a shift against the flow of the nervous impulse (Fig. 403). Such a directed and oriented response has been named a *neurobiotaxis*. It presumably proceeds under the influence of some unknown attracting and orienting force. Examples of neurobiotactic shifting are furnished by the migration of the visceral motor nuclei of the cranial nerves to a lateral position (Figs. 410 and 414).

Primary Divisions.—The neural axis in embryos 2 mm. long (and with somites just appearing) is still nearly straight, but its rostral end is enlarging into the primitive brain (Fig. 393 *B*). Even before this region of the neural groove begins to close, three points of expansion, separated by two retarded zones of relative constriction, subdivide the brain into three parts (*C, D*): the fore-brain (*prosencephalon*); the mid-brain (*mesencephalon*); and the hind-brain (*rhombencephalon*). When the brain becomes a closed tube these divisions are referred to as the primary brain vesicles (Fig. 404 *A*). The human brain at this stage is shown in Fig. 405 *A*, but the three divi-

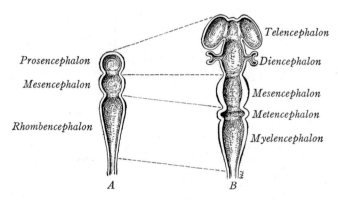

FIG. 404.—Subdivisions of the brain. *A,* Three-vesicle stage; *B,* five-vesicle stage.

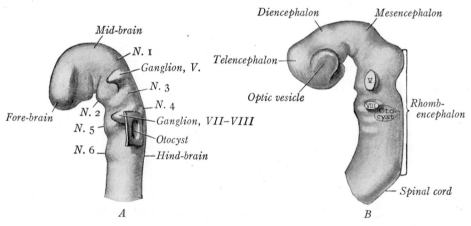

FIG. 405.—Early human brains, viewed from the left side. *A,* At 3 mm., with eighteen somites (after Politzer; × 55); *B,* at 4 mm. (after Hochstetter; × 17). N.1–6, Neuromeres.

sions are not so clearly demarcated, as they are, for example, in the chick (Fig. 508).[41]

Both the fore- and the hind-brain vesicle promptly give rise to two secondary vesicles, whereas the mid-brain remains permanently undivided (Fig. 404 *B*). In embryos of about 3 mm. (early fourth week) the fore-brain shows indication dorsally of a groove that subdivides it into the *telencephalon*, with its primitive cerebral hemispheres, and the *diencephalon*

which bears the optic vesicles (Fig. 405 *B*).   The mid-brain retains its
original designation, the *mesencephalon*.   Somewhat later the hind-brain
specializes into the *metencephalon*, or future region of the cerebellum and
pons, and into the *myelencephalon* or medulla oblongata (Fig. 406).   A
constricted region, the *isthmus*, unites mesencephalon with metencephalon.
The further separation and growth of these five brain vesicles can be
followed easily in Fig. 408.

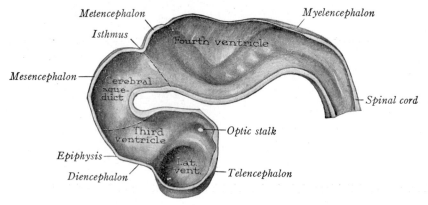

FIG. 406.—Cavities of the human brain, at 11 mm., shown in a hemisection.   × 10.

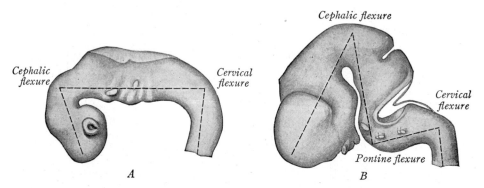

FIG. 407.—Flexures of the human brain.   *A*, At 6 mm. (× 13); *B*, at 14 mm. (× 7).

Cavities.—The lumen of the tubular brain undergoes change simultaneously with the walls (Figs. 404 and 406).   The cavity of the telencephalon extends into the paired hemispheres as the *lateral ventricles;* that
of the diencephalon (and the median portion of the telencephalon) is designated the *third ventricle;* the narrow canal of the mesencephalon becomes
the *cerebral aqueduct;* the lumen of the metencephalon and myelencephalon
is the *fourth ventricle*.   The latter is continuous with the central canal of
the spinal cord.   A cast of these cavities from the brain of a newborn is
shown in Fig. 428 *B*.

Flexures.—While the several divisions of the brain are differentiating, certain flexures appear in its roof and floor, due largely to unequal growth

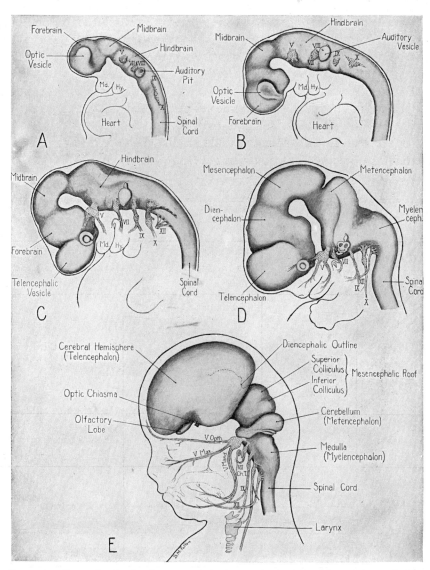

FIG. 408:—Stages in the development of the human brain (Patten). *A*, At 3 mm.; *B*, at 4 mm.; *C*, at 8 mm.; *D*, at seven weeks; *E*, at three months. In *B* and *C*, the parts labelled 'fore-brain' are telencephalon and diencephalon, respectively. In *C*, the 'hind-brain' is differentiating into metencephalon and myelencephalon.

processes. In part these correspond to those external bendings seen in the head and neck regions of young embryos. The first, or *cephalic flexure* occurs in the mid-brain region of embryos 3 to 4 mm. long where the end

of the primitive head takes a sharp bend ventrad (Fig. 405). Soon the
angle is so acute that the long axes of the fore- and hind-brains are nearly
parallel (Fig. 407). At about the same time a *cervical flexure* appears at
the junction of the brain and spinal cord. It is produced by the entire
head flexing ventrad at the level of junction with the future neck. The
pontine flexure begins to gain prominence at the 10 mm. stage. It bends
in a direction opposite to the others and is limited to the brain wall (Fig. 407
B). Eventually these flexures straighten and practically disappear, but the
diencephalon and hemispheres become set permanently at an angle with the
rest of the brain axis (Figs. 408 and 420).

Derivatives.—In the appended table are listed the primary subdivisions
of the neural tube and the parts derived from them:

DERIVATIVES OF THE NEURAL TUBE

Primary divisions	Subdivisions	Derivatives	Cavities
Prosencephalon	Telencephalon	Rhinencephalon Corpora striata Cerebral cortex	Lateral ventricles Rostral portion of the third ventricle

	Diencephalon	Epithalamus
		Thalamus (including
		  Metathalamus)
		Hypothalamus
		  Optic chiasma
		  Hypophysis
		  Tuber cinereum
		  Mammillary bodies
			Most of the third ventricle

Mesencephalon	Mesencephalon	Corpora quadrigemina Tegmentum Crura cerebri	Cerebral aqueduct
Rhombencephalon	Metencephalon	Cerebellum Pons	Fourth ventricle
	Myelencephalon	Medulla oblongata	
Spinal cord	Spinal cord	Spinal cord	Central canal

The Myelencephalon.—This most caudal part of the brain, commonly
called the *medulla oblongata*, is bounded rostrally by the early pontine
flexure; this level is identified later by the caudal border of the pons. The
caudal limit of the medulla is the first cervical nerve.

The myelencephalon is transitional in structure between the spinal
cord and the more highly specialized parts rostrad. Among other func-

tions it is notable for serving as a great pathway linking brain and cord into a functional whole. All the typical features of the cord are continued into the medulla oblongata where they are gradually displaced to new positions and relations, are altered to a greater or less degree, and in most instances receive new names. Other elements, not represented at lower levels, also appear and enter into association with these basic structures. So it is that as one progresses rostrad through the myelencephalon the familiar picture of the cord becomes more and more confused.

Among the more obvious differences from the spinal cord may be mentioned several features: (1) First is the loss of the serially segmental repetitions of the cord. To be sure, in the fifth and sixth weeks the floor of the rhombencephalon is furrowed transversely by *rhombic grooves*, seven in number,[40] whose intervals are the so-called *rhombomeres*, or *neuromeres*

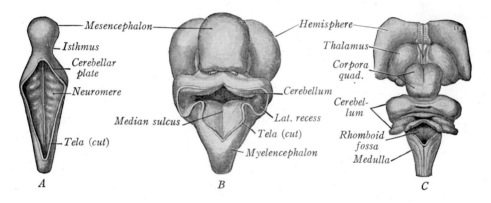

FIG. 409.—Mesencephalon, metencephalon and myelencephalon of human brains, in dorsal view (largely after Hochstetter). *A*, At five weeks (× 7); *B*, at nine weeks (× 4.5); *C*, at fifteen weeks (× 1.3).

(Figs. 405 *A* and 409 *A*). Some view these as evidential of a primitive segmented condition of the head (p. 398).[3] It seems more probable, however, that their approximate segmental arrangement is secondary and that they represent the expression of a combination of growth factors[11] by which they stand in rather regular relation to the branchial arches.[41, 43] (2) Another difference is the addition of a lateral row of nerves, intermediate in position between the dorsal sensory and the ventral motor series. These lateral cranial nerves are by number: *V, VII, IX, X* and *XI*. They are associated primarily with the branchial arches—rather than with the segmental trunk and its appendages, like spinal nerves (Fig. 408). (3) Still another difference is the disappearance of a sharp demarcation between gray and white substance. Nerve fibers, crossing in every direction, break up the gray substance into a mixture of gray and white known as the *reticular formation;* nevertheless, some is spared to form definite but isolated nuclear masses (Figs. 410 and 411).

The wall of the myelencephalon differentiates much like that of the spinal cord. Dorsally and ventrally there are comparable *roof-* and *floor plates;* the lateral wall is separated similarly by the *sulcus limitans* into *alar-* and *basal plates* (Figs. 410 and 411).

All but the roof plate are fairly comparable to their homologues in the spinal cord. By contrast, this dorsal region becomes a broad and flattened layer of thin ependymal tissue (Fig. 410). Coincidental with the formation of a marked pontine flexure, at about the middle of the second month, the alar plates bulge laterally and the thinner roof plate is widened; espe-

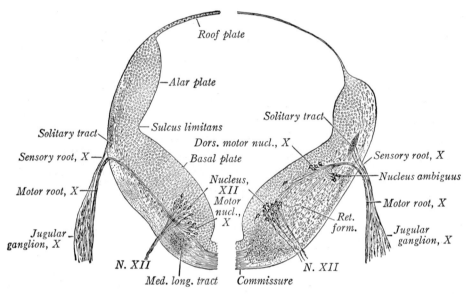

Roof plate

Alar plate

Solitary tract

Solitary tract

Solitary tract

Sulcus limitans

Sensory root, X

Dors. motor nucl., X

Basal plate

Sensory root, X

Nucleus ambiguus

Motor root, X

Nucleus, XII

Motor nucl., X

Ret. form.

Motor root, X

Jugular ganglion, X

Jugular ganglion, X

N. XII

N. XII

Med. long. tract

Commissure

FIG. 410.—Human myelencephalon, in transverse section. Left half, at 10 mm. (× 75); right half, at 12 mm. (× 45).

cially is this true in the rostral portion of the myelencephalon (Fig. 409 *B*). The cavity of the rhombencephalon (fourth ventricle) is thereby spread out from side to side and flattened dorsoventrally, a change most marked rostrally where the *lateral recesses* of the fourth ventricle occur.

Blood vessels grow into the mesenchymal layer that lies upon the ependymal roof of the myelencephalon; this combined membrane is the *tela chorioidea.* Moreover, vascular tufts of this tela invaginate into the cavity of the myelencephalon and form there the *chorioid plexus* of the fourth ventricle (Fig. 418). Through local resorptions, paired lateral apertures (*foramina of Luschka*) and a mesial aperture (*foramen of Magendie*) appear rostrally; they permit communication with the subarachnoid space. The ridge where the tela joins the alar plate is known as the *rhombic lip* (Fig. 415 *A, B*).

As the roof plate expands into a non-nervous cover, the alar- and basal plates are spread laterally like an opened book whose hinge is the floor plate (Figs. 410 and 411). Both the alar- and basal plates are at first represented by distinct ependymal-, mantle- and marginal zones, but the rapid proliferation of neuroblasts, the complex courses of fibers extending from them, and the invasion of fibers from without all tend soon to mask the primitive layering. It will be convenient to consider the paired cranial nerves *V* to *XII* all at one time, since they occur as a natural series in the rhombencephalon. Actually, nerves *V* to *VIII* belong to the metencephalic subdivision.

Sensory nerve fibers, entering the rhombencephalic alar plates from the cranial nerves, group into definite tracts in the marginal zone; *tractus*

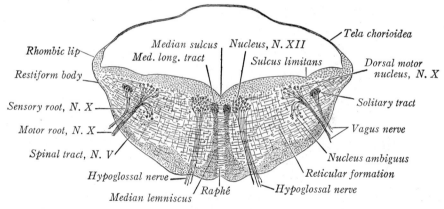

FIG. 411.—Human myelencephalon, at two months, in transverse section. × 18.

solitarius; spinal tract of the fifth nerve; *restiform body,* or inferior peduncle of the cerebellum (Figs. 410, 411 and 414). Alar-plate neuroblasts migrate into the primitive marginal zone and surround these terminal tracts of the sensory cranial nerves (tracts which correspond to the dorsal root fibers of the spinal nerves); here they organize into the receptive or *terminal nuclei* of nerves *V, VII, VIII, IX* and *X*. More caudally the *nucleus gracilis* and *nucleus cuneatus* are developed as terminal nuclei for the sensory fibers which ascend through the spinal cord from its nerves. Still other nuclei differentiate; it may be, however, that the conspicuous *olivary nuclei* are of basal- rather than alar-plate origin.

The basal plates of the rhombencephalon differentiate a little earlier than the alar plates. In embryos of the sixth week their neuroblasts give rise to the *motor nuclei* of origin for seven cranial nerves, arranged in two linear groups (Fig. 443). Laterally, nearer the sulcus limitans, are located

the nuclei of the visceral motor nerves *V*, *VII*, *IX*, *X* and *XI* (Fig. 414).
More mesad (primitively, ventrad) lie the nuclei of somatic motor nerves
VI and *XII* (Fig. 411). Some of these nuclei produce swellings in the
floor of the fourth ventricle. Among the motor nerve fibers coursing in
the marginal layer are those descending from the motor cortex which produce the prominent *pyramids* (Fig. 412). Since in early embryos the
rhombencephalon lies directly above the pharynx, fore-gut and heart (Fig.
148), it comes to pass that the centers concerned with the regulation of chewing, swallowing, digestion, respiration and circulation remain located in the
rhombencephalon, even though the organs innervated become considerably
dislocated in position.

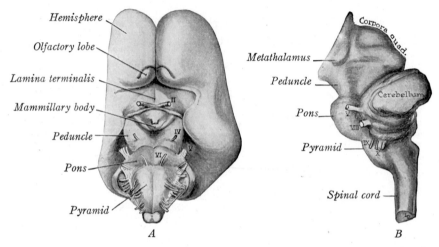

FIG. 412.—Human brain, at fourteen weeks (after Hochstetter). *A*, Ventral aspect (× 2). *B*,
Left lateral aspect, caudal to the diencephalon (× 2.5).

The ependymal cells of the floor plate elongate to keep pace with the
thickening of the ventral wall of the medulla oblongata. Their processes
extend from lumen to surface as the septum-like *raphé* (Fig. 411). On the
floor of the medulla this raphé lies at the bottom of the *median sulcus*
(Fig. 409).

Having considered the differentiation of the neuroblasts in the alar and
basal plates of the rhombencephalon, it is instructive to indicate some of the
more important connections their processes make in the myelencephalon.
The primary sensory nuclei of this part of the brain effect four general types
of communication: (1) correlating connections with the motor nuclei of the
myelencephalon by means of the reticular formation; (2) descending connections with the motor centers of the spinal cord; (3) connections with the
cerebellum; and (4) connections with the diencephalon which, in turn, are
relayed to the cerebral cortex. Other important tracts are found in the

medulla oblongata, but they are merely passing through to terminate at higher or lower levels.

The Metencephalon.—This division of the brain extends from the isthmus to the pontine flexure (caudal border of pons). The metencephalon continues the general structure of the myelencephalon upward. It, however, adds two specialized and superposed secondary parts. These are the cerebellum dorsally and the *pons* ventrally (Fig. 412). They are not especially conspicuous except in animals with finely adjusted equilibrium and well-developed muscular coördination. The metencephalon reaches its highest expression in primates, but is also large in flying and swimming vertebrates. The cerebellum and pons have evolved through association with the adjacent otocysts, which are organs not only for hearing but also for the balancing mechanism; the latter sense is the prime factor in so far as the evolution of the cerebellum and pons is concerned. Besides its intimate connection with all the sensory centers that are concerned with body equilibrium and the maintenance of muscle tone, the cerebellum also receives afferent fibers from the cerebral cortex and gives off efferent fibers to the motor centers of the brain stem. All these fibers enter and leave the cerebellum by three stalks, or *peduncles*, on each side. The pons not only contains important sensory and motor nuclei belonging to certain cranial nerves, but it also develops the pontine nuclei which relay to the cerebellum the efferent impulses descending from the motor cortex. Many fibers from higher and lower levels pass uninterruptedly through the pons toward their destinations. Most imposing are the pyramidal tracts.

The early metencephalon of man is made up of the six typical plates of the neural tube, but the primitive relations are soon profoundly modified. The roof plate transforms into a thin sheet of white matter both in front of the cerebellum and behind it. This tissue constitutes, respectively, the *anterior* and the *posterior medullary velum* (Fig. 413). The rest of the roof plate is lost in the substance of the cerebellum. The alar plates feature prominently; they elaborate the cerebellum and its nuclei, contribute to the three cerebellar peduncles, and produce the sensory nuclei of cranial nerve *V*, and *VII* and *VIII* in part. The basal plates supply the motor nuclei of origin of the nerves derived from this region and elaborate much of the reticular formation (Fig. 414). The floor plate forms a raphé, as in the medulla.

The part of the metencephalon that most resembles the medulla oblongata lies just beneath the continuation of the fourth ventricle into this region (Fig. 414). Here are found several distinct nuclei; of these, the *motor nuclei* of nerves *V*, *VI* and *VII*, along with the *reticular formation*, are derivatives of the basal plate. In this location are also found such alar-plate derivatives as the terminal *sensory nucleus* of the fifth nerve, continuous with extensions into both mesencephalon and medulla, and the *cochlear* and *vestibular nuclei* of the eighth nerve. The two latter (acoustic) nuclei originate in embryos of two months through the proliferation of neuroblasts from the margin of the rhombic lip. The cochlear nucleus is pushed ventrad; other small nuclei differentiating from the rhombic lip in the same manner but displaced even to a greater degree, are the numerous *pontine nuclei*.

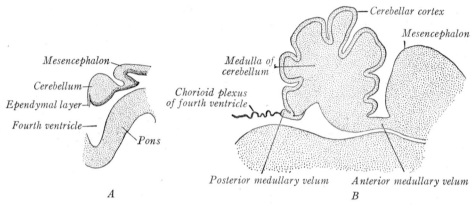

FIG. 413.—Human metencephalon, in sagittal section (after Prentiss). *A*, At two months (× 5); *B*, at five months (× 8).

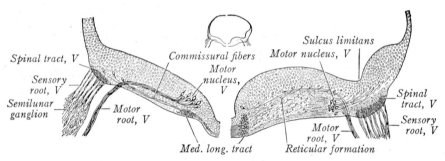

FIG. 414.—Human metencephalon, in transverse section. Left half, at 6 mm. (× 66); right half, at 11 mm. (× 57). Above is an orientation drawing of the total half-sections.

The Cerebellum.[44]—The alar plates of the metencephalon are bent out laterally by the pontine flexure and assume a transverse position. During the second month they thicken and bulge into the fourth ventricle (Fig. 415 *A*). Near the midline paired swellings indicate the future *vermis*, while the more lateral portions are destined to become *cerebellar hemispheres* (*B*). During the third month the cerebellar mass everts and forms on each side a convex cerebellar hemisphere (*C*) connected with the pons by the *brachium pontis*, or middle cerebellar peduncle. In the meantime the paired primordia of the vermis have fused in the midline, thereby producing a single structure. The rhombic lip of this region gives rise to those parts of the cerebellum known as the *flocculus* and *nodulus* (*D*). Between the third and fifth months the cerebellar cortex grows faster than the deeper layers, and in this way the principal lobes and fissures are produced (*C*, *D*). The hemispheres are the last to undergo such specialization; their fissures do not appear until the fifth month, but in fetuses of seven months the cerebellum has attained its final configuration.

The cerebellum shows at first a differentiation into the same three layers that typify the neural tube as a whole. During the second and third months

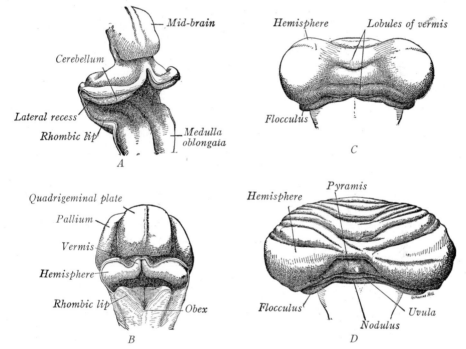

FIG. 415.—Human cerebellum, in dorsal view (*A*, His; *B–D*, Prentiss). *A*, At six weeks (× 8); *B*, at two months (× 4); *C*, at four months (× 3); *D*, at five months (2.8).

proliferating cells from the rhombic lip, and perhaps from the mantle layer of the cerebellum as well, migrate into the marginal layer; here they organize the *cerebellar cortex* with its characteristic molecular and granular layers (Fig. 413 *B*). The final differentiation of the cortex is not completed until after birth. The axons of Purkinje cells and those of entering afferent fibers comprise the deep *medullary layer* of the cerebellum. Many cells of the primitive mantle layer take no part in the development of the cerebellar cortex, but give rise to neuroglial tissue and to the internal nuclei. Of these latter, the largest is the *dentate nucleus* which is seen at the end of the third month.[45]

The Mesencephalon.—A plane passing just caudal to the posterior commissure dorsally, and the mammillary bodies ventrally, defines the rostral limits of the mesencephalon; its caudal limit is the isthmus (Fig. 420).

The mid-brain is the least modified part of the brain (Fig. 418). After the third month it is soon overshadowed and concealed by the much bulkier fore- and hind-brains and then serves chiefly to interconnect them (Fig. 428). The roof-, alar- and basal plates are all represented, but the floor plate is now said to terminate with the metencephalon (Fig. 402 B).[30,37] The roof plate of young specimens constitutes a mere seam uniting the alar plates, yet even this loses its identity in later stages. The primitive neural cavity is reduced to the slender *cerebral aqueduct*, which after the third month narrows both relatively and absolutely (Fig. 420).

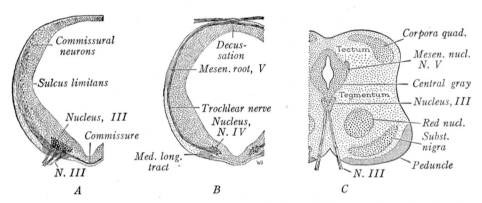

Fig. 416.—Human mesencephalon, in transverse section. *A*, At 10 mm., level of oculomotor nucleus ($\times$ 48). *B*, At 10 mm., level of trochlear nucleus and decussation ($\times$ 48). *C*, Later stage (semidiagrammatic).

As at other levels, the alar plates develop more tardily than the basal plates. The alar plates of the mesencephalon give rise to a common lamina which bears the *corpora quadrigemina* (Figs. 409 and 412 *B*). These are two pairs of rounded eminences appearing in the fourth month to serve as centers for visual and auditory correlation. The rostral pair (the superior colliculi) are primary receptive centers for the optic tracts; they are linked to the caudal pair (the inferior colliculi) which, in turn, connect with the cochlear nuclei of the pons. Neuroblasts migrate to the surfaces of the corpora quadrigemina and there organize stratified ganglionic layers, which are comparable to the cortical layers of the cerebellum; the deeper cell masses correspond to the metencephalic nuclei (Fig. 416 *C*). The continuation to this level of the sensory nucleus (here the *mesencephalic nucleus*) of the fifth nerve, already mentioned, is worthy of note; it furnishes the only instance in which sensory fibers of a peripheral nerve have their cell bodies implanted in the wall of the neural tube (Fig. 416).[46]

Early in the second month neuroblasts of the basal plate condense into the *motor nuclei* of the third and fourth cranial nerves (Fig. 416 *A*, *B*). The *tegmentum*, continued upward from the pons, is similar to the reticular formation of lower levels (*C*). The *red nucleus* and the *substantia nigra* presumably differentiate *in situ*, although the former has commonly been said to originate from migratory, alar-plate neuroblasts.

The mesencephalon is primarily associated with the mechanism of sight. The rostral pair of quadrigeminal bodies receives fibers from the retina, and from deep motor nuclei is derived the chief nerve supply of the muscles of the eyeball. The mid-brain also becomes the main highway for motor fibers that unite the fore-brain with the nuclei of lower levels, and for sensory paths that connect in the reverse direction. Such ascending and descending motor tracts course in two rounded strands known as the *cere-*

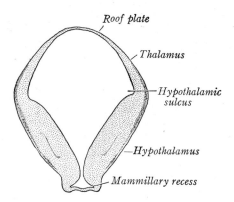

FIG. 417.—Human diencephalon, at 12 mm., in transverse section. × 33.

bral peduncles; they are conspicuous structures on the ventral surface of the brain (Fig. 412).

The Diencephalon.—The rostral extent of the diencephalon is established by folds that set caudal limits to the hemispheres and the corpora striata; on the floor of the brain this boundary passes just rostral to the optic chiasma (Fig. 419 *A*). The caudal limit includes the posterior commissure dorsally and the mammillary bodies ventrally (*B*).

Though prominent during the second month (Figs. 418 *A* and 419 *A*), the diencephalon becomes largely concealed by the greater expansion of adjoining parts of the brain (Fig. 420). It is wholly given over to various kinds of correlations, and through it pass all the nervous impulses which reach the cerebral cortex with the single exception of those from the olfactory organs.

The wall of the diencephalon differentiates a dorsal roof plate and paired alar plates, the latter including both the sides and the floor of the tube (Fig. 417). It seems probable that neither the basal plate nor floor plate of lower levels extends this far rostrad (Fig. 402 *B*).[30,37] Except for this difference, and the absence of typical nerves, the diencephalon appears in early stages not unlike the primitive spinal cord. It remains preponderatingly composed of gray nuclear matter. The cavity of the diencephalon is the *third ventricle;* for a time it is relatively broad (Fig. 419 *A*), but the strongly thickening lateral walls later compress it to a narrow, median cleft (Fig. 420).

The roof plate becomes the thin ependymal lining of the *tela chorioidea* (Fig. 417). Blood vessels growing into the folded tela form the *chorioid plexus* which invaginates into the third ventricle during the second month (Figs. 419 *A* and 423). The rest of the diencephalon consists of three main regions (Fig. 419): the *epithalamus*, dorsally; the *thalamus* (including a subdivision called the *metathalamus*), laterally; and the *hypothalamus*, ven-

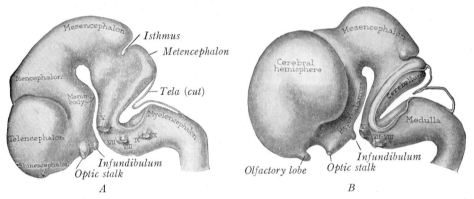

FIG. 418.—Human brain, in left lateral view (after Hochstetter). *A*, At 14 mm. (× 7.5); *B*, at 27 mm. (× 5).

trally. The epithalamus and hypothalamus are the more primitive in character and their differentiation precedes that of the thalamus which is best developed in higher vertebrates.

At the junction of the caudal portion of the roof plate with the alar plate is the area designated the epithalamus (Fig. 419). It is a synaptic region for the correlation of olfactory impulses. An interesting derivative is the *epiphysis*, or pineal body, which evaginates during the seventh week and in man becomes solid and conical (Fig. 421). [47,48] It lies between the *habenular* and *posterior commissures* (Fig. 420). The epiphysis of mammals, birds and some reptiles is interpreted as a fundamentally glandular organ that has differentiated in quite a different direction from the median parietal eye of certain fishes, amphibia and reptiles. In this sense it is not a vestigial or degenerated parietal eye; the latter even develops from an entirely separate primordium.[49]

The thickened alar plate proper is divided by the *hypothalamic sulcus* into a dorsal thalamus and a ventral hypothalamus (Figs. 419 and 420). Ingrowing nerve fibers separate the massive gray substance into numerous nuclei. The thalamus consists of a more ancient part, which can act independently of the cerebral cortex in effecting reflexes having to do with

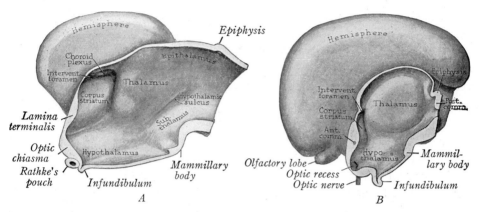

FIG. 419.—Human telencephalon and diencephalon, hemisected and viewed from the left side (after Hochstetter). *A*, At seven weeks (× 10); *B*, at ten weeks (× 4.5).

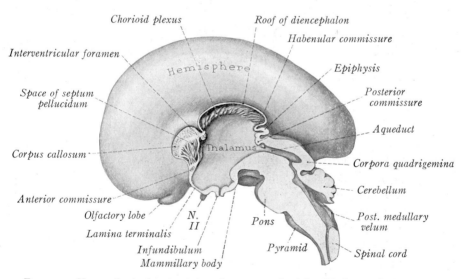

FIG. 420.—Human brain, hemisected, at fourteen weeks (after Hochstetter). × 2.5.

pleasurable and painful sensations, and a newer part which is the larger by far in man. The latter portion is the main corridor through which impulses of cutaneous, visual and auditory sensibility are relayed by new neurons to the cerebral cortex. The so-called metathalamic subdivision of the newer thalamus contains the *geniculate bodies* which are concerned with the transmission of impulses of visual and auditory sensibility.   The two thalami grow into close approximation and usually unite across the median plane (massa intermedia).

Several structures develop from the hypothalamic floor.   From the rostral end of the early diencephalon evaginate the paired optic vesicles (Fig. 422); the cavity of each stalk obliterates and its wall affords a pathway for the centrally growing fibers of an optic nerve.   The crossing nerve fibers form a chiasma plate in this region (pars optica) of the hypothalamus (Figs. 412 *A* and 419 *A*).   Next caudad is the *infundibulum* which specializes into the stalk and neural lobe of the hypophysis; for the development of this organ, see p. 204.   Next in line is the *tuber cinereum*, while farthest caudad a protuberance marks the site of the *mammillary bodies*.   The hypothalamus is the headquarters of the sympathetic system which controls the vegetative functions of the body (*e.g.*, digestion; sleep; heat regulation; emotional behavior).   A transitional region, interposed between the hypothalamus and the tegmentum of the mesencephalon, is often recognized as a definite region, the *subthalamus*.

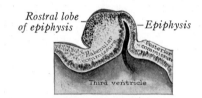

FIG. 421.—Human epiphysis, at ten weeks, longitudinally hemisected (after Hochstetter). × 27.

The Telencephalon.—The caudal boundary of this rostral end of the brain has already been defined (p. 443).   The telencephalon consists of a median portion, continuous with the diencephalon and containing the rostral part of the third ventricle, and of two lateral hemispheric outpouchings from it (Fig. 423).   The telencephalon becomes in higher animals the most specialized and complex region of the brain.   Practically all the nervous mechanisms of lower levels are concerned with rigid responses involving reflex and instinctive activities.   In lower vertebrates the telencephalon is still of this nature, but in mammals the characteristically variable types of response (acquired and mostly consciously performed) are mediated through the thin gray covering of the hemispheres known as the *cerebral cortex;* accordingly, this substance becomes increasingly prominent until its elaboration reaches a climax in man.

The telencephalon consists of three regional parts.   One is the *corpus striatum*, directly continuous with the thalamus and, like it, a reflex and reinforcing center but of a higher order (Figs. 419 and 423).   The second division is the *rhinencephalon*, or *archipallium*, while the remainder makes up the *neopallium* (Fig. 420). The last two portions comprise all of the externally visible hemispheres, and together may be called the *pallium*. The rhinencephalon is the olfactory part of the brain; in fishes it represents almost the entire cerebral hemisphere, but in higher forms it becomes progressively subordinate as smell declines as the dominant sense. The neopallium, or non-olfactory cortex, advances in importance in reptiles and birds, becomes very large in mammals and constitutes almost all the exposed portions of the human cerebrum.

Like the diencephalon, the telencephalon is a product of greatly expanded alar plates. Basal and floor plates are lacking, and the roof plate

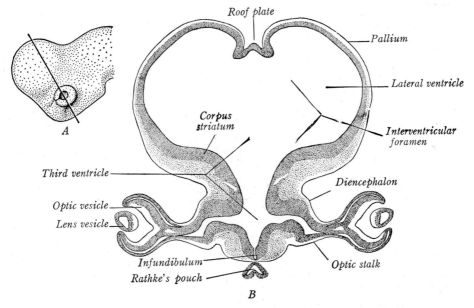

FIG. 422.—Human telencephalon, at 10 mm. *A*, Left lateral view (× 10). *B*, Transverse section, at the level indicated on *A* (after Prentiss; × 30).

is largely concerned with the formation of a chorioid plexus (*cf.* p. 444). The roof of the original telencephalon is inconsiderable in comparison to the evaginated hemispheres and does not take part in their extensive development (Fig. 422). The cerebral hemispheres begin to be prominent during the sixth week and expand rapidly until, at the middle of fetal life, they overgrow the diencephalon and mesencephalon and overlie the cerebellum somewhat (Figs. 418 and 420). During this period of enlargement the original rostral end of the neural tube remains a mesial band, relatively unchanged in position; for this reason it is named the *lamina terminalis* (Figs. 419 and 420). Since the two hemispheres grow forward on each side of it, the lamina becomes buried at the bottom of the resulting *longitudinal fissure* that separates them (Fig. 423 *A*). The *lateral ventricles*, or cavities of the hemispheres, at first communicate broadly with the third ventricle

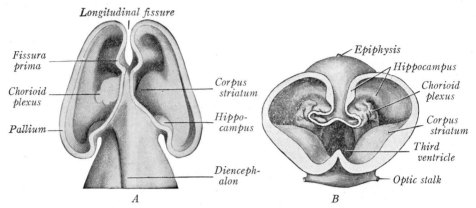

FIG. 423.—Human fore-brain, with a portion of the wall removed. *A*, At six weeks, in dorsal view (His; × 13). *B*, At seven weeks, in front view (after Hochstetter; × 9).

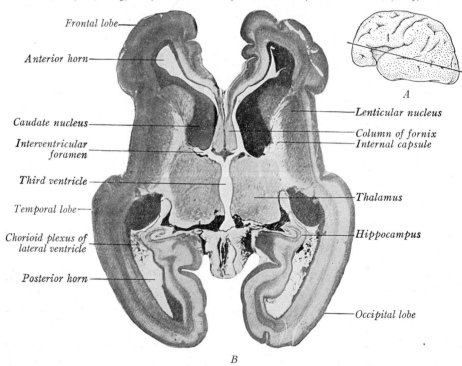

FIG. 424.—Human telencephalon and diencephalon, at five months. *A*, Left lateral view. *B*, Horizontal section, at the level indicated on *A* (His; × 2).

through the paired *interventricular foramina* of Monro (Fig. 422 *B*). Later each foramen is narrowed to a slit, not by constriction but because its boundaries grow more slowly than the rest of the telencephalon (Fig. 419).

The Corpus Striatum.—The floor of each hemisphere produces a thickening, which at six weeks bulges prominently into the lateral ventricle (Fig. 423). The *corpus striatum*, so formed, is in line caudally with the thalamus of the diencephalon and is closely related to it both developmentally and functionally (Fig. 419). The thalamus and corpus striatum are separated by a deep groove until the end of the third month. As the two structures enlarge, the groove between them disappears and they then seem like one continuous mass (Fig. 424). The thickening of the corpus striatum is due to an active proliferation in its ependymal layer; this gives rise to a prominent mass of mantle-layer cells.

Nerve fibers, passing in both directions between the thalamus and the cerebral cortex, course through the corpus striatum; here they are arranged

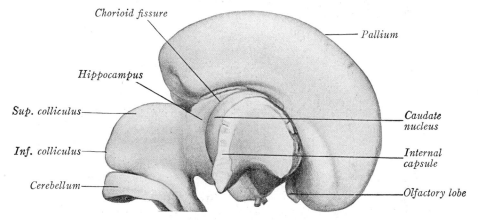

FIG. 425.—Human brain, at nearly three months, viewed from the right side after removal of most of the right pallium (His). × 5.

in a lamina that takes the form of a wide **V**, open laterally. This band-like tract of white fibers is the *internal capsule*. Its rostral limb partly divides the corpus striatum into the *caudate* and *lenticular nuclei;* the caudal limb of the capsule extends between the lenticular nucleus and the thalamus (Fig. 424). The corpus striatum elongates in company with the cerebral hemispheres, its caudal portion curving around to the tip of the inferior horn of the lateral ventricle and forming the slender tail of the caudate nucleus (Fig. 425). By the middle of fetal life the corpus striatum has attained its adult shape and relations.

The Rhinencephalon and Neopallium.—During the sixth week a swelling appears on the ventral surface of each cerebral hemisphere (Fig. 418). These enlarge into distinct *olfactory lobes* which, however, remain small in man (Fig. 425). Each lobe is arbitrarily divided into a rostral and caudal division. The pars anterior represents the *olfactory bulb* and *tract*, of which the latter receives the backward-growing olfactory fibers and loses its original lumen (Fig. 426). The pars posterior is a thickening of this brain wall, which matures into the *anterior perforated substance* and the *parolfactory area* mesial and dorsal to it (Figs. 426 and 427). The olfactory apparatus includes also a pallial portion. It is termed the *archipallium* because it embodies nearly the entire fore-brain of lower vertebrates. In

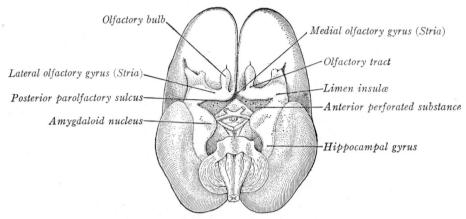

FIG. 426.—Human brain, at eighteen weeks, showing the rhinencephalon in ventral view (Hardesty after Retzius). × 1.5.

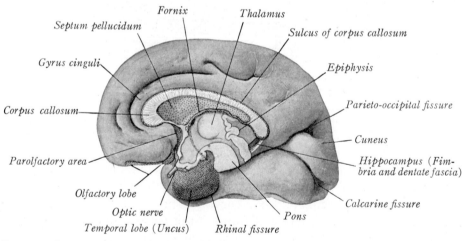

FIG. 427.—Human brain, at seven months, hemisected (adapted from Kollmann). × 1. The rhinencephalon is designated by stipple.

reptiles the non-olfactory cortex begins to emerge, and in mammals this neopallium becomes dominant while the archipallium is represented chiefly by the hippocampal system, including the *hippocampus* proper (Figs. 423 and 425), the *dentate fascia* and the *hippocampal gyrus* in part (Fig. 427).

External Form of the Hemispheres.—The telencephalon expands in such a fashion that four lobes can be distinguished in each hemisphere (Fig. 428 *A*). These have no functional significance but are convenient for descriptive purposes. They are: (1) a rostral *frontal lobe;* (2) a dorsal *parietal lobe;* (3) a caudal *occipital lobe;* and (4) a ventrolateral *temporal lobe,* derived by a part of the primitive occipital lobe turning ventrad and rostrad. The original ventricle of the telencephalon expands into *lateral ventricles,* which follow the development of the hemispheres and extend into their four pairs of lobes; the body of each lateral ventricle occupies the corre-

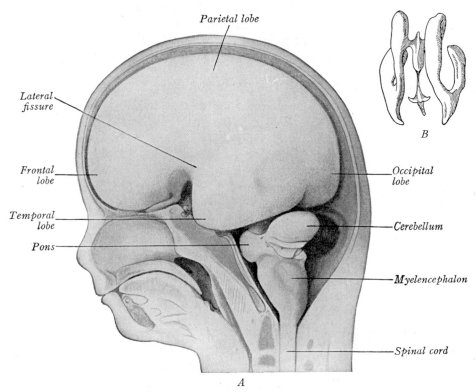

Parietal lobe

Lateral fissure

Frontal lobe

Temporal lobe

Pons

Occipital lobe

Cerebellum

Myelencephalon

Spinal cord

B

A

Fig. 428.—Form and relations of the human cerebral hemisphere. *A*, Left lateral view of the brain, at fourteen weeks, *in situ* (His; × 2.5). *B*, Cast of the newborn ventricles (after Welker; × ½).

sponding parietal lobe, while the anterior, posterior and inferior horns make up the remainder (*B*).

The surface extent of the cerebral wall, the thin gray cortex, increases more rapidly than the white medullary layer which underlies it. As a result, the cortex is folded into *gyri,* or *convolutions,* between which are prominent furrows. The larger furrows are *fissures;* the smaller, *sulci.* The first fissures to appear are the *rhinal* (Fig. 427) and *hippocampal fissures,* which develop during the fourth month in association with the rhinencephalon. The hippocampal fissure represents a curved infolding along the mesial wall of the temporal lobe; the corresponding elevation on the internal surface of the pallium is the hippocampus itself (Figs. 424 and 425). At about the same time, the *lateral fissure* (of Sylvius) makes its appearance but is not completed until after birth (Fig. 428). Its development is due to the fact that the cortex overlying the corpus striatum expands more slowly than do the surrounding areas; this region is consequently overgrown by opercular (covering) folds of the frontal, parietal and temporal lobes. The area thus incompletely enclosed is the *insula* (island of Reil), and the depression so formed is the lateral fissure (Fig. 429). These opercula do not close-in over the insula and come into contact until after birth. The *chorioid fissure* results from the ingrowth of the chorioid plexus (Fig. 425). Since the temporal lobe carries with it the chorioid plexus and the fissure

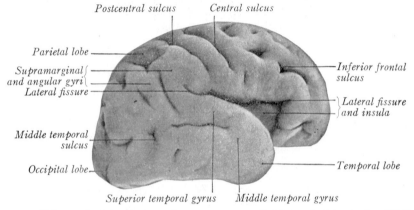

FIG. 429.—Right cerebral hemisphere, from a seven-months' fetus, in lateral view (Kollmann). × 1.

through which it entered, the chorioid fissure is transferred to the under aspect of the hemisphere.

Until the middle of fetal life the exposed surface of the brain is quite smooth, but at the stage of six to seven months four other neopallial depressions appear, which later become important landmarks in cerebral topography. They are: (1) the *central sulcus*, or fissure of Rolando, which forms the dorsolateral boundary between the frontal and parietal lobes (Fig. 429); (2) the *parieto-occipital fissure* which, on the median wall of the hemisphere, is the line of separation between the occipital and parietal lobes (Fig. 427); (3) the *calcarine fissure*, which marks the position of the visual area of the cerebrum (Fig. 427) and internally causes that convexity termed the calcar avis; and (4) the *collateral fissure*, on the ventral surface of the temporal lobe, which produces the inward bulging on the floor of the posterior horn of the ventricle known as the collateral eminence.

Simultaneously with the establishment of this last group of fissures occur those shallower depressions known as sulci (Figs. 427 and 429). The secondary and tertiary sulci peculiar to the human brain are developments of the final fetal months. Previous to their appearance the brain resembles that of the adult monkey. Although the gyri and sulci have a definite and regular arrangement, they bear only a general relation to 'functional areas.'

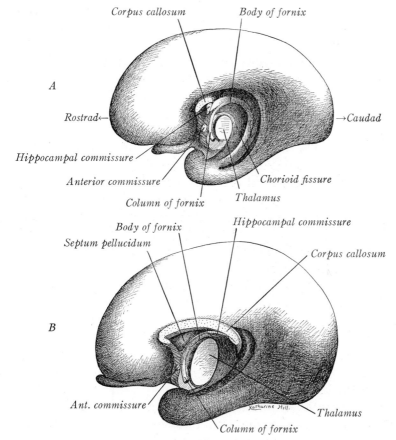

FIG. 430.—Development of the commissures, shown in hemisected human brains, viewed from the left side (adapted by Prentiss). × about 2. *A*, At three months; *B*, at four months.

Commissures.—For the purpose of securing coördination, the reflex centers of the two sides of the neural tube are connected by bands of crossing fibers called *commissures.* They occur both in the brain and in the spinal cord. Besides the optic chiasma (Fig. 419 *A*) and the habenular and posterior commissures of the diencephalon (Fig. 421), already mentioned, there are three in the telencephalon (Fig. 430). The *hippocampal* and *anterior commissures* are the more ancient cross connections for the archipallium, while the larger *corpus collosum* is the great transverse bridge of the neopallium. These commissures develop in relation to the lamina terminalis, since this is the natural, direct path from one cerebral vesicle to the other (Fig. 419). They cross partly in the lamina and partly in the fused adjacent portions of the median pallial walls. Owing to the union of the pallial walls dorsal and rostral to the lamina, the latter thickens rapidly during the fourth and fifth months. It is at this time that the significant development of the commissures occurs.

In the rostral portion of the lamina terminalis, fibers crossing the midplane unite the two hippocampi and produce the *hippocampal commissure* (Fig. 430 *A*); with the later growth of the corpus callosum this commissure shifts farther caudad (*B*) The hippocampal commissure is closely associated with the *fornix* which is made up of paired symmetrical fiber tracts that pursue arching courses to connect the hippocampi with the hypothalamus.

The fibers of the *anterior commissure* cross in the lamina terminalis, ventral to the primitive hippocampal commissure (Fig. 430). They arise in paired rostral and caudal divisions which unite into a common bundle near the midplane. The rostral part interconnects the olfactory bulbs in a horse-shoe bow of fibers. The caudal division passes ventrally between the corpora striata and the cerebral cortex and may be derived from one or both of these regions.

The *corpus callosum* develops in the roof-region of the thickened lamina terminalis, located both rostral and dorsal to the primitive hippocampal commissure (Fig. 430 *A*). Within a short time it has extended particularly in the caudal direction, and thereafter constitutes a conspicuous landmark of the telencephalon (*B*). Through its fibers, which grow out from neuroblasts in the wall of the neopallium, nearly all regions of one hemisphere are associated eventually with corresponding regions of the other. In fetuses of five months this great commissure has attained the structure and shape that is characteristic of the adult (Fig. 427).

The triangular interval between the fornix and corpus callosum contains a thin partition that separates the two lateral ventricles (Fig. 430 *B*). This *septum pellucidum* is a membranous portion of the lamina terminalis and really consists of thinned, median pallial wall (Fig. 427). As a result of stretching, caused by the growth of the corpus callosum, the septum sometimes splits and contains a cleft-like cavity bounded by distinct laminæ. The space is designated the *space of the septum pellucidum*, or often, inappropriately, the fifth ventricle (Fig. 420).

Histogenesis.—In the wall of the pallium are differentiated the ependymal, mantle and marginal layers typical of the neural tube in general. During the first two months the cortex remains thin and differentiation is slow. At eight weeks neuroblasts migrate from the ependymal and mantle zones into the superficial marginal zone and there give rise to layers of pyramidal and other cells typical of the *cerebral cortex* (Fig. 431). The differentiation of these layers is most active during the third and fourth months, but probably continues until after birth.[50] Beginning with the fourth month the pallial wall thickens rapidly, owing both to the intrusion of fibers from the thalamus and to fibers derived from the neuroblasts of the cortex itself. The fibers as a whole are arranged in an inner medullary layer, white in color and surrounded by the gray cortex; this *medulla* is homologous to the mantle zone of the spinal cord (Fig. 431 *B*). Myelination begins shortly after birth, but some fibers do not acquire their sheaths until the end of puberty. As the cerebral wall increases in thickness, the size of the lateral ventricles diminishes relatively; especially is this true of their lateral diameters.

Myelination.—The brain of a newborn is largely unmyelinated. Only the fibers of the basal ganglia and those that continue the structure of the spinal cord possess myelin sheaths. As in the cord, the various tracts

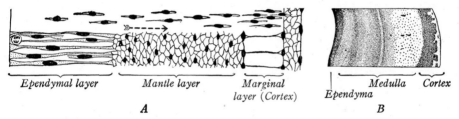

| Ependymal layer | Mantle layer | Marginal layer (Cortex) | Ependyma | Medulla | Cortex |

A   B

FIG. 431.—Histogenesis of the human pallial wall. *A*, Schematic section, at three months (after His). Below is the spongioblastic framework only; above are wandering neuroblasts migrating into the cortical layer. *B*, Vertical section of the pallium, at four months, with its cortex thickening rapidly ($\times$ 15).

myelinate in definite sequence; the process begins chiefly after birth and continues through puberty. First to acquire sheaths are the primary sensory-motor fields—that is, the olfactory, optic and auditory cortical fields and the motor cortex. The projectional and commissural fibers myelinate last.

The Chorioid Plexus of the Lateral Ventricles.[51]—Just as the chorioid plexus of the third ventricle develops in the folded roof plate of the diencephalon, so the thin median wall of the pallium (originally dorsal, and largely roof plate) at its junction with the wall of the diencephalon is folded into each lateral ventricle (Fig. 423). A vascular plexus, continuous with that of the third ventricle, grows into this fold and projects into the corresponding lateral ventricle (Fig. 432). The entire plexus system is a paired structure which, with the plexus of the third ventricle, makes a ϒ-shaped figure; the stem of the ϒ overlies the third ventricle, and its curved arms project into the lateral ventricles just caudal to the interventricular foramen. Later, as the pallium expands, the chorioid plexus is extended far into the temporal lobes, where it protrudes into the inferior horns of the lateral ventricles.

Anomalies.—A severe arrest of brain development often accompanies those types of defective skull formation (*cranioschisis*) that are specifically designated *acrania* or *hemicrania* (Fig. 357 *A*). Such virtual absence of the brain is called *anencephaly*. Herniation of the brain wall through a defective cranial roof is *encephalocœle*, or cerebral hernia (Fig. 433 *A*). Protrusion of the meninges is *meningocœle;* a sacculation of both, as most commonly occurs, constitutes *meningo-encephalocœle*.

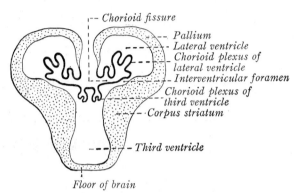

FIG. 432.—Invagination of the human chorioid plexuses into the lateral and third ventricles, shown by a diagrammatic transverse section through a fetal brain (after Smith).

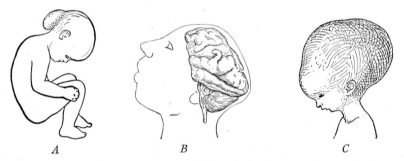

A   *B*   *C*

FIG. 433.—Anomalies of the human brain. *A*, Encephalocœle. *B*, Micrencephaly, associated with a microcephalic head. *C*, Hydrocephalus, producing a macrocephalic head.

Abnormal smallness of the brain is *micrencephaly;* it is associated with an undersized cranium (*microcephalus*) (Fig. 433 *B*). Excessive brain size is usually due to *hydrencephaly*, which is characterized by a distention of the head (*macrocephalus*) through the increase of cerebral fluid (*C*); the same condition, as well as the resulting individual, also is called *hydrocephalus*.

REFERENCES CITED

1. Glaser, O. W. 1914. Anat. Rec., 8, 525–551.
2. Landacre, F. L. 1931. Jour. Comp. Neurol., 56, 215–255.
3. Bartelmez, G. W. and Evans, H. M. 1926. Carnegie Contrib. Embryol., 17, No. 85, 1–67.
4. Bailey, P., and Cushing, H. 1926. A Classification of Tumors, etc. Lippincott, Phila.
5. Penfield, W. 1928. Sect. 30 in Cowdry's 'Special Cytology.' Hoeber, N. Y.

6. Hardesty, I. 1904. Am. Jour. Anat., **3**, 230–268.

7. Cajal, S. R. 1909; 1911. Histologie du système nerveux, etc. Maloine, Paris.

8. Sauer, F. C. 1935. Jour. Comp. Neurol., **63**, 13–23.

9. Weiss, P. and Wang, H. 1936. Anat. Rec., **67**, 105–117.

10. Murnaghan, D. P. 1941. Anat. Rec., **81**, 183–204.

11. Adelmann, H. B. 1925. Jour. Comp. Neurol., **39**, 19–171.

12. Holmdahl, D. E. 1928. Zeitschr. f. mikr.-anat. Forsch., **14**, 99–298.

13. Truex, R. C. 1939. Jour. Comp. Neurol., **71**, 473–486.

14. Stone, L. S. 1922. Jour. Exp. Zoöl., **35**, 421–496.

15. Metz, A. and Spatz, H. 1924. Zeitschr. f. gesam. Neurol. u. Psychiat., **89**, 138–170.

16. Schaffer, K. 1926. Zeitschr. f. Anat. u. Entwickl., **81**, 715–719.

17. Kershman, J. 1939. Arch. Neurol. and Psychiat., **41**, 24–50.

18. Juba, A. 1934. Zeitschr. f. Anat. u. Entwickl., **103**, 245–258.

19. Detwiler, S. R. and Kehoe, K. 1939. Jour. Exp. Zoöl., **81**, 415–435.

20. Raven, C. D. 1937. Jour. Comp. Neurol., **67**, 221–240.

21. Jones, D. S. 1939; 1941. Anat. Rec., **73**, 343–357; **79**, 7–15.

22. Langworthy, O. R. 1933. Carnegie Contrib. Embryol., **24**, No. 139, 1–57.

23. Speidel, C. C. 1933. Am. Jour. Anat., **52**, 1–79.

24. Harrison, R. G. 1910. Jour. Exp. Zoöl., **9**, 787–848.

25. Harrison, R. G. 1924. Jour. Comp. Neurol., **37**, 123–205.

26. Bodian, D. 1937. Jour. Comp. Neurol., **68**, 117–159.

27. Cajal, S. R. 1928. Degeneration and Regeneration of the Nervous System. Oxford Univ. Press, London.

28. Holmdahl, D. E. 1925–26. Morph. Jahrb., **54**, 333–386; **55**, 112–208.

29. Sternberg, H. 1927. Zeitschr. f. Anat. u. Entwickl., **82**, 747–780.

30. Kingsbury, B. F. 1922. Jour. Comp. Neurol., **34**, 461–491.

31. Weed, L. H. 1917. Carnegie Contrib. Embryol., **5**, No. 14, 1–116.

32. Harvey, S. C. *et al.* 1933. Arch. Neurol. and Psychiat., **29**, 683–690.

33. Raven, C. R. 1936. Arch. f. Entwickl.-mech. d. Organ., **134**, 122–146.

34. Streeter, G. L. 1919. Am. Jour. Anat., **25**, 1–11.

35. Kunitomo, K. 1918. Carnegie Contrib. Embryol., **8**, No. 26, 167–198.

36. Alegais and Peyron. 1920. Compt. rend. Soc. biol., **83**, 230–232.

37. Kingsbury, B. F. 1920. Jour. Comp. Neurol., **32**, 113–135.

38. Schulte, H. W. and Tilney, F. 1915. Annals New York Acad. Sci., **24**, 319–346.

39. Kappers, C. U. A. 1917. Jour. Comp. Neurol., **27**, 261–298.

40. Windle, W. F. 1933. Jour. Comp. Neurol., **58**, 643–723.

41. Streeter, G. L. 1933. Jour. Comp. Neurol., **57**, 455–475.

42. Nilsson, F. 1926. Zeitschr. f. mikr.-anat. Forsch., **7**, 191–230.

43. Neal, H. V. 1918. Jour. Morph., **31**, 293–315.

44. Ingvar, S. 1918. Folia Neuro-biol., **11**, 205–495.

45. Dowd, L. W. 1929. Jour. Comp. Neurol., **48**, 471–499.

46. Sheinin, J. J. 1930. Jour. Comp. Neurol., **50**, 109–131.

47. Hochstetter, F. 1929. Beiträge zur Entwicklungsgeschichte des menschlichen Gehirns. Deuticke, Wien.

48. Gladstone, R. J. and Wakeley, C. P. G. 1935. Jour. Anat., **69**, 427–454.

49. Tilney, F. and Warren, L. F. 1919. Am. Anat. Memoirs, No. 9, Pt. 1, 257 pp.

50. Mellus, E. L. 1912. Am. Jour. Anat., **14**, 107–117.

51. Bailey, P. 1916. Jour. Comp. Neurol., **26**, 79–120.

CHAPTER XX

THE PERIPHERAL NERVOUS SYSTEM

The peripheral nervous system consists of bundles of myelinated and unmyelinated *nerve fibers*, and aggregations of nerve cells known as *ganglia*. The fibers are of two types: *afferent fibers*, which carry sensory impulses to the central nervous system, and *efferent fibers* which dispatch motor impulses away from the nervous centers. The peripheral afferent fibers originate from nerve cells located in the ganglion crest (p. 417) alongside the neural

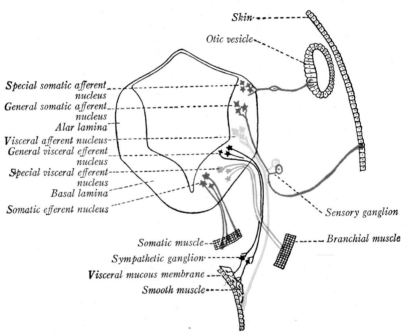

FIG. 434.—Arrangement of the functional cell columns and the origin, course and termination of the functional components of the cranial nerves, illustrated by a diagrammatic section through the embryonic myelencephalon (Ranson).

tube. The efferent fibers develop from neuroblasts in the basal plate of the tube and grow ventrolaterad to the outside. Fibers of one or both sorts converge into distinct cables called *nerves*, which are arranged in pairs to innervate corresponding regions of the bilaterally symmetrical body. The nerves belong to two main systems: the *cerebro-spinal* series and the *sympathetic* division.

Functional Classification of Fibers.—The early observation that sensory impulses travel in the dorsal root fibers and motor impulses in ventral root fibers (Fig. 435) has been supplemented by a more complete analysis (Fig. 434). All neurons fall within four chief functional groups, which are further subdivided as indicated in the following list. No single nerve contains representatives of all fiber types; those components designated 'special' are peculiar to the cranial nerves alone.

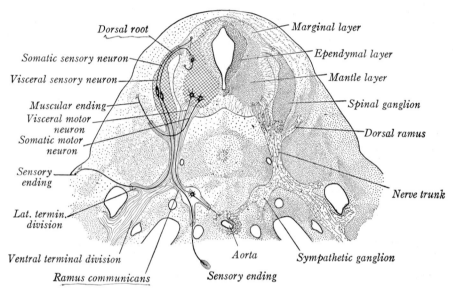

FIG. 435.—Typical spinal nerve (on right) and its functional components (on left), shown in a transverse section of a 10 mm. human embryo. × 30.

1. *Somatic afferent.*
    (a) *General* (fibers ending chiefly in the integument).
    (b) *Special* (fibers from the sensory epithelia of the eye and ear).

2. *Visceral afferent.*
    (a) *General* (sensory fibers from the viscera).
    (b) *Special* (fibers of smell and taste).

3. *Somatic efferent.* (Fibers ending on skeletal muscle).

4. *Visceral efferent.*
    (a) *General* (fibers ending about sympathetic ganglion cells which, in turn, control smooth muscle, cardiac muscle and glandular tissue).
    (b) *Special* (cranial nerve fibers terminating on the striated musculature derived from branchial arches).

THE SPINAL NERVES

The spinal nerves are arranged segmentally in agreement with the myotomes they supply. Each is attached to the spinal cord by two *roots*. One root is dorsal (posterior) in position and has a spinal ganglion associated with it; the other is ventral, or anterior (Fig. 435). Toward the end of the

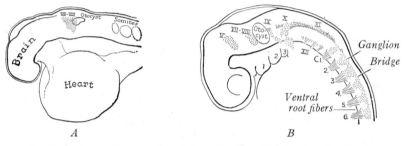

Fig. 436.—Early human brains, viewed from the left side, showing the developing cerebro-spinal nerves (adapted). *A*, At 2 mm., with ten somites (× 30); *B*, at 3.5 mm., with twenty-five somites (× 14).

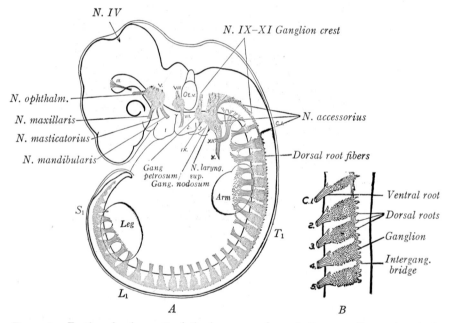

Fig. 437.—Further development of the human cerebro-spinal nerves (Streeter). *A*, At 7 mm. (× 12); the first nerve of each spinal group is numbered. *B*, At 10 mm., showing cervical spinal nerves (× 17).

fourth week (4 mm.) the ventral root fibers can be seen growing out from neuroblasts located in the mantle layer of the spinal cord (Fig. 436 *B*). At this time the spinal ganglia are represented by local enlargements along the continuous ganglion crest. Slightly later (5 mm.) the cells of the spinal ganglia begin to develop centrally directed processes, which enter the marginal zone of the cord as dorsal root fibers (Fig. 437). Peripheral processes of the ganglion cells join the ventral root fibers to complete the serially repeated nerve trunks (Figs. 388 and 390).

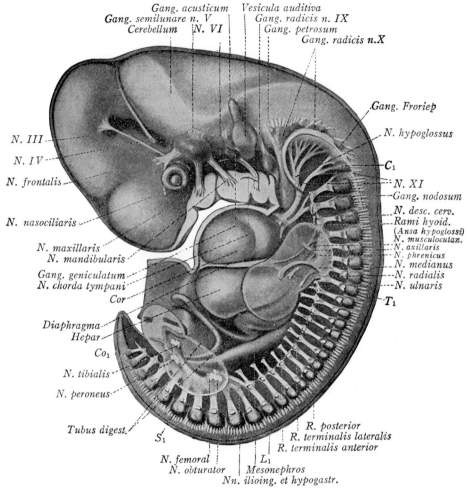

FIG. 438.—Nervous system of a 10 mm. human embryo, dissected superficially from the left side (Streeter). × 12.

At the 10 mm. stage (Fig. 438) the cellular bridges of the ganglion crest, which previously interconnected the spinal ganglia, have begun to disappear, and the several parts of a typical spinal nerve become evident (Fig. 435). In this differentiation the nerves more cephalic in position maintain a slight advance over those at lower levels. Just beyond the union of the dorsal and ventral roots, the trunk of a nerve gives off laterally the *dorsal ramus;* its fibers supply the dorsal muscles and integument. The stouter *ventral ramus*, continuing distad, branches off mesially the *ramus communicans* to the sympathetic ganglion and then divides into the lateral and ventral *terminal divisions*. The efferent fibers of the terminal divisions supply the muscles of the lateral and ventral body wall, while the afferent fibers end in the integument of the same regions (Fig. 371).

Nerve Plexuses.—At the points where the ventral and lateral terminal divisions arise, connecting loops may extend from one spinal nerve to another, thereby forming distinct nerve plexuses (Fig. 438). Regions favorable for this condition are those where the muscles of the limbs superimpose themselves on the ordinary regularity of the trunk musculature. In this manner the first four pairs of cervical nerves produce the *cervical plexus*. The nerves supplying the arm and leg also unite into plexuses, clearly indicated in embryos of six weeks. The plexus related to the arm is the brachial plexus; the one to the leg is the lumbo-sacral plexus. Both of these divide into dorsal and ventral divisions, whose branches are distributed respectively to the dorsal and ventral surfaces of the appendages. The dorsal nerves innervate the extensor muscles of the dorsal side, the ventral nerves the flexor muscles of the ventral side. The cutaneous innervation of these regions is shown in Fig. 371.

As additional detail, it may be said that the trunks of the last four cervical nerves, together with the first thoracic, unite into a flattened plate that represents the primitive *brachial plexus*. From this plate nerve cords extend into the intermuscular spaces and end in the premuscle masses. The developing skeleton of the shoulder splits the brachial plexus into dorsal and ventral laminæ. From the dorsal lamina arise the axillary and radial nerves; from the ventral lamina the musculo-cutaneous, median and ulnar nerves. Similarly the lumbar and sacral nerves to the leg associate in a plate-like mass that differentiates into the *lumbo-sacral plexus*. This plate is divided by the skeletal elements of the pelvis and femur into two lateral (primitively dorsal) and two medial (primitively ventral) trunks. Of the cranial pair, the lateral component becomes the femoral nerve; the medial, the obturator nerve. The caudal pair constitutes the primitive sciatic nerve; its lateral trunk will be the peroneal nerve, the medial trunk the tibial nerve.

THE CRANIAL NERVES

Twelve pairs of cranial nerves appear during the fifth and sixth weeks (Fig. 438). They are not arranged segmentally, and all attempts to interpret them satisfactorily as serial homologues of spinal nerves have failed. In addition to the general sensory and motor components of spinal nerves, the cranial group contains special fibers distributed to the major sense organs and to muscles derived from branchial arches. The several sensory and motor nuclei are arranged in definite masses and columns within the respective alar- or basal plate (Fig. 434). Unlike the nerves of the spinal series, which are fundamentally alike, the several cranial nerves vary widely in functional composition. Those in the first two groups of the subjoined list have but a single kind of fiber. Quite different is the third group, all of whose representatives are mixed; notable are the ninth and tenth nerves, which contain five different fiber types each.

SPECIAL SENSORY	SOMATIC MOTOR	VISCERAL SENSORY AND MOTOR
I. Olfactory.	III. Oculomotor.	V. Trigeminal.
II. Optic.	IV. Trochlear.	VII. Facial.
VIII. Acoustic.	VI. Abducens.	IX. Glossopharyngeal.
	XII. Hypoglossal.	X. Vagus complex (including XI, Spinal Accessory).

THE SPECIAL SENSORY NERVES

I. The **Olfactory Nerve**, though purely sensory, has no ganglion. Its nerve cells lie at first wholly within the epithelial lining of the nose and are of the bipolar type (Fig. 439). From them short peripheral processes develop which end in bristles at the surface of the olfactory epithelium. Proximal processes grow brainward during the fifth week and gather into the strands of the olfactory nerve, around which the cribriform plate of the ethmoid bone later develops. These fibers end in the *glomeruli* of the olfactory bulb in contact with dendrites of the *mitral cells,* or

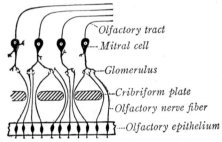

FIG. 439.—Diagram of the relations of the olfactory nerve to the nasal epithelium and olfactory tract.

olfactory neurons of the second order (Fig. 439). Some olfactory cells migrate inward from the epithelium, with which, however, they retain peripheral connections. Such bipolar elements, found along the entire course of the nerve, resemble ordinary dorsal ganglion cells. The olfactory nerve fibers remain unmyelinated.

The poorly understood *terminal nerve* courses in close association with the olfactory nerve but evidently is distinct from it. Ganglion cells occur along its extent, and its unmyelinated fibers end in the epithelium of the vomero-nasal organ and nasal septum.[1,2]

II. The **Optic Nerve** is formed by fibers that grow from neuroblasts in the nervous layer of the retina. Since the retina differentiates from the evaginated wall of the fore-brain (Fig. 422), the optic nerve is not a true peripheral nerve but belongs rather to the central system of cerebral tracts. The neuroblasts from which the optic nerve fibers develop constitute the ganglion cell layer of the retina. During the sixth and seventh weeks these cells give rise to central processes which spread out on the free surface of the retina, there to organize the *nerve fiber layer* (Fig. 464). The optic fibers converge toward the optic stalk and grow through the substance of its wall back to the brain (Fig. 440 *A*). The cells of the optic stalk are converted into a neuroglial framework, and its central cavity is rapidly obliterated (*B*). In the floor of the diencephalon, at its boundary with the telencephalon, the two optic nerves unite at about the end of the second month to produce

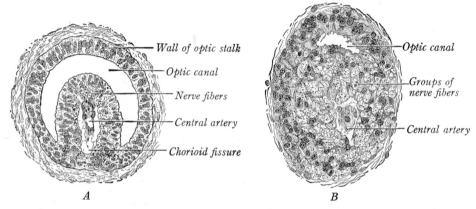

Wall of optic stalk

Optic canal

Nerve fibers

Central artery

Chorioid fissure

Optic canal

Groups of nerve fibers

Central artery

A   *B*

Fig. 440.—Transformation of the human optic stalk into the optic nerve, shown by transverse sections (after Bach and Seefelder). *A*, At 14.5 mm. (× 275); *B*, at 19 mm. (× 350).

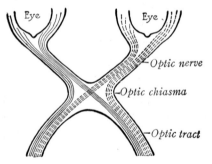

Eye   Eye

Optic nerve

Optic chiasma

Optic tract

Fig. 441.—Diagram to illustrate the course of the human optic nerve fibers in the region of the optic chiasma.

the *optic chiasma*. This is a region where there is a partial crossing of optic nerve fibers; those from the medial half of each retina pass over to the opposite side of the chiasm, whereupon the recombined nerves again separate and continue into the brain as the *optic tracts* (Fig. 441). Optic nerve fibers are all myelinated but lack neurilemma sheaths.[3]

Efferent fibers ending in the retina may be present in the optic nerves of lower vertebrates, but the evidence for their existence in mammals is less clear.[4,5]

VIII. The **Acoustic Nerve** is composed of fibers that grow out of the acoustic ganglion, located opposite the fourth neuromere. Its cells arise from a portion of the neural crest which, at its earliest appearance in embryos of some four somites, still lies within the brain wall but soon separates off and locates just rostral to the otic vesicle (Fig. 436);[6] a placodal origin from the wall of the otocyst has also been described.[7] This is the

first sensory primordium that can be identified in an embryo. The cells
remain bipolar—central processes uniting the ganglion to the tuberculum
acusticum of the myelencephalon and peripheral fibers connecting it with
the wall of the otocyst.

The primitive acoustic ganglion is differentiated into *vestibular* and
spiral ganglia in the following manner (Fig. 442): The original ganglion
elongates and is subdivided into superior and inferior portions in 7 mm.

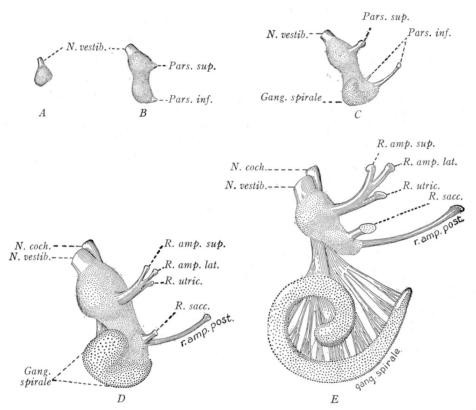

Fig. 442.—Differentiation of the primitive left acoustic ganglion and nerve of man (Streeter).
× 30. The vestibular ganglion is finely stippled, the spiral ganglion coarsely stippled. *A*, At
4 mm.; *B*, at 7 mm.; *C*, at 9 mm.; *D*, at 20 mm.; *E*, at 30 mm.

embryos (*A*, *B*). The superior part and some of the inferior portion co-
operate in innervating the utriculus, sacculus and the semicircular ducts; the
combined ganglionic mass becomes known as the vestibular ganglion (*C–E*).
Most of the pars inferior, however, differentiates into the spiral ganglion,
the peripheral fibers of which innervate the auditory hair cells of the spiral
organ (of Corti) in the cochlea. The spiral ganglion is recognizable in
9 mm. embryos and conforms to the spiral turns of the cochlea—hence
its name. Its centrally directed nerve fibers produce the cochlear division

of the acoustic nerve. This is distinctly separated from the corresponding fibers of the vestibular ganglion, which constitute the vestibular division of the acoustic nerve, equilibratory in function. In spite of this, the component of the vestibular ganglion derived from the pars inferior does become closely connected with the n. cochlearis, and thus in the adult it appears as though the sacculus and posterior ampulla were supplied by the cochlear nerve.

THE SOMATIC MOTOR NERVES

This group, consisting of the three nerves to the eye muscles and the hypoglossal nerve to the tongue, is purely motor; the nuclei of origin are colored red in Fig. 443. They are regarded as homologues of the ventral

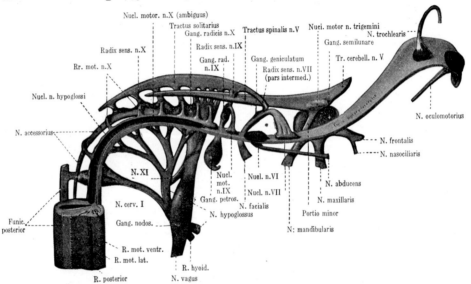

FIG. 443.—Reconstruction of the nuclei of origin and termination of the cranial nerves in a 10 mm. human embryo (Streeter). × 30. The somatic motor nuclei are colored red.

motor roots of the spinal cord that have lost their segmental arrangement and are otherwise modified. All of the motor components of the cranial nerves originate from neuroblasts located at first in the basal plate, near the floor plate. Somatic motor nuclei retain this position, while visceral motor neuroblasts migrate to a more lateral position (Figs. 410 and 411).

III. The **Oculomotor Nerve** develops from neuroblasts in the basal plate of the mesencephalon (Figs 416 *A* and 443). The fibers emerge ventrally as small fascicles, located in the concavity under the mid-brain brought about by the cephalic flexure (Fig. 438). The fascicles collect into a nerve trunk and end in the premuscle masses of the eye. The nerve eventually supplies all of the extrinsic eye muscles, save the superior oblique and external rectus.

IV. The **Trochlear Nerve** fibers arise from neuroblasts located just caudal to the nucleus of the oculomotor nerve (Fig. 443). They are directed dorsad and curve around the cerebral aqueduct within the neural wall; crossing in the roof of the mesencephalon, the two nerves leave the brain at the isthmus (Fig. 416 *B*). From such a superficial origin, at the level of the first neuromere, each passes ventrad as a slender nerve that connects with the superior oblique muscle of the corresponding eye (Fig. 438); this, however, is on the side opposite to its nucleus of origin. The reason for this interesting crossing is quite obscure.

VI. The **Abducens Nerve** takes origin from a motor nucleus located directly beneath the fourth neuromere in the pontine region of the metencephalon (Fig. 443). The converging fibers pass out ventrally at a point caudal to the pons and, as a single trunk, course rostrad to end in the external rectus muscle of the eye (Fig. 438). Vestigial rootlets of the abducens and hypoglossal nerves tend to fill in the gap between these two nerves.[8]

XII. The **Hypoglossal Nerve** results from the fusion of the ventral root fibers of three to five nerves rostral to those commonly recognized as belonging to the cervical series (Figs. 436 *B* and 443). The corresponding dorsal roots have dropped out, and the motor fibers leave the ventral wall of the myelencephalon in several groups. In embryos of 7 mm. these fibers have converged ventrally to form the common trunk of the nerve (Fig. 437 *A*). Later they grow rostrad and eventually end in the muscles of the tongue.

That the hypoglossus is a composite nerve, homologous with the ventral roots of the spinal nerves, is shown:[9] (1) by the segmental origin of its fibers; (2) from the fact that its nucleus of origin is a rostral continuation of the ventral gray column, or nucleus of origin for the ventral spinal roots; and (3) from the presence in mammalian embryos (pig; sheep; cat; etc.) of rudimentary dorsal ganglia, one of which at least (Froriep's ganglion) sends a dorsal root to the hypoglossus. In human embryos, Froriep's ganglion may be present as a rudimentary structure (Fig. 446), or it may be absent and the ganglion of the first cervical nerve also be missing. In pig embryos there are one to four accessory ganglia (including Froriep's) from which dorsal roots extend to the root fascicles of the hypoglossal nerve (Fig. 550).

THE VISCERAL MIXED NERVES

The motor roots of this group arise in a lateral series, distinct from the roots encountered hitherto in other nerves. This position is the result of an early migration of motor neuroblasts from an originally ventral location (Figs. 410, 411 and 414). The sensory elements are derivatives of a neural crest partly continuous with that of the spinal cord (Fig. 436 *B*).

The trigeminal nerve contains not only visceral efferent fibers to muscles originating in the first branchial arch, but also numerous somatic sensory neurons from the head. The facial, glossopharyngeal and vagus nerves are almost wholly visceral in function. Their sensory fibers supply the sense organs of the branchial arches and viscera; their motor components innervate such muscles as are derived from the second to fifth branchial arches; in addition, these nerves contain a few somatic sensory fibers. The primitive relation of the visceral nerves to the branchial arches is illustrated in Fig. 369 *A*, the final relation in Fig. 444.

V. The **Trigeminal Nerve** is chiefly sensory. Its large *semilunar ganglion* lies near the rostral end of the hind-brain, opposite the second neuromere (Fig. 436 *B*). Centrally directed processes from the ganglion form the large sensory root that enters the wall of the metencephalon at the level of the pontine flexure (Fig. 414). These fibers make connections with the sensory nuclei, some of them turning caudad to constitute the *spinal tract* of the trigeminal nerve (Fig. 443). The processes peripheral to the ganglion separate into three large divisions (the *ophthalmic, maxillary* and *mandibular nerves;* Fig. 438) and supply the integument of the head as well as the epithelium of the nose and mouth. An interesting tract of sensory nerve fibers arises in the *mesencephalic nucleus,* which is made up of unipolar cells similar to ganglion cells;[10] it furnishes the only instance of a peripheral sensory nerve with cells of origin buried in the central nervous system (Fig. 416 *C*). The mesencephalic root comes to be an integral part of the mandibular division of the fifth nerve.

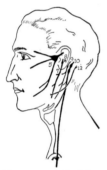

The motor fibers of the trigeminal nerve arise largely from a *motor nucleus* that lies within the pons at the same level as the external ganglion (Figs.

FIG. 444.—Position of certain cranial nerves with respect to the head.

414 and 443). In the embryo its fibers leave the brain wall as a separate motor root alongside the semilunar ganglion and, as a distinct trunk, supply the premuscle masses derived from the first pair of branchial arches. These transform into the muscles of mastication. Later the motor fibers are incorporated into the mandibular division.

VII. The **Facial Nerve** is composed for the most part of efferent fibers arising from a cluster of neuroblasts that comprise its *motor nucleus;* this is located in the pons beneath the third neuromere of the rhombencephalon (Fig. 443). Its fibers at first grow straight laterad, passing rostral to the nucleus of the abducens (Fig. 445 *A*). The nuclei of the two nerves later shift their positions, that of the facial nerve moving caudad and laterad while the nucleus of the abducens shifts rostrad (*B*). As a result, the motor root of the facial nerve bends around the nucleus of the abducens (*C*), producing the *genu*, or knee, of the former. The motor fibers leave the brain just mesial to the acoustic ganglion (Fig. 437 *A*). From here they continue ventrad and are lost in the tissue of the hyoid (second) branchial arch.

Most of the efferent fibers of the facial nerve innervate the muscles of facial expression, all derivatives of the second branchial arch; other fibers pass to the salivary glands.

The sensory fibers of the facial nerve grow from the cells of the *geniculate ganglion*, which develops from neural-crest material in close association with the acoustic ganglion (p. 464). In fact, at the start the two ganglion masses are combined in a common acustico-facial primordium (Fig. 436). However, in 7 mm. embryos the geniculate ganglion is a separate entity, located rostral to the acoustic ganglion (Fig. 437 *A*). The proximal processes from the geniculate ganglion enter the alar plate and form part of the *solitary tract* (Fig. 443). Some peripheral fibers accompany the motor fibers of the *chorda tympani*, join the mandibular branch of the trigeminal nerve, and end in the sense organs of the tongue.

IX. The **Glossopharyngeal Nerve** takes its superficial origin just caudal to the otic vesicle, at the level of the sixth neuromere (Figs. 436 *B* and 446).

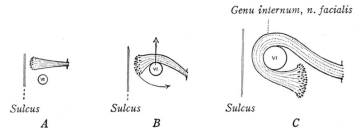

FIG. 445.—Diagram illustrating three stages in the development of the genu of the human facial nerve (Streeter). *A*, At 10 mm.; *B*, at 13 mm.; *C*, at 20 mm.

Its few efferent fibers arise from neuroblasts in the basal plate beneath the fifth neuromeric groove. These neuroblasts help form the *nucleus ambiguus*, a nucleus of origin which the glossopharyngeal shares with the vagus (Fig. 443). The motor fibers pass outward beneath the spinal tract of the trigeminal nerve. They later innervate such muscles of the pharynx as are derived from the third branchial arch, and also activate the salivary glands.

The sensory fibers of the glossopharyngeal nerve arise from two ganglia, the *superior ganglion* closer to the brain and the *petrosal ganglion* farther distad on the trunk (Fig. 446). These fibers represent the greater part of the nerve; they separate peripherally into *tympanic* and *lingual rami*, which pass to the second and third branchial arches. Proximally the sensory fibers enter the alar plate of the myelencephalon and join similar fibers of the facial nerve coursing caudad in the *solitary tract* (Fig. 443).

X, XI. The **Vagus and Spinal Accessory.**—The vagus nerve, like the hypoglossus, is composite. It represents the union of several nerves that supply the branchial arches of aquatic vertebrates (Fig. 446). The more caudal fascicles of motor fibers begin in the lateral gray column of the cervical cord as far down as the fourth cervical segment. These fibers emerge from the cord laterally and, as the *spinal accessory* trunk (considered a distinct nerve in adult amniotes), course rostrad along the line of the neural crest (Figs. 437 *A* and 446). The motor fibers of the vagus proper spring from the neuroblasts of the *nucleus ambiguus* of the myelencephalon (Fig. 443); still others arise from a *dorsal motor nucleus* (Fig. 411). The fibers from these two sources pass out as separate fascicles and join the fibers of the spinal accessory in the main trunk of the vagus nerve. The accessory

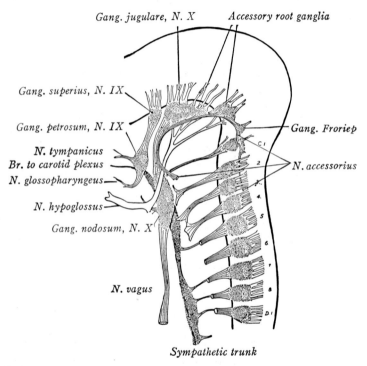

FIG. 446.—Peripheral nerves in the occipital region of an 18 mm. human embryo (Streeter). × 12.

fibers soon separate off and are distributed laterally and caudally to the premuscle masses of branchial-arch origin that later form the sterno-mastoid and trapezius muscles of the shoulder. The motor fibers of the vagus proper innervate most of the muscles of the pharynx and larynx; all these are derivatives of the fourth and fifth pairs of branchial arches. Other vagal fibers supply the smooth muscle of the viscera.

Since the vagus is a composite nerve, it has several ganglia which arise as local enlargements along the course of the ganglion crest (Fig. 446). The most dorsal and rostral of these is the *jugular ganglion*, at the level of the seventh neuromere. The other dorsal ones, termed *accessory ganglia,* are vestigial structures which are not segmentally arranged. In addition to such root ganglia of the vagus there is the *nodose ganglion* located farther distad on the trunk. The trunk ganglia of both the vagus and glossopharyngeal nerves are believed to be derivatives of the ganglion crest, their cells migrating ventrad in early stages. The central processes from the neuroblasts of the vagal ganglia enter the wall of the myelencephalon, turn caudad and, with the sensory fibers of the facial and glossopharyngeal nerves, complete the *solitary tract* (Figs. 411 and 443). The peripheral processes of the ganglion cells form the greater part of the vagal trunks after the spinal accessory fibers have separated from it.

Placodes.—In lower vertebrates there are two series of ectodermal thickenings in connection with certain cranial nerves.[11,12] Their plate-like nature has suggested the designation 'placode' for them. The *dorsolateral placode* is developed in relation to the auditory placode as a focal point; spreading rostrad and caudad, it is responsible for the sense organs and nerves of the acoustic and lateral-line systems. *Epibranchial placodes* originate at the dorsal ends of the branchial clefts, and in some lower vertebrates cellular proliferation from them clearly adds to the neighboring ganglia. In higher animals, including man, the relations are less plain. The dorsolateral system is probably not represented beyond the sense organs of the internal ear. Indications of contributions from the epibranchial placodes to the ganglia of nerves *V, VII, IX* and *X* have been reported,[6,13,14] but the evidence is circumstantial and not beyond dispute.[15]

Anomalies.—There are many variations in the arrangement and distribution of the peripheral nerves. The more striking anomalies are usually accompanied by correlated disturbances of the central nervous system and axial skeleton.

THE SYMPATHETIC NERVOUS SYSTEM

The sympathetic nervous system is composed of a series of ganglia and peripheral nerves, the fibers of which supply gland cells and the cardiac and smooth muscle fibers of the viscera and blood vessels. The nerve cells are of the multipolar ganglion type and their axons remain unmyelinated.

The exact source of the sympathetic ganglia has caused much controversy among those who have sought by observation and experiment to solve this problem. Both the neural crest and the neural tube have been identified as the source of origin. There are no mass movements, as in sharks, but rather a migration of individual cells. Some describe these as emerging out of the masses of neural-crest substance that mostly become spinal ganglia. At an early stage these particular crest cells migrate down the dorsal nerve roots and the peripheral nerve trunks to form paired ganglionic clusters dorsolateral to the aorta (Fig. 447 *A, B*).[16] Others hold that neuroblasts pass out of the neural tube, chiefly by way of the ventral roots, and become the sympathetic ganglia.[17,18] Sheath and capsule cells come from both sources.

The ganglia of the trunk develop before those of the head and neck region. In embryos of 5 mm. the sympathetic primordia are present in the vicinity of the aorta throughout most of the extent of the trunk; the earliest cells migrate outward as indifferent elements before the differentiation of nerve processes has occurred. The prospective ganglion cells aggre-

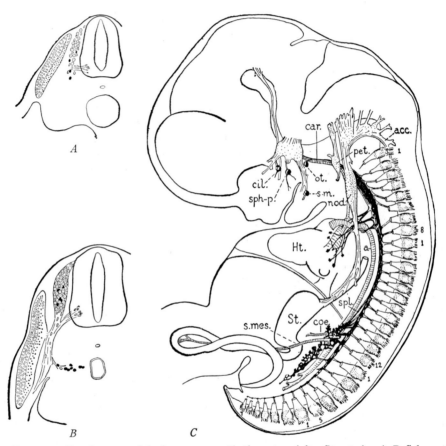

Fig. 447.—Development of the human sympathetic system (after Streeter). *A, B*, Schematic sections through the lumbar and thoracic levels of a 7 mm. embryo (× 40). *C*, Sympathetic system of a 16 mm. human embryo (× 7); the ganglionated trunk is heavily shaded.

cil., Ciliary ganglion; *cœ.*, cœliac artery and plexus; *Ht.*, heart and cardiac plexus; *ot.*, otic ganglion; *pet.*, petrosal ganglion; *s-m.*, submaxillary ganglion; *sph-p.*, spheno-palatine ganglion. In *A* and *B* spinal ganglion cells are represented by dotted circles, sympathetic cells by black ovals, and sheath cells by white rings.

gate in segmental masses during the seventh week, whereupon further migration ceases and the primitive ganglia of each side become linked, chain-fashion, by a longitudinal nerve cord. The resulting ganglionated cords are the sympathetic trunks (Fig. 447 *C*). In the neck region primary sympathetic ganglia develop in the lower cervical segments only; growth cephalad then carries the sympathetic trunks to higher cervical levels (Fig. 446).[19] The sympathetic (*i.e.*, cranial autonomic) ganglia related to the brain are at no time segmental. They are derived chiefly from the primitive semilunar ganglia, although the geniculate and petrosal ganglia also contribute (Fig. 447 *C*).[19, 27]

Root fibers from the cerebro-spinal nerves pass into or through the adjacent ganglia of the sympathetic trunks (Figs. 435 and 447 *C*). Some are efferent and terminate about the ganglion cells, whence their impulses are relayed by unmyelinated sympathetic neurons to their destinations. Others are afferent, bringing visceral sensory impulses directly from the viscera to the spinal ganglia and central nervous system. Both fiber types acquire myelin sheaths and so constitute the *white communicating rami*. Some of the unmyelinated sympathetic fibers grow back into the spinal nerves by way of separate *gray communicating rami*. These fibers are efferent in function and are distributed with the spinal nerves.

In addition to the primary ganglia of the paired sympathetic trunks, which lie dorsolateral to the aorta, there are other more peripheral ones, known as *collateral ganglia*, belonging to the great *prevertebral plexuses*, such as the cardiac, cœliac and hypogastric (Fig. 447 *C*). Still farther distad are the *terminal ganglia*, located near or even within the structures they innervate; this group includes the ciliary and cardiac ganglia, and the small ganglion masses of the myenteric and submucous plexuses. Each cell in these several types of ganglion is in direct relation with the axon of a cerebro-spinal cell, so that every sympathetic neuron forms a terminal link in a chain whose first link is a neuron belonging to the central nervous system (Fig. 435). The ganglion cells of the prevertebral plexuses originate like those of the sympathetic trunks and differ only in migrating greater distances; they are conspicuous about a week after the trunk ganglia appear. At about the same time the terminal ganglia related to the cardiac, pulmonary and enteric plexuses are organized. The component cells advance peripherad along the vagus nerves, except those of the gastro-intestinal region which come from the prevertebral ganglia.[20]

THE CHROMAFFIN BODIES AND SUPRARENAL GLAND

Certain cells of the primitive sympathetic ganglia are transformed into peculiar endocrine glands, rather than into neurons. The secretion formed by these elements causes them to stain brown when treated with chrome salts—hence the designation, *chromaffin cells*. Cells of this type give rise to structures known as *chromaffin bodies;* the most conspicuous member of this system is the suprarenal gland (Fig. 448 *A*).

Some chromaffin bodies are rounded, cellular masses partly embedded in the dorsal surfaces of the sympathetic ganglia; because of this association

21

they have received the appropriate name *paraganglia* (Fig. 448 *C*). They appear during the third month and at birth attain a diameter of a millimeter or more.[21]

Other chromaffin bodies, similar in nature, occur on the sympathetic plexuses. The largest, found on the abdominal sympathetic plexus, is the pair of *aortic chromaffin bodies* (of Zuckerkandl). These are first recognizable toward the end of the second month about the root of the inferior mesenteric artery (Fig. 448 *A*, *B*). At birth they are about 1 cm. long. All representatives of this group are composed of cords of chromaffin cells intermingled with strands of connective tissue; the whole mass is surrounded

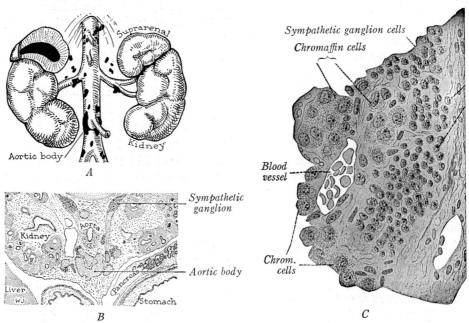

FIG. 448.—Human chromaffin bodies. *A*, Distribution of chromaffin tissue (in black), at six months (× 1.5). *B*, Aortic body, at eight weeks, shown in a transverse section (× 22). *C*, Sectioned paraganglion, at ten weeks (after Kohn). × 450.

by a connective-tissue capsule. After birth the chromaffin bodies decline but do not disappear entirely.

Associated with the aortic-arch derivatives are several problematical masses, one of which, at least, belongs in the chromaffin category. Best known is the *carotid body*, which organizes in the seventh week from a mesodermal condensation on the wall of the internal carotid artery;[22] it apparently lacks true chromaffin cells.

Each **Suprarenal Gland** has a double origin and in reality is two distinct glands secondarily combined as one within a common capsule. The *cortex* is derived from mesoderm, the *medulla* from ectodermal chromaffin tissue.

In an embryo of 8 mm. the material of the cortical portion of each gland begins to gather beneath the peritoneal epithelium at the root of the dorsal mesentery (Fig. 449 *A*, *B*).[23,24] At this period there is direct continuity between the surface epithelium and the subjacent mesenchyme.   Hence the cortical primordium originates from the proliferating epithelium in the same way that mesenchyme bordering the serous cavities, in general, has this origin.   Rapid growth of the two cortical primordia produces a pair of prominent mesenchymal condensations (*C*, *D*).   These then enter on a

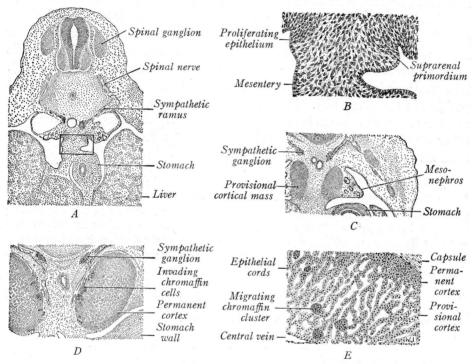

FIG. 449.—Development of the human suprarenal gland, shown in transverse sections. *A*, At 8 mm. (× 24); *B*, detail of area marked by a rectangle in *A* (× 75); *C*, at 12 mm. (× 20); *D*, at 16 mm. (× 24); *E*, at four months (× 70).

course of specialization leading to the differentiation of distinctive, well vascularized organs.   The enlarging suprarenals soon project from the dorsal wall of the cœlom, between the urogenital organs and mesentery.   Here they become relatively huge, encapsulated organs (Fig. 267 *A*), and even at birth they are one-third the size of the kidney.

No sooner has the original cortical primordium established itself as a cellular mass (Fig. 449 *C*) than it begins to become enveloped by cells of another type (*D*, *E*).   Yet both kinds trace origin to the same proliferative focus.[24]   The internal mass is a *provisional cortex* that is especially characteristic of the fetus. It constitutes the chief bulk of the organ at birth, although entering on a rapid decline at this time; its involution is not completed until two years later.[28] This provisional, or 'fetal cortex' has also been called the X- or androgenic zone; the latter term is applied because it has certain hormonal functions like the testis.[26] Simultaneously with the regression of the provisional cortex, the enveloping *permanent cortex* grows farther centrad. The glomerular zone, next the capsule, is already present at birth, and there is the beginning of a fasciculate zone as well. The fasciculate and the reticular zones become well defined within a few months.[25]

The chromaffin cells of the medulla are descended from the primitive ganglia of the cœliac plexus of the sympathetic system. In embryos of seven weeks, when the cortex is already prominent, masses of these cells begin to invade the medial side of the cortical primordium (Fig. 449 *D*). The continued migration of these cell clusters brings them to a central position in the gland (*E*). Such immigration ceases at the end of fetal life and the chromaffin tissue becomes grouped in cords and masses. Like most other ductless glands, the suprarenal tissue is permeated with a profuse network of sinusoidal capillaries.

Anomalies.—Multiple primordia or secondarily separated portions of the parent gland frequently form *accessory suprarenals*. As a rule, such accessory glands are composed of cortical substance only; they may migrate some distance from their original position, often accompanying the genital glands and also locating within the kidney. In fishes the cortex and medulla occur normally as separate organs; in higher animals there is an increasingly intimate association between the two parts until the climax is reached in mammals where the cortex encapsulates the medulla.

REFERENCES CITED

1. Pearson, A. A. 1941. Jour. Comp. Neurol., **75**, 39–66.
2. Simonetta, B. 1931. Zeitschr. f. Anat. u. Entwickl., **97**, 425–463.
3. Bruesch, S. R. and Arey, L. B. 1942. Jour. Comp. Neurol., **77**, 631–665.
4. Arey, L. B. 1916. Jour. Comp. Neurol., **26**, 213–245.
5. Arey, L. B. and Smith, H. V. 1937. Anat. Rec., **67** (Suppl.), 4.
6. Bartelmez, G. W. and Evans, H. M. 1926. Carnegie Contrib. Embryol., **17**, No. 85, 1–67.
7. Van Campenhout, E. 1935. Arch. Biol., **46**, 273–286.
8. Bremer, J. L. 1908. Jour. Comp. Neurol. and Psychol., **18**, 619–639.
9. Prentiss, C. W. 1910. Jour. Comp. Neurol. and Psychol., **20**, 265–282.
10. Sheinin, J. J. 1930. Jour. Comp. Neurol., **50**, 109–131.
11. Landacre, F. L. 1910. Jour. Comp. Neurol. and Psychol., **20**, 309–411.
12. Stone, L. S. 1922. Jour. Exp. Zoöl., **35**, 421–496.
13. Landacre, F. L. 1932. Jour. Comp. Neurol., **56**, 215–255.
14. Van Campenhout, E. 1935. Comp. rend. Soc. biol., **118**, 1653–1654.
15. Adelmann, H. B. 1925. Jour. Comp. Neurol., **39**, 19–171.
16. Yntema, C. L. and Hammond, W. S. 1945. Jour. Exp. Zoöl., **100**, 237–263.
17. Raven, C. D. 1937. Jour. Comp. Neurol., **67**, 221–240.
18. Jones, D. S. 1939; 1941. Anat. Rec., **73**, 343–357; **79**, 7–15.
19. Kuntz, A. 1920. Jour. Comp. Neurol., **32**, 173–229.
20. Van Campenhout, E. 1932. Physiol. Zoöl., **5**, 333–353.

21. Iwanow, G.   1927.   Zeitschr. f. Anat. u. Entwickl., **84**, 238–260.
22. Boyd, J. D.   1937.   Carnegie Contrib. Embryol., **26**, No. 152, 1–31.
23. Politzer, G.   1937.   Zeitschr. f. Anat. u. Entwickl., **106**, 40–48.
24. Uotila, U. U.   1940.   Anat. Rec., **76**, 183–203.
25. Keene, M. F. L. and Hewer, E. E.   1927.   Jour. Anat., **61**, 302–324.
26. Howard, E.   1938.   Am. Jour. Anat., **65**, 105–150.
27. Cowgill, E. J. and Windle, W. F.   1942.   Jour. Comp. Neurol., **77**, 619–630.
28. Swinyard, C. A.   1943.   Anat. Rec., **87**, 141–150.

CHAPTER XXI

THE SENSE ORGANS

The sense cells of primitive animals, such as worms, are ectodermal in origin and position and generalized in their receptive capacities. Only the sensory cells of the vertebrate olfactory organ retain this primitive location, even though the germ-layer origin has remained unchanged. During evolutionary history the cell-bodies of all other primary sensory neurons are believed to have migrated inward to form the dorsal ganglia.[1] As a result of such centralization the peripheral processes have assumed new relations: they end freely in the epithelium and connective tissue, become enclosed within connective-tissue capsules, or appropriate new epithelial cells that serve as sensory receptors (taste; hearing).

Among the sense organs are receptive elements of general sensibility which belong to the integument, muscles, tendons and viscera; these mediate such general sensations as touch, pressure, muscle and tendon sensibility, temperature and pain. Other organs, of a special sensory nature, are responsible for the sensations of taste, smell, vision and hearing. Each is attuned to a specific and exclusive kind of stimulus. The organs of smell, vision and hearing are distance receptors; they stand in contrast to all others that collect information from the organism itself, and especially from its integument. The apparatus for smell and taste consists of little more than the special sensory cells and fibers alone; at the other extreme are the eye and ear which possess elaborate accessory mechanisms for receiving the external stimulus and converting it into a form suitable to affect the sensory cells proper.

GENERAL SENSORY ORGANS

Free nerve terminations are by far the commonest of all the general sensory organs. There is no definite specialization, the terminal branches of the sensory nerve fibers merely ending among the cells of the epithelium or in the connective tissue. Free nerve endings begin to invade the epidermis at the end of the third month, while Merkel's tactile discs organize one month later.[2]

Lamellated corpuscles include several variant types, but all are fundamentally alike. Their differentiation begins in fetuses four months old and is completed at eight months.[2] A corpuscle starts as a mass of mesenchymal cells clustered around a nerve termination (Fig. 450 *A*). These cells multiply, flatten and give rise to concentric fibrous lamellæ which increase in number from without inward.[3]   In the cat, lamellar corpuscles increase in number by budding.

A *tactile corpuscle* originates with a looping plexus of terminal nerve fibers located just beneath the epidermis (Fig. 450 *B*); this plexus becomes encapsulated along with a cluster of mesenchymal cells.   Differentiation begins at four months, but is not completed until a year after birth.[2]   The history of certain specialized variants, such as Ruffini's terminal cylinders, Krause's end bulbs and the genital corpuscles is less well known.

Neuromuscular spindles probably begin their differentiation during the third month.[3],[4]   A plexus of nerve fibers first comes into relation with a group of myoblasts.   The latter take the form of a tapering bundle and the whole is encased in a connective-tissue capsule (Fig. 450 *C*).

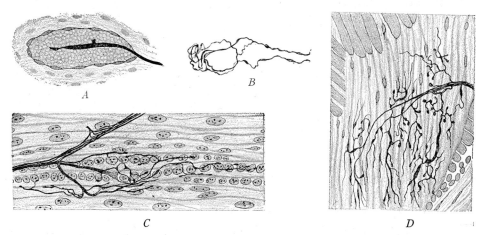

FIG. 450.—Differentiation of sensory nerve endings (after Tello and Szymonowicz).   *A*, Lamellated (Pacinian) corpuscle, from a chick embryo of fifteen days (× 275).   *B*, Nerve loops of a tactile corpuscle, from a human fetus of seven months (× 500).   *C*, Neuromuscular spindle, from a chick embryo of twelve days (× 500).   *D*, Neurotendinous spindle, from a human fetus of six months (× 400).

Neurotendinous end organs develop concurrently with muscle spindles.[3]   Their branching nerve fibers end on an encapsulated bundle of tendon fibers (Fig. 450 *D*).

THE GUSTATORY ORGAN

In fetuses of two months local thickenings of the lingual epithelium represent the first *taste buds*.[5]   The parent tissue is mostly entoderm, yet some buds are located in ectodermal territory.   The basal cells of such a thickened spot lengthen and extend toward the surface of the epithelium (Fig. 451).   This produces an epithelial cluster which, in later fetal months, differentiates further.   Some of the elements specialize into slender *taste cells*, ending in hair-like receptive tips, while others become columnar 'supporting' cells, supposedly nonsensory. Taste buds are supplied by nerve fibers of the seventh, ninth or tenth cranial nerves; the fibers branch and end about the periphery of the taste cells. However, the functional relationship between nerve and epithelium is more intimate than one might assume, since the nerve seems to exert an organizing influence on the development of taste buds.[6] Moreover, a taste bud degenerates when its nerve is cut and does not reform until the nerve regenerates.

Between the fifth and seventh fetal months taste buds are more widely distributed in the mouth and pharynx than in the adult. It is possible that this represents a transitory recapitulation of the more widespread distribution occurring in lower vertebrates. In late fetuses and after birth many taste buds degenerate; those that survive are to be found on the vallate and foliate papillæ, on a few fungiform papillæ and on the soft palate and laryngeal surface of the epiglottis. Their location at the brink of the pharynx, just before swallowing becomes an involuntary act, is advantageous. The sense of taste is present in a premature infant of eight months.

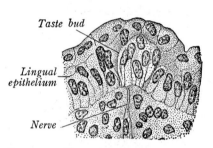

FIG. 451.—Human taste bud, at two months, in vertical section. × 300.

The development of the lingual papillæ has been described in an earlier chapter (p. 208).

THE NOSE

The development of the nose is bound up with the changes that produce the face and mouth. The first indication of the olfactory organ is an oval area of thickened ectoderm occurring on each ventrolateral surface of the head in embryos about 4 mm. long (Fig. 452 A). This *olfactory placode* straightway becomes an *olfactory pit* bounded by an elevated margin (B). Actually the early pit is more like a groove, since it is deficient ventrally and communicates with the oral cavity, as in sharks. At this period it is convenient to designate the marginal wall as a *median* and a *lateral nasal process*, separated by the olfactory pit. Figure 453 shows similar stages as they appear in sections. Close at hand laterally are the *maxillary processes* of the first branchial arches, while in the midplane is the tissue that represents the future *nasal septum* (Fig. 452 B). How these parts combine to produce the nose is shown clearly in Fig. 138.

When the fusions of the maxillary and nasal processes convert the nasal grooves into blind sacs, the opening is the *external naris* (Fig. 454 A). At its deep end the olfactory sac is separated from the mouth cavity by an epithelial plate which thins caudally and ruptures during the seventh week

(*B*). Each nasal cavity then opens to the outside through an external naris and communicates internally through its *primitive choana* with the oral

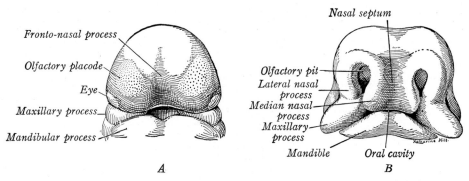

FIG. 452.—Development of the human olfactory pits (after Peter). *A,* At 5 mm. (× 24); *B,* at 11 mm. (× 12).

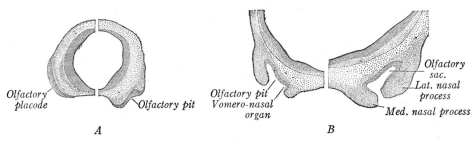

FIG. 453.—Development of the human olfactory pits, shown in transverse sections. *A,* Left half, at 5 mm. (× 25); right half, at 7 mm. (× 17). *B,* Left half, at 9 mm. (× 21); right half, at 12 mm. (× 21).

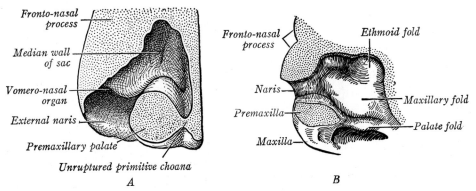

FIG. 454.—Early nasal cavity of man, illustrated by hemisections. *A,* Medial half of left cavity, at 12 mm. (after Schaeffer; × 55). *B,* Lateral half of right cavity, at seven weeks (after Frazer).

cavity. Mesenchyme proliferates beneath the floor of the sac, thereby forming the primitive palate (*A*, *B*). This differentiates both into a median part of the lip and into the so-called *premaxillary palate*.

22

Paralleling these changes comes a broadening of the head, so that the olfactory pits take a more ventral position and seem to approach the midplane. In accomplishing this, the region between is relatively compressed; it becomes the *nasal septum* (Fig. 455). Additions to the original nasal sacs are gained when the palate halves unite and separate a dorsal portion

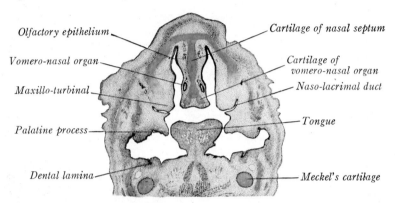

FIG. 455.—Human nasal cavities, before the completion of the palate, shown in a section at seven weeks (Prentiss). × 20.

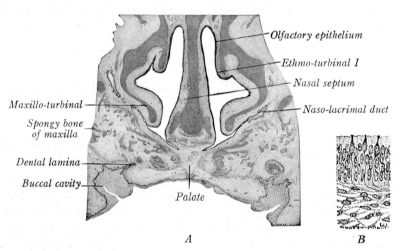

FIG. 456.—*A*, Human nasal cavities, after the union of the septum and palate, shown in a section at three months (after Prentiss; × 10). *B*, Olfactory epithelium, at seven weeks, showing three neurons in vertical section (× 200).

of the primitive mouth cavity from the rest (Fig. 163). The nasal septum grows caudad correspondingly and presently fuses with both the primary (premaxillary) and secondary palate, thus completing the separation of the two nasal passages (Figs. 456 *A* and 457*A*). The permanent nasal passages thus consist of the original nasal sacs plus a portion of the primitive mouth cavity that has been appropriated secondarily by the development of the palate (Fig. 457 *B* and 459 *A*). Their internal opening into the pharynx is by secondary, permanent *choanæ*, or posterior nares. From the second to the sixth month the external nares are closed by epithelial plugs.

The lining of the upper part of the nasal cavity is transformed into olfactory epithelium (Figs. 455 to 457). Many of its cells become elongate sensory elements which are really bipolar nerve cells (Fig. 456 *B*). At the bulbous free end a diplosome divides to produce six to eight basal bodies, each of which sends forth a fine sensory bristle. The basal end of the cell tapers into an olfactory nerve fiber which joins others and grows brainward (Fig. 439). Interspersed between the olfactory cells are inert, supporting elements. The rest of the nasal epithelium is ciliated and glandular in structure, and respiratory in function; it covers most of the septum and conchæ and lines the ethmoidal cells and paranasal sinuses (Fig. 459).

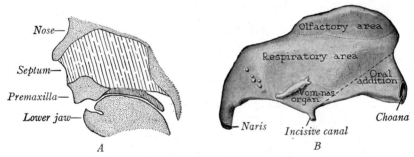

FIG. 457.—*A*, Relation of the human nasal septum and palate, shown in a sagittal section of a fetal head (after Frazer). *B*, Right nasal cavity, in median view, shown by a cast at 11 weeks (after Broman; × 12).

The *Vomero-nasal Organs* (of Jacobson) are rudimentary epithelial structures which first appear in 8 mm. embryos as a pair of grooves, one on the median wall of each nasal cavity (Figs. 453 *B* and 454 *A*). The grooves deepen and close caudally to produce blind tubular sacs which open toward the front of the nasal septum (Fig. 458 *B*). Nerve fibers, arising from the epithelial cells of the organ, join the olfactory nerve, and still other fibers from the terminal nerve end in its epithelium. Special cartilages are developed for the support of the vomero-nasal organ (Fig. 455), and during the sixth month it attains a length of 4 mm. In late fetal stages the vomero-nasal organ often degenerates, but it may persist in the adult. This organ is not functional in man, yet in many animals it evidently constitutes a special olfactory apparatus, perhaps useful in sampling odors.[7]

The human *conchæ* are poorly developed in comparison to those of some mammals. They include several elevated folds on the walls of the nasal passages—folds that secondarily become supported first by cartilage and then by bone. The *maxillo-turbinal* develops first and is followed by five

ethmo-turbinals arranged in a series of decreasing size (Figs. 456 *A* and 458
A). The ethmo-turbinals arise wholly[8] or in part[9] on the median walls,
and by a process of unequal growth are transferred to the lateral walls.

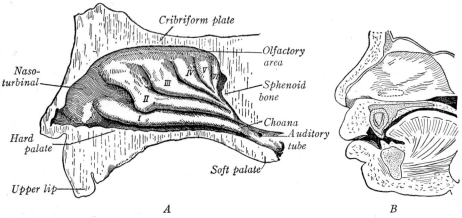

FIG. 458.—Nasal walls in human fetuses near term. *A*, Reconstruction of the lateral wall
of the right nasal passage (Prentiss, after Killian); *I*, maxillo-turbinal; *II–VI*, ethmo-turbinals.
B, Left surface of the nasal septum, with the vomero-nasal organ indicated (after Corning).

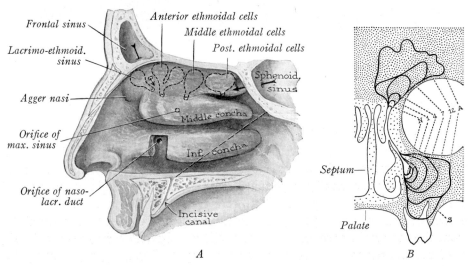

FIG. 459.—Later relations of the human nasal wall. *A*, Conchæ and paranasal sinuses, shown
on the right half of a longitudinally sectioned head; the broken, straight line indicates the position
of the primitive choana. *B*, Postnatal growth of the frontal and maxillary sinuses, indicated on
a frontal section (after Torrigiani). *A*, Adult; *N*, newborn; *S*, old age; *1–12*, years.

The *naso-turbinal* is very rudimentary and appears merely as a slight elevation near the rostral end of the maxillo-turbinal. Important growth
changes continue even into childhood. In adult anatomy (Fig. 459 *A*)
the *inferior concha* forms from the maxillo-turbinal (Fig. 458 *A*, *I*), the

middle concha from the first ethmo-turbinal (*II*), and the *superior concha* from the second and third ethmo-turbinals (*III, IV*). Often a *supreme concha* remains as the representative of the highest ethmo-turbinals. The naso-turbinal becomes the inconspicuous *agger nasi* of man.

In communication with the nasal cavity are several irregular chambers known collectively as the *paranasal sinuses* (Fig. 459 *A*). All are first indicated at about the fourth month, but most of their expansion occurs after birth (*B*).[10] Destruction of bone neighboring the nasal cavities, in order to make room for the expanding sinuses, proceeds apparently under the influence of the lining epithelium. This nasal epithelium advances at equal pace with the destruction, and its invaginated sacculations serve thereafter as a lining to the sinuses. The *ethmoidal cells* develop in the grooves between the primitive ethmo-turbinals and are fairly well differentiated in the later fetal months. The *maxillary sinus* invaginates from the groove between the maxillo-turbinal and first ethmo-turbinal and is of appreciable size in the newborn. The superior portion of the same furrow gives rise to the *frontal sinus* which undergoes most of its development after birth. The caudal end of each nasal fossa is set aside as a *sphenoidal sinus*, but actual invasion of the sphenoid bone does not occur until the third year of childhood.

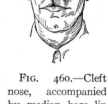

Fig. 460.—Cleft nose, accompanied by median hare lip and an abnormally large mouth.

Anomalies.—Stenosis of the nares or an incomplete septum represents the retention of normally temporary fetal conditions. Failure of the region between the nasal sacs to consolidate into a typical septum leads to a doubling of the nose; this ranges from mere apical bifurcation to complete duplicity (Fig. 460). The most striking anomaly is associated with cyclopia (p. 497); in such cases the nose is a tubular proboscis attached above the single median eye (Fig. 472 *C*). Other malformations may be introduced by hare lip and cleft palate, as already described.

THE EYE

Comparative anatomy fails to give any clue to the evolution of the vertebrate eye, since it is highly organized even in the lowest groups. Its materials come from three sources: (1) the optic nerve and retina are derivatives of the fore-brain; (2) the lens arises from the ectoderm of the head; and (3) the accessory tunics and the mechanism of accommodation differentiate from the adjacent mesenchyme.

In embryos with eight somites a vaguely expressed optic field can be identified on each of the widely spread halves of the future fore-brain (*cf.* Fig. 393 *C*). A little later a definite pit occurs in this region, but the actual optic field is larger than this, as the outlined areas on Fig. 461 *A* show.[11] A frontal section at this period demonstrates how shallow the pit is (*B*), but slightly later the evagination (*optic vesicle*) is more extensive (*C, D*); concomitantly the union of the neural folds into a tubular brain is advancing to completion.

Embryos not quite 4 mm. long have progressed to the extent that the swollen optic vesicles are attached to the brain wall by relatively constricted *optic stalks* (Fig. 408 *A, B*). This condition is followed quickly by the stage of the *optic cup*, which is characterized by an indenting of the distal wall of the vesicle brought about by rapid, marginal growth. The result is a double-layered cup, connected to the diencephalon by a tubular optic

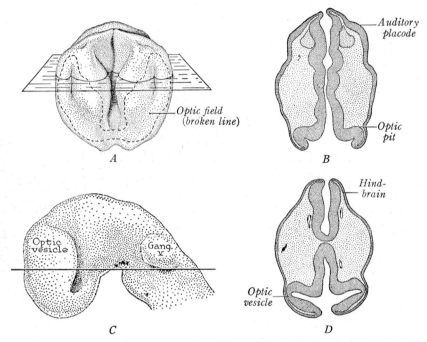

FIG. 461.—Development of the human optic vesicles. *A*, Brain, at twelve somites, in front view (after Bartelmez; × 50). *B*, Section, at fourteen somites, in the plane indicated on *A* (× 50). *C*, Brain, at fifteen somites, in lateral view (after Wen; × 66). *D*, Section, at sixteen somites, in the plane indicated on *C* (× 50).

stalk (Figs. 462 and 463). The optic cup is destined to become the retina, or the essential sensory epithelium of the eye, while the optic nerve will grow from it back through the stalk to the brain. Meanwhile, the surface ectoderm overlying the optic vesicle thickens into a *lens placode*. This straightway pockets inward to produce the *lens vesicle*, or lens primordium, which then occupies the concavity of the optic cup (Fig. 462). While these fundamental parts are differentiating further, the accessory vascular and fibrous coats of the eyeball organize from the surrounding mesoderm (Fig. 469). The axes of the primitive eyes in an embryo not yet six weeks old are set at an angle of 160° to each other; at ten weeks broadening of the head has reduced this to 72°, which is not much greater than the permanent angular divergence.   Such relative convergence makes possible the binocular vision of primates.

With this introductory statement for a background, the details of the development of the eye will now be set forth.

The preprimordium of the eyes is a common optic field on which the substrate normally acts to establish two bilaterally situated centers of eye-formation.   In itself, the prepri-mordium is neither 'single and median' nor 'double and bilateral'; rather, the normal pro-duction of two eyes depends upon factors operating during development.[12]

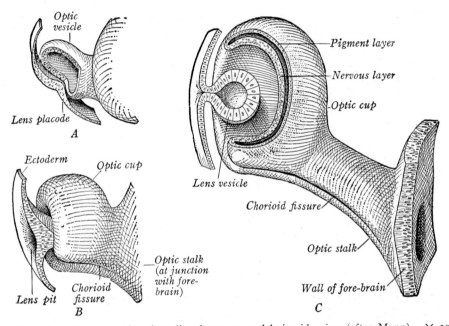

FIG. 462.—Human optic primordia, shown as models in side view (after Mann). × 100. The lens is sectioned and the optic cup in *A* and *C* has been partly cut away. *A*, At 4.5 mm.; *B*, at 5.5 mm.; *C*, at 7.5 mm.

The invagination of the optic vesicle is a self-governed process, which takes place even after transplantation to a strange locality.   Moreover, the optic vesicle possesses the ability to act as an organizer and induce lens formation in the overlying ectoderm; it may even do this in regions that normally never differentiate a lens.   Nevertheless, the ectoderm of dif-ferent species possesses a capacity for independent lens formation in varying degrees; in some a lens does differentiate after removal of the optic vesicle.[13]

Differentiation of the Optic Cup.—From its beginning, the optic cup is imperfect because of a notch that affects both layers of its double wall. This defect is brought about by the original invagination extending at one point past the cup and continuing as a groove that courses along the optic stalk (Fig. 462 *B*, *C*).   The meridionally located defect in the cup and the furrow-like groove of the stalk together comprise what has been inappropriately named the *chorioid fissure*. As a necessary result of this type of invagination, the internal as well as the external layer of the optic cup is continued into a corresponding component of the stalk (Fig. 463). It will be noticed that the optic stalk meets the cup below its central axis; this fact and the presence of the chorioid fissure account for the varying appearances obtained in sections cut through different planes at early stages.

During the seventh week the lips of the chorioid fissure close, so that the double-walled cup is complete and symmetrical, while the stalk becomes a tube within a tube (Fig. 466). By the formation and closure of the chorioid fissure the inner layer of the optic cup is continued directly back-

Mesenchyme   Lens vesicle   Vitreous body   Optic stalk   Optic recess of brain

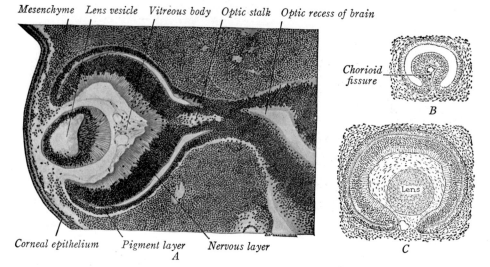

Corneal epithelium   *Pigment layer*   *Nervous layer*
                              A

FIG. 463.—Optic primordia of a 10 mm. human embryo. *A*, Longitudinal section (Prentiss; × 80). *B*, *C*, Optic stalk and optic cup, respectively, sectioned transversely to show the chorioid fissure (× 65).

ward within the optic stalk. This continuity creates a direct path along which optic nerve fibers, originating in the inner layer of the retina, pass to the brain. The same arrangement likewise furnishes a tunnel which the hyaloid artery utilizes in reaching the interior of the eyeball without piercing its layers (Fig. 468).

Returning to the stage of the optic vesicle, it is obvious that its continued deepening as an optic cup will bring the invaginating layer progressively closer to the external layer. Soon the two come to lie in apposition, thereby obliterating the primitive lumen of the cup (Fig. 463 *A*). These layers now transform into an epithelial *retina*,[14] while the rim of the cup represents the primitive, epithelial *iris*. The circular opening into the cup is the *pupil*.

The outer, thinner component of the optic cup becomes a simple epithelium known as the *pigment layer*. Pigment granules, elaborated from the cytoplasm,[15, 16] appear in its cells in embryos of 7 mm. and the pigmentation is soon dense (Fig. 468). It extends even to the pupillary margin of the optic cup.

The internal, thicker layer of the optic cup becomes the *nervous layer*. In it may soon be recognized (Fig. 470): (1) the thinner *pars cæca*, a non-nervous zone bordering the rim; and (2) the thicker *pars optica*, a truly nervous portion lining most of the cup. The line of demarcation between these two regions makes a wavy circle, the *ora serrata*. Through the development of radial folds, just peripheral to the ora serrata, the ciliary bodies are foreshadowed. The pars cæca of the retina is thereby subdivided into a *pars ciliaris* and *pars iridica*. The pars ciliaris, with a co-extensive zone

Cone cell—
Rod cell—
Rod cell—
Fiber of Müller—
Amacrine cell—
Ganglion cell—
Optic fibers—

External limiting membrane
Layer of rod and cone cells
Ganglionic layer
Fibrous layer
Internal limiting membrane

FIG. 464.—Early differentiation of the nervous layer of the human retina, shown in a vertical section at three months (Prentiss). × 440. At left, Cajal's analysis of the component element after silver impregnation; at right, the appearance with ordinary stains.

of the pigment layer, covers the definitive, vascular *ciliary bodies*. The pars iridica, bordering the pupil, owes its existence to the continued growth of the margin of the optic cup.[17, 18] It blends intimately with the similarly extended pigment layer and becomes pigmented like the latter. These two layers constitute the epithelial basis of the iris.

The *pars optica*, or nervous portion of the retina, begins its peculiar differentiation near the optic stalk, from which center the process extends progressively peripherad. An outer, nuclear layer (next the pigment coat) and an inner, fibrous layer (next the cavity of the cup) can be distinguished in 12 mm. embryos (Fig. 463 A). These correspond respectively to the cellular layer (ependymal and mantle zones) and marginal layer of the neural tube. In the third month the retina shows three strata, large ganglion cells in the meantime having migrated inward from the outer layer of rod and cone cells (Fig. 464). In a fetus of the seventh month all the layers of the adult retina can be recognized (Fig. 465 A), and at this time it is known that light perception is possible.

As in the wall of the neural tube, both supporting and nervous tissues appear (Fig. 464). The supporting elements, or *fibers of Müller*, superficially resemble ependymal cells and are arranged vertically. Their terminations unite with the *internal* and *external limiting membranes* which bound the nervous retina; the actual membranes are described as a formed product, after the nature of terminal bars.[19, 20] The outermost neuroblasts of the

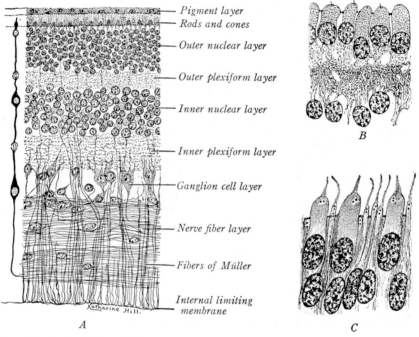

Pigment layer
Rods and cones

Outer nuclear layer

Outer plexiform layer

Inner nuclear layer

Inner plexiform layer

Ganglion cell layer

Nerve fiber layer

Fibers of Müller

Internal limiting membrane

A   C

FIG. 465.—Later differentiation of the human retina. *A,* At seven months, in vertical section (after Prentiss). × 440; at left, the chief neurons shown by silver technique; at right, appearance with ordinary stains. *B,* Early cone cells during the fifth month (after Magitot; × about 750). *C,* Rods and cones during the seventh month (after Seefelder; × 750).

retina transform into *rod* and *cone cells*, which are at first unipolar. In fetuses of seven months specialized processes protruding from them through the external limiting membrane have differentiated into the visual *rods* and *cones* (Fig. 465).[21, 22] These are the receptive, visual elements of the retina. How the retina became inverted so that light has to pass through it before encountering the rods and cones is a matter of speculation.[23] Next in position internally comes an intermediate layer, composed mostly of bipolar cells; these make connections both with the layer above and with the one below. The innermost stratum of nerve cells is the so-called *ganglion cell layer;* axons from its multipolar cells comprise the *nerve fiber layer.* The nerve fibers converge to the optic stalk, and in embryos seven weeks old grow back in its wall to the brain (Fig. 466 *A*). The cells of the optic stalk are converted into a scaffolding of neuroglial supporting tissue, and the cavity in the stalk is rapidly obliterated (*B*). The optic stalk is thus transformed into the *optic nerve,* containing a central artery and vein which originally coursed along its open groove (chorioid fissure).

The site of keenest vision in the retina is a small area, known as the *macula lutea,* that differentiates late in fetal life and in early infancy. The macula lies in the direct visual axis; this spot is particularly characterized by a thinner, highly specialized center which lies at the bottom of a shallow pit, or *fovea centralis.* These structures and the partial crossing of optic fibers at the chiasma are associated with binocular vision and the fusion of

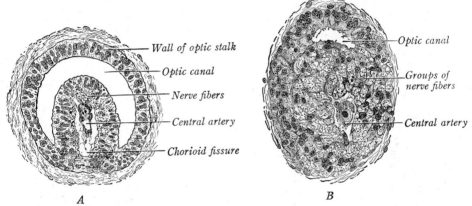

FIG. 466.—Transformation of the human optic stalk into the optic nerve, shown in transverse sections (after Bach and Seefelder). *A*, At 14.5 mm. (× 275); *B*, at 19 mm. (× 350).

images in higher primates. The human eye is sensitive to light in the seventh month, but form perception and color discrimination are not acquired until some time after birth.

The Lens.—For a short time the saccular primordium of the lens is still attached to the parent ectoderm and nearly fills the cavity of the optic cup (Fig. 462). In embryos of 8 mm. it has detached and lies free as the *lens vesicle;* at this stage it is a hollow spheroid whose inner wall is already thicker than the outer one next the surface epithelium (Fig. 463 *A*). The cells of the outer wall remain a low columnar type and constitute the permanent *lens epithelium.* The cells of the inner wall are also single-layered. They increase rapidly in height and at about seven weeks obliterate the original cavity (Figs. 468 *A* and 467 *A*). These cells transform into transparent *lens fibers.* Toward the end of the third month such primary lens

fibers attain a length of 0.18 mm., whereupon they cease dividing into new
fibers and their nuclei degenerate.   All additional fibers arise from prolifer-

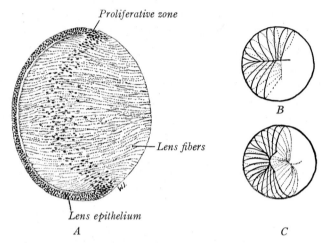

FIG. 467.—Differentiation of the human lens. *A*, Section through the lens of a 20 mm.
embryo (× 100). *B, C*, Diagrams of the formation of sutures (Mann); *B*, represents a stage when
sutures are linear, like the adult dogfish lens (front suture, horizontal; back suture, vertical); *C*,
shows a four-pointed star of the early adult.

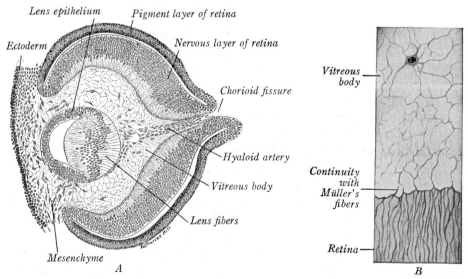

FIG. 468.—Differentiation of the human vitreous body. *A*, Optic cup, at 12 mm., in longitudinal section (after Prentiss; × 100). *B*, Detail of the vitreous body and its relation to the
retina, at two months.

ating cells located in an equatorial zone where the less specialized lens
epithelium joins the lens-fiber mass (Fig. 467 *A*).

Every lens fiber extends the whole distance from the back surface to the front. As new fibers are progressively superposed in meridional series, they necessarily become longer and longer. The characteristic *lens sutures* make their appearance on the proximal and distal faces of the lens when the longer, newer fibers overlap the ends of the shorter and older ones (Fig. 470). By an intricate yet orderly arrangement of fibers the simple linear sutures first laid down (Fig. 467 *B*) expand into *lens stars* containing three, and finally six or even nine rays (*C*). Lens fibers continue to be added throughout life, but the size of the lens does not increase much in the adult years. The structureless *capsule* of the lens is apparently derived from the cells of the lens vesicle. The lens of the early fetal months is spherical and relatively large.

The Vitreous Body and Intraocular Vessels.—The concavity between the lens and the optic cup becomes filled during the second month with a

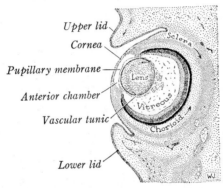

Fig. 469.—Human eyeball and eyelids, at two months, in longitudinal section. $\times$ 15.

hyaline, fibrillar jelly which comes to be known as the *vitreous body* (Fig. 469). Modern investigations agree that this substance is primarily an epithelial product.[17,24] Its early 'secretion' from lens tissue soon ceases, but the vitreous substance is progressively increased by fibrillar processes that project from the surface of the retina; they probably grow out from the young supporting cells of Müller (Fig. 468 *B*). Those fibers laid down by the pars ciliaris retinæ seemingly become the *zonula ciliaris*, or suspensory ligament of the lens.

Only when the primitive vitreous body is partly developed does mesenchyme first appear within the optic cup. Some of it enters through the chorioid fissure with the hyaloid artery (Fig. 468 *A*). Still other mesenchymal cells gain entrance around the edge of the cup in association with the lens. The fate of all this invading mesenchyme—whether it contributes significantly to the structure of the vitreous or whether it degenerates—is not yet decided beyond question.

The lens tissue proper is at all periods wholly nonvascular. However, blood vessels do spread over its surface. Some of these come from the *hyaloid artery*. This is a continuation of the *central artery*, which in 6 mm. embryos courses along the gutter-like groove of the optic stalk, enters the back of the optic cup through the chorioid fissure, and (renamed the hyaloid artery) extends to the back surface of the lens (Fig. 468 *A*). Other vessels from the region of the iris supply the front of the lens in a corresponding mesenchymal layer called the *pupillary membrane* (Fig. 470). The invest-ment as a whole constitutes the *vascular tunic of the lens*. It flourishes during the period of chief growth of the lens and attains its highest develop-

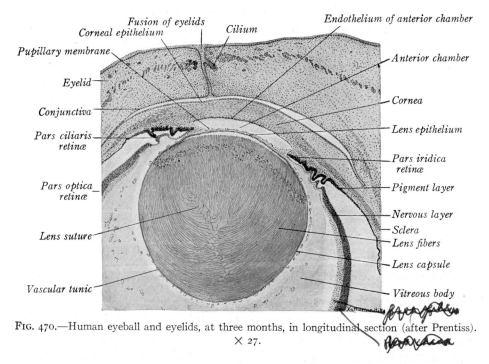

FIG. 470.—Human eyeball and eyelids, at three months, in longitudinal section (after Prentiss).
× 27.

ment in the seventh month; at birth the tunic has usually disappeared. The hyaloid artery also degenerates completely, the only permanent trace being the lymph path of the *hyaloid canal* through the vitreous body.

The Fibrous and Vascular Coats.[25]—During the seventh week the mes-enchyme surrounding the optic cup begins to specialize into two accessory coats (Fig. 469). The outer one is more compact and becomes a definitely fibrous tunic—the sclera and cornea. The inner, looser covering organizes into the vascular chorioid; it also contributes to the ciliary body and iris.

The mesenchymal *sclera* transforms into dense, white-fibrous tissue. It covers the base and sides of the eyeball. The sclerotic coat corresponds to the dura mater of the brain, with which it is continuous by way of the sheath of the optic nerve. Toward the front of the eyeball the fibrous coat is designated the *cornea* (Fig. 470). This consists of transparent connective tissue, surfaced externally with ectodermal *corneal epithelium* and lined internally with the *endothelium of the anterior chamber*. The latter represents the first mesenchymal cells that grow in from the sides, whereas the main substance of the cornea fills in secondarily between ectoderm and endothelium.[26, 27]

The *chorioid* is the inner of the two primary, mesenchymal tunics of the eyeball (Fig. 469). It is located between the sclerotic coat and the pigment layer of the retina. The chorioid primordium acquires a high vascularity in embryos as young as six weeks; moreover, its cells become stellate and pigmented, so that the tissue is loose and reticulate. This vascular layer, in which course the chief vessels of the eye, corresponds to the pia mater of the brain. Distal to the level of the ora serrata, the primitive vascular coat differentiates into (Fig. 470): (1) the connective tissue of the *ciliary bodies;* (2) the unstriped fibers of the *ciliary muscle;* and (3) the connective-tissue stroma of the *iris*. The pigmented layers of the iris are derived both from the pars iridica retinæ and from a corresponding zone of the pigment epithelium. Certain cells of this region, derived from the external (original pigment) layer of the optic cup, give rise to the *pupillary muscles* of the iris, which are thus exceptional by virtue of their ectodermal origin.[18] The lustrous *tapetum*, which reflects light in lower mammals, is not represented in the chorioid of man.

The *anterior chamber* is not a simple cleft occurring in the mesenchyme between ectoderm and lens (Figs. 469 and 470). Rather, the cornea differentiates first, whereas the mesoderm overlying the lens is an independent and secondary ingrowth from all sides.[27] This mesodermal tissue between the anterior chamber and the lens is the *pupillary membrane* (p. 494). The continued peripheral extension of the anterior chamber is responsible for the separation of a definite *iris* from the cornea. Close to the margin of the anterior chamber, at the junction of cornea and sclera, there is an important, ring-shaped drainage space, the *scleral venous sinus* (canal of Schlemm). The *posterior chamber*, between the iris and the lens, makes a relatively tardy appearance.

Accessory Apparatus.—The *Eyelids* develop as folds of the integument adjacent to the eyeball (Fig. 469). These folds are indicated at the end of the seventh week, and two weeks later their edges have met and fused (Fig. 470). This epidermal union begins to break down in fetuses five months old, but the eyes do not reopen until the seventh or eighth month; in some mammals this is delayed until after birth. A third, rudimentary eyelid, perhaps incorrectly homologized with the functional nictitating membrane of lower vertebrates,[28] is represented by the adult *plica semi-*

lunaris at the inner angle of the eye. The ectoderm of the outside of the lid differentiates into epidermis. Contrasted is the continuation of ectoderm on the internal surface of the lid and its reflection over the front half of the sclera and all of the cornea; this is a mucous membrane named the *conjunctiva* (Fig. 470). The *cilia*, or eyelashes, develop like ordinary hairs at the edges of the lids; they are provided both with sebaceous glands (of Zeis) and with modified sweat glands (of Moll). About thirty *tarsal glands* also arise along the edge of each lid (Fig. 471); these glands (of Meibom) are sebaceous in nature. The hair follicles for the cilia begin developing during the tenth week. They are followed closely by the several glands associated with the cilia and eyelids. These start budding early in the fourth month while the eyelids are still fused.

The *Lacrimal Glands* appear during the ninth week as approximately six knobbed outgrowths of the conjunctiva (Fig. 471). They lie dorsally

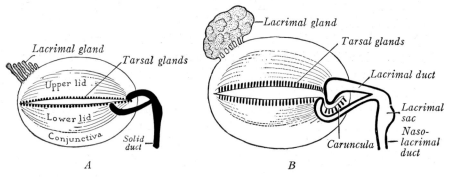

FIG. 471.—Development of the tarsal and lacrimal glands and the lacrimal-duct system of the human eye, shown by diagrams (adapted after Ask).

near the external angle of the eye. At first the primordia are solid epithelial cords, but they soon branch and acquire lumina.

Each *Naso-lacrimal Duct* arises in 12 mm. embryos as a ridge-like thickening of the epithelial lining of the naso-lacrimal groove (Fig. 366 A).[29] This groove, it will be remembered, extends from the inner angle of the eye to the primitive olfactory sac and separates the maxillary and lateral nasal processes of its respective side. The duct-thickening becomes cut off and, as a solid cord, sinks into the underlying mesenchyme. A secondary sprout grows out to each eyelid to comprise the *lacrimal ducts* (Fig. 471), while an extension in the opposite direction connects with the nose (Fig. 456 A). The nasal end of the lumen is not completed until birth. The *caruncula* (the reddish elevated mass at the inner angle of the eye) is a part of the lower lid, secondarily elevated by the corresponding lacrimal duct (Fig. 471 B).[30]

Anomalies.—Absence of the eye (*anophthalmia*) and reduction in its size (*microphthalmia*) are known, as is the virtual absence of the lens (*aphakia*). Opacities of the lens and cornea are said to be acquired aberrations, since there is no normal stage of development when these tissues are not clear.[17] Retained portions of the pupillary membrane may cross the pupil and so interfere with vision (Fig. 472 A); a similar obstruction in the visual path is presented by a persistent hyaloid artery. Lack of pigment in the retina and iris is usually associated with general albinism. Congenital *glaucoma* results when the canal of Schlemm fails to develop and furnish normal drainage for the intraocular fluid. The absence of a sector (or any local area) of the iris, ciliary body or chorioid tunic produces a defect known as *coloboma* (B); contrary to common belief, gaps in the retina proper do not occur.[17] Coloboma is usually said to result from improper closure of the embryonic chorioid fissure, but such a simple explanation is not in accord with all the facts.[17] Of eyelid defects, the best known is a cleft or split in the upper lid. In *cyclopia* a single, median eye replaces the usual paired condition (C); all intergrades exist from closely approximated eyes to perfect unity. This is the result of faulty organization of paired optic centers in a primitive, common 'eye field' (p. 487). In cases of cyclopia the nose is usually a cylindrical proboscis, situated at the base of the forehead above the median eye.

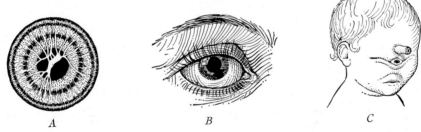

A   *B*   *C*

FIG. 472.—Anomalies of the human eye. *A*, Persistent pupillary membrane in an adult. *B*, Coloboma of the iris. *C*, Cyclopia of a newborn, with a single eyeball but partial doubling of the lids; above the eye is the proboscis-like nose.

THE EAR

The human ear consists of a sound-conducting apparatus and a receptive sense organ (Fig. 479 *B*). The reception and transmission of sound waves is the function of the *external* and *middle ears*. The end organ proper is the *internal ear*, with auditory sensibility residing in its cochlear duct. The remainder of the internal ear (semicircular ducts; utriculus; sacculus) serves as an organ of equilibration; this apparatus constitutes the entire ear of fishes.

The Internal Ear.—The epithelium of the internal ear is derived from the ectoderm. Its first occurrence is in the form of a thickened ectodermal plate, the *auditory placode*, located midway alongside the hind-brain (Fig. 473 *A*). The paired placodes have been recognized in embryos with as few as two somites, but they are not prominent until about the nine-somite stage.[11] Similarly, when 11 somites are attained the placodes already are beginning to bend inward feebly, whereas distinct *auditory pits* are better seen somewhat later (*B*). In embryos of about 24 somites (nearly 4 mm.) the cup-like pits close into *otocysts* which, however, still remain in temporary union with the ectoderm (*C*).   At the close of the fourth week (5 mm.) the otocyst, or auditory vesicle, is a detached, ovoid sac.   It lies opposite the fifth neuromere and is in contact rostrally with the acustico-facial ganglionic mass (Fig. 405).

Approximately at the point where the otocyst joined the ectoderm, a tubular recess, the *endolymph duct*, straightway pushes out as a new growth and then shifts to a mesial position (Fig. 474).[31]   Hence the human endolymph duct may not correspond precisely to that of selachian fishes which

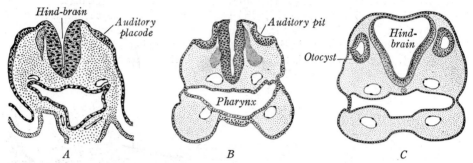

FIG. 473.—Development of the human otocyst, illustrated in transverse sections. *A*, At nine somites (× 80); *B*, at sixteen somites (× 60); *C*, at about 4 mm. (× 40).

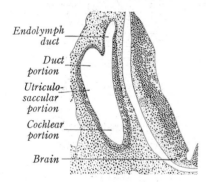

FIG. 474.—Human otocyst, at 7 mm., in longitudinal section (His).   × 50.

connects the otocyst permanently with the exterior.   In higher vertebrates its blind extremity dilates into the *endolymph sac* (Fig. 475).   In the fifth week the ovoid otocyst elongates still further in a dorsoventral direction (Figs. 474 and 475 *A*).   Its narrower, ventral part then begins coiling into the *cochlear duct* (*B–D*).   In the fifth week the most dorsal portion of the otocyst already shows indications of the developing *semicircular ducts* (*A*), while an intermediate region is destined soon to subdivide into *utricle* and *saccule* (*B–D*).

The semicircular ducts are well outlined at six weeks as two pouches— the anterior and posterior ducts from a single pouch at the dorsal border of the otocyst, the lateral duct from a horizontal outpocketing (Fig. 475 *A*, *B*).   The seventh week is occupied with the rough modeling of the otocyst into an approximation of the definitive *membranous labyrinth* (*C*). Centrally the walls of the two secondary pouches, just mentioned, flatten and fuse into epithelial plates, but canals are left at the periphery communicating with the remainder of the otic vesicle.   Soon the solid, central portions of the epithelial plates break down, leaving the semicircular ducts free.

Early in the eighth week (Fig. 475 *C*) the endolymph duct and the three semicircular ducts are well represented; at the same time the main sac is dividing into utricle and saccule, and the cochlear duct has begun to coil like a snail's shell. It will be noticed that the anterior and posterior ducts have a common limb opening dorsally into the utricle, their opposite

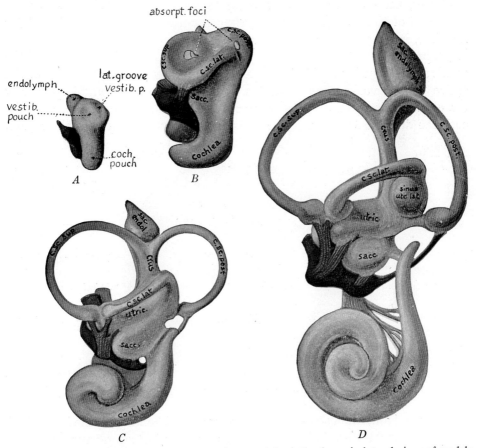

FIG. 475.—Development of the left membranous labyrinth, shown in lateral views of models (Streeter). × 25. *A*, At 6.6 mm.; *B*, at 13 mm.; *C*, at 20 mm.; *D*, at 30 mm. The colors, yellow and red, indicate respectively the cochlear and vestibular divisions of the acoustic nerve and its ganglia.

absorpt. foci. Area where absorption is complete; *crus*, crus commune; *c, sc. lat., c. sc. post., c. sc. sup.*, lateral, posterior and anterior semicircular ducts; *endolymph*, endolymph duct; *sacc.*, sacculus; *sac. endol.*, endolymph sac; *utric.*, utriculus.

ends and the rostral end of the lateral duct are dilated to form *ampullæ*. Constriction separates the utriculo-saccular region (*C*) into a dorsal portion, the *utriculus*, to which are attached the semicircular ducts, and a ventral portion, the *sacculus*, connected with the cochlear duct. Early in the third month the general adult form of the internal ear is nearly attained (*D*). At this time the sacculus and utriculus are less broadly connected; the semicircular ducts are relatively longer, their ampullæ more prominent, and the cochlear duct is coiled to its final extent of two and one-half turns. In the adult the utriculus and sacculus are completely separated from each other, but each remains attached to the endolymph duct by a slender canal. Similarly, the cochlear duct is further constricted from the sacculus; the basal end of the former becomes a blind process, while a canal, the *ductus reuniens*, is the sole connection between the two.

The totally differentiated otocyst, with all its subdivisions, is called the *membranous labyrinth*. The utriculus and sacculus alone correspond to the entire 'ear' of various invertebrates, in which the organ functions merely for equilibration and not for hearing. The semicircular ducts and the cochlear duct historically are secondary outgrowths from this older part.

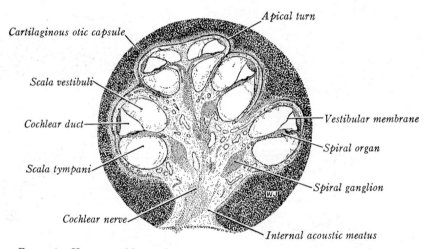

Fig. 476.—Human cochlea, at four months, in longitudinal section. × 12.

In fishes and amphibia the cochlear portion is rudimentary, while in reptiles, birds and monotremes it is a straight tube; only in true mammals does a coiled canal differentiate. The epithelium of the membranous labyrinth is composed at first of a single layer of low columnar cells. At an early stage, fibers from the acoustic nerve grow between the epithelial cells in certain regions, and these areas are then thickened and modified into special sense organs. Such end organs are the *cristæ ampullares* in the ampullæ of the semicircular ducts, the *maculæ acusticæ* in the utriculus and sacculus, and the *spiral organ* (of Corti) in the cochlear duct (Figs. 476 to 478).

The cristæ and maculæ are sense organs for maintaining equilibrium and giving information concerning the direction and extent of body movements. They differentiate during the seventh week. In each ampulla, transverse to the long axis of the duct, the epithelium and underlying tissue form a curved ridge, the *crista* (Fig. 478 *B*). The cells of the epithelium differentiate both into sense cells, which bear bristle-like hairs at their ends, and into supporting cells. The latter elements secrete a jelly-like substance (the *cupula*) upon the free surface; into it the sensory bristles project. The *macula* of the utriculus or sacculus resembles the cristæ in its development, save that larger areas of the epithelium specialize into cushion-like end organs. The free surface becomes covered with a gelatinous *otolithic membrane* which bears superficial calcareous deposits, the *otoconia*.

The true organ of hearing, the *spiral organ*, develops slowly in the epithelium of the coiled cochlear duct.[32] The spiral organ is a continuous strip that lies on the basal side of the duct, basal here signifying in a direction away from the apex of the conical cochlea (Fig. 476). Differentiation begins as an epithelial thickening in the basal turn and advances progressively toward the apex.

The epithelial primordium of the spiral organ soon divides longitudinally into an inner, larger ridge and an outer, smaller ridge (Fig. 477 *A*). The inner cells of the inner ridge be-

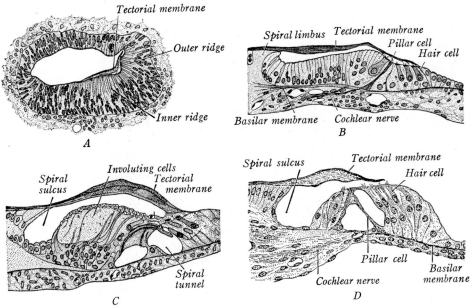

FIG. 477.—Differentiation of the human spiral organ, at ten to twenty weeks, in the basal turn of the cochlear duct (after Kolmer and Alexander). X about 150.

come the tall constituents of the *spiral limbus* (*B*); by contrast, the outer part of the ridge undergoes a peculiar autolytic involution until only the thin lining of the *inner spiral sulcus* remains (*C, D*). The outer, smaller ridge is the primordium of the *spiral organ* (of Corti). In it appear the flask-shaped *inner* and *outer hair cells*, while the remaining elements become the various *supporting cells* (*B–D*). The *spiral tunnel* results from a partial destruction of the supporting cells (*C*). Both ridges are from the beginning covered with the gradually thickening *tectorial membrane*. It is a fibrillar and gelatinous substance secreted by the epithelium.[33,34] As the spiral sulcus becomes deeper by the cellular dissolution already mentioned, the membrane spans across its trough (*C, D*).

The development of the acoustic nerve and the distribution of its vestibular and cochlear divisions are described on p. 464 and illustrated in

Figs. 442 and 475. Nerve fibers arborize about the bases of the sensory cells of the cristæ, maculæ and spiral organ. A newborn child hears imperfectly because the external auditory meatus is not entirely free and the middle ear cavity is filled almost completely with a gelatinous tissue. Following the progressive resorption of this material, normally acute hearing enters in the first weeks after birth.

The mesenchyme surrounding the membranous labyrinth is differentiated into a fibrous basement membrane, which lies next the epithelium, and into cartilage which envelops the whole labyrinth. At about the tenth week the cartilage immediately bordering the labyrinth begins a secondary reversal of development whereby it returns first to precartilage and then to

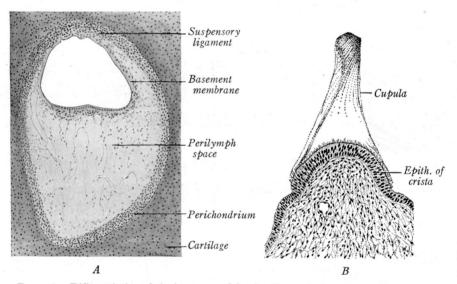

Suspensory ligament

Basement membrane

Perilymph space

Perichondrium

Cartilage

Cupula

Epith. of crista

A

B

FIG. 478.—Differentiation of the human semicircular duct. A, Appearance of the perilymph space, at four months, shown in a transverse section (after Streeter; × 75). B, Crista and its cupula, at five months, sectioned vertically (after Alexander).

a syncytial reticulum; the latter becomes the open tissue of the *perilymph spaces* (Fig. 478 A).[35] The membranous labyrinth is henceforth suspended in the fluid of the perilymph spaces. The cochlear duct appears triangular in section, for its lateral wall remains attached to the peripheral bony labyrinth while its inner angle is adherent to the bony axis (modiolus) of the cochlea (Fig. 476). Large perilymph spaces are formed above and below the cochlear duct.[36] The upper is the *scala vestibuli*, the lower the *scala tympani;* both are lined with flattened mesenchymal cells, arranged like an epithelium. The thin wall separating the cavity of the cochlear duct from that of the scala vestibuli is the *vestibular membrane* (of Reissner). Beneath the basal epithelium of the cochlear duct, a fibrous *basilar membrane* is differentiated by the mesenchyme. The *bony labyrinth* is produced in the fifth fetal month by the replacement of the cartilage capsule by bone. The central axis of the bony cochlea is exceptional, however, in that it develops directly from mesenchyme as a membrane bone.

The Middle Ear.—Each auditory tube and tympanic cavity represents a drawn-out first pharyngeal pouch (with which the second perhaps merges, as well).[37] The entodermal pouches appear in embryos of 3 mm., enlarge rapidly, flatten dorsoventrally, and are in temporary contact with the ectoderm (Fig. 479 *A*). During the last days of the second month the proximal stalk of each pouch undergoes actual constriction to form the more cylindrical *auditory tube*. This canal lengthens and its lumen becomes slit-like during the fourth month. The blind, outer end of the pouch enlarges into

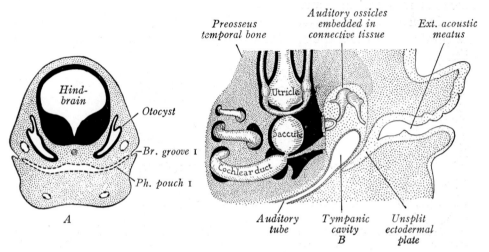

Preosseus temporal bone

Auditory ossicles embedded in connective tissue

Ext. acoustic meatus

Hind-brain

Otocyst

-Br. groove I

Ph. pouch I

Utricle

Saccu

Cochlear duct

A

Auditory tube

Tympanic cavity

B

Unsplit ectodermal plate

FIG. 479.—Progressive association of the primordia of the external, middle and internal ears, illustrated by partly schematic sections. *A*, At six weeks; *B*, at three months.

the *tympanic cavity* (Fig. 479 *B*). It is surrounded by loose connective tissue in which the auditory ossicles develop and for a considerable time lie embedded. In the last fetal months, however, the peculiar spongy tissue that surrounds the ossicles undergoes degeneration, while the tympanic cavity expands correspondingly to occupy the new space thus made available; yet at birth this process is still incomplete. The tympanic epithelium on encountering the ossicles wraps itself around them, mesentery-fashion. Even in the adult, the ossicles, their muscles and the chorda tympani nerve (all of which appear to have invaded the tympanic cavity) really are outside, since they retain a covering of mucous epithelium continuous with that lining the cavity. The pneumatic cells of the mastoid wall result from epithelial invaginations, which at the close of fetal life begin to invade the simultaneously excavated temporal bone.

With few exceptions[38, 39] modern investigators adhere to a primary origin of the *auditory ossicles* from the condensed mesenchyme of the first and second branchial arches.[40] When these primordial ossicles are chondrifying from single centers, they are still in direct continuation with their respective cartilaginous arches (Fig. 480). Soon the ear bones lose connection with the rest of the arch, and articulations are developed where the ossicles touch each other. The *malleus* (hammer) attaches to the ear drum; the *stapes* (stirrup) is inserted into the oval window of the perilymph space; the *incus* (anvil), intermediate in position, articulates with the other two. Of these ear bones, the malleus and incus are differentiated in serial order from the dorsal end of the first arch (Meckel's cartilage). Similarly, the stapes is derived from the second branchial arch (Reichert's cartilage) (Fig. 480). Since its mesenchymal and cartilaginous stages are perforated by the stapedial artery, the early shape is that of a ring. This form persists well into the third month when the stapedial artery disappears and the assumption of the final shape is begun.

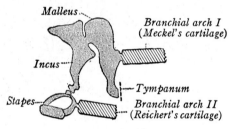

FIG. 480.—Origin of the auditory ossicles from branchial arches, illustrated in a diagram.

Certain collateral data tend to strengthen the belief in a branchial arch origin for the auditory ossicles. For instance, the muscle of the malleus, the *tensor tympani*, is derived from the first branchial arch; the *stapedial muscle* of the stapes, from the second arch. These muscles are innervated by the trigeminal and facial nerves, which are respectively the nerves of the first and second arches.

The External Ear.—The external ear is a modification of the first branchial groove, together with additions from the branchial arches bounding the groove. In a sense, the *external acoustic meatus* represents the ectodermal groove itself, which for a time is in contact with the entoderm of the first pharyngeal pouch. Later, however, this contact is lost and growth of the head in thickness tends to separate the meatus from the middle ear cavity. Toward the end of the second month the groove deepens centrally to produce a funnel-shaped pit; the whole canal, thus formed, corresponds to the outer portion of the definitive meatus. From the bottom of the pit just described, an ectodermal cellular plate grows still deeper until it reaches the wall of the tympanic cavity (Fig. 479 *B*). During the seventh month the plate splits, and the additional cleft acquired in this fashion constitutes the innermost portion of the external meatus. Even at birth a plug of cast-off cells may fill the lumen.

The *tympanic membrane* (ear drum) results from a thinning out of the mesodermal tissue in the region where the blind end of the external acoustic meatus is coming to abut against the wall of the tympanic cavity. Hence the permanent membrane is a fibrous sheet covered externally by ecto-dermal epithelium and internally by entoderm. The area of apposition between these layers does not correspond to any part of the primary tym-panic cavity, but is at a region added secondarily through the process of

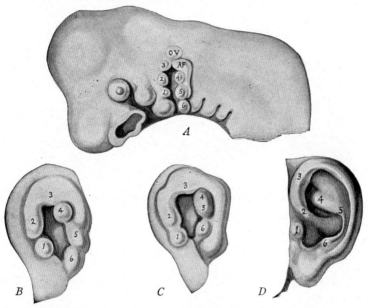

FIG. 481.—Development of the human auricle (partly after His). *A*, At 11 mm.; *B*, at 13.5 mm.; *C*, at 15 mm.; *D*, adult.

AF, Auricular fold; *OV*, otic vesicle; 1–6, elevations on the mandibular and hyoid arches which respectively become: 1, tragus; 2, 3, helix; 4, 5, anthelix; 6, antitragus.

expansion already described (p. 211). At birth the ear drum is set so obliquely that it almost lies upon the meatal floor; it erects gradually as the meatus lengthens.

The *auricle* develops around the first branchial groove. Its tissue is furnished both by the first (mandibular) branchial arch and the second (hyoid) arch. During the sixth week six hillocks appear on these arches— three on the caudal border of the first and three on the second (Fig. 481 *A*). Unfortunately, however, there is no agreement as to the exact value and fate of these parts. For many years it was held that the auricle develops in a rather precise manner from the six elevations and from an auricular fold of the hyoid integument.[41]   The progressive steps in this remodeling process are illustrated in Fig. 481.   A later restudy of the problem agrees in the main with these interpretations; however, the tubercles, except 1 and 6, are said to be erased early and so possess only a general topographical significance.[42]   The latest contribution to this topic makes the entire auricle, except the tragus, of hyoid origin.[43]

Anomalies.—Congenital deafness may be the result of imperfect nerve connections, of faulty development of the auditory ossicles or membranous labyrinth, or of atresia of the external meatus.   Defective combination of the several primordial parts is responsible for variously malformed auricles (Fig. 482 A).   Fetal types of auricle are occasionally seen in adults as the result of inhibited development, but are without further significance. Alleged cases of inherited, pierced ear lobes are really clefts between the incompletely fused tragus and antitragus; similar pits may occur between the other primordia, while the whole group

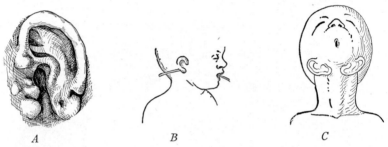

A   B   C

FIG. 482.—Anomalies of the human auricle.   A, Malformed auricle.   B, Fistula auris, probed to show its relations.   C, Synotus, combined with microstomus and agnathus.

is included among the fistulæ of the ear.   A complete fistula, connecting with the middle ear cavity, is of the greatest rarity (B).   The extremely rare condition of *synotus* shows the ears fused, or near the midventral line at the upper part of the neck (C); it is associated with agnathus (p. 181) and illustrates the primitive location of the ear primordia before being wedged apart by the growing mandible.

REFERENCES CITED

1. Parker, G. H.   1918.   The Elementary Nervous System.   Lippincott, Phila.
2. Jalowy, B.   1939.   Zeitschr. f. Anat. u. Entwickl., **109**, 344–359.
3. Tello, J. F.   1922.   Zeitschr. f. Anat. u. Entwickl., **64**, 348–440.
4. Cuajunco, F.   1927.   Carnegie Contrib. Embryol., **19**, No. 99, 45–72.
5. Hellman, T. J.   1921.   Upsala läkaref. Förhandl., **26**, No. 11, 1–72.
6. Torrey, T. W.   1941.   Proc. Nat. Acad. Sci., **26**, 627–634.
7. Broman, I.   1920.   Anat. Hefte, **58**, 137–191.
8. Peter, K.   1912.   Arch. f. mikr. Anat., **79**, 478–559.
9. Schaeffer, J. P.   1920.   The Nose, etc., in Man.   Blakiston, Phila.
10. Torrigiani, C. A.   1914.   Arch. Ital. Anat. e. Embriol., **12**, 153–253.
11. Bartelmez, G. W.   1922.   Jour. Comp. Neurol., **34**, 201–232.
12. Adelmann, H. B.   1936.   Quart. Rev. Biol., **11**, 161–182; 284–304.
13. Spemann, H.   1938.   Embryonic Development and Induction.   Yale Univ. Press, New Haven.
14. Arey, L. B.   1928.   Sect. 25 in Cowdry's 'Special Cytology.'   Hoeber, N. Y.
15. Hooker, D.   1915.   Anat. Rec., **9**, 393–402.

16. Smith, D. T. 1920. Johns Hopkins Hosp. Bull., **31,** 239–246.
17. Mann, I. C. 1928. The Development of the Human Eye. Cambridge Univ. Press.
18. Special-Cirincione, S. 1922. Annali di ottal. e clin. oculist, **50,** 2–49.
19. Leboucq, G. 1909. Ann. Soc. de Med. de Gand., **89,** 66–99.
20. van der Stricht, O. 1922. Compt. rend. Soc. biol., **86,** 264–266; 266–269.
21. Magitot, A. 1910. Ann. d'oculist, **143,** 241–282.
22. Seefelder, R. 1910. Arch. f. Ophthal., **73,** 419–537.
23. Parker, G. H. 1908. Am. Nat., **42,** 601–609.
24. Mawas, J. and Magitot, A. 1912. Arch. d'Anat. micros., **14,** 41–144.
25. Glücksmann, A. 1929. Zeitschr. f. Anat. u. Entwickl., **88,** 529–610.
26. Rones, B. 1932. Arch. Ophthal., **8,** 568–575.
27. Mann, I. 1931. Trans. Ophthal. Soc. Un. King., **51,** 63–85.
28. Stibbe, E. P. 1928. Jour. Anat., **62,** 159–176.
29. Schaeffer, J. P. 1912. Am. Jour. Anat., **13,** 1–24.
30. Contino, A. 1909. Arch. f. Ophthal., **71,** 1–51.
31. Anson, B. J. and Black, W. T. 1934. Anat. Rec., **58,** 127–137.
32. Kolmer, W. 1927. Bd. 3, Teil 1 in Möllendorff's 'Handbuch der mikroskopischen Anatomie des Menschen.' Springer, Berlin.
33. Prentiss, C. W. 1913. Am. Jour. Anat., **14,** 425–459.
34. van der Stricht, O. 1918. Carnegie Contrib. Embryol., **7,** No. 21, 55–86.
35. Streeter, G. L. 1918. Carnegie Contrib. Embryol., **7,** No. 20, 5–54.
36. Streeter, G. L. 1917. Am. Jour. Anat., **21,** 299–320.
37. Frazer, J. E. 1914. Jour. Anat. and Physiol., **48,** 391–408.
38. Fuchs, H. 1905. Arch. f. Anat. u. Physiol. (Anat. Abt.), Suppl.-bd., Jahrg., 1905 1–178.
39. Eschweiler, R. 1911. Arch. f. mikr. Anat., **77,** 52–77.
40. van der Klaauw, C. J. 1924. Ergebn. d. Anat. u. Entwickl., **25,** 565–622.
41. Schwalbe, G. 1897. Bd. 5, Abt. 2 in Bardeleben's 'Handbuch der Anatomie des Menschen.' Fisher, Jena.
42. Streeter, G. L. 1922. Carnegie Contrib. Embryol., **14,** No. 69, 111–138.
43. Wood-Jones, F. and I-Chuan, Wen. 1934. Jour. Anat., **68,** 525–535.

PART III. A LABORATORY MANUAL OF EMBRYOLOGY[1]

CHAPTER XXII

THE STUDY OF CHICK EMBRYOS

(A) THE UNINCUBATED OVUM AND EMBRYOS OF THE FIRST DAY

The Unincubated Egg.—The 'yolk' of the hen's egg is a single ovum, enormously expanded with stored food material. When this egg cell is expelled from the ovary at the time of *ovulation* it is enveloped by the *vitelline membrane*, secreted by the cytoplasm of the egg itself (Fig. 483), and by the delicate *zona pellucida* commonly held to be a product of the follicle cells among which the growing egg lay. By the time the liberated ovum passes into the oviduct, the process of *matura-*

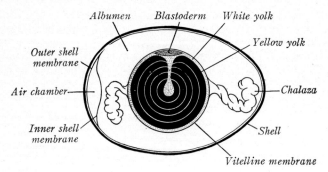

FIG. 483.—Diagrammatic longitudinal section of an unincubated hen's egg (after Lillie). × 1.

tion has progressed to the point where one polar cell is given off. If spermatozoa lie in wait, *fertilization* ensues; at the same time the second polar cell is extruded, thereby completing maturation. As the egg continues down the oviduct, the viscid *albumen*, papery *shell membrane* and calcareous *shell* are progressively secreted by the epithelial lining of the duct and are added about the yolk as accessory investments (Fig. 483). During this journey, which ends with the laying of the egg, a start has been made toward the formation of a visible embryo. Thus it is that, before external incubation begins, the processes of *cleavage* and entoderm formation are complete; when laid, the embryonic area is represented by the familiar whitish disc to be seen on the surface of the yolk and technically designated the *blastoderm*. The egg is ready to be laid about 18 hours after its discharge from the ovary; at this time the relations of its several components are as indicated in Fig. 483.

Cleavage and the Blastula.—The protoplasmic part of the egg is a tiny disc or cap at its upper pole. Fertilization promptly initiates a series of orderly cell

---

[1] About one-half of the illustrations in this section are copies or adaptations of drawings originally published by Professor C. W. Prentiss in 1915.

divisions which divide the thin disc into an increasingly large number of cells. This sequence of mitoses comprises the process of *cleavage*, while the component cells are known as *blastomeres* (Fig. 484). The result is a cellular disc, separated from the yolk beneath by a cleft-like space (Fig. 485); the whole makes an asymmetrical hollow sphere which is called a *blastula*.

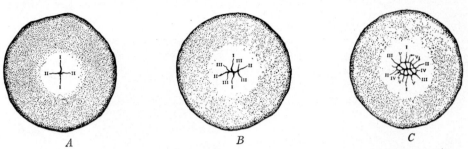

FIG. 484.—Cleavage of the pigeon's ovum, seen in surface view (Patten, after Blount). × 4. The order of appearance of cleavage furrows on the blastoderm is indicated by Roman numerals. *A*, Second cleavage; *B*, third cleavage; *C*, fifth cleavage.

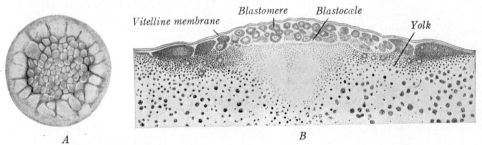

FIG. 485.—Early blastula stage in the pigeon (after Blount). *A*, Blastoderm in surface view; *B*, in vertical section.

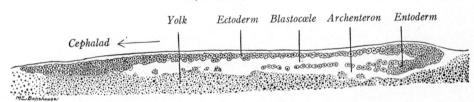

FIG. 486.—Entoderm formation in the pigeon, shown by a longitudinal section of the blastoderm (after Patterson). × 50.

Gastrulation and the Primitive Streak.—Two different processes accomplish gastrulation in birds. The first occurs when an under layer, the *entoderm*, splits away from the blastodermic disc (Fig. 486). In this condition the egg is laid, and without incubation there is no further development. On the commencement of incubation, even though days of dormancy have elapsed since laying, gastrulation continues into its second phase. This consists in the movement of certain cells, destined to become the *mesoderm* and *notochord*, out of the outer layer to a middle-layer position (Fig. 41). The residual outer layer, when these departures are completed, is *ectoderm*.

The crowding toward the midline, as the cells of the future chorda-mesoderm flow and turn beneath, produces an opaque band named the *primitive streak* (Fig. 487 *A*). It is first seen after 16 hours of incubation. Directly following the earliest appearance of the streak, a *primitive groove* courses lengthwise along its surface (*B*). In the future cephalic direction this gutter ends in the deeper *primitive pit*. At the extreme front end of the streak is a clubbed expansion, known as the *primitive knot* (of Hensen).

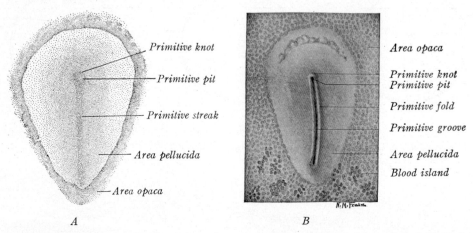

A   *B*

FIG. 487.—Chick blastoderms, in surface view, at the stage of the primitive streak (16 hours). × 17.   *A*, Before the appearance of the primitive groove; *B*, with a prominent groove.

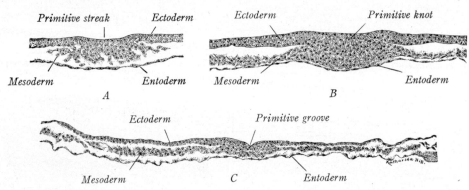

FIG. 488.—Transverse sections of chick blastoderms, at the stage of the primitive streak. × 165.   *A*, Through the early primitive streak; *B*, *C*, through the later primitive knot and groove.

Microscopic sections, cut across the primitive streak, show it to be a thickening from which the mesoderm spreads laterad (Fig. 488). The first mesodermal cells are sparse, migratory elements (*A*), but they soon aggregate into distinct plates (*C*) extending both in a lateral and caudal direction. Later the mesoderm invades the region ahead of the streak. At the primitive knot all three germ layers fuse intimately (*B*), but in the caudal half of the streak the entoderm tends to be free (*C*). The primitive groove is the mechanical consequence of this rapid spread of mesoderm which produces a trough through cellular depletion. From the three germ layers, whose origins have been thus briefly outlined, all the tissues and organs will develop.

Head Process and Head Fold.—Embryos of about 19 hours' incubation show an axial strand of cells extending forward from the primitive knot (Fig. 489 *A*). This is the so-called *head process*; it is also termed the *notochordal plate* because it becomes the cylindrical notochord, destined to serve as the primitive axis about which the embryo differentiates. The head process results from the turning under of cells, originally located in the outer layer, which pass through the substance of the primitive knot and extend forward in the midline. Their movement constitutes a late phase of gastrulation. A longitudinal section shows the relation of head

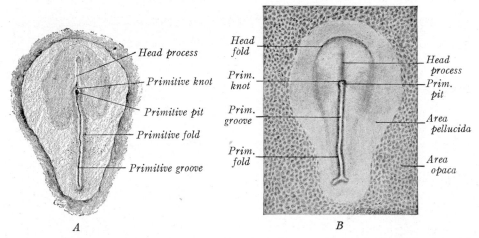

A   B

FIG. 489.—Chick blastoderm and embryo, in surface view. *A*, Stage of the head process (18 hours) (× 16). *B*, Stage of the head fold (19 hours) × 15.

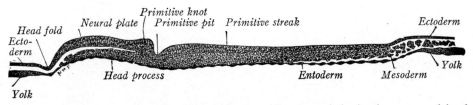

FIG. 490.—Midsagittal section of a chick embryo, at the stage of the head process and head fold (19 hours). × 100.

process to primitive knot (Fig. 490); a transverse section demonstrates it as a median, thicker mass, continuous laterally with mesoderm which has grown into this region (Fig. 491). Both sections illustrate the independence of the head process from the ectoderm above, and the temporary fusion that it makes with the entoderm beneath.

After the head process has become prominent, a curved fold begins to show in a position still more cephalad (Fig. 489 *B*). It is the *head fold*, which at first involves ectoderm and entoderm alone (Fig. 490). The further development of this important structure will establish the gut internally and definitely delimit the upper body externally (Fig. 492).

Neural Groove and Mesodermal Segments.—Even embryos of the previous stage exhibit a broad zone of thickening in the ectoderm overlying the head process. This region constitutes the *neural plate* (Fig. 491). In an embryo of 21 hours the plate begins to fold lengthwise to form a shallow, gutter-like trough, called the *neural groove* (Fig. 492 *A*). Within the next hour or two this groove becomes flanked by elevated, marginal ridges, the *neural folds* (Fig. 492 *B*), which later will unite progressively until the brain and spinal cord are laid down as a continuous tube. The *notochord* is now a definite rod, seen through the transparent ectoderm at the bottom of the neural groove.

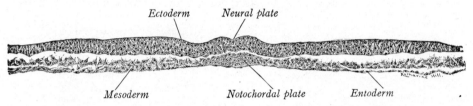

Fig. 491.—Transverse section through the head process of a nineteen-hour chick embryo. × 165.

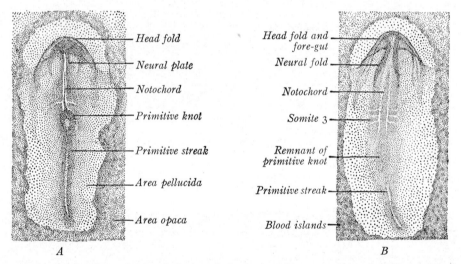

Fig. 492.—Chick embryos, in dorsal view, at the beginning of segmentation. *A*, Embryo with the first intersomitic groove (21 hours) (× 25). *B*, Embryo of three somites (23 hours) (× 16).

The wings of mesoderm, which grew from the sides of the primitive streak, have continued to spread peripherad to the margin of the blastoderm, but have not yet reached the region just in front of the *head fold* (Fig. 492). Alongside the notochord the mesoderm is thick, and in it are appearing pairs of vertical clefts; these separate the mesoderm into successive masses (the first incomplete cranially) which will be seen better in older stages. They are the *somites*, or *mesodermal segments*.

(B) EMBRYO OF FIVE SEGMENTS (TWENTY-FOUR HOURS)

In an embryo one day old it is evident that an embryonic and an extra-embryonic region of the blastoderm are becoming more sharply defined (Fig. 493).

Of the extra-embryonic territory (*i.e.*, the region of the blastoderm not destined to become a part of the embryo proper), that nearest the embryo comprises the clearer *area pellucida*. More peripherad lies the *area opaca*, darker because of its adherence to the yolk beneath. In a zone of the opaque area bordering the area pellucida are mottled masses, the *blood islands*, already observed in younger

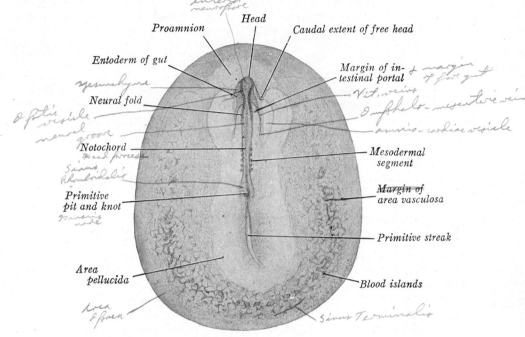

FIG. 493.—Chick blastoderm and embryo with five segments (24 hours), in dorsal view. × 14.

stages but now fusing into an incomplete network. This mesh is best developed caudally; when complete, it will comprise a distinct subdivision of the area opaca to be called the *area vasculosa*. Mesoderm is still lacking in a clearer region in front of the head; to it the quite unsuitable name of *proamnion* has been given.

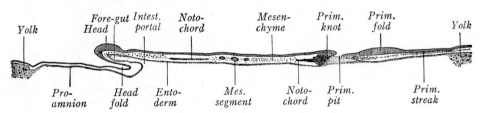

FIG. 494.—Longitudinal section of a chick embryo with five segments (after Patten). × 25.

At this period the *head* is growing rapidly. It rises above the blastoderm and projects cephalad as a somewhat cylindrical part of the embryo which, at its cephalic end, is entirely free (Fig. 493). In accomplishing this result, the shallow head fold of earlier stages appears to have grown caudad and to have liberated the head by undercutting (Fig. 494). A more important factor, however, is a true forward overgrowth on the part of the head itself. Simultaneously with the extension of the head, the entodermal component of the original head fold is elongated as an internal tubular pocket; this is the primitive *fore-gut*. Cranially it is a blind sac; caudally it opens out onto the yolk through an arched aperture which resembles a tunnel-entrance and is termed the *intestinal portal*. In Fig. 493 the lateral limits of the darker fore-gut (labelled 'entoderm') and its relation to the arching intestinal portal are shown plainly. Figure 494 illustrates how the entoderm is reflected into the fore-gut at the level of the portal.

The *neural groove* is both broad and deep (Fig. 493). Midway along its extent the component neural folds have approached and are ready to fuse. Caudally the folds diverge and become increasingly indistinct.

The *mesodermal segments* are clearly defined and block-like. The *notochord* shows through the transparent ectoderm, and the *primitive streak* is shorter, both relatively and actually. Later, when the body form is further indicated by the formation of the tail fold, the primitive streak will disappear. It is a notable fact that the head not only arises soonest but also retains its early advantage over lower levels of the body. The progressive differentiation, leading to the establishment of body form, advances in a caudal direction; it first reaches the end of the trunk at a considerably later period than the stage under consideration.

(C) EMBRYO OF SEVEN SEGMENTS (TWENTY-FIVE HOURS)

Although a total view of a chick embryo at this stage much resembles the one last described, it does show certain distinct advances (Figs. 495 and 496). Nevertheless, the descriptions that follow will apply in all essentials to embryos having between five and ten primitive segments. Among the changes encountered, it is noteworthy that the vascular area of the blastoderm is better organized than before and extends far cephalad. In front of the head there is a light area, not yet invaded by mesoderm, known by the poorly chosen name *proamnion*. The *primitive streak* is still prominent caudally, but it now measures only about one-fourth the length of the embryo. The *notochord* can be followed cephalad from the primitive knot until it is lost beneath the neural tube.

Neural Tube.—The lips of the neural folds have met throughout the cranial two-thirds of the embryo, but have not fused to any extent. The *neural tube*, formed thus by the closing of ectodermal folds, is open at each end; the closure of its cranial opening is characteristically delayed, and this leaves a temporary communication to the outside which has been designated the *anterior neuropore*. In succeeding stages the more caudal regions of the present neural groove will be rolled progressively together and added to the tube already completed. At the head end the neural tube has begun to expand into the brain; only the *fore-brain* is at all prominent, and from it the *optic vesicles* are bulging laterally.

Fore-Gut.—Except for an increase in size, the *fore-gut* is little changed. Near its blind end the floor of the gut is applied to the ectoderm of the under surface of the head; the two comprise the temporary *pharyngeal membrane* (*cf.* Fig. 510) which later ruptures to make the permanent opening into the mouth. The fore-gut will ultimately specialize into the several divisions of the alimentary canal that extend as far as the middle of the small intestine. The way in which the entoderm is folded up from the blastoderm and carried forward into the head is shown well in Figs. 494 and 510. The fore-gut opens caudally through the arched *anterior intestinal portal*.

Mesoderm and Cœlom.—The tissue of the middle germ layer assumes two different forms. Throughout most of the head region it makes up a diffuse mesh-work of cells that fills in the spaces between the various epithelial layers. This tissue is *mesenchyme* (Fig. 506). In the caudal part of the head and in the remainder of the body, the mesoderm at this stage is organizing more definitely. Nearest the midplane it is already divided by transverse furrows into seven block-like *primitive segments*, four of which belong to the future head (Figs. 495 and 497).

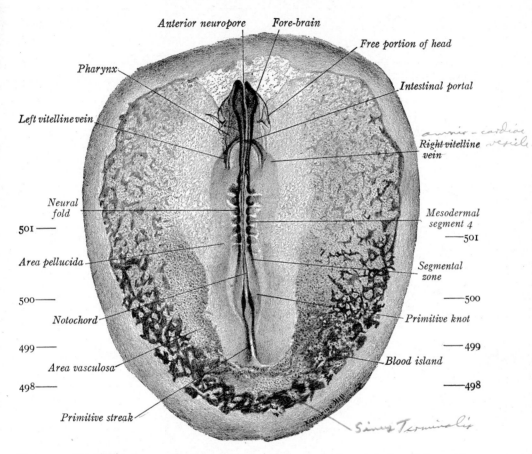

FIG. 495.—Chick blastoderm and embryo with seven segments (25 hours), in dorsal view. × 20. The numbered lines indicate the levels of the sections, Figs. 498–501.

Caudad, between the segments and the primitive streak, there is the undifferentiated mesoderm of the *segmental zone*, but new pairs of segments are developing progressively in this region. Lateral to each segment is a plate of unsegmented mesoderm, termed the *intermediate cell mass;* it is also called the *nephrotome* because it will play an important rôle in the development of the excretory system (Fig. 497). The nephrotome plate serves as a bridge between the segments and the unsegmented *lateral mesoderm*. When first proliferated, the lateral mesoderm of each side was a solid plate (Fig. 488). However, in stages like the present embryo these have split secondarily into two lamellæ, separated by a space (Figs. 497 and 500). The dorsal layer comprises the *somatic mesoderm*, the ventral layer the *splanchnic mesoderm*. It is in the splanchnic layer that the blood vessels are forming. The somatic mesoderm and the ectoderm are closely associated in development, and together are designated the *somatopleure;* it makes up the body wall. Similarly, the splanchnic mesoderm and entoderm are jointly termed

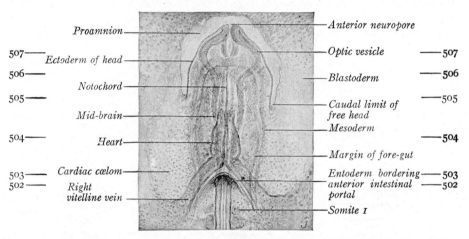

Fig. 496.—Head of a chick embryo with seven segments (25 hours), in ventral view. × 43. The numbered lines indicate the levels of the sections, Figs. 502–507.

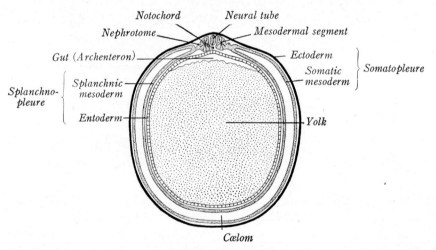

Fig. 497.—Diagrammatic transverse section of an early vertebrate embryo (Prentiss, after Minot).

the *splanchnopleure;* it is primarily concerned with the development of the gut and its derivatives. Both the mesodermal segments and the unsegmented mesodermal layers contribute to the loose mesenchymal cells, which play such an important part in development.

The space between the two mesodermal layers first occurs in the form of isolated clefts, but these soon unite on each side into a continuous *body cavity*, or *cœlom*. The originally bilateral cœlomic chambers will later become confluent beneath the gut, thus forming a common cavity (Fig. 497). In the region of the heart the cœlom is already enlarged locally, anticipating its destiny as the pericardial cavity. Other, more caudal portions will become the pleural cavities of the thorax and the peritoneal cavity of the abdomen.

Heart and Blood Vessels.—The *heart* is a simple straight tube, lying in the midplane and ventral to the gut (Fig. 496). Traced caudad it is continuous with the converging *vitelline veins*, which enter the body from the area vasculosa by following along the margins of the intestinal portal; the two veins unite as they join the heart. From the cephalic end of the heart is given off the *ventral aorta*. Dorsal to the gut course paired *dorsal aortæ*.

TRANSVERSE SECTIONS

The first embryo to be studied in serial section is most easily understood if the student begins at the caudal end, where differentiation has entered least, and

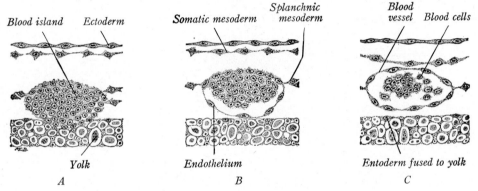

FIG. 498.—Transverse sections through the area vasculosa of a seven-segment chick embryo. × 225.

works toward the head. Important facts pertaining to the germ layers, as well as the principles underlying the development of the neural tube, gut, heart and head are then made simple. The following illustrations and descriptions can be used to interpret sections of chick embryos between the stages of five and ten somites. The level of each section can be determined by applying a straight edge across the correspondingly numbered lines on Figs. 495 and 496.

Sections through the Area Vasculosa (Fig. 498).—The illustrations show, at medium magnification, a sample of the extra-embryonic territory (*area opaca*), peripheral to the area pellucida. In this region the entoderm is associated intimately with the coarsely granular *yolk*. The splanchnic mesoderm contains aggregations of cells known as *blood islands*, many of which are fusing into the network characteristic of the *area vasculosa* (Figs. 495 and 498 *A*). The cellular thickenings of the blood islands undergo differentiation into two distinct cell types. Fluid-filled vacuoles first appear within the islands and then expand, so as to set free the innermost cells. These cells soon separate and float about as primitive *blood corpuscles*, while the general process of vacuolization flattens the peripheral cells into an *endothelium* (Fig. 498 *B*, *C*). The endothelial spaces both coalesce and bud out new vascular sprouts, and in this way the system of extra-embryonic vessels is extended. All blood vessels at first consist of an endothelial layer only.

Section through the Primitive Streak (Fig. 499).—The *primitive streak* is a mesial thickening of the blastoderm in which the layers of *ectoderm*, *mesoderm* and *entoderm* all merge. A prominent *primitive groove* indents the streak in its midplane, and this groove is bounded on each side by a *primitive fold*.

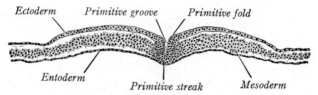

Ectoderm   *Primitive groove*   *Primitive fold*

Entoderm   *Primitive streak*   *Mesoderm*

FIG. 499.—Transverse section through the primitive streak of a seven-segment chick embryo. × 90.

Section through the Primitive Knot (Fig. 500).—The enlarged cephalic end of the primitive streak is the *primitive knot*. Its common cellular mass separates at higher levels into the three typical germ layers; especially notable is the direct continuity into the notochord. The thickened and grooved *neural plate* of higher levels also extends downward to the region of the knot

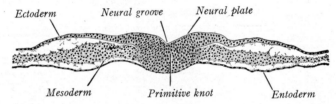

Ectoderm   *Neural groove*   *Neural plate*

Mesoderm   *Primitive knot*   *Entoderm*

FIG. 500.—Transverse section through the primitive knot of a seven-segment chick embryo. × 90.

and even overlies it. This *neural groove* should not be confused with the smaller and fundamentally different primitive groove of lower levels.

Section through the Fifth Primitive Segment (Fig. 501).—The general level of the somites is characterized by the greater specialization of the mesoderm, the elevation of high *neural folds*, and the presence of a *dorsal aorta* on each side between the mesodermal segments and the entoderm. The neural folds are thick, as is the adjoining ectoderm to a less degree. The *notochord*

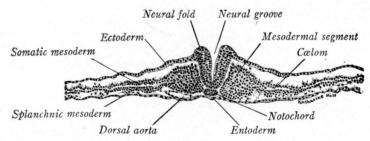

Neural fold   *Neural groove*

Ectoderm   *Mesodermal segment*

Somatic mesoderm   *Cœlom*

Splanchnic mesoderm   *Notochord*

Dorsal aorta   *Entoderm*

FIG. 501.—Transverse section through the fifth pair of somites of a seven-segment chick embryo. × 90.

is a sharply defined, oval mass of cells which will be observed just below the *neural groove;* it appears in all sections of the series, except those through the tip of the head and the primitive streak. The *mesodermal segments* are somewhat triangular in outline; each is connected with the *lateral mesoderm* by the *intermediate cell mass*, or *nephrotome*. The lateral mesoderm is partially divided by irregular, flattened spaces into two sheets; the dorsal of these is the *somatic layer*, the ventral the *splanchnic layer*. When the spaces unite to form a definite *cœlom*, or primitive body cavity, the mesodermal lining of the cavity specializes into a flat epithelium called *mesothelium*.

In the higher segments of the series the differentiation of mesoderm and cœlom is more advanced (*cf.* Fig. 519). Caudal to the seventh segment, in the region of the *segmental zone*, the mesoderm still forms solid plates (*cf.* Fig. 520).

Section Caudal to the Intestinal Portal (Fig. 502).—The section is characterized: (1) by the meeting of the neural folds preparatory to closing the *neural tube;* (2) by the arching of the entoderm which, a few sections nearer the head end, folds forward into the *fore-gut;* (3) by the presence of *vitelline veins* between the entoderm and folds of the splanchnic mesoderm; (4) by the

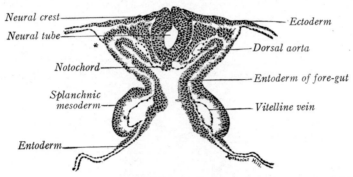

Neural crest — ———— Ectoderm
Neural tube — ———— Dorsal aorta
Notochord — ———— Entoderm of fore-gut
Splanchnic mesoderm — ———— Vitelline vein
Entoderm —

Fig. 502.—Transverse section caudal to the intestinal portal of a seven-segment chick embryo.
× 90.

wide separation of the somatic and splanchnic mesoderm and the consequent increase in the size of the cœlom. In this location the cœlom later surrounds the heart and is converted into the pericardial cavity. The neural tube at this level is transforming into the third brain vesicle,

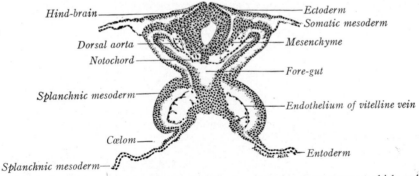

Hind-brain — ———— Ectoderm
———— Somatic mesoderm
Dorsal aorta — ———— Mesenchyme
Notochord —
———— Fore-gut
Splanchnic mesoderm — ———— Endothelium of vitelline vein
Cœlom — ———— Entoderm
Splanchnic mesoderm —

FIG. 503.—Transverse section through the intestinal portal of a seven-segment chick embryo.
× 90.

or *hind-brain*. The neural folds have not yet fused, and at their dorsal angles are located the *neural crests*, the forerunners of the spinal ganglia. Mesodermal segments never develop as far cephalad as this region; instead, diffuse masses of mesenchyme occupy comparable positions adjacent to the neural tube. On the left of the section an asterisk marks the point of junction between somatic and splanchnic mesoderm.

Section through the Intestinal Portal (Fig. 503).—This section passes through a vertical fold of entoderm at the exact point where the latter is reflected into the head as the *fore-gut* (*cf.* Figs. 494 and 510). Since the entoderm is here cut on the flat, it appears as a continuous sheet of tissue; it is located between the vitelline veins and closes the fore-gut ventrally. On each side, lateral to the endothelial layer of the veins, the splanchnic mesoderm is thrown into a thick-walled, bulging fold.

A few sections cephalad the reflection of the entodermal layer no longer shows, and the gut is quite separate from the general entoderm; this separation allows first the endothelial heart tubes to meet, and then the flanking folds of splanchnic mesoderm.

Section through the Heart (Fig. 504).—Passing cephalad in the series to a level just above the intestinal portal, one finds that the vitelline veins converge and open into the *heart*. The entoderm of the original head fold can now be identified as the crescentic *pharynx* of the fore-gut; it is separated by the heart, cœlom and splanchnic mesoderm from the entoderm of the general blastoderm. The *dorsal aortæ* are larger, making conspicuous spaces between the neural tube (*hind-brain*) and the pharynx. The heart has resulted from the union of two endothelial tubes,

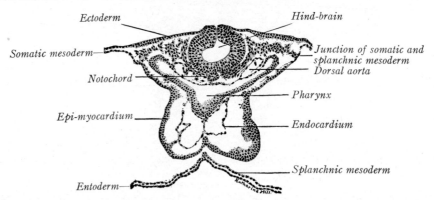

Ectoderm

Hind-brain

Somatic mesoderm—

Junction of somatic and splanchnic mesoderm

Dorsal aorta

Notochord

Pharynx

Epi-myocardium

Endocardium

Splanchnic mesoderm

Entoderm—

FIG. 504.—Tranverse section through the heart of a seven-segment chick embryo. × 90.

continuous with those constituting the vitelline veins in sections already studied. The median walls of these tubes fuse and disappear at a slightly older stage; this union establishes a single tube, the *endocardium*. Thickened layers of splanchnic mesoderm, which in the preceding section invested the vitelline veins laterally, now form the mesothelial wall of the heart; such tissue will give rise to both the *myocardium* and the *epicardium*. In the midventral plane the layers of cardiac mesoderm of each side have fused and separated from the splanchnic mesoderm of the germinal disc; in such a fashion are the two halves of the future pericardial cavity put in communication. Dorsal to the heart the paired layers of splanchnic mesoderm approach slightly; this presages the *dorsal mesocardium*, or mesentery of the heart, which will be seen more characteristically in older embryos. Continuing still more dorsad, the splanchnic mesoderm extends to a point where the original cœlomic split separated it from the somatic layer; this junction is labeled on the right side of Fig. 504.

Origin of the Heart and Embryonic Vessels.—From the two sections last described, it is seen that the heart arises as a pair of endothelial tubes which lie in folds of the splanchnic mesoderm. These tubes are continuous with paired veins entering from lower levels and paired arteries leaving for higher ones; hence, the vascular system is primitively a paired system throughout. Later the endothelial heart tubes fuse, and the mesodermal folds are also brought together. The heart then consists of a single endothelial tube within a thick-walled investment of mesoderm. The endothelial cells of the heart often appear to be splitting off from the entoderm (Fig. 503) but this is perhaps a deception, for elsewhere endothelium is mesodermal in origin. Primarily the blood vessels of the body are delicate endothelial channels which originate as clefts in the mesenchyme. Coalescence and budding produce a continuous plexus from which definite vessels are then selected (Fig. 282).

Section through the Head Fold (Fig. 505).—It will be remembered that an ectodermal *head fold* undercuts the head both from in front and at the sides (Figs. 494 and 495). The portion of the body cephalad of this fold is necessarily free from the blastoderm. The present section is located just cephalad of the heart at a level into which the central portion of the head fold has not yet extended. The inspection of a few sections both in front of and behind this critical region will demonstrate how the embryonic and extra-embryonic territories are related and how they become separate. The cœlom does not extend into the head. Midway of the blastoderm is a

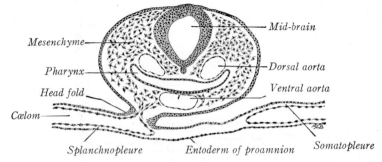

FIG. 505.—Transverse section through the head fold of a seven-segment chick embryo. × 90.

region that lacks mesoderm; it is the so-called *proamnion*. Ventral to the pharynx occurs the *ventral aorta*, here transitional between a single vessel which is continuous with the heart in one direction and the separate vessels which pass cephalad in the other direction. Above the pharynx is the dilated middle brain vesicle, or *mid-brain*.

Section through the Pharyngeal Membrane (Fig. 506).—This section shows the head free from the underlying blastoderm (*cf.* Fig. 510). Ectoderm surrounds the head completely. Near the midventral line it is bent dorsad, thickened somewhat and comes in contact with the thick entoderm of the pharynx. The area of contact between ectoderm and pharyngeal entoderm

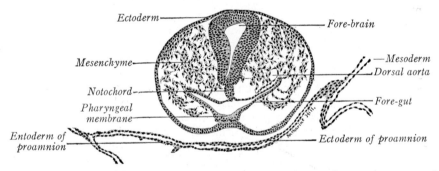

FIG. 506.—Transverse section through the pharyngeal membrane of a seven-segment chick embryo. × 90.

constitutes the *pharyngeal membrane*. Later this plate breaks through and establishes the oral opening. As in the previous section, the neural tube is closed and entirely separate from the superficial ectoderm. In this region it forms the caudal, slender portion of the *fore-brain*. The *dorsal aortæ* are represented by small vessels just above the lateral wings of the pharynx. The blastoderm directly beneath the head is the broad *proamnion*. Far laterad may be seen the layers of the mesoderm as well.

Section through the Fore-brain and Optic Vesicle (Fig. 507).—The neural tube is open here, and the section is chiefly made up of a continuous double layer of ectoderm, infolded gastrula-fashion. The opening from the first brain vesicle, or *fore-brain*, to the outside is the temporary *anterior neuropore*. The ectoderm on the surface of the head is continuous at the neuropore with the much thicker wall of the fore-brain. These two ectodermal layers are in contact with each other, except in the midventral region where the mesenchyme is beginning to penetrate and separate them. The lateral expansions of the fore-brain are the *optic vesicles*, which eventually give rise to the retina of the eye.

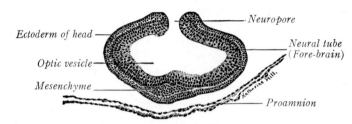

Fig. 507.—Transverse section through the fore-brain and optic vesicles of a seven-segment chick embryo. × 90.

(D) EMBRYO OF SEVENTEEN SEGMENTS (THIRTY-EIGHT HOURS)

The stage selected as a type for illustrating the significant advances since the seven-segment embryo is a chick of about 38 hours' incubation which possesses 17 primitive segments (Fig. 508 *B, C*). Since at this time the somites are developing rapidly, the descriptions that follow will apply satisfactorily to embryos between 33 hours (12 segments) and 40 hours (18 segments). Intermediate conditions between seven and 17 somites are illustrated by the embryo shown in Fig. 508 *A*.

The long axis of the embryo is still nearly straight, but specimens of full 17 segments should show a flexing of the head ventrad (Fig. 511) and a slight turning of the tip of the head on its left side (Fig. 508 *C*). In these respects the embryo in Fig. 508 *B* is slightly backward. The area pellucida is dumb-bell shaped and is developing a vascular network. The extra-embryonic vessels of the area opaca are well differentiated and the vascular area ends in a bordering *terminal sinus*. Adjacent to the caudal end of the heart, the vascular networks of the blastoderm converge and become continuous with the stems of the vitelline veins. Connections have been established also between the dorsal aortæ and the vascular area at the level of the lowest segments, but as yet these have not organized as distinct vitelline arteries (Fig. 509). The tubular heart is enlarged and bent to the embryo's right; the head is more prominent than formerly and the three primary vesicles of the brain are easily distinguishable; seen through the brain walls is the notochord which extends in the midplane as far cephalad as the fore-brain; the proamniotic area is reduced to a small region in front of the head; the primitive streak is short and relatively inconspicuous.

Central Nervous System and Sense Organs.—The tardy sealing of the anterior neuropore has occurred and the neural tube is closed, save at its caudal end where the divergent neural folds bound the so-called *rhomboidal sinus* (Fig. 508 *B*). In the head the neural tube has differentiated into three brain vesicles, set off from one another by constrictions. The *fore-brain* (prosencephalon) is characterized by the outgrowing *optic vesicles*. The *mid-brain* (mesencephalon) is a simple dilatation. The elongate *hind-brain* (rhombencephalon) gradually passes into the *spinal cord;* it shows a number of secondary dilatations, the *neuromeres*.

The ectoderm is thickened into a *lens placode* where it overlies the lateral wall of each *optic vesicle* (Fig. 513). The optic vesicle flattens at this point and will soon invaginate to produce the optic cup. Dorsolaterally, in the hind-brain region, the ectoderm is also thickened into *auditory placodes* which are already indented as the *auditory pits* (Fig. 509). Each pit will become an otocyst, or otic vesicle, from which differentiates the sensory epithelium of the internal ear (membranous labyrinth).

Fore-gut.—Caudal to the intestinal portal, the entoderm is still flattened over the surface of the yolk. In Fig. 509 the greater part of the entoderm is cut away. The broad *fore-gut*, folded inward at the portal, shows indications of three lateral

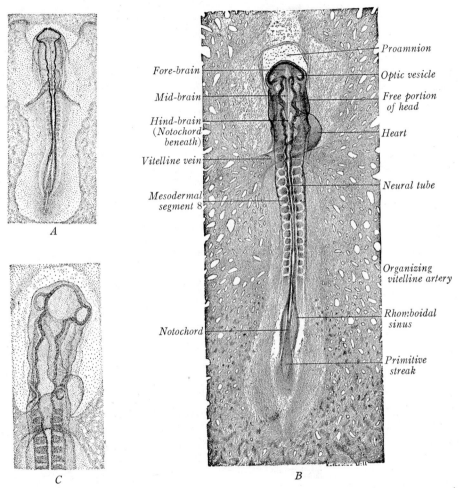

A

C   *B*

Fore-brain
Mid-brain
Hind-brain
(*Notochord beneath*)
Vitelline vein
Mesodermal segment 8
Notochord

Proamnion
Optic vesicle
Free portion of head
Heart
Neural tube
Organizing vitelline artery
Rhomboidal sinus
Primitive streak

FIG. 508.—Chick embryos of 30 to 38 hours, in dorsal view. *A*, At eleven segments (30 hours) (× 13). *B*, At seventeen segments (38 hours) (× 20). *C*, At seventeen segments, with head slightly rotated and bent (38 hours) (× 25).

diverticula, the *pharyngeal pouches*, which will be much plainer in the next embryo studied. At its cephalic end the pharynx is closed ventrally by the double-layered *pharyngeal membrane;* the ectodermal depression external to it is the *stomodeum* (Fig. 510).

Heart and Blood Vessels.—The heart tube is flexed, yet does not vary in structure throughout its length. Nevertheless, certain regions can be identified with the later subdivisions (Fig. 509). The caudal end of the tube, where the vitelline and cardinal veins open, is the *sinus venosus*. This dilates into the *atrium*, which bends ventrad and to the embryo's right. The tube then bends dorsad and to the midplane, as the *ventricle*, thereby completing a **U**-shaped bend. Con-

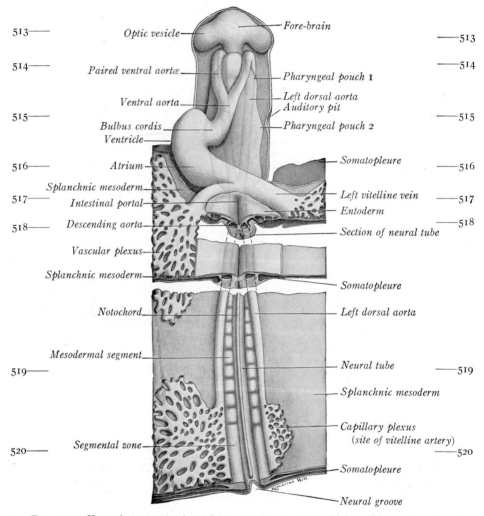

513——
514——
515——
516——
517——
518——
519——
520——

Optic vesicle——
Paired ventral aortæ——
Ventral aorta——
Bulbus cordis——
Ventricle——
Atrium——
Splanchnic mesoderm——
Intestinal portal——
Descending aorta——
Vascular plexus——
Splanchnic mesoderm——
Notochord——
Mesodermal segment——
Segmental zone——

—Fore-brain
Pharyngeal pouch 1
—Left dorsal aorta
Auditory pit
—Pharyngeal pouch 2
Somatopleure
Left vitelline vein
Entoderm
Section of neural tube
Somatopleure
Left dorsal aorta
Neural tube
Splanchnic mesoderm
Capillary plexus
(site of vitelline artery)
Somatopleure
Neural groove

——513
——514
——515
——516
——517
——518
——519
——520

FIG. 509.—Ventral reconstruction of a seventeen-segment chick embryo. × 38. The ectoderm of the ventral surface of the head, the mesoderm of the head and heart regions, and the entoderm except about the intestinal portal have been removed. Numbered lines indicate the levels of Figs. 513–520.

tinuing cephalad, the ventricle narrows into the *bulbus* which, in turn, passes over into the *ventral aorta*. The latter vessel lies beneath the pharynx and divides into two trunks. Near the tip of the pharynx these paired ventral aortæ bend dorsad around the sides of the pharynx as the first pair of *aortic arches*. The arches then turn sharply caudad as the paired *dorsal aortæ*. In the region of the intestinal portal they not only lie close together but also have fused for a short distance to form a single vessel, the *descending aorta*. Below this level they separate again, and opposite the lowest somites connect by numerous capillaries with the general vascular network. It is in this connecting region that paired *vitelline arteries* presently will be differentiated. The heart already beats spasmodically at this stage. Blood drains from the vascular area by way of the *vitelline veins* to the heart; here it is pumped around the aortæ and flows through the organizing vitelline arteries back again to the area vasculosa. This circuit constitutes the vitelline circulation; through it the embryo receives nutriment from the yolk for its continued development.

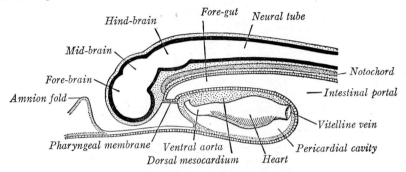

FIG. 510.—Midsagittal section of the head-end of a seventeen-segment chick embryo. × about 50.

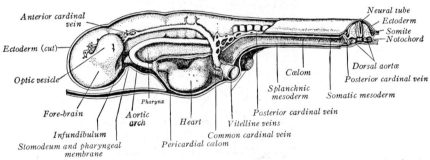

FIG. 511.—Reconstructed lateral dissection of a seventeen-segment chick embryo (Patten). × 33.

Heretofore the body of the embryo has been without definite veins, but now two pairs of vessels are developing for the purpose of returning blood to the heart (Fig. 511). The *anterior cardinal veins* collect blood from the head region; the *posterior cardinals*, just appearing at this stage, will perform a similar function for the lower body. The two vessels on each side unite into a *common cardinal vein* (duct of Cuvier) which enters the sinus venosus.

Differentiation of Mesoderm and Cœlom.—The production of early mesodermal segments and the addition of new ones by a progressive furrowing of the *segmental zone* have been observed in previous stages. The somites, thus formed, are block-like with rounded corners when viewed dorsally; in transverse sections they appear triangular (Fig. 512). In higher vertebrates the primitive segments contain indications of a space that represents a cavity continuous in lower vertebrates with the general cœlom. In the chick this rudiment is a minute, central cleft which is mostly filled with a cellular core; the other cells of the somite form a thick, radially-arranged shell about it (Fig. 519). The ventral wall and a portion of the medial wall of each somite break down into a mass of mesenchyme termed the *sclerotome;* these later surround the notochord and neural tube where they transform into the axial skeleton. The remaining portions of the somite constitute the *dermo-myotome* (Fig. 516). The cells of the dorsomesial wall of this plate, the *myotome,* eventually give rise to the skeletal musculature of the body. The lateral plate is the *dermatome* which contributes to the connective tissue of the integument.

The cellular plate connecting a primitive segment with the lateral meso-dermal layers is the *intermediate cell mass,* or *nephrotome* (Fig. 512). In the chick the nephrotomes of the fifth to sixteenth segments give rise to segmental pairs of bud-like sprouts which extend dorsad (Fig. 519). These are the *pronephric tubules* of a rudimentary type of kidney. Although functionless as excretory

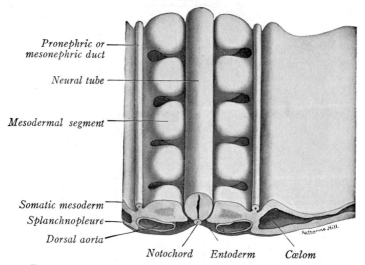

Pronephric or
mesonephric duct

Neural tube

Mesodermal segment

Somatic mesoderm
Splanchnopleure
Dorsal aorta

Notochord   Entoderm   Cœlom

FIG. 512.—Reconstruction through the lower mesodermal segments of a two-day chick embryo. The ectoderm is removed from the dorsal surface.

tubules their ends turn caudad and link into a tube, known as the *pronephric duct,* which grows to the cloaca (Fig. 512). More caudal nephrotomes will soon dif-ferentiate a temporary functional kidney, the *mesonephros;* its tubules open into the pronephric duct which thereafter is called the *mesonephric duct.* Later still, the permanent kidney develops partly from the pronephric duct and partly from nephrotome tissue of a lower level. Accordingly, the intermediate cell masses may be regarded as the source of the urogenital glands and ducts—all mesodermal in origin.

In the previous embryo of seven somites the lateral mesoderm was observed to split into two layers, the dorsal somatic and the ventral splanchnic mesoderm. These layers persist as components of the *somatopleure* and *splanchnopleure;* the somatic mesoderm will give rise to the parietal walls of the pericardial, pleural and peritoneal cavities, while the splanchnic layer forms the epi-myocardium, the visceral pleura, and the mesenteries and mesodermal layers of the gut.

The *cœlom* has not progressed much beyond its condition in the previous stage (Fig. 511), although a beginning has been made toward the isolation of a portion of it within the body of the embryo (Fig. 517).

TRANSVERSE SECTIONS

In studying serial sections of an embryo it is not sufficient merely to identify the structures seen. The student should determine also the exact level of each significant section with respect to drawings or models of the total embryo; this has been done along the margins of Fig. 509 for the particular series that follows. It is also important to trace the several organs and parts faithfully from section to section in a series. The novice is then ready to reconstruct mentally the complete picture of a part and to interpret its origin and relations.

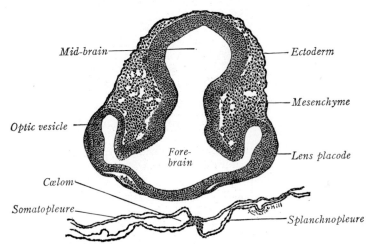

FIG. 513.—Transverse section through the fore-brain and optic vesicles of a seventeen-segment chick embryo. × 75.

The following sections are drawn as if viewed from the cephalic surface; hence, the right side of the embryo is at the reader's left. These illustrations and descriptions may be used for guidance in the study of chick embryos between 33 hours (12 segments) and 40 hours (18 segments).

Section through the Fore-brain and Optic Vesicles (Fig. 513).—The first sections encountered in the series are shavings through the tip of the free head. The brain cavity straightway enlarges, and about midway along the fore-brain the present level is reached. Here the *optic stalks* connect the *optic vesicles* laterally with the lateral portion of the *fore-brain*. Dorsally the section passes through the *mid-brain*, due to the somewhat ventral flexion of the head (*cf.* Fig. 510). The *lens placodes* are thickenings of the surface ectoderm over the optic vesicles. Note that there is now a considerable amount of mesenchyme filling in between the ectoderm and the neural tube; the small spaces seen are terminal branches of the *anterior cardinal veins*. Layers of mesoderm extend to the midplane in the underlying blastoderm.

Section through the Mid-brain and Pharyngeal Membrane (Fig. 514).—At this level the fore-brain has been passed and the *mid-brain* alone is included. In the midventral line the thickened ectoderm bends up into contact with the entoderm of the tubular *pharynx* of the fore-gut. The resulting plate is the *pharyngeal membrane*, and the ectodermal pit leading to it is the *stomo-*

deum. The membrane is transient because at this point the *oral opening* will break through and make the stomodeum continuous with the rest of the mouth cavity (which is entodermal). Lateral to the pharynx two pairs of large vessels are seen. The ventral pair is the *ventral aortæ*, while *dorsal aortæ* make up the dorsal pair. Two sections cephalad in the series, the two sets become continuous around the first *aortic arches*. The caudal end of the *mesencephalon* is the portion of the neural tube showing; its thick walls surround an oval cavity. Notice the large amount of

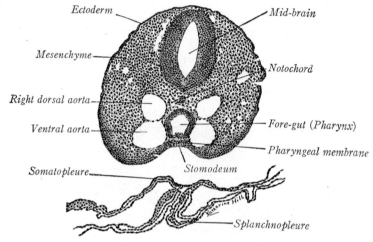

FIG. 514.—Transverse section through the mid-brain and pharyngeal membrane of a seventeen-segment chick embryo. × 75.

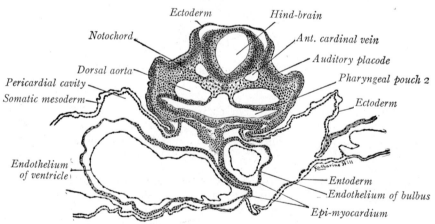

FIG. 515.—Transverse section through the hind-brain, auditory pits and heart of a seventeen-segment chick embryo. × 75.

unspecialized mesenchyme throughout the section. The structure of the blastoderm is complicated laterally by the presence of collapsed blood vessels in the splanchnopleure.

Section through the Hind-brain, Auditory Pits and Heart (Fig. 515).—Between the plane of the last section and this one, the head fold ceases to separate the body from the blastoderm. Nevertheless, lateral prolongations of the head fold continue to indent the somatopleure for some distance caudad.

The section selected is characterized by: (1) the *auditory placodes*, already deepening into pits which represent the beginnings of the internal ears; (2) the large *hind-brain*, somewhat thin and flattened dorsally; (3) the broad *pharynx*, cut through its second pair of pharyngeal pouches, above which on each side lie the *dorsal aortæ*; (4) definite *anterior cardinal veins*, ventrolateral to the brain, which return blood from the head region; (5) the presence of two portions of the *heart*, cut near its cephalic end. Due to its sinuous shape, the heart is sectioned twice. The smaller

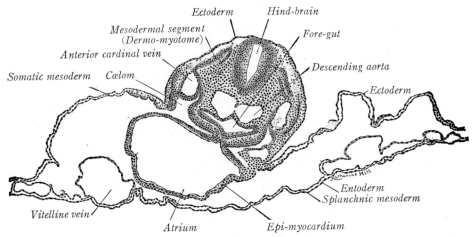

FIG. 516.—Transverse section through the atrial end of the heart of a seventeen-segment chick embryo. × 75.

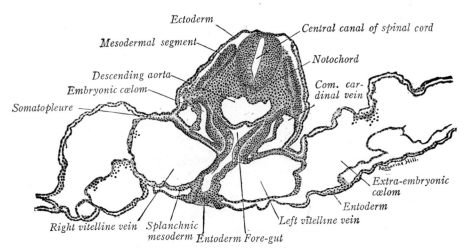

FIG. 517.—Transverse section through the intestinal portal and venous stems of a seventeen-segment chick embryo. × 90.

part is the single *bulbus*, which now replaces the paired ventral aortæ of higher levels. The large *ventricle* lies on the right side of the embryo; a few sections caudad in the series it is continuous with the bulbus (*cf.* Fig. 509). Between the somatic and splanchnic mesoderm is the large potential *pericardial cavity* surrounding the heart.

Section through the Atrial End of the Heart (Fig. 516).—The section is toward the caudal end of the *pharynx*, but the lower end of the *hind-brain* is still included. The *dorsal aortæ* are separated merely by a thin septum which has ruptured at this level. The *anterior cardinal veins* are cut where they bend ventrad to connect with the common cardinal veins. The mesodermal wall of the *atrium* continues dorsad into two layers that then fold laterad, right and left, and join the general splanchnic mesoderm of the embryo. Beneath the pharynx these approximated folds constitute the *dorsal mesocardium*, which serves as a transient mesentery to the heart. On the right side of the section there is fusion between the *epi-myocardium* of the heart and the somatic mesoderm; this is separating off an embryonic portion of the cœlom. *Mesodermal segments*

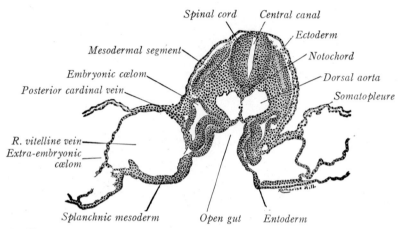

FIG. 518.—Transverse section through the open gut of a seventeen-segment chick embryo. × 90.

were not observed at higher levels, but now they appear alongside the hind-brain. The ventro-mesial part of the segment is breaking down into the *sclerotome;* the dorsomesial wall represents the *myotome*, while the lateral plate is the *dermatome*.

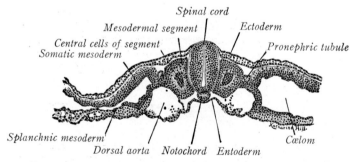

FIG. 519.—Transverse section through the fourteenth pair of somites of a seventeen-segment chick embryo. × 90.

Section through the Intestinal Portal and Venous Stems (Fig. 517).—Both heart and brain have been passed, but the *spinal cord* now becomes a prominent feature. The dorsal aortæ lose their separating median septum and combine into a single vessel, henceforth to be known as the *descending aorta*. The section cuts through the entoderm at the point where it is folded dorsad and cephalad into the head as the *fore-gut* (*cf.* Fig. 510). Two sections caudad is found the opening (*intestinal portal*) where the fore-gut communicates with the progressively flattened, open gut spreading out between the entoderm and the yolk. On each side of the fore-gut is a large *vitelline vein*, sectioned obliquely as it diverges from the heart. The splanchnic mesoderm overlying these veins is pressed by them against the somatic mesoderm, and the cavity of the cœlom is thus interrupted on each side; the portions lying within the embryo's body are the beginnings of an *embryonic cœlom*. The *common cardinal veins* are cut near the level where they join the sinus venosus.

Section through the Open Gut (Fig. 518).—In general this section resembles the preceding, save that the gut is clearly open and without a ventral wall. Its lining is directly continuous with the splanchnopleure, and in this region one speaks of the *mid-gut*. The *vitelline veins* are still large and may be traced laterad into the vascular plexus of the blastoderm. Lateral to the enclosed cœlom, on each side, are rounded spaces which represent the *posterior cardinal veins*, just differentiating. The *dorsal aortæ* are about to become separate once more.

Section through the Fourteenth Pair of Primitive Segments (Fig. 519).—The body of the embryo is now flattened on the surface of the yolk, and the section is characterized by its relative simplicity. Here the *dorsal aortæ* are again separate. Other prominent features are the *spinal cord, notochord, somites, nephrotomes*, and layers of *somatic* and *splanchnic mesoderm*. These

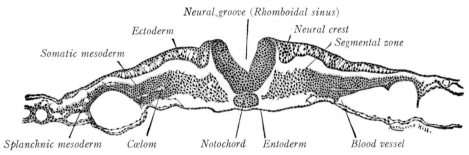

FIG. 520.—Transverse section through the rhomboidal sinus and segmental zone of a seventeen-segment chick embryo. × 90.

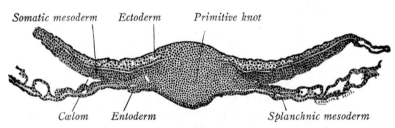

FIG. 521.—Transverse section through the primitive knot of a seventeen-segment chick embryo. × 90.

somites are much less specialized than the older ones at higher levels. Arising from the neph-rotomes are sprout-like *pronephric tubules*. The tips of these hollow out and unite to produce the *pronephric duct*, which is the primary excretory duct of the embryo.

Section through the Rhomboidal Sinus and Segmental Zone (Fig. 520).—The section passes through the *segmental zone*, which is a region of unsegmented mesoderm destined to be cut up into additional somites. Large blood vessels (of the area vasculosa) occur in the splanchnic mesoderm, next the entoderm. The dorsal aortæ of higher levels lose their identity in this plexus, which precedes the appearance of a definite *vitelline artery*. The lateral mesoderm is separated by narrow, cœlomic clefts. The open neural groove is called the *rhomboidal sinus*. The ectoderm is notable for the columnar form of its cells. At the point where the general ectoderm of each side joins the neural fold, a cellular ridge projects ventrally. This tissue constitutes the *neural crests*, and from them the spinal ganglia will differentiate.

Section through the Primitive Knot (of Hensen) (Fig. 521).—The three germ layers merge at the *primitive knot* into a common mass of unspecialized tissue. This knob of formative tissue

is also to be known as the *end bud*, or *tail bud*, since it gives rise to the lower body. The lateral
mesoderm is split into somatic and splanchnic layers; the splanchnic mesoderm contains numerous
small blood vessels of the vascular network.

Section through the Primitive Streak (Fig. 522).—In the mid-dorsal line is the *primitive
groove*. The four germ layers can be seen in direct continuity with the undifferentiated tissue

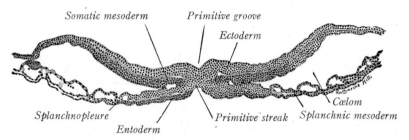

Somatic mesoderm   Primitive groove

Ectoderm

Splanchnopleure   Primitive streak   Splanchnic mesoderm

Cœlom

Entoderm

FIG. 522.—Transverse section through the primitive streak of a seventeen-segment chick embryo.
× 90.

of the *primitive streak* beneath. Laterally, between the splanchnic mesoderm and entoderm,
blood vessels are present as in the preceding sections.

(E) EMBRYO OF TWENTY-SEVEN SEGMENTS (TWO DAYS)

Although a chick embryo with 27 segments (50 hours) is chosen as the norm
(Fig. 523 *B*), the descriptions that follow are applicable to stages between 45
hours (23 segments) and 60 hours (32 segments). An earlier and a later stage are
shown in Fig. 523 *A* and *C*, respectively.

During the latter half of the second day a remarkable change occurs in the
appearance of the embryo and in its position with respect to the blastoderm (Fig.
523 *B*). The bending of the head, already begun in the stage last studied, has
continued until the fore- and hind-brains are nearly parallel. This marked *cephalic
flexure* occurs at the region of the mid-brain. It is manifest that as long as the
embryo retained its original prone position with respect to the yolk it would be
difficult for the head to bend greatly ventrad. In order to facilitate such flexion,
and to allow it to proceed to completion, the upper body has twisted about its
long axis until the left side lies flat upon the yolk. In a dorsal view, therefore,
one sees the right side of the head but the dorsal side of the lower body. The
actual region of torsion, now half way down the trunk, will advance caudad progressively until the whole embryo lies on its left side. Additional curvatures then
bend it into the shape of the letter **C**. One of these flexures is already appearing
opposite the lower end of the heart, at the junction of head and trunk; for this
reason it is named the *cervical flexure*.

Most of the body is rather sharply delimited from the blastoderm; the head
is free; much of the midbody is bounded by deep *lateral folds;* caudally the *tail
bud* indicates the material for the future hind end of the body; it is bordered by a
tail fold. The further overgrowth of the embryo beyond the limits of the head-,
lateral- and tail folds will appear to constrict the embryo from extra-embryonic
blastoderm.

The head is now covered by a double fold of the somatopleure, the head fold
of the *amnion;* it envelops the upper half of the body like a veil. The heart bends
in the form of a letter **S**, and distinct *vitelline arteries* and *vitelline veins* connect

with a profuse plexus of extra-embryonic vessels. Three ectodermal furrows form *branchial grooves* on the sides of the neck. *Eye* and *ear* are prominent. Additional somites, produced from the former segmental zone, extend far down the embryo.

Central Nervous System and Sense Organs.—The brain region of the neural tube is separated by constrictions into five vesicles, but these subdivisions are not so distinct as they will be somewhat later (Fig. 523 *B*). The first subdivision of the primitive fore-brain is the *telencephalon;* the rest constitutes the *diencephalon.* The *mesencephalon* remains undivided, but is bent at its middle by the cephalic

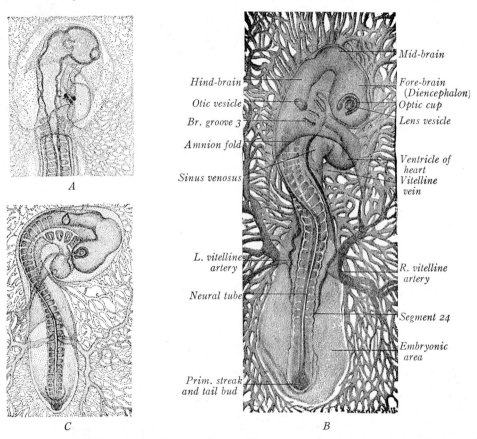

A

Hind-brain

Otic vesicle

Br. groove 3

Amnion fold

Sinus venosus

L. vitelline artery

Neural tube

Prim. streak and tail bud

C

Mid-brain

Fore-brain (*Diencephalon*)

Optic cup

Lens vesicle

Ventricle of heart

Vitelline vein

R. vitelline artery

Segment 24

Embryonic area

B

FIG. 523.—Chick embryos of 43 to 60 hours. The upper portion is in lateral view, the lower in dorsal view. *A*, At twenty segments (43 hours) (× 19). *B*, At twenty-seven segments (50 hours) (× 14). *C*, At thirty-one segments (60 hours) (× 8).

flexure. The hind-brain shows indistinctly two regions of specialization. A short segment with a thick roof, adjoining the mid-brain, is the *metencephalon;* the thin-roofed remainder is the *myelencephalon.* The *spinal cord* is now closed to its extreme end, and consequently the rhomboidal sinus no longer exists.

The lens placode has become a *lens vesicle;* coincidental with its invagination, the outer wall of the optic vesicle also folds inward, thereby making a double-walled structure, the *optic cup.* The latter is not a complete cup, for on one side a segment of the wall is missing; this *chorioid fissure* gives the cup a horseshoe-

shaped outline in surface view (Fig. 523). The auditory placode of earlier stages
has become a sac, the *otocyst* or *otic vesicle;* it, however, still retains connection
with the body ectoderm.

Digestive System.—The entodermal canal shows two (or three?) regional divisions. Of these, the *fore-gut* is best differentiated; it will be described more fully in
the next paragraph. In Fig. 524 most of the entoderm has been removed, so that

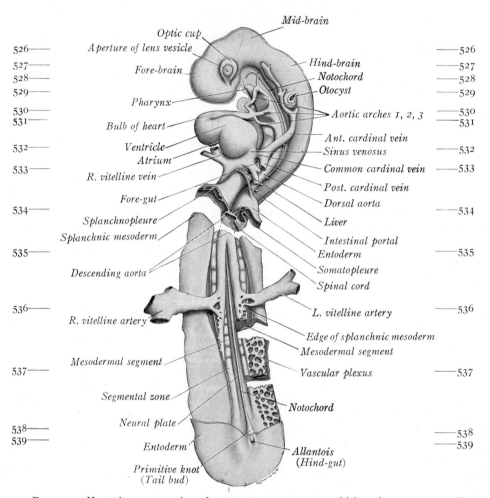

Fig. 524.—Ventral reconstruction of a twenty-seven-segment chick embryo. × 18. The
ectoderm and mesoderm of the upper body and the entoderm of the lower body have been mostly
removed. Numbered lines indicate the levels of Figs. 526–539.

the open *mid-gut* scarcely shows; it extends from the *anterior intestinal portal* to
the tail bud and, lacking a ventral wall, lies directly upon the yolk. At the caudal
end a shallow pocket opens ventrally, just caudal to the main mass of the tail bud.
This is commonly designated *hind-gut* and *posterior intestinal portal*, but there are
reasons for suspecting it to be the first indication of the sacculating *allantois* (p. 546).

The *pharyngeal membrane* lies at the bottom of a deep pit, the *stomodeum,* formed by depressed ectoderm. A median ectodermal sac, just in front of the pharyngeal membrane, is *Rathke's pouch*. It extends along the ventral surface of the diencephalon where it will develop into the epithelial portion of the hypophysis. The entodermal *pharynx* bears three pairs of lateral outpocketings known as *pharyngeal pouches* (Fig. 524). They occur opposite the three external *branchial grooves*, and here ectoderm of the groove and entoderm of the pouch are in contact, forming *closing plates* (Fig. 523). At about this age the first pair of plates ruptures, thereby making a free opening, or *branchial cleft*, into the pharynx. These transitory apertures correspond to the gill clefts in lower, aquatic vertebrates. Between the successive pouches lie solid, bar-like portions of the body wall, the *branchial arches;* in animals with aquatic respiration the arches bear gills, and even in higher embryos, like the chick, an artery courses through each (*cf.* Fig. 303 *A*). At the level of the second pair of pouches, a broadly open pocket grows away from the median floor of the pharynx; it is the *thyroid gland* (Fig. 531). Beyond the pharynx the fore-gut narrows, but esophagus, stomach and small intestine are not yet clearly distinguishable. Toward the anterior intestinal portal the fore-gut is flattened from side to side, and before it opens into the mid-gut there is budded off the bilobed diverticulum of the *liver* (Fig. 524). This lies between the vitelline veins, which later break up into the sinusoidal spaces of the liver.

Vascular System.—The disappearance of the dorsal mesocardium leaves the large, tubular heart attached solely by its two ends. Since the heart tube is growing faster than the surrounding body, it of necessity bends; when viewed from the ventral side it comes to look like the letter **S** (Fig. 524). Four regions can be distinguished: (1) the *sinus venosus*, into which the veins open; (2) a dilated, dorsal chamber, the *atrium;* (3) a tubular, ventral portion, bent in the form of a **U**, of which the left limb is the *ventricle*, the right limb (4) the *bulbus cordis*. From the bulbus is given off the *ventral aorta*. There are now three pairs of *aortic arches*, which open into the paired *dorsal aortæ*. The first aortic arch runs axially through the first branchial arch, located just cranial to the first pharyngeal pouch; it is the same vessel seen in the 38-hour embryo connecting ventral and dorsal aortæ. The second and third aortic arches course in the second and third branchial arches, which stand similarly cephalad of the second and third pharyngeal pouches. They are developed by the enlargement of channels in primitive capillary networks between the ventral and dorsal aortæ. At the level of the sinus venosus the paired dorsal trunks fuse to form the single *descending aorta*, which extends as far back as the fifteenth pair of primitive segments. At this point the aortæ again separate; opposite the twenty-second segments each connects with the trunk of a *vitelline artery*, which conveys blood to the vascular area (Fig. 524). Caudal to the vitelline arteries the aortæ decrease rapidly in size and soon end.

As in the previous stage, the blood is returned from the vascular area to the heart by the *vitelline veins*, now two large trunks (Fig. 524). In the body of the embryo the *anterior cardinal veins* course ventrolateral to the brain, and already are of large size. The smaller *posterior cardinal veins* are developing caudal to the atrium. They lie in the mesenchyme of the somatopleure, lateral in position (Fig. 533). Opposite the sinus venosus the anterior and posterior cardinal veins of each side unite to form the *common cardinal veins* (ducts of Cuvier), which open into the dorsal wall of the sinus venosus (Fig. 524). The set of primitive veins is thus paired like the arteries, and like them develops by the enlargement of channels in a network of capillaries.

Differentiation of Mesoderm and Cœlom.—The formation of new mesodermal segments and the progressive differentiation of older ones into sclerotome,
myotome and dermatome continue as described for the preceding embryo (p. 525).
The nephrotome region shows the beginning of additional features. The *pronephric duct* has continued beyond its original site of formation and extends tailward as a blindly growing cord. A second set of kidney tubules is now starting
to differentiate between the thirteenth and thirtieth segments. They arise from
the intermediate cell masses caudal to the pronephric group. At first taking the
shape of vesicles, they later will become *mesonephric tubules* and join the pronephric (hereafter mesonephric) duct. The mesonephros constitutes the functional
kidney of the embryo, but not the definitive one.

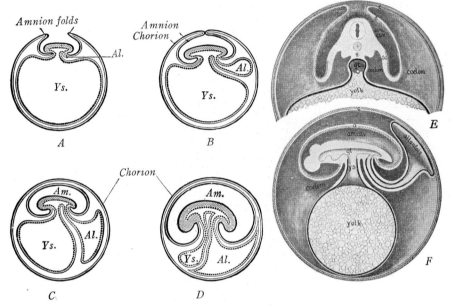

FIG. 525.—Diagrams illustrating the development of the fetal membranes in the chick
(after McMurrich and Kingsley). In *A–D* ectoderm, mesoderm and entoderm are represented
by heavy, light and dotted lines respectively; in *E, F* ectoderm is hatched, mesoderm gray and
entoderm black.

a, Amnion, *al*, allantois; *am*, amniotic cavity; *c*, chorion; *gt*, gut; *so*, somatopleure; *ys*, yolk
stalk and sac.

The splanchnopleure of this stage is chiefly involved in gut formation. Below
the level of the free head the somatopleure is continuous with the extra-embryonic
blastoderm, but it is already being indented deeply by *lateral body folds* whose
union will progressively close the ventral body wall (Fig. 534). The establishment
of a complete body wall is the chief factor in separating embryonic from extra-
embryonic cœlom. Up to the present time this closure has not occurred. The
only stretch of embryonic cœlom is due to fusions between somatopleure and
splanchnopleure at the caudal level of the heart. Since the lungs will bud out
here, these paired cœlomic canals are potentially pleural cavities.

Amnion and Chorion.—At the end of the second day two extra-embryonic
protective membranes have become prominent. They are the *amnion* which

will form a membranous fluid-filled sac about the embryo itself, and the *chorion* which eventually encloses both embryo and all extra-embryonic structures. Developmentally the two membranes are nothing more than the outer and inner layers of a circular fold thrown up around the embryo from the extra-embryonic somatopleure. The two membranes arise simultaneously by a single process of folding (Fig. 525). The first indication of them is a fold in front of the embryo, followed later by lateral and caudal ones (*A*). These hood-like, arching folds close in from all sides (*B*, *E*) until they meet and fuse over the embryo (*C*, *D*, *F*). The inner somatopleuric layer is the amnion; the outer somatopleuric layer constitutes the

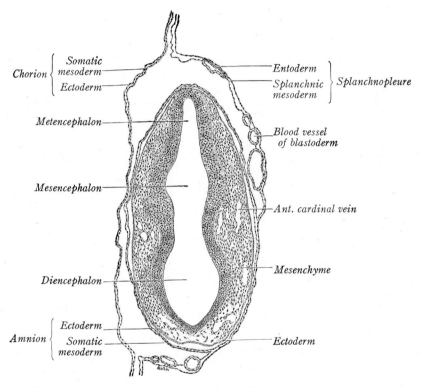

FIG. 526.—Transverse section through the flexed brain of a twenty-seven-segment chick embryo. × 50.

chorion, of little importance to the chick. It should be noted that, while the folding brings the mesodermal components of these membranes facing each other, the two are separated by the extra-embryonic cœlom.

The *head fold* of the amnion had begun in the chick of the previous stage (Fig. 510); at the end of the second day it is continuous along a crescentic margin with the *lateral folds* and envelops the upper half of the body (Figs. 523 and 534). As yet the *tail fold* of the amnion has scarcely started.

TRANSVERSE SECTIONS

The following series of transverse sections from a two-day chick shows the fundamentally important structures; the illustrations and descriptions are equally applicable to the study of embryos between 45 hours (23 segments) and 60 hours (32 segments). The sections used are drawn from the cephalic surface; hence, the right side of the embryo is at the reader's left. The precise level of each significant section in the student's slides should be determined with respect to Figs. 523 *B* and 524; for the sections about to be described this has been indicated along the margins of Fig. 524. Since the head is bending rapidly during the last hours of the second day, minor variations in the appearance of different series of sections through the head are unavoidable; this, however, is chiefly a question of which particular structures happen to appear together in the fore-brain and hind-brain portions of a section.

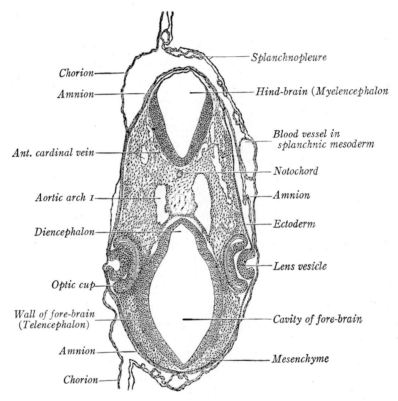

FIG. 527.—Transverse section through the optic cups and first aortic arches of a twenty-seven-segment chick embryo. × 50.

Section through the Flexed Brain (Fig. 526).—Due to flexion of the head, the first sections encountered pass through the *mesencephalon*. A little farther down the series the *metencephalon* of the hind-brain and the *diencephalon* of the fore-brain are included as well; constrictions mark the boundaries between these divisions, as in Fig. 526. The blood vessels seen in the mesenchyme are branches of the *anterior cardinal veins*. The splanchnopleure is characterized in this and subsequent sections by the presence of blood vessels in its mesodermal layer; these obvious structures make easy the identification of the yolk-side of the blastoderm.

The entire head is enveloped by the *amnion;* by contrast, the *chorion* surrounds both embryo and yolk, and consequently is in relation with the right side of the head only (*i.e.*, the free side of the head, away from the yolk). In each of these membranes a layer of ectoderm and a separate layer of mesoderm can be identified; the mesodermal components of the amnion and chorion face each other across the extra-embryonic cœlom, but due to collapse in the process of preparation they may be found partly in contact.

Section through the Optic Cups and First Aortic Arches (Fig. 527).—Continuing down the series, the mid-brain is passed and the brain becomes cut twice in each section; the *myelencephalon* is always recognized by its thin roof and its close association with the notochord. Observe that in these sections through the bent head, progress is caudad down the hind-brain half of the section, but rostrad toward the tip of the fore-brain.

Since the section illustrated passes above the level of the optic stalks, the *optic cups* appear unconnected with the fore-brain. The overlying ectoderm has thickened and invaginated to form the *lens vesicles*. The thicker wall of the optic cup, next the lens, will give rise to the nervous layer

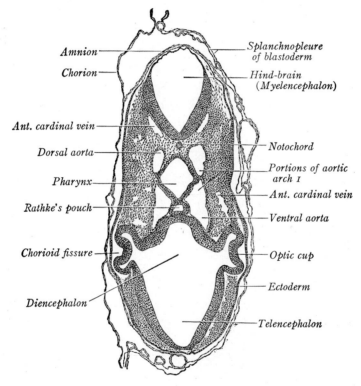

Fig. 528.—Transverse section through Rathke's pouch and the optic stalks of a twenty-seven-segment chick embryo. × 50.

of the retina; the thinner outer wall becomes the pigmented epithelium. Ventrally in the section is the *telencephalon* and *diencephalon*. Dorsally occurs the *myelencephalon* of the hind-brain, with its roof a thin *ependymal layer*. Between the brain vesicles are longitudinal sections of the first pair of *aortic arches*. Lateral to the hind-brain are portions of the *anterior cardinal veins*, which convey blood from the head to the heart.

Section through Rathke's Pouch and the Optic Stalks (Fig. 528).—The section passes just caudal to the lens, but it includes the caudal margins of the *optic cups*. The shallow concavity on the margin is the *chorioid fissure*. Each cup is connected with the wall of the fore-brain (specifically the *diencephalon*) by an eccentrically attached *optic stalk*; this stalk will furnish the path through which optic nerve fibers grow from retina to brain. Both the *ventral* and *dorsal aortæ* are seen. Parts of the first pair of aortic arches, cut along their caudal borders, connect with them.

Between the ventral wall of the fore-brain and the *pharynx* is an invagination of the stomodeal ectoderm, *Rathke's pouch;* it will become the epithelial lobe of the hypophysis. The *anterior cardinal veins* have assumed their characteristic positions ventrolateral to the hind-brain.

Section through the Stomodeum and Pharyngeal Membrane (Fig. 529).—The most important feature of this level is the head, cut in two separate sections. One part includes the *hind-brain* and *pharynx;* the other, the *fore-brain* and end of the bent head. The space between these two parts is the region of the *stomodeum.* Here the *pharyngeal membrane,* composed of fused ectoderm and entoderm, still separates stomodeum from pharynx. Here, also, the mouth of *Rathke's pouch* opens. *Dorsal* and *ventral aortæ* show their characteristic positions with respect to the pharynx. This is about the lowest section to include the *optic stalks.*

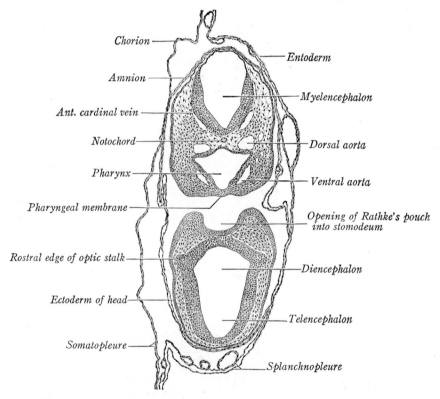

Chorion

Amnion

Ant. cardinal vein

Notochord

Pharynx

Pharyngeal membrane

Rostral edge of optic stalk

Ectoderm of head

Somatopleure

Entoderm

Myelencephalon

Dorsal aorta

Ventral aorta

Opening of Rathke's pouch into stomodeum

Diencephalon

Telencephalon

Splanchnopleure

FIG. 529.—Transverse section through the stomodeum and pharyngeal membrane of a twenty-seven-segment chick embryo. × 50.

Section through the Otocysts, Bulbus and Second Aortic Arches (Fig. 530).—The bent part of the head of the Γ-shaped embryo has been passed. The *otocysts* are sectioned caudal to their apertures, and so appear as closed sacs alongside the hind-brain. Ventral to the *pharynx,* the *bulbus cordis* is sectioned obliquely. Continuous with the bulbus is the unpaired *ventral aorta,* which gives off the second pair of *aortic arches;* these pass around the sides of the pharynx and connect with the *dorsal aortæ.* Surrounding the bulbus cordis is the *cœlom,* which is not yet enclosed by body wall and for this reason is not yet specifically a pericardial cavity. The *amnion* attaches to the body on each side; on the right it is folded upon itself. This is because the primitive amniotic folds fuse directly over the original dorsal line, regardless of the turning of the embryo; consequently, on the right there is 'slack.'

Section through the Pharyngeal Pouches, Thyroid Gland and Ventricle (Fig. 531).—As the

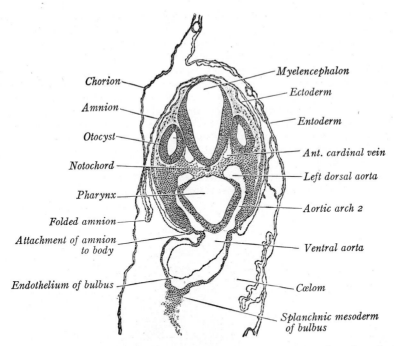

Chorion
Amnion
Otocyst
Notochord
Pharynx
Folded amnion
Attachment of amnion
to body
Endothelium of bulbus

Myelencephalon
Ectoderm
Entoderm
Ant. cardinal vein
Left dorsal aorta
Aortic arch 2
Ventral aorta
Cœlom
Splanchnic mesoderm
of bulbus

FIG. 530.—Transverse section through the otocysts, bulbus and second aortic arches of a twenty-seven-segment chick embryo.   × 50.

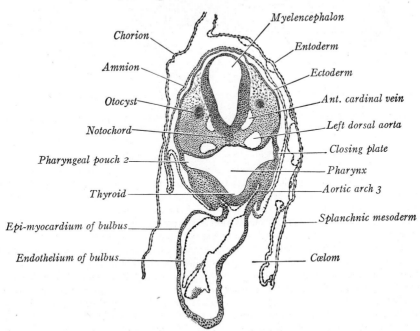

Chorion
Amnion
Otocyst
Notochord
Pharyngeal pouch 2
Thyroid
Epi-myocardium of bulbus
Endothelium of bulbus

Myelencephalon
Entoderm
Ectoderm
Ant. cardinal vein
Left dorsal aorta
Closing plate
Pharynx
Aortic arch 3
Splanchnic mesoderm
Cœlom

FIG. 531.—Transverse section through the second pharyngeal pouches, thyroid gland and ventricle of a twenty-seven-segment chick embryo.   × 50.

section figured is taken at a level between the second and third aortic arches, the *dorsal aortæ* and heart are unconnected; nevertheless, the ventral ends of the third pair of *aortic arches* have been grazed and do show. Tangential shavings have also been cut from the caudal walls of the *otocysts*, just as they are being left behind. Extending laterad from the pharynx is the second pair of *pharyngeal pouches*, which have already come in contact with the ectoderm to form *closing plates;* the complementary, external *branchial grooves* are not well seen in the present instance. A pocket-like depression in the midventral floor of the pharynx indicates the beginning of the *thyroid gland;* later it becomes saccular and loses its connection with the pharyngeal entoderm. The splanchnic mesodermal wall of the heart is destined to give rise to the *epicardium* and *myocardium*. Only the beginning of the *ventricle* appears, but a short distance down the series its large loop is met; the main part of the ventricle is free and no longer suspended by the former dorsal mesocardium.

Section through the Atrium, Venous Stems and Pleural Cavities (Fig. 532).—Between the previous level and this one, the third aortic arches and much of the heart have been passed. Also the anterior cardinal veins have bent downward to join the posterior cardinal veins in a stem

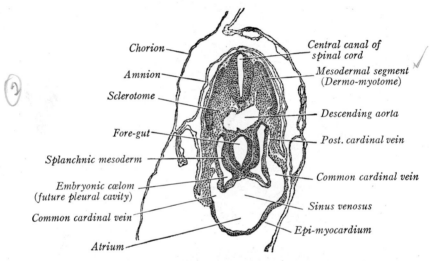

FIG. 532.—Transverse section through the atrium, venous stems and pleural cavities of a twenty-seven-segment chick embryo. × 50.

known as the common cardinal. The present level shows the *posterior* and *common cardinal veins*, the latter opening into the thin-walled *sinus venosus*. The sinus receives all of the blood being returned to the heart and is separated from the larger *atrium* by a slight constriction only. Passing a few sections lower, the opening of the *vitelline veins* into the sinus may also be demonstrated. The dorsal aortæ have united to form the single *descending aorta*.

On each side of the pharynx is a subdivision of the cœlom which will serve as a *pleural cavity* when the lung buds appear. These canals are partially separated from the pericardial cavity by the *septum transversum* (primitive diaphragm), through which the common cardinal veins cross to the sinus venosus. Since the last section the myelencephalon has given way to the *spinal cord*, and here the highest *mesodermal segments* are seen. These somites have differentiated into a *dermo-myotome* plate and a more diffuse *sclerotome*. At all higher levels the general mesoderm was purely mesenchyme and without visible specialization. The mesodermal components of the two amnion folds are not fused at this level.

Section through the Vitelline Veins and Liver (Fig. 533).—The fore-gut is now flattened from side to side and its cavity is narrow; a few sections caudad it bends downward to open through the *anterior intestinal portal* onto the yolk sac. Midventrally there is evaginated from the gut-entoderm a pair of diverticula which constitutes the earliest indication of the *liver*. At the side of each bud is a *vitelline vein* (the left, cut as it swings in from the blastoderm); their destina-

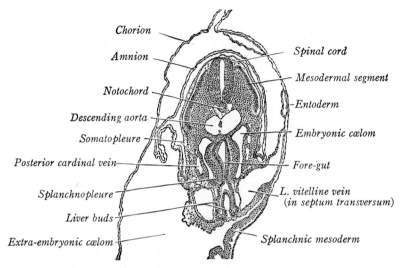

FIG. 533.—Transverse section through the vitelline veins and liver of a twenty-seven-segment chick embryo.   × 50.

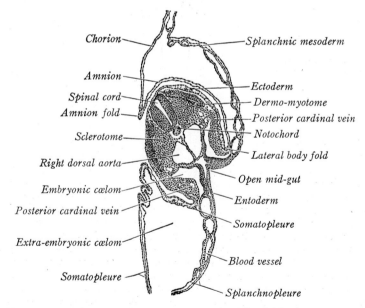

FIG. 534.—Transverse section through the open gut and amnion folds of a twenty-seven-segment chick embryo.   × 50.

tion in the sinus venosus has already been traced. The primitive liver bud does not always appear bilobed; at a slightly later stage it is found ventral to the united vitelline veins, and a second bud, more cephalic in origin, lies dorsal to the vein. Note the intimate relation between the entodermal epithelium of the liver and the endothelium of the vitelline veins; this is significant since later there will be a mutual intergrowth between the two to give the characteristic relation of hepatic cords and sinuses.

The *septum transversum* is still present at this level; in fact, it was originally produced through the bulging vitelline veins fusing with the somatopleure. Lateral to the fore-gut are small *cœlomic cavities*, and lateral to these, in turn, appear portions of the *posterior cardinal veins*.

Section through the Open Gut and Amnion Folds (Fig. 534).—The intestine has opened ventrally as the *mid-gut*, its splanchnopleuric wall passing directly over onto the vascular blastoderm. The descending aorta is again divided by a septum into its primitive components, the right and left *dorsal aortæ*. Lateral to the aortæ and in the somatopleure are the small *posterior cardinal veins*. The embryonic cœlom is in communication with the extra-embryonic cœlom. Deep *lateral body folds* of somatopleure indicate how, by their ventral union, the body becomes established free from the blastoderm.

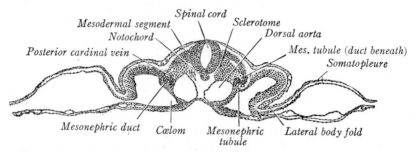

FIG. 535.—Transverse section through the seventeenth pair of somites of a twenty-seven-segment chick embryo. × 50.

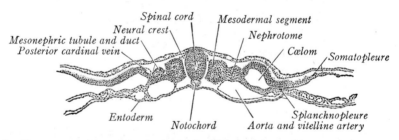

FIG. 536.—Transverse section through the twenty-third somites and the vitelline arteries of a twenty-seven-segment chick embryo. × 50.

The *amnion folds* have not joined at this level, thus leaving the amniotic cavity open; some variation may be found in the exact level where closure is occurring. In such a section as this the somatopleuric components of the amnion and chorion are easily traced, and a few sections cephalad the manner of union of the two folds is illustrated.

Section through the Seventeenth Pair of Somites (Fig. 535).—The body of the embryo is no longer rotated. On the left side of the embryo the mesodermal segment is specializing into a *dermo-myotome* plate and a diffuse *sclerotome;* on the right side the section merely grazes the edge of a somite. Lateral to each aorta appears a section of the *pronephric (mesonephric) duct* and a *mesonephric tubule*. The space nearby is the *posterior cardinal vein*. The embryonic somatopleure is arched and infolded, preparatory to forming the ventrolateral body wall of the embryo and separating the embryo from the underlying layers of the blastoderm.

Section through the Twenty-third Somites and the Vitelline Arteries (Fig. 536).—In this region the embryo is flatter and simpler in structure, corresponding to the condition at higher levels in younger embryos. Mesodermal segments, nephrotomes and lateral layers of somatic and splanchnic mesoderm are little changed from their original appearance. The amniotic folds have not appeared. On the left side the *vitelline artery* leaves the aorta; on the right side this connection has been passed. The right *posterior cardinal vein* is present just lateral to the *mesonephric tubule* and *duct*. The small clusters of cells dorsolateral to the spinal cord are the *neural crests*, which will differentiate into spinal ganglia.

Section through the Segmental Zone (Fig. 537).—The mesodermal segments are replaced by the *segmental zone*. This is a somewhat triangular column of primitive mesoderm, ready to serve as the source from which both somites and nephrotomes will be progressively blocked out. The

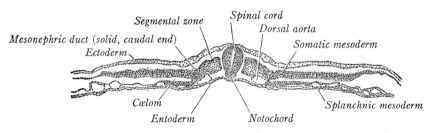

Fig. 537.—Transverse section through the segmental zone of a twenty-seven-segment chick embryo. × 50.

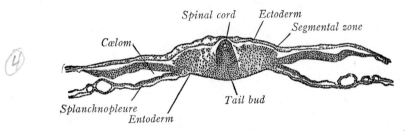

Fig. 538.—Transverse section through the tail bud of a twenty-seven-segment chick embryo. × 50.

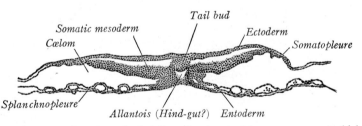

Fig. 539.—Transverse section through the allantois of a twenty-seven-segment chick embryo. × 50.

solid, caudal ends of the free-growing *mesonephric ducts* appear at this level. The *aortæ* are smaller than heretofore, and a short distance caudad they disappear in the plexus of the area vasculosa. Laterally the *somatopleure* and *splanchnopleure* are flat and separated by the slit-like *cœlom*.

Section through the Tail Bud (Fig. 538).—In embryos of two days the neural groove has rolled into a tube and is cut off from the surface ectoderm throughout its full length. At the present level the caudal tip of the spinal canal is seen, and the ventral wall of the neural tube is merged with an undifferentiated mass of dense tissue which is a common meeting ground for the ectoderm, mesoderm and entoderm. This tissue has the essential relations of the primitive knot of earlier stages, and like it is a region of progressive proliferation and differentiation; the entire formative mass has been called the *tail bud*, since the caudal end of the body develops from its substance.

Section through the Allantois (Fig. 539).—A short pocket, located in the midplane, is cut across at this level; a few sections cephalad in the series it opens and becomes continuous with the entoderm. Some interpret this diverticulum as the beginning *hind-gut* and *posterior intestinal portal*. Since, however, it is largely caudal to the tail bud, it more probably is the first indication of the sacculating *allantois* (which precedes the reversal of relations at the caudal end of the embryo and the establishment of a hind-gut by folding; *cf.* Fig. 70).

Also in the midplane may be seen the caudal end of the *tail bud*. It is continuous dorsally with the *ectoderm*, ventrally with the *entoderm* of the hind-gut, and laterally with the **mesoderm**.

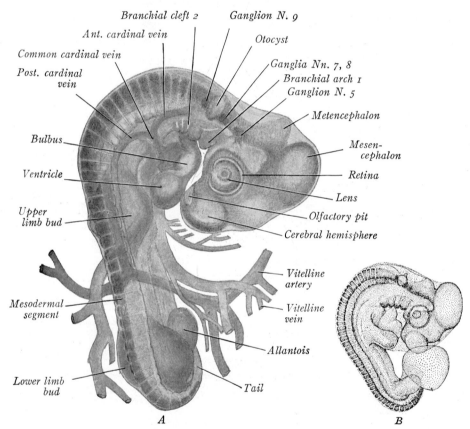

FIG. 540.—Chick embryos of three and four days, viewed from the right side. *A*, At three days (× 14). *B*, At four days (× 6).

(F) EMBRYOS OF THREE TO FOUR DAYS

During the third and fourth days of incubation the chick attains a stage of development corresponding to the youngest pig embryos customarily studied. It will be sufficient, therefore, to describe only such essential features of developmental advance in these older chick embryos as are necessary for introducing the detailed pig studies that follow.

External Form.—The whole body shows the effect of continued torsion, and the embryo now lies on its left side (Fig. 540). The former flexures, especially the cervical, are pronounced, and new *dorsal* and *caudal flexures* have appeared; as a result, the embryo becomes so curved that its head and tail approach. The final number of 42 primitive segments is present and the body ends in a distinct *tail*. Upper and lower *limb buds* project from the body wall, and the saccular *allantois* extends beyond the unclosed lower abdomen. Four *branchial clefts* show, separated by prominent *branchial arches*. The area of attachment with the yolk sac is the relatively slender *yolk stalk* (Fig. 541). Continued overgrowth on the part of the embryo and undercutting by the body folds, especially the more recent *tail fold*, have led to an increasingly sharp delimitation of embryo from blastoderm.

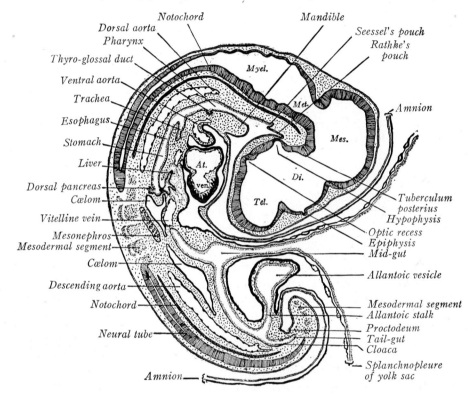

FIG. 541.—Midsagittal section of a chick embryo of four days, viewed from the right side (Patten). × 14.

Central Nervous System and Sense Organs.—The five secondary divisions of the brain are easily identified; the telencephalon bears lateral *hemispheres*, and the distinction between metencephalon and myelencephalon is now plain. Most of the *cranial nerves* and *ganglia* have begun to appear (Fig. 540). From the roof of the diencephalon protrudes the evagination of the *epiphysis;* in the floor is the neural lobe of the *hypophysis* (Fig. 541).

The *eye* is a prominent organ, with its lens freed from the ectoderm but with the narrowed *chorioid fissure* still showing (Fig. 540 A). The *otic vesicle* is a detached and closed sac, from which the tubular *endolymph duct* is growing. Olfactory organs, not seen hitherto, have not only appeared as ectodermal placodes on the ventrolateral sides of the head, but also they are now depressed into *olfactory pits*.

Digestive and Respiratory Systems.—The fore-gut and hind-gut are closed-in tubes, while the open mid-gut is a relatively short segment connected by the *yolk stalk* with the *yolk sac* (Fig. 541). As the pharyngeal membrane has ruptured, the stomodeum becomes an integral part of the *mouth cavity*. Four *pharyngeal pouches* are prominent; in all but the fourth, the closing plates perforate and form temporary *branchial clefts*. By the end of the fourth day the *thyroid* diverticulum loses its connection with the median floor of the pharynx. The *trachea* has arisen from a midventral groove which separates from the caudal end of the pharynx and bifurcates into two *lung buds*. The *esophagus* is a short and slender tube, and the *stomach* is a slightly spindle-shaped dilatation. Both *liver* buds have fused into a common branching mass, while at the same level the *pancreas* is appearing.

Except for the attachment of the slender *yolk stalk* to the nearly straight *intestine*, there are no additional features of special interest above the caudal end of the hind-gut. Here the gut is separated from an ectodermal pit, the *proctodeum*, by a thin *cloacal membrane* which later perforates (Fig. 541). The mesonephric ducts join the hind-gut, and a stalked vesicle, the *allantois*, grows from its ventral floor. This terminal portion of the original hind-gut, which will receive not only the contents of the intestine but also the secretions of the urinary and reproductive glands, is the *cloaca*.

Urinary System.—The pronephric tubules disappear on the fourth day. *Mesonephric tubules* are still developing. Each consists of an elongate, coiled tubule, which is associated with a knot of blood vessels (glomerulus) at one end and drains into the mesonephric duct at the other. The *metanephros*, or permanent kidney, is just appearing; its collecting tubules and ureter arise as a bud from the mesonephric duct near the cloaca; the secretory tubules will develop from adjacent nephrotome tissue, located more caudally than the mesonephros.

Vascular System.—The ventricular loop has moved caudad and the atrial region cephalad, thus reversing the original relations of these parts (Fig. 540). Both *atrium* and *ventricle* show external indications of a beginning division into right and left chambers; the myocardial wall is assuming the characteristics of muscle cells. As a whole, the heart has sunk caudad considerably from its early cephalic position.

Below the heart, the primitive aortæ are fused throughout their lengths. Since the second day, a fourth pair of *aortic arches*, a rudimentary fifth and a sixth pair have developed; of the full set, only the third (carotid), fourth (aortic) and sixth (pulmonary) arches remain. The *cardinal veins* are well developed, and the paired *vitelline arteries* and *veins* have each fused inside the body into single vessels. New *allantoic arteries* pass to the allantois, and *allantoic veins* return the same blood by way of the lateral body wall to the heart. These vessels are also termed umbilical; they become still more important in the mammal.

Extra-embryonic Membranes.—During the third day the tail-fold of the *amnion* develops, and soon the embryo becomes enclosed by a complete fluid-filled sac which is protective in function (Fig. 525); the *chorion*, formed by the same process but of little significance, ultimately surrounds the embryo and all extra-embryonic structures. Much of the yolk mass is covered by advancing splanchnopleure (*yolk sac*), which is continuous over a narrow *yolk stalk* with the gut (Fig. 541). As the embryo elongates, the yolk stalk appears relatively narrower. Through the vitelline vessels the yolk supplies all the food material for embryonic growth. The *allantois* arises late in the third day as a diverticulum of the splanchnopleuric floor of the hind-gut (Figs. 540 and 541). It later becomes a large, stalked sac occupying the space beneath the shell. Allantoic (umbilical) blood vessels ramify in its walls, and the allantois serves as the principal fetal organ of respiration and excretion.

(G) EMBRYOS OF SEVEN AND TEN DAYS

Fig. 541½ illustrates the advances in form acquired up to the middle of the incubation period. By the end of this time the fetus becomes unmistakably bird-like in its external characteristics. The original cervical flexure has been lost, and a distinct *neck* now separates head from thorax. The first branchial arches remain

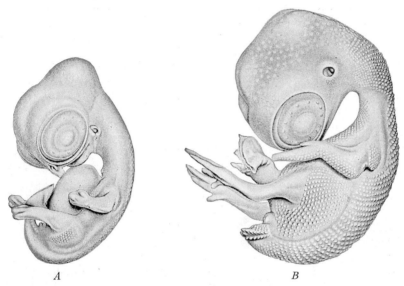

A B

Fig. 541½.—Later chick embryos, viewed from the left side (after Keibel and Abraham). × 3. *A*, At seven days; *B*, at ten days.

as the primitive *jaws*, which assume the appearance of a beak, and the first branchial cleft is retained as the *external acoustic meatus*, about which no auricle develops. The other arches and clefts have disappeared. The ventral surface of the body bulges prominently as the viscera become more protuberant. *Feather* primordia appear in definite patterns. The contours of the body, including the head and tail, become recognizably avian, and the fore limbs are wing-like.

RECOMMENDED COLLATERAL READING

Lillie, F. R. The Development of the Chick. Holt.
Patten, B. M. The Early Embryology of the Chick. Blakiston.

CHAPTER XXIII

THE STUDY OF PIG EMBRYOS

The maturing eggs of the pig are expelled from the ovary during the period of heat, following which they become promptly fertilized (*cf.* Fig. 27). Cleavage and the formation of a blastocyst are illustrated in Fig. 33. Gastrulation (the segregation of entoderm and mesoderm) is essentially like the stages shown in Figs. 46 and 48, while the organization of a typical blastoderm is illustrated in Fig. 49.

At the completion of germ-layer formation the embryonic disc possesses a typical primitive streak (Fig. 542 *A*). This is quickly followed by the appearance of neural folds (*B*, *C*). Coincidently with their closure into a neural tube, meso-

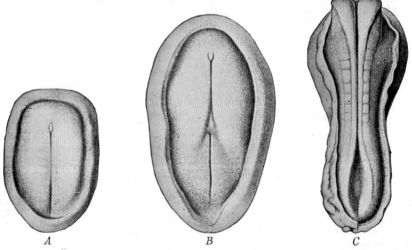

| *A* | *B* | *C* |

FIG. 542.—Early pig embryos, in dorsal view (Keibel). × 20. *A*, Blastoderm at twelve days, with primitive streak and knot. *B*, Blastoderm at thirteen days, with primitive streak and neural groove. *C*, Embryo of fourteen days, with seven segments.

dermal segments are appearing progressively (Fig. 543 *A*). The fundamental similarity of these stages to chick embryos of the first two days is apparent (*B*). The stages immediately succeeding correspond to those of three-day chick embryos, but are complicated by flexion and spiral twisting (*C*); this makes sections difficult for the beginner to interpret. However, in embryos about 6 mm. long the twist of the body has disappeared sufficiently so that its structure may be studied to better advantage. At this time the state of development is generally comparable to that of a four-day chick (Fig. 544). Notice the similarity of Figs. 542 and 543 to the human stages shown as Figs. 65, 71, 72 and 73.

The fetal membranes of the pig stand somewhat intermediate between the chick and man. The amnion, chorion and allantois develop very much as in the chick (Fig. 53). The yolk sac for a time grows rapidly, but its functions are soon

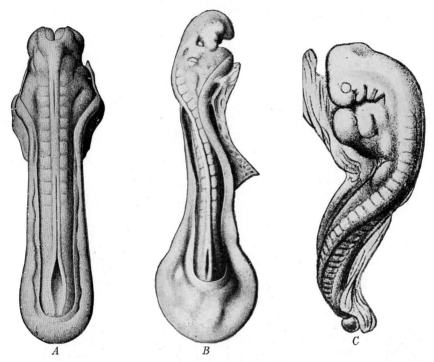

A B C

FIG. 543.—Early pig embryos, in dorsal view (Keibel). A, At fifteen days with eleven segments ($\times$ 20). B, At sixteen days, with seventeen segments ($\times$ 15). C, At seventeen days, approximately 4 mm. long, with about the full number of segments ($\times$ 12).

transferred to the allantois which fuses with the chorion; the two constitute a placenta, which is the organ of fetal respiration, nutrition and excretion (Fig. 57 A, B). The development and relations of these extra-embryonic structures are described on pp. 80–89.

(A) THE ANATOMY OF A SIX MM. PIG EMBRYO

The general structure of a 6 mm. pig embryo is illustrated in Figs. 544 to 547. This should be compared with the chick embryo of four days (Figs. 540 and 541) and the 5 and 8 mm. human embryos (Fig. 74). Familiarity with Figs. 544 to 547 will make the detailed study of the 10 mm. pig embryo, which follows, easier to understand.

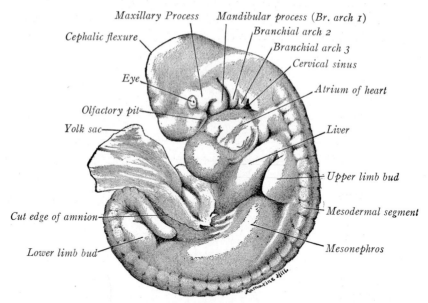

FIG. 544.—Pig embryo of 6 mm., with the amnion removed, viewed from the left side. × 12.

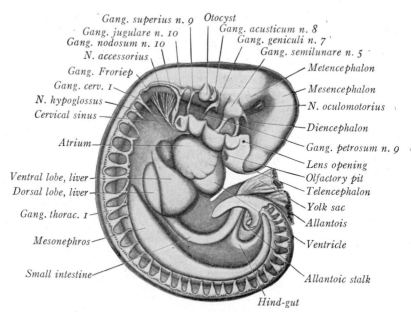

FIG. 545.—Lateral dissection of a 5.5 mm. pig embryo, viewed from the right side. × 12.

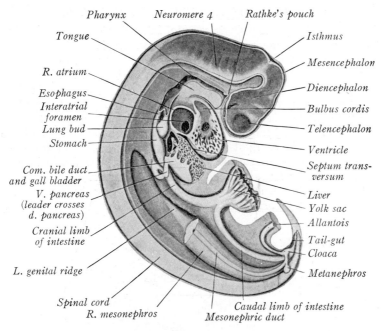

FIG. 546.—Median dissection of a 6 mm. pig embryo, after removal of the right half. × 12.

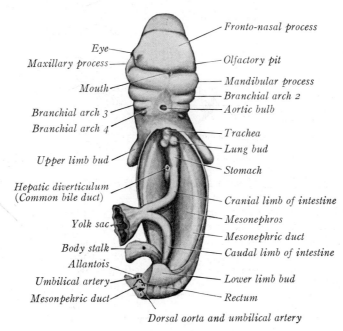

FIG. 547.—Ventral dissection of a 6 mm. pig embryo. × 11. The head is bent dorsad.

25

(B) THE ANATOMY OF A TEN MM. PIG EMBRYO

This is the most instructive single stage of later development. Nearly all the important organs are represented, and yet the embryo is not so complex as to confuse unduly a beginner. Embryos between 8 and 14 mm. long may be used satisfactorily in conjunction with the descriptions that follow. Human embryos of 8 mm. and 12 mm. are shown in Figs. 74 *B* and 75, respectively. At this period a human embryo is slightly further advanced than a pig embryo of equal size, but at corresponding stages of development they are fundamentally alike.

External Form.—The head, which is relatively large on account of the dominance of the brain, makes a right-angled bend at the *cephalic flexure* (Fig. 548). On the under surface of the head are the *olfactory pits*, now drawn into elongate grooves and bounded by *lateral* and *median nasal processes*. The lens of the *eye* is prominent as it lies beneath the ectoderm, surrounded by the optic cup. At the sides of the head are four *branchial arches*, separated by three *branchial grooves*.

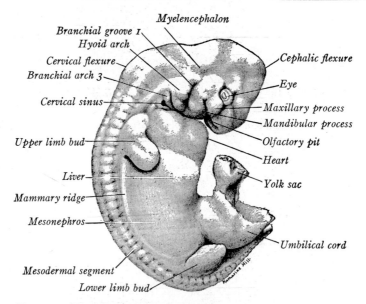

FIG. 548.—Pig embryo of 10 mm., viewed from the right side. × 7.

The first branchial arch of each side forks ventrally into two parts. The smaller *maxillary processes* show signs of fusing with the median nasal processes to form the upper jaw, while the larger *mandibular processes* have united already into the lower jaw (*cf.* Fig. 554). Next caudad is the prominent second, or hyoid arch. Small tubercles, which will combine into the *auricle* of the external ear, bound the first branchial groove; the groove itself will become the *external acoustic meatus*. The third branchial arch is still visible in the future neck region, but the fourth arch has sunk into the *cervical sinus;* both disappear at a slightly later stage.

At the *cervical flexure* the head is bent at right angles to the body, thus bringing the ventral surface of the head close to the trunk (Fig. 548); it is probably owing to this flexure that the third and fourth branchial arches buckle inward to give rise to the *cervical sinus* (Fig. 554). Along its dorsal surface the trunk curves convexly, but this feature is not so prominent as at 6 mm. The reduction in the trunk flexures results from the increased size of the heart, liver and mesonephroi. These organs are plainly indicated through the translucent body wall, while the position of the septum transversum may be noted between the heart and the liver (*cf.* Fig. 549). The *limb buds* are growing rapidly; due to the dominance of the head they seem to be located far down the body. The *umbilical cord* is relatively large; it contains the yolk sac and allantoic stalk. Dorsally the *mesodermal segments* occur in serial order; toward the tail they become progressively smaller. Paralleling them and extending in a curve between the bases of the limb buds is

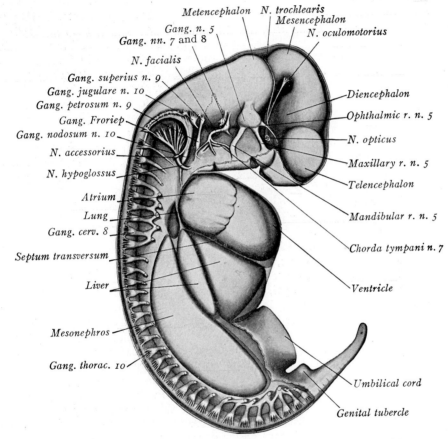

FIG. 549.—Lateral dissection of a 10 mm. pig embryo, viewed from the right side. × 11.

the *mammary ridge;* on this thickened band of ectoderm will differentiate the mammary glands. The *tail* is long and tapering. Between its base and the umbilical cord is the *genital tubercle* (Fig. 549).

Nervous System and Sense Organs.—*The Brain and Spinal Cord.*—Five distinct regions of the brain can be distinguished (Figs. 549 and 551): (1) The *telencephalon* with its rounded lateral outgrowths, the *cerebral hemispheres*. Their cavities, the *lateral ventricles*, communicate by interventricular foramina with the third ventricle. (2) The *diencephalon* shows a laterally flattened cavity, the *third ventricle*. From the ventrolateral side of the diencephalon pass off the optic stalks, while an evagination of the midventral wall (the infundibulum) will produce the neural lobe of the *hypophysis*. (3) The *mesencephalon* never subdivides, and its cavity becomes the *cerebral aqueduct* leading caudad into the fourth ventricle. (4) The *metencephalon* is separated from the mesencephalon by a constriction, the *isthmus*. Dorsolaterally it becomes the *cerebellum*, ventrally the *pons*. (5) The elongate *myelencephalon* is roofed over by a thin and non-nervous ependymal layer. Its ventrolateral wall is thickened and still gives internal indication of the *neuromeres*. The cavity of the metencephalon and myelencephalon is the *fourth ventricle*.

The *spinal cord* begins without specific demarcation and extends into the tapering tail. Just beneath the hind-brain and spinal cord lies the *notochord*.

The Cranial Nerves.—Of the twelve pairs of cranial nerves, all but the olfactory and abducens are represented on Fig. 549, where they occur in the order listed: (1) The *olfactory nerve* is not grossly demonstrable at this stage. (2) The *n. opticus* fibers are growing brainward within the optic stalk, cut through in this illustration. (3) The *n. oculomotorius*, a motor nerve to four of the eye muscles, takes origin from the ventrolateral wall of the mesencephalon and passes downward between the two parts of the bent brain. (4) The *n. trochlearis*, motor and destined for the superior oblique muscle of the eye, really arises from the ventral wall of the mesencephalon but emerges dorsally at the isthmus. The next eight pairs of nerves pass off from the rhombencephalon; since four of these are rostral to the otocyst in the metencephalon and four lie caudally in the myelencephalon, the otocyst becomes a convenient landmark. (5) The *n. trigeminus* is conspicuous because of its large *semilunar ganglion* and three branches (ophthalmic, maxillary and mandibular rami) which carry motor impulses to the jaw muscles and bring sensory impulses from the head. (6) The *n. abducens* originates from the ventral brain wall and passes to the eye, where it will innervate the external rectus muscle. (7) The *n. facialis* is mixed, sensory and motor; it bears the *geniculate ganglion* and divides into chorda tympani, facial and superficial petrosal rami in the order named; most of the nerve has to do with the motor innervation of the face, whereas the sensory supply goes to the tongue. (8) The *n. acusticus* arises just rostral to the otocyst; it bears the *acoustic ganglion* which will send sensory fibers to the internal ear. The postotic nerves are displayed in greater detail in Fig. 550. (9) Caudal to the otocyst is the *n. glossopharyngeus*, showing a proximal *superior* and a more distal *petrosal ganglion;* its sensory and motor fibers innervate both tongue and pharynx. (10) The *n. vagus* is mixed in function and has both a *jugular* and a *nodose ganglion;* its fibers innervate chiefly the viscera. (11) The *n. accessorius* has motor fibers which take origin both from the lateral wall of the myelencephalon and from the spinal cord as far caudad as the sixth cervical ganglion; an internal branch accompanies the vagus, while the external branch is distributed to the sterno-mastoid and trapezius muscles. (12) The *n. hypoglossus* arises by five or six rootlets from the ventral wall of the myelencephalon; it is purely motor and supplies the muscles of the tongue.

It should be noted that the fifth, seventh, ninth and tenth cranial nerves pass into the four branchial arches in the order named. This primitive relation, better seen in Fig. 545, is maintained in the adult when the nerves innervate the derivatives of these arches.

A nodular chain of ganglion cells extends caudad from the jugular ganglion of the vagus (Fig. 550). These have been interpreted as *accessory vagus ganglia*. They may, however, be continuous with *Froriep's ganglion* which sends sensory fibers to the n. hypoglossus. In pig embryos of 15 mm. this chain is frequently divided into four or five ganglionic masses, of which occasionally two or three (including Froriep's ganglion) contribute fibers to the root fascicles of the hypoglossal nerve (Fig. 550).

The Spinal Nerves.—Each nerve has a single *spinal ganglion*, from which the sensory *dorsal root* fibers are developed (Figs. 549 and 569). The motor fibers take origin from the ventral cells of the neural tube; they form the *ventral roots* which join the dorsal roots in the common *nerve trunk*. In the region of the upper and lower limb buds the spinal nerves unite and give rise respectively to the *brachial* and *lumbo-sacral plexuses.*

The Sense Organs.—The *olfactory pits* are deep fossæ, flanked by the median and lateral nasal processes (Fig. 548). The stalked *optic cup* is prominent and the

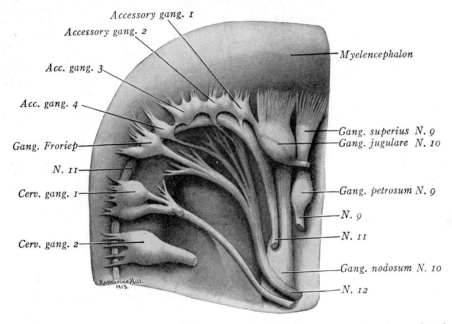

FIG. 550.—Dissection of the postotic cranial nerves and ganglia of a 15 mm. pig embryo, viewed from the right side. × 25.

lens vesicle detached from the ectoderm. The *otocyst* is a compressed oval vesicle with a tubular *endolymph duct* growing from its medial side.

Digestive and Respiratory Systems.—*Mouth and Pharynx.*—The pharyngeal membrane disappeared at a considerably earlier stage and the stomodeum is now continuous with the pharynx. From the dorsal wall of the ectodermal mouth cavity, *Rathke's pouch* (epithelial hypophysis) extends as a long, stalked sac which forks at its end near the neural hypophyseal lobe (Fig. 551). The floor of the mouth and pharynx is occupied by the *tongue* and *epiglottis* (Fig. 552). From the mandibular arches arise paired *lateral swellings* that become the body of the tongue. Lying between these thickenings is the transient *tuberculum impar.* The thyroglossal duct, which formerly opened just caudal to the tuberculum impar, is already obliterated; the *thyroid gland* itself, composed of branching epithelial cords, is now

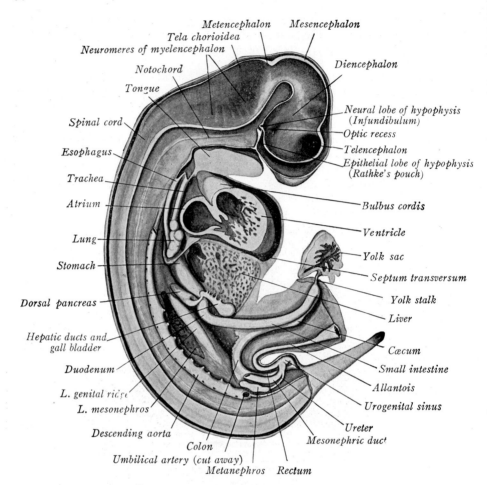

FIG. 551.—Median dissection of a 10 mm. pig embryo, after removal of the right half. × 10.

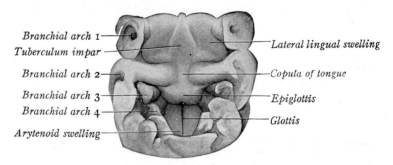

FIG. 552.—Floor of the mouth and pharynx of a 10 mm. pig embryo, after removing the upper half of the head. × 12.

located in the midplane between the second and third branchial arches (Fig. 553). A median ridge, named the *copula*, unites the second arches and represents the primitive root of the tongue; it connects the tuberculum impar with the epiglottis which develops from the bases of the third and fourth branchial arches (Fig. 552). On each side of the slit-like *glottis* is an *arytenoid fold* of the larynx.

The pharynx is flattened dorsoventrally; it is broad at the oral end. Opposite the third branchial arch the pharynx bends sharply in conformity with the cervical

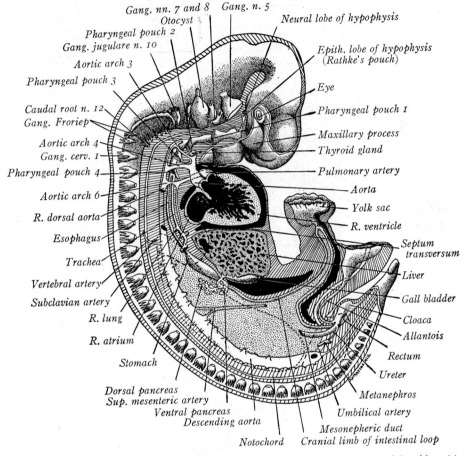

Gang. nn. 7 and 8   Gang. n. 5
Otocyst   *Neural lobe of hypophysis*
Pharyngeal pouch 2
Gang. jugulare n. 10
Aortic arch 3   *Epith. lobe of hypophysis*
                                    (Rathke's pouch)
Pharyngeal pouch 3
                                    Eye
Caudal root n. 12
Gang. Froriep   *Pharyngeal pouch 1*
Aortic arch 4   *Maxillary process*
Gang. cerv. 1   *Thyroid gland*
Pharyngeal pouch 4   *Pulmonary artery*
Aortic arch 6   *Aorta*
R. dorsal aorta   *Yolk sac*
Esophagus   *R. ventricle*
Trachea   *Septum*
                                    transversum
Vertebral artery   *Liver*
Subclavian artery   *Gall bladder*
R. lung   *Cloaca*
R. atrium   *Allantois*
                                    Rectum
Stomach   *Ureter*
Dorsal pancreas
Sup. mesenteric artery   *Metanephros*
Ventral pancreas   *Umbilical artery*
Descending aorta
                    Mesonepheric duct
Notochord   Cranial limb of intestinal loop

FIG. 553.—Reconstruction of a 10 mm. pig embryo, viewed from the right side. × 10. The veins are not included; broken lines indicate the outline of the left mesonephros and the positions of the limb buds.

flexure. The *pharyngeal pouches* are large, and each bears a dorsal and a ventral wing (Fig. 553). The first pouch persists as the *auditory tube* and *tympanic cavity;* the 'closing plate' between it and the first branchial groove forms the *tympanic membrane*, while the ectodermal groove becomes the *external acoustic meatus*. The second pouch is destined largely to disappear; about it develops the *palatine tonsil*. The dorsal wing of each tubular third pouch forms a *parathyroid gland;* the ventral wings differentiate into the *thymus*. The fourth pouch is smaller; its dorsal wing gives rise to another parathyroid on each side, while the ventral wing is rudimentary. A tubular outgrowth, just caudal to the fourth pouch, is commonly regarded as a *fifth pharyngeal pouch*; it forms an *ultimobranchial body* on each side.

Larynx, Trachea and Lungs.—The *larynx* and *epiglottis* are indicated (Fig. 552), and the *trachea* is a definite tube (Figs. 551 and 553). Terminally the trachea bifurcates into *primary bronchi;* each of these has already divided again into secondary bronchial buds which indicate the two lobes of the left lung and the middle and lower lobes of the right lung (Fig. 554). From the right side of the

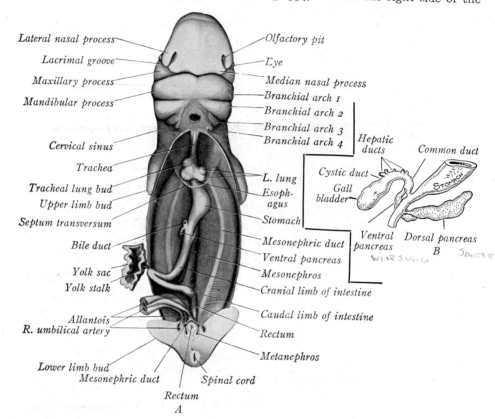

Lateral nasal process — Olfactory pit
Lacrimal groove — Eye
Maxillary process — Median nasal process
Mandibular process — Branchial arch 1
— Branchial arch 2
— Branchial arch 3
Cervical sinus — Branchial arch 4 | Hepatic ducts | Common duct
Trachea — Cystic duct
L. lung — Gall bladder
Tracheal lung bud — Esoph- agus
Upper limb bud — Stomach
Septum transversum — Stomach
Bile duct — Ventral Dorsal pancreas
Mesonephric duct — Ventral pancreas | B
Yolk sac — Ventral pancreas | WIRSUNG | SANTORINI
Yolk stalk — Mesonephros
— Cranial limb of intestine
Allantois — Caudal limb of intestine
R. umbilical artery — Rectum
— Metanephros
Lower limb bud
Mesonephric duct — Spinal cord
Rectum
A

FIG. 554.—Ventral dissections of a 10 mm. pig embryo. *A*, General view, with head bent dorsad (× 9). *B*, Detail of duodenal region (× 20).

trachea itself appears another bud which, in the pig, represents the upper lobe of the right lung.

Esophagus and Stomach.—The *esophagus* extends as a narrow tube past the lungs, whereupon it dilates into the laterally flattened *stomach* (Figs. 551 and 553). The entire stomach has so rotated that the original dorsal border, now the convex greater curvature, lies to the left and the primitive ventral border (lesser curvature) to the right (Fig. 554). At this stage the rotation is incomplete.

Intestine.—The pyloric end of the stomach opens into the *duodenum* which also shows the effect of stomach rotation, so that the stem of the *hepatic diver-*

ticulum, originating from it, now lies to the right (Fig. 554 *A*). The diverticulum itself has differentiated into various things. From its tip has come the four-lobed *liver*, filling in the space between the heart, stomach and duodenum (Fig. 551). One of the several ducts now connecting the liver with the parent diverticulum will persist as the *hepatic duct*. The main stem of the diverticulum is the *common bile duct*, while a side sacculation is the *cystic duct* and *gall bladder* (Figs. 553 and 554). The *ventral pancreas* springs from the common bile duct near its point of origin. It is directed dorsad and caudad, to the right of the duodenum. The *dorsal pancreas* arises a little more caudally (in man, cranially) from the dorsal wall of the duodenum; its larger, lobulated body grows dorsad and cephalad (Figs. 553 and 554). The two glands will interlock into a single organ; in the pig it is the duct of the dorsal pancreas that persists as the functional duct.

Beyond the duodenum the intestine is thrown into a loop, which extends well into the umbilical cord and connects with the *yolk stalk* there (Figs. 551 and 553). Owing to rotation in the entire loop, the cranial limb of the intestine lies to the right, the caudal limb to the left. The small intestine (jejunum and ileum) extends as far as a slight enlargment on the caudal limb of the loop (Fig. 551). This is the *cæcum* which marks the beginning of the *large intestine* (colon and rectum). The cloaca is now subdividing into the *rectum* and *urogenital sinus*.

Cœlom and Mesenteries.—The cœlom is a continuous, communicating system which includes the single *pericardial* and *peritoneal cavities*, still connected by paired *pleural canals*. Between the heart and liver is a prominent partition, the *septum transversum;* the liver is broadly fused to this septum which will comprise much of the diaphragm (Fig. 551). The double sheet of splanchnic mesoderm that serves as the primitive dorsal mesentery receives special names at different levels. Where it suspends the stomach it is known as the *mesogastrium*, or *greater omentum*. Then in order come the *mesoduodenum*, the *mesentery* proper of the small intestine, and the *mesocolon*. The last two divisions follow the intestinal loop out into the umbilical cord (Fig. 553). The ventral mesentery is limited in extent. It persists as the *lesser omentum* between stomach and liver, encloses the liver, and continues as the *falciform ligament* between the liver and ventral body wall. A saccular recess, between the caval mesentery and liver on the right and the stomach and its mesenteries on the left, is the *omental bursa*. It opens through a narrowed *epiploic foramen* (of Winslow) (*cf.* Fig. 211 *A*).

Urogenital System.—The *mesonephroi* are large and complex in the pig (Figs. 549 and 554). Along the middle of their ventromesial surfaces *genital ridges* have become prominent (Fig. 551). In a ventral dissection the course of the *mesonephric ducts* can be traced along the ventral margins of the mesonephroi and into the urogenital sinus (Fig. 554). The *allantois* is a conspicuous, stalked sac which communicates with the ventral part of the urogenital sinus (Fig. 551).

The *metanephroi*, or permanent kidneys, lie far caudad between the roots of the umbilical arteries (Figs. 551 and 553). At the present stage each consists of a tubular epithelial portion, surrounded by a mass of condensed mesenchyme. The epithelial tube has budded off the mesonephric duct, near its ending; proximally there is a slender duct, the *ureter*, while a distal dilatation is the *pelvis*. From the renal pelvis grow out later the calyces and collecting tubules of the kidney. Encasing the pelvic primordium is a layer of condensed mesenchyme, derived from the lower nephrotomes and destined to differentiate into the secretory tubules.

Vascular System.—*The Heart.*—This organ lies within the pericardial cavity. Its general form and relations are illustrated in Figs. 549 and 553. There are two *atria* and two thicker-walled *ventricles*. In addition, a small chamber, the *sinus venosus*, receives all the blood returned to the heart and directs it into the right atrium while the *bulbus cordis* still serves as a common arterial outlet (Fig. 555 *B*).

From the two hemisections shown in Fig. 555 the internal structure of the heart can be understood. The entrance from the sinus venosus into the right atrium is a sagittal slit, guarded by right and left *valves of the sinus venosus.* Dorsally the two valves join and continue a short distance as the temporary *septum spurium.* Somewhat later the sinus largely loses its identity by merging with the right atrium, although its middle part does persist as the *coronary sinus.* The dorsal wall of the left atrium is receiving a single *pulmonary vein* (not shown). The two *atria* are incompletely partitioned by the *septum primum* which contains an opening, the *foramen ovale I.* On the right side of this partition a second sickle-like fold, the *septum secundum,* is forming. It also becomes an incomplete septum

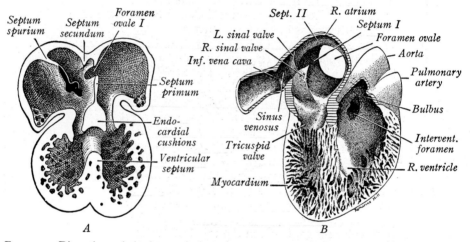

FIG. 555.—Dissections of the heart of pig embryos. × 20. *A*, At 10 mm., with ventral wall removed (after Patten). *B*, At 12 mm., with right wall removed.

which bears an opening, known as the *foramen ovale II.* After birth these two septa, together with the left valve of the sinus venosus, will fuse to complete the final atrial septum. Slightly earlier the atria and ventricles communicated through a common canal, bounded by two thickenings named *endocardial cushions.* At the present stage the two cushions have joined midway, have received the septum primum, and now subdivide this passage into two *atrio-ventricular canals.* About the right canal the endocardium is already undermined and in the process of forming the *tricuspid valve;* similarly, on the left is the developing *bicuspid valve.* The two *ventricles* are separated by a *ventricular septum;* it is complete except for the *interventricular foramen* which connects the left ventricle with the bulbar part of the right. The *bulbus cordis* separates distally into *ascending aorta* and *pulmonary artery,* but proximally it is still undivided. The ventricular walls are thick and spongy, forming a meshwork of muscular trabeculæ, separated by sinusoids. Until later when coronary vessels are developed, the heart receives all its nourishment from the blood circulating in the sinusoids.

The Arteries.—The aortic-arch system is still represented, although some-what modified and in process of transforming into its permanent derivatives (Fig. 556). The first two pairs of arches have disappeared. The third pair and the extensions of the dorsal aortæ into the head constitute a continuous channel to be known as the *internal carotids.* Near their bases arise the *external carotid arteries*, which extend into the region of the lower jaw. The fourth aortic arch is largest,

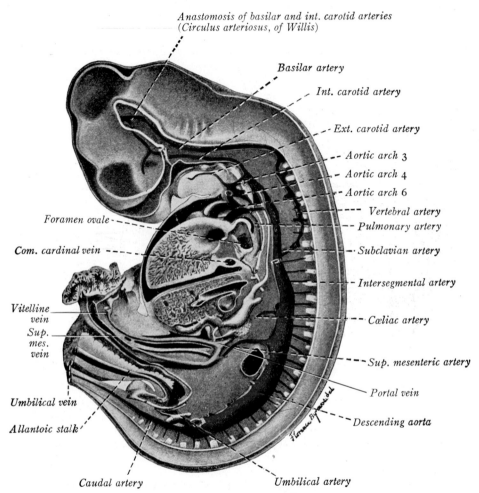

Anastomosis of basilar and int. carotid arteries
(*Circulus arteriosus, of Willis*)

Basilar artery

Int. carotid artery

Ext. carotid artery

Aortic arch 3

Aortic arch 4

Aortic arch 6

Vertebral artery

Pulmonary artery

Foramen ovale

Com. cardinal vein

Subclavian artery

Intersegmental artery

Vitelline
vein

Cœliac artery

Sup.
mes.
vein

Sup. mesenteric artery

Portal vein

Umbilical vein

Descending aorta

Allantoic stalk

Caudal artery

Umbilical artery

FIG. 556.—Reconstruction of the arteries of a 12 mm. pig embryo, viewed from the left side (after Patten, from Lewis). × 9.

and on the left side it will form the permanent *arch of the aorta*. The sixth (fifth?) aortic arches connect with the pulmonary trunk, and from them small *pulmonary arteries* pass to the lungs; the left arch continues until birth as the *ductus arteriosus*.

The paired *dorsal aortæ* unite opposite the eighth segments and continue caudad as the median *descending aorta* (Fig. 556). The aorta shows dorsal, lateral and ventral branches. The dorsal branches pass upward between the somites, and accordingly can be called *intersegmental arteries*. From the seventh pair, which is located just where the dorsal aortæ combine, the _subclavian arteries_ pass off to the upper limb buds, and _vertebral arteries_ run cephalad into the head. The latter vessels are formed by longitudinal anastomoses between the first seven pairs on each side, after which the stems of the first six atrophy. Under the brain the vertebrals are continuous with the unpaired _basilar artery;_ the latter connects with the internal carotids beneath the diencephalon. Lateral branches of the descending aorta supply the mesonephroi and genital ridges. Ventral branches form the _cœliac artery_ to the stomach region, the _superior mesenteric_ artery (primitive

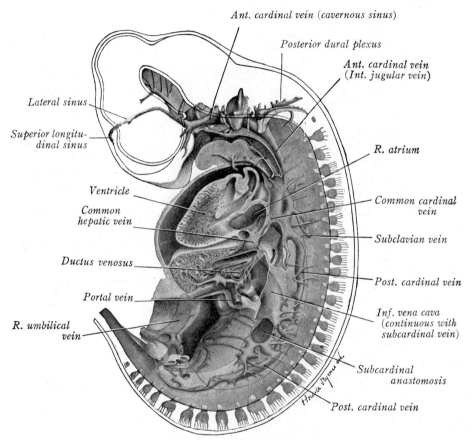

FIG. 557.—Reconstruction of the veins of a 12 mm. pig embryo, viewed from the left side (after Lewis). × 9.

vitelline) to the small intestine and the _inferior mesenteric artery_ to the large intestine. The _umbilical arteries_ (to the allantois and placenta) belong in this ventral series, but they now arise laterally from secondary trunks which persist as the _common iliacs._ Beyond this point the aorta narrows into the diminutive _caudal artery_ extending into the tail.

  The Veins.—Three sets of plexuses, which are the forerunners of the _dural sinuses,_ occur alongside the brain. They drain into the _anterior cardinal veins,_ now becoming the _internal jugular veins_ (Fig. 557). After receiving the newer *external jugular veins* from the mandibular region and the *subclavian veins* from the upper limb buds, the anterior cardinals open into the *common cardinal veins* (ducts of Cuvier). The latter empty into the sinus venosus.

The *posterior cardinal veins* are the most primitive veins caudal to the level of the heart. They course dorsal to the mesonephroi and drain the mesonephric sinusoids (Fig. 557). However, the posterior cardinal veins are already beginning to decline, and midway along their lengths an interruption occurs; for this reason only the cranial halves communicate with the common cardinal stems.

Considerable diversion of blood from the posterior cardinal veins has been brought about by the development of *subcardinal veins* along the ventromesial

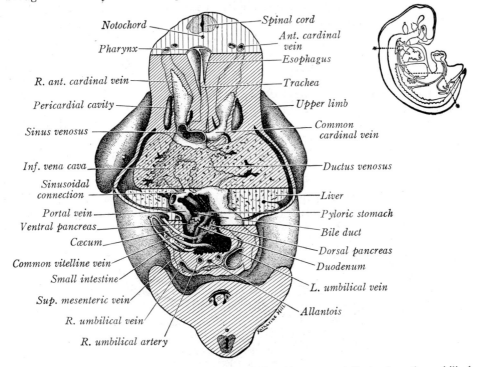

Notochord
Pharynx
R. ant. cardinal vein
Pericardial cavity
Sinus venosus
Inf. vena cava
Sinusoidal connection
Portal vein
Ventral pancreas
Cæcum
Common vitelline vein
Small intestine
Sup. mesenteric vein
R. umbilical vein
R. umbilical artery

Spinal cord
Ant. cardinal vein
Esophagus
Trachea
Upper limb
Common cardinal vein
Ductus venosus
Liver
Pyloric stomach
Bile duct
Dorsal pancreas
Duodenum
L. umbilical vein
Allantois

FIG. 558.—Ventral reconstruction of a 10 mm. pig embryo, especially to show the umbilical and vitelline veins. × 15. In the small orientation figure (*cf.* Fig. 553) the various planes are indicated by broken lines—*- - - - - -*.

surfaces of the mesonephroi. These vessels arose as longitudinal channels in a mesonephric plexus that was originally tributary to the posterior cardinal veins. Connections between the post- and subcardinal systems of each side still exist, while the two subcardinals also communicate by a prominent anastomosis across the midplane of the body. A fairly prominent *ventral vein* of the mesonephros follows the ventral border of this organ, but it soon disappears.

The *inferior vena cava* is becoming established at this stage. It has a compound origin. In the mesonephric region the larger right subcardinal is an important component (Fig. 557). More cephalad a vein has developed in a specialized portion (caval mesentery) of the mesogastrium. This vessel connects the subcardinal with the hepatic (vitelline) sinusoids. The blood flow through the sinusoids is already consolidating into a definite channel, and this is the hepatic part of the inferior vena cava (Fig. 558); it empties into the common hepatic vein (primitive right vitelline).

The *umbilical veins* follow the allantoic stalk back from the placenta. In the umbilical cord they have merged into a common vessel, but they separate again on entering the embryo where they course in the ventrolateral body wall of each side to the level of the liver (Fig. 557). Cephalad of the liver the original stems that connected with the sinus venosus have disappeared. The umbilical blood is now routed through the liver in enlarged sinusoidal channels. The left umbilical is the larger of the two, and it alone persists in older fetuses. An important fetal passage, connecting the left umbilical with the inferior vena cava, is the *ductus venosus* (Fig. 558).

Distally the two *vitelline veins* are fused. Passing inward from the regressive yolk sac, they course cephalad of the intestinal loop (Figs. 556 and 558). In the pancreas region the left vein receives the *superior mesenteric vein* which is a new vessel arising in the mesentery of the intestinal loop. Above this junction a cross anastomosis, and a continuation of the right vein make a new channel which is known as the *portal vein*. It gives off branches to the hepatic sinusoids, which have arisen much earlier from a breaking up of the vitelline veins in this region, and connects with the left umbilical vein within the liver. Beyond the sinusoids the vitelline vessels are retained as *hepatic veins* and the stem of the *inferior vena cava*.

TRANSVERSE SECTIONS OF A TEN MM. PIG EMBRYO

The more important levels, as indicated by guide lines on Fig. 559, are illustrated and described. These are useful for the identification of organs, but the student must interpret his sections with reference to the dissections and recon-

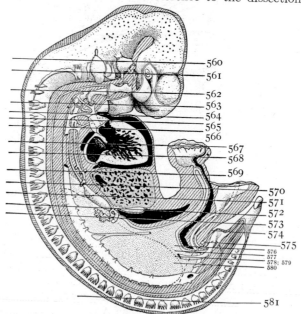

FIG. 559.—Reconstruction of a 10 mm. pig embryo (*cf.* Fig. 553). × 8. The numbered lines indicate the levels of transverse sections shown as Figs. 560–581.

structions, and especially Fig. 553. All sections are drawn from the cephalic surface; accordingly, the right side of the embryo is at the reader's left.

Sections through the Cephalic Flexure.—Due to the flexed head, the sections first encountered pass through the *mesencephalon* and *metencephalon*. At a slightly lower level the metencephalon also becomes continuous with the thin-roofed *myelencephalon*, but presently the midbrain gives way to the *diencephalon* as the brain becomes cut twice. Several important structures should be identified in the mesenchyme between these two portions of the brain. In the midplane, but nearer the metencephalon, is the single *basilar artery*; ventrolateral to the diencephalon are the paired *internal carotids* (*cf.* Fig. 560). These three vessels unite at the location of the

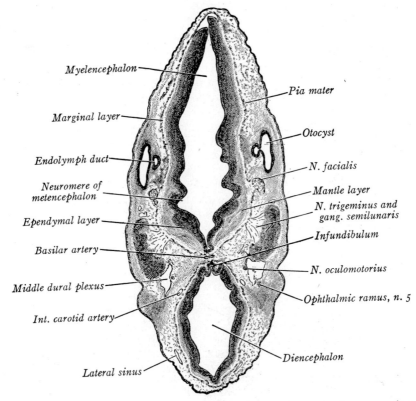

FIG. 560.—Transverse section through the semilunar ganglia and otocysts of a 10 mm. pig embryo.
× 23.

future *arterial circle* (of Willis). About halfway between the midplane and the lateral wall appear branches of the *anterior cardinal veins* and the *oculomotor* and *trochlear nerves*. Of the two nerves, the trochlear is smaller and slightly more lateral in position; in some series it extends only a slight distance. The origin and relations of these nerves show plainly in Fig. 549.

Section through the Infundibulum, Semilunar Ganglia and Otocysts (Fig. 560).—The brain is sectioned twice. At the bottom of the section is the *diencephalon*, cut transversely; its cavity is the *third ventricle*. Midventrally the diencephalon gives off the *infundibulum* which furnishes the neural lobe of the *hypophysis*. The *metencephalon* and *myelencephalon* are sectioned frontally; there is no clear demarcation between the two. Their walls bear the prominent scalloping of the *neuromeres*, while the common cavity is the *fourth ventricle*. The wall of the entire neural tube now shows a differentiation into three layers: (1) an inner *ependymal layer*, densely cellular, next the central canal; (2) a middle *mantle layer*, of nerve cells and fibers; and (3) an outer *marginal layer*, chiefly fibrous. A thin, vascular layer surrounds the brain wall as the primitive *pia mater*.

The interval between the two portions of the brain contains several structures, sectioned transversely. Next the metencephalon is the unpaired *basilar artery;* ventrolateral to the dien- cephalon are the paired *internal carotid arteries*. Near the latter are *oculomotor nerves;* in this embryo the trochlear nerves had not grown down to this level. On the left side is a part of the ophthalmic branch of the *trigeminal nerve*. Tributaries of the *anterior cardinal veins* occur, the largest in the region of the semilunar ganglia. This is the stem of the *middle dural plexus*, while alongside the diencephalon the *lateral sinus* is cut.

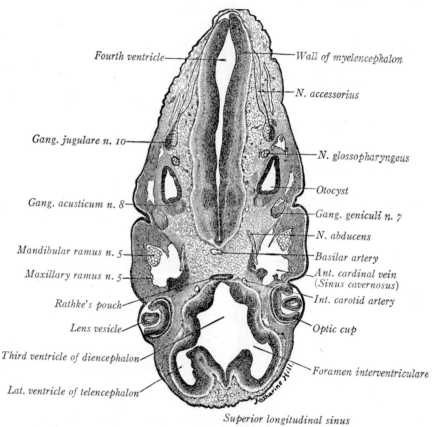

Fourth ventricle — Wall of myelencephalon

N. accessorius

Gang. jugulare n. 10 — N. glossopharyngeus

Otocyst

Gang. acusticum n. 8 — Gang. geniculi n. 7

N. abducens

Mandibular ramus n. 5 — Basilar artery

Maxillary ramus n. 5 — Ant. cardinal vein (Sinus cavernosus)

Rathke's pouch — Int. carotid artery

Lens vesicle — Optic cup

Third ventricle of diencephalon —

Foramen interventriculare

Lat. ventricle of telencephalon —

Superior longitudinal sinus

FIG. 561.—Transverse section through the cerebral hemispheres and eyes of a 10 mm. pig embryo. × 23.

Near the beginning of the hind-brain are the large *semilunar ganglia;* from their medial sides nerve fibers of the *trigeminal nerves* join the brain wall. This ganglion, situated at the pontine flexure of the metencephalon, constitutes one of the most important landmarks of the embryonic head. Slightly caudad lie the *facial nerves;* the left is cut just as it leaves the brain wall. Midway along each side of the hind-brain will be seen the apex of an *otocyst*, and mesial to it the *endolymph duct;* on the left side the two communicate.

Section through the Cerebral Hemispheres and Eyes (Fig. 561).—This level shows some important new features. The *diencephalon* is now continuous with the *telencephalon*. The latter consists of a mesial region which has evaginated paired *cerebral hemipsheres;* their cavities, the *lateral ventricles,* connect through the *interventricular foramina* with the *third ventricle* of the dien-cephalon. Close to the ventral wall of the diencephalon is a section of the epithelial lobe of the hypophysis (*Rathke's pouch*), near which are the *internal carotid arteries.* Lateral to the dien-cephalon are the *optic cups,* sectioned caudal to their stalks. The double wall of the optic cup comprises the *retina;* the thin outer layer is the pigmented epithelium, the inner and thicker coat is the nervous layer. The *lens* is now a closed vesicle, distinct from the overlying *corneal ectoderm.*

The irregular vascular spaces are tributaries of the *anterior cardinal veins.* The largest space is the *cavernous sinus,* in the vicinity of the fifth nerve. The upper half of the section contains

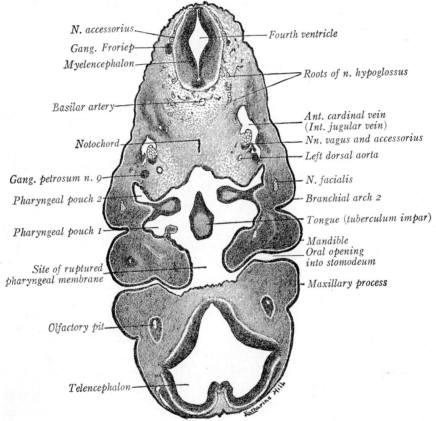

FIG. 562.—Transverse section through the mouth, tongue and first and second pharyngeal pouches of a 10 mm. pig embryo. × 23.

portions of the *posterior dural plexus,* while the two small vessels between the cerebral hemispheres at the bottom of the section represent the *superior longitudinal sinus.*

By working above and below the present level all the cranial nerves and ganglia, as well as the central connections and peripheral courses of these nerves, will be observed. In Fig. 561 transverse sections of the maxillary and mandibular branches of the *trigeminal nerve* are seen, while the *abducens nerve* is sectioned longitudinally as it passes from the under surface of the hind-brain toward the eyes. On the rostral side of the otocyst occur the *geniculate ganglion* of the *n. facialis* and the *acoustic ganglia* of the *n. acusticus.* The *otocyst* is a sharply defined, epithelial sac which lies at the junction of the metencephalon and myelencephalon and makes a convenient landmark in identifying ganglia and nerves. Caudal to the otocyst, the *n. glosso-*

pharyngeus and the *jugular ganglion* of the *vagus nerve* are cut transversely while the trunk of the *n. accessorius* is sectioned lengthwise as it curves forward from the level of the spinal cord.

Section through the Mouth, Tongue and First and Second Pouches (Fig. 562).—The end of the head, with parts of the *telencephalon* and *olfactory pits*, is now separate from the rest of the section. Since the level last described, Rathke's pouch has opened into the ectodermal *stomodeum* between the jaws; the present section is at the actual *oral opening*, bounded by the *maxillary* and *mandibular processes* of the *first branchial arches*. With the disappearance of the pharyngeal membrane, the stomodeum and entodermal mouth cavity have become continuous. The *pharynx* shows ventral portions of the *first* and *second pharyngeal pouches*, destined to be utilized as auditory tubes and tonsillar fossæ, respectively. Opposite the first pouch, externally, is the *first branchial groove*, or future external acoustic meatus. A shaving has been cut from the tuber-

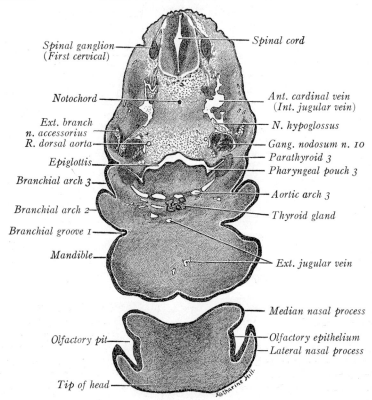

Spinal ganglion — (*First cervical*)

Spinal cord

Notochord —

Ant. cardinal vein (*Int. jugular vein*)

Ext. branch n. accessorius — *R. dorsal aorta* —

N. hypoglossus

Gang. nodosum n. 10

Epiglottis —

Parathyroid 3

Pharyngeal pouch 3

Branchial arch 3 —

Branchial arch 2 —

Aortic arch 3

Thyroid gland

Branchial groove 1 —

Mandible —

Ext. jugular vein

Median nasal process

Olfactory pit —

Olfactory epithelium

Lateral nasal process

Tip of head —

FIG. 563.—Transverse section through the third pharyngeal pouches, thyroid gland and olfactory pits of a 10 mm. pig embryo.   × 23.

culum impar of the *tongue* as it rises above the floor of the pharynx. The *facial nerves* of the *second branchial arches* are cut across, but since the previous level the trigeminal nerves have ended in the maxillary and mandibular processes of the first arches.

The *myelencephalon* is sectioned close to its continuation into the spinal cord; *Froriep's ganglion* and some of the *accessory nerve* are included. Between the myelencephalon and the pharynx are seen on each side the several rootlets of the *n. hypoglossus*, the fibers of the *nn. vagus* and *accessorius*, and the *petrosal ganglion* of the *n. glossopharyngeus*. Mesial to the ganglia are the *dorsal aortæ*, and lateral to the vagi are the *anterior cardinal veins*. In the midplane is a bit of the *notochord*, cut lengthwise. The *basilar artery* still lies beneath the myelencephalon, but a short distance caudad it is replaced by the paired *vertebral arteries*.

Section through the Third Pouches and Olfactory Pits (Fig. 563).—The tip of the head is now small and includes on either side the open *olfactory pits*, lined with thickened epithelium. Each pit is bordered by a *lateral* and a *median nasal process*, which assist in the formation of the nose and upper jaw. The first three pairs of *branchial arches* show; the first is fused as the *mandible*, and the third is slightly sunken in the *cervical sinus*. The dorsal wings of the *third pharyngeal pouches* extend toward the ectoderm of the *third branchial grooves;* attached to these wings are prominent *parathyroid* primordia. The ventral wings are large, epithelial sacs that can be followed in sections caudal to this one. They give rise to the *thymus*. The floor of the pharynx is sectioned through the epiglottis.

Ventral to the pharynx are portions of the *third aortic arches* (internal carotids) and the solid cords of the *thyroid gland*. (*External carotid arteries* arise at a slightly higher level, close to the ventral origins of the third aortic arches; they can be traced for a variable distance into the substance of the lower jaw.) Beneath the thyroid and in the mandible are portions of the *external jugular veins*. Dorsally the section passes through the *spinal cord* and the first pair of *cervical ganglia*. Between the cord and pharynx, named in order, are the *anterior cardinal veins*, the *hypoglossal nerve* and the *nodose ganglia* of the *vagi*. Lateral to each ganglion is the external branch of the *n. accessorius*, and mesial to the ganglia are the small *dorsal aortæ*.

Section through the Glottis and Fourth Aortic Arches (Fig. 564).—At this level the first three branchial arches have been passed and the cephalic border of the heart is coming into view. The

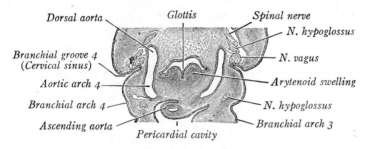

FIG. 564.—Transverse section through the glottis and fourth aortic arches of a 10 mm. pig embryo. × 23.

illustration includes only the region of the *fourth branchial arches*, and the fourth pair of *aortic arches* which course through them. The left aortic arch will become the permanent *arch of the aorta*, the right the stem of the *subclavian artery*. The *ascending aorta* connects with these aortic arches a little cephalad in the series. The *fourth branchial groove* opens off the *cervical sinus*. It extends for some distance before coming in contact with the fourth pharyngeal pouch of Fig. 565. The section cuts across the *pharynx*, the *glottis* (entrance to the larynx), and its bordering *arytenoid swellings*. In addition to a spinal nerve, sections of the *vagus* and *hypoglossal nerves* are encountered.

Section through the Fourth Pouches and Larynx (Fig. 565).—The head has been passed and the section is now dominated by the *heart*, lying within its *pericardial cavity*. The tips of the *atria* are sectioned as they project at the sides of the *bulbus cordis*. The bulbus is dividing into the aortic stem and the pulmonary trunk. The *pulmonary trunk* is cut twice; its distal portion can be followed caudad into connection with the sixth aortic arches (Fig. 566). The small section of the *ascending aorta* traces cephalad to the fourth aortic arches (Fig. 564) and caudad into the ventricle (Fig. 566).

The crescentic *pharynx* is continued laterad as the small *fourth pharyngeal pouches*. Each gives origin to a dorsal wing (*parathyroid*), encountered a few sections cephalad in the series and shown here as a separate drawing. At the level of the main section the pharynx is also continuous with a saccular *ultimobranchial body* (pouch 5?). From the midventral wall of the pharynx arises the solid epithelial plate of the *larynx*. A section of the *vagus nerve* is located between the dorsal aorta and the *anterior cardinal vein* of each side. Ventral to the anterior cardinals (soon to be

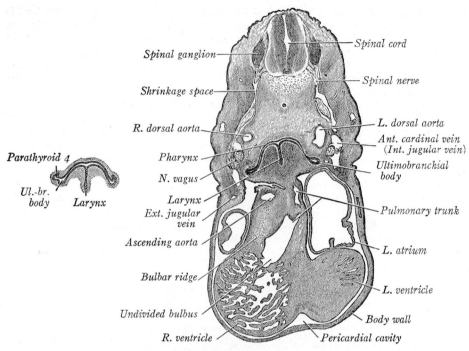

Spinal ganglion

Shrinkage space

R. dorsal aorta

Parathyroid 4

Pharynx

N. vagus

Ul.-br.
body   Larynx

Larynx
Ext. jugular
vein

Ascending aorta

Bulbar ridge

Undivided bulbus

R. ventricle

Spinal cord

Spinal nerve

L. dorsal aorta

Ant. cardinal vein
(Int. jugular vein)

Ultimobranchial
body

Pulmonary trunk

L. atrium

L. ventricle

Body wall

Pericardial cavity

FIG. 565.—Transverse section through the fourth pharyngeal pouches and larynx of a 10 mm. pig embryo.   × 23.

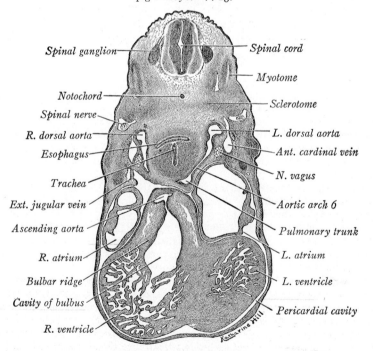

Spinal ganglion

Notochord

Spinal nerve

R. dorsal aorta

Esophagus

Trachea

Ext. jugular vein

Ascending aorta

R. atrium

Bulbar ridge

Cavity of bulbus

R. ventricle

Spinal cord

Myotome

Sclerotome

L. dorsal aorta

Ant. cardinal vein

N. vagus

Aortic arch 6

Pulmonary trunk

L. atrium

L. ventricle

Pericardial cavity

FIG. 566.—Transverse section through the pulmonary arches and bulbus cordis of a 10 mm. pig embryo.   × 23.

called the *internal jugular veins*) are small *external jugular veins*. The left *dorsal aorta* is larger than the right in anticipation of its conversion into the permanent descending aorta of this level.

Section through the Pulmonary Arches and Bulbus Cordis (Fig. 566).—The heart is little changed from the last level. However, the *aorta* communicates with the *bulbus*, while the latter shows on each side the thickened internal ridges that will progressively meet and continue the separation of the aortic and pulmonary trunks. The *sixth aortic arches* connect the dorsal aortæ with the main pulmonary stem, already traced in the preceding section. On the left side of the embryo the arch is complete; it represents the *ductus arteriosus*, which remains patent until birth. From these pulmonary arches small *pulmonary arteries* may be traced caudad in the series toward the lungs. The *esophagus* is now separate from the *trachea*; both are cut through their extreme cephalic ends. Ventrolateral to the spinal cord are diffuse *myotomes*, while *sclerotome* masses surround the notochord. The *vagus nerves* are prominent. At about this level the *external jugular veins* join the *anterior cardinals*.

Section through the Heart and Foramen Ovale (Fig. 567).—Only the heart is figured, taken from a total section much like Fig. 568. All four chambers are shown. The *atria* are partially separated by the *septum primum*, which is incomplete because of the *foramen oval I;* this foramen will remain open until birth. Each atrium communicates with the ventricle of the same side

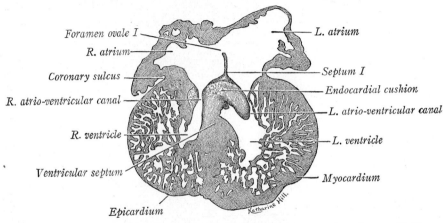

FIG. 567.—Transverse section through the heart of a 10 mm. pig embryo. × 23.

through an *atrio-ventricular canal*. Between these openings is the fused portion of the *endocardial cushions*. At an earlier stage these cushions were double, but they have fused midway and thus divide the originally single canal into two; they will *also help in the formation of the bicuspid* and *tricuspid valves*. The atria are marked off externally from the ventricles by the *coronary sulcus*. Between the two ventricles is the *ventricular septum*, which is perforated by the *interventricular foramen* a little higher in the series (cf. Fig. 555 B). The ventricular walls are thick and spongy, forming a network of muscular trabeculæ surrounded by blood spaces, or sinusoids. This muscular layer constitutes the *myocardium*. It is lined by an endothelial layer, the *endocardium*, while the entire heart is surrounded by a layer of mesothelium, the *epicardium*, or visceral pericardium. The latter sac is continuous with the parietal pericardium, which lines the body wall.

Section through the Common Cardinals and Sinus Venosus (Fig. 568).—The section is also marked by the large *heart* and the bases of the *upper limb buds*. Dorsal to the atria are the *common cardinal veins*. The right vein empties into the *sinus venosus;* the left crosses the midplane and connects with the sinus at a lower level. Just above the plane of this section the right common cardinal has received the right *subclavian vein* from the limb bud; the left subclavian is still separate. The sinus venosus drains into the right atrium through a slit-like opening in the dorsal and caudal atrial wall. The opening is guarded by the right and left *valves of the sinus venosus*, both of which project into the atrium. The *septum primum* completely divides the two atria at this level, which is a little caudal to the foramen ovale and the atrio-ventricular canals. The septum joins the fused *endocardial cushions*, as does the *ventricular septum* from below.

The *esophagus* and *trachea* are tubular. Around the epithelium of both are condensations of mesenchyme from which their fibrous and muscular layers are to be differentiated; laterally in this mass lie the *vagus nerves*, unlabeled in the illustration. Ventral to the trachea are the *pulmonary arteries*. The left *dorsal aorta* is large and is here continuing the arch of the aorta caudad; the right dorsal aorta at this level forms a part of the right subclavian artery. Dorso-lateral to the aortæ are *sympathetic ganglia*. The condensation of mesenchyme about the noto-chord foreshadows a *future vertebra*.

Section through the Brachial Plexus and Tracheal Bifurcation (Fig. 569).—Distinctive features are the presence of *upper limb buds* and the *liver*, and the bifurcation of the trachea into

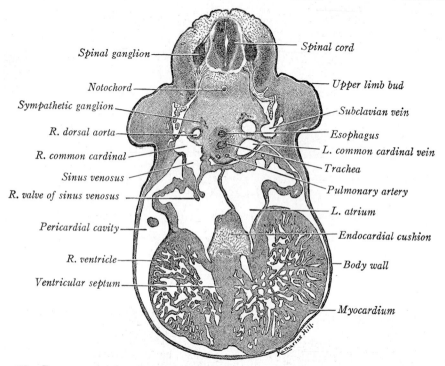

Spinal ganglion

Notochord

Sympathetic ganglion

R. dorsal aorta

R. common cardinal

Sinus venosus

R. valve of sinus venosus

Pericardial cavity

R. ventricle

Ventricular septum

Spinal cord

Upper limb bud

Subclavian vein

Esophagus

L. common cardinal vein

Trachea

Pulmonary artery

L. atrium

Endocardial cushion

Body wall

Myocardium

FIG. 568.—Transverse section through the common cardinals and sinus venosus of a 10 mm. pig embryo. × 23.

primary bronchi. The seventh pair of cervical *spinal nerves* is cut lengthwise in diagrammatic fashion. The spindle-shaped ganglion is associated with the *dorsal root* whose fibers grow out from its cells; the fibers of the *ventral root* arise from the middle, cellular layer of the cord and join the dorsal root in the common *nerve trunk*. On the right side, a short *dorsal ramus* supplies the dorsal muscle mass close by the ganglion. The much larger *ventral ramus* unites with similar rami of several other nerves to form the *brachial plexus*, a part of which is seen.

The *descending aorta* shows its manner of origin from paired vessels. From the seventh pair of *intersegmental arteries*, which arise dorsally from it, the *subclavian arteries* are given off two sections caudad in the series. Traced cephalad these seventh intersegmentals become continuous with the *vertebral arteries*. The latter lie mesial to the stem portions of the spinal nerves. In some embryos they are imperfectly developed at this stage. Lateral to the aorta are the *posterior cardinal veins*, easily traced to the common cardinals of the previous figure. Adjacent to the

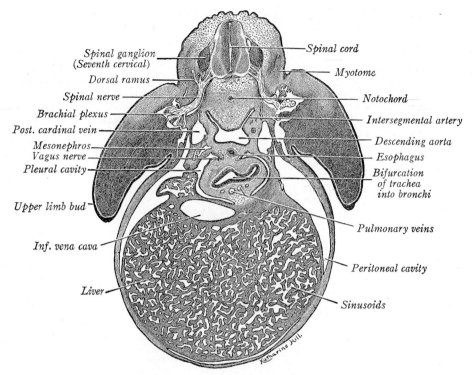

FIG. 569.—Transverse section through the brachial plexus and tracheal bifurcation of a 10 mm. pig embryo.   × 23.

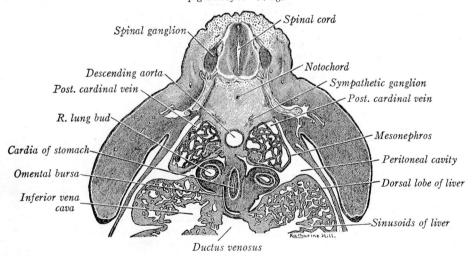

FIG. 570.—Dorsal half of a transverse section through the lungs, upper limbs and sympathetic ganglia of a 10 mm. pig embryo.   × 23.

esophagus are the cut *vagus nerves*. The branching trachea continues laterally into short buds which represent the upper left and middle right lobes of the *lungs*. The upper right bud (unpaired) comes off the trachea a little cephalad in the series (*cf.* Fig. 554); the paired lower lobes are more caudad (Fig. 570). Crescentic *pleural cavities* bound the bulging pulmonary tissue laterally. On the embryo's left this cavity is separated from the peritoneal cavity by the *septum transversum*, and here the parietal and visceral pleura assume typical relations. Ventral to the bronchi are sections of the *pulmonary veins*, which can be traced into the left atrium at a slightly higher level. The liver, with its close network of trabeculæ and sinusoids, is large and nearly fills the *peritoneal cavity*. The prominent vein within the liver is that portion of the *inferior vena cava* that is, in reality, the common hepatic vein (stem of the primitive right vitelline).

Section through the Lungs, Upper Limbs and Sympathetic Ganglia (Fig. 570).—The *limb buds* are ectodermal sacs stuffed with dense, undifferentiated mesenchyme. At their tips the ectoderm is characteristically thickened; some think this is homologous with the fin fold of fishes. Flanking the now circular *descending aorta* are the cranial ends of the *mesonephroi,* while above

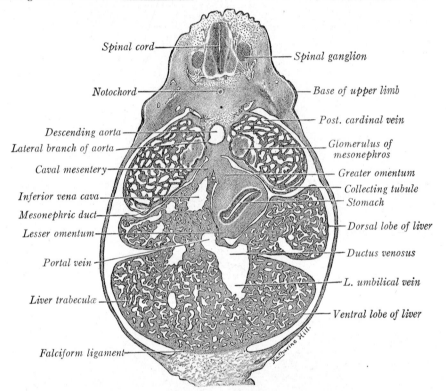

FIG. 571.—Transverse section through the stomach and liver of a 10 mm. pig embryo. × 23.

the aorta is a pair of *sympathetic ganglia;* the *sympathetic rami* connecting with the spinal nerve trunks do not appear but can be seen in neighboring sections, like the one shown in Fig. 572. The esophagus is just beginning to dilate into the *stomach,* and at this level the *omental bursa* appears as a crescentic slit to the right and below it. The *lungs* are sectioned through their caudal ends (*i.e.,* lower lobes). Both *pleural cavities* still communicate freely with the peritoneal cavity. In the right dorsal lobe of the liver is located more of the intrahepatic portion of the *inferior vena cava;* this particular segment is organizing from enlarged hepatic sinusoids. Near the midplane is the large *ductus venosus*, which traces into union with the vena cava a short distance cephalad. The *posterior cardinal veins* are coming into intimate relation with the dorsal surfaces of the mesonephroi.

Section through the Stomach and Liver (Fig. 571).—It is the *stomach* and lobate *liver* that feature this level. The stomach has rotated partially, so that its original dorsal margin is now dropping to a lateral position on the embryo's left and the primitive ventral margin is rising to a corresponding level on the right. These margins are to be the *greater* and *lesser curvatures*, respectively. The stomach is attached dorsally by the *greater omentum;* ventrally the *lesser omentum* passes to the liver. This ventral mesentery splits into halves and is continued as a peritoneal reflection around the liver; the component layers then come together again as the *falciform ligament*, attaching the midventral border of the liver to the body wall. Both the body wall and the abdominal viscera are thus seen to be surfaced with a continuous sheet of mesothelium underlaid by mesenchyme; this serous investment is the *peritoneum*, in which a parietal and a visceral division is recognized.

The liver shows paired dorsal and ventral lobes. The right dorsal lobe is fused dorsally to the greater omentum. This connection forms the *caval mesentery*, in which courses the *inferior*

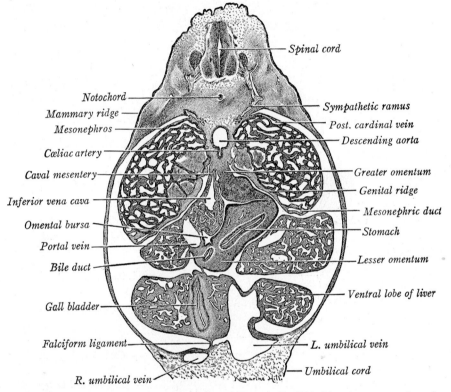

FIG. 572.—Transverse section through the omental bursa and gall bladder of a 10 mm. pig embryo.
× 23.

vena cava. Between the attachments of the stomach and liver, and to the right of the stomach, is the *omental bursa*. Midventrally in the liver is the *ductus venosus*, sectioned just at the point where it receives the left *umbilical vein* and a branch from the *portal vein*. The liver tissue is a complicated network of trabeculæ and sinusoids; the component *liver cords* are composed of liver cells, surrounded by the endothelium of the sinusoids; red blood cells are developing here at this stage.

The *mesonephroi* are becoming prominent organs. Along their ventral margins course the *mesonephric ducts;* each shows a connection laterally with the terminal segment of a *collecting tubule*.

Section through the Omental Bursa and Gall Bladder (Fig. 572).—The section passes slantingly through the pyloric end of the *stomach*, then cuts the *common bile duct*, and finally passes lengthwise through the *gall bladder* superficially embedded in the substance of the *liver*. Within the distance of a few sections it is easy to demonstrate the continuity of these parts. The *greater omentum* of the stomach is larger and more folded than in the previous illustration, and the *omental bursa* is correspondingly expansive. Traced caudad a short distance it opens into the

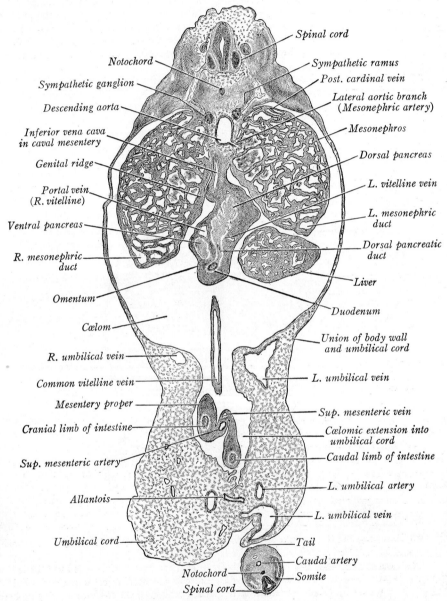

FIG. 573.—Transverse section through the mesonephroi, pancreas and intestinal loop of a 10 mm. pig embryo. × 23.

peritoneal cavity through the *epiploic foramen* (of Winslow). Between stomach and duodenum is a caudal portion of the *lesser omentum.* The blood supply of the stomach-pancreas region comes from the *cœliac artery*, seen emerging as a ventral branch of the aorta.

The liver has nearly been left behind, and its dorsal and ventral sets of lobes are now separate. Associated with the liver are several veins. Dorsally is the *inferior vena cava*, about to leave the liver within a lip-like fold, the *caval mesentery*. Also in the right upper lobe is the *portal vein*. Ventrally in the body wall are the *umbilical veins*, the left entering the left ventral lobe of the liver on its way to the ductus venosus. On each dorsolateral surface of the trunk is a thickened ecto-dermal ridge, poorly shown in Fig. 572, which represents the *mammary ridge*. At the same hor-izontal level a *sympathetic ramus* passes from the left nerve trunk to a *sympathetic ganglion*. The bottom of the figure includes a little of the insertion of the *umbilical cord* on the abdominal wall.

Section through the Mesonephroi, Pancreas and Intestinal Loop (Fig. 573).—The bulging *mesonephroi* are conspicuous. *Mesonephric corpuscles*, with vascular *glomeruli* indenting them, are medial in position; the glomeruli receive *mesonephric arteries*, arising as lateral branches from the aorta. The *mesonephric tubules* are contorted and variously sectioned; they are lined with a cuboidal epithelium and empty into the *mesonephric duct* coursing along the ventral margin of the gland. A reconstruction of a complete tubule is shown in Fig. 239 C. On the mesial surface of each mesonephros the epithelium is thickened; from these *genital ridges* the sex glands will differentiate. The *posterior cardinal veins* lie on the dorsal surfaces of the mesonephroi, and the transient *ventral veins* of the mesonephroi course along the ventral borders. The *inferior vena cava* is a vertical slit in the caval mesentery. Traced caudad a short distance it joins the right subcardinal vein, which continues this important venous channel down the trunk. The *sub-*

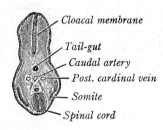

FIG. 574.—Transverse section through the cloacal membrane of a 10 mm. pig embryo. × 23.

Cloacal membrane
Tail-gut
Caudal artery
Post. cardinal vein
Somite
Spinal cord

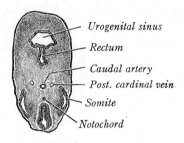

FIG. 575.—Transverse section through the subdividing cloaca of a 10 mm. pig embryo. × 23.

Urogenital sinus
Rectum
Caudal artery
Post. cardinal vein
Somite
Notochord

cardinal veins are prominent vessels, seen well at a slightly lower level on the ventromesial surfaces of the mesonephroi. There they interconnect by a large anastomosis (*cf.* Fig. 557).

The *duodenum* lies within its dorsal mesentery (*mesoduodenum*). The duct of the lobulated *dorsal pancreas* is shown arising directly from the duodenal wall. More to the right is a section of the *ventral pancreas* which traces cephalad to its origin from the stem of the common bile duct. On each side of the dorsal pancreas are portions of the *vitelline veins*, the right at this level being a part of the *portal vein*. A few sections caudad this vessel can be followed across a transverse anastomosis to the left vitelline vein where the *superior mesenteric vein* from the mesentery at-taches. Beyond the duodenum the vitelline veins have fused into a common vessel, cut lengthwise in the present section; it can be followed to the yolk sac, where the right and left components again separate (*cf.* Fig. 556).

The ventral body wall is continuous with the *umbilical cord*. This contains an extension of the embryonic *cœlom*, and a portion of the *intestinal loop* within its *mesentery*. Between the two intestinal limbs are the *superior mesenteric artery* and *vein*. The former is a ventral branch of the aorta; the latter joins the portal vein. The *allantois* is flanked by *umbilical arteries*, while *umbilical veins* are cut in the cord and again as they enter the body wall. The tip of the recurved *tail* shows as a separate section.

Section through the Cloacal Membrane (Fig. 574).—To maintain the proper relations with sections already studied, this and succeeding sections through the curved, caudal region are shown dorsal side down. The caudal end of the embryo is small. Its laggard differentiation, in comparison to higher levels, is reflected in the less specialized *spinal cord* and *somites*. The slender *tail-gut* is cut across. Between the *notochord* and tail-gut is the continuation of the aorta, known here as the *caudal artery*. On each side of the latter lies the termination of a *posterior cardinal vein*. The ventral half of the section is featured by an *epithelial plate* that represents the solid *cloacal membrane*. Since the plane of section largely parallels the surface ectoderm, the fusion of ectoderm with entoderm in the plate is shown only at one end.

Section through the Subdividing Cloaca (Fig. 575).—Tracing a short distance down the series from the previous level, the tail-gut joins the *cloaca* and the latter gains a cavity. Still

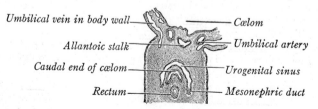

Umbilical vein in body wall—— ————— Cœlom

Allantoic stalk—— ——Umbilical artery

Caudal end of cœlom—— ——Urogenital sinus

Rectum—— ——Mesonephric duct

FIG. 576.—Transverse section through the allantois, urogenital sinus and rectum of a 10 mm. pig embryo. × 23.

farther, at the present level, the cloaca is separating into a dorsal *rectum* and a ventral *urogenital sinus*. (It should be understood that the recurvation of the tail-end of the embryo makes caudal progress in the sectioned series actually cephalad on this part of the embryo; *cf.* Fig. 559.)

Section through the Allantois, Urogenital Sinus and Rectum (Fig. 576).—Only part of the whole section is shown. It is but a few sections cephalad of Fig. 577 and resembles it closely. In the ventral body wall is seen the *allantoic stalk*, accompanied by the *umbilical arteries*. More dorsad are the crescentic *urogenital sinus* and the *rectum*, now separate. The caudalmost portion of the cœlom tapers to an end between the two.

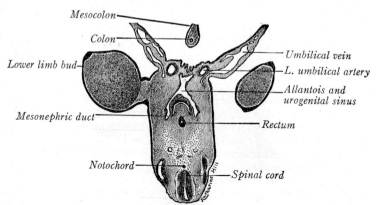

Mesocolon——

Colon——

Lower limb bud—— ——Umbilical vein

——L. umbilical artery

——Allantois and urogenital sinus

Mesonephric duct—— ——Rectum

Notochord—— ——Spinal cord

FIG. 577.—Transverse section through the stems of the mesonephric ducts and allantois of a 10 mm. pig embryo. × 23.

Section through the Stems of the Mesonephric Ducts and Allantois (Fig. 577).—This illustration and the three that follow include only the caudal, recurved part of the embryo. In the present section the *colon* is contained within a portion of the mesentery that is specifically named the *mesocolon*. In the body wall are tributaries of the *umbilical veins*, and mesial to them are the *umbilical arteries;* both are about to enter the umbilical cord. The *allantoic stalk* is sectioned as it opens into the *urogenital sinus*. Dorsal to the sinus is a section of the *rectum*, separated from the sinus by a crescentic prolongation of the *cœlom*. The horns of the urogenital sinus receive the *mesonephric ducts*.

Section through the Lower Limb Buds and Ureteric Stems (Fig. 578).—The section cuts through the middle of both _lower limb buds_. Like the upper set already studied, they consist of sacs of undifferentiated mesenchyme. Mesial to the limb buds are the _umbilical arteries_, which in turn lie lateral to the _mesonephric ducts_. The left mesonephric duct is cut at just the proper plane to show the _ureter_, or duct of the metanephros, being given off dorsally. The right ureter appears as a separate tube, since it is sectioned transversely.

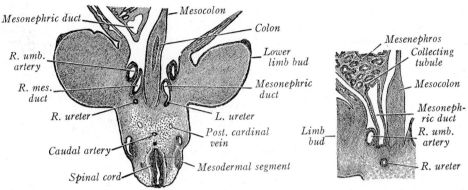

FIG. 578.—Transverse section through the lower limb buds and ureteric stems of a 10 mm. pig embryo. × 23.

FIG. 579.—Transverse section through the right mesonephric duct and ureter of a 10 mm. pig embryo. × 23.

Section through the Mesonephric Ducts and Ureters (Fig. 579).—Continuing down the series the ureters can be traced for some distance. The present illustration is a small part of a section close to Fig. 578. In it the right _ureter_ is seen. Also the right _mesonephric duct_ is cut lengthwise (frontally) as it leaves the mesonephros on its way to connect with the urogenital sinus.

Section through the Metanephroi (Fig. 580).—The ureters are found to terminate in the _metanephroi,_ figured here. Each of these kidney primordia consists of two parts. Internally

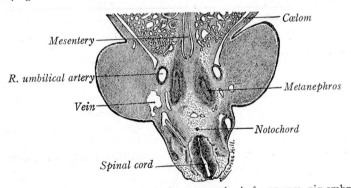

FIG. 580.—Transverse section through the metanephroi of a 10 mm. pig embryo. × 23.

there is a dilated expansion of the ureter that represents the renal _pelvis;_ from it the _calyces_ and the system of _collecting tubules_ will bud and grow. The periphery of the double primordium is a mass of condensed mesenchyme, derived from nearby nephrotomes; this tissue will differentiate into the _secretory tubules_ of the kidney.

Section through the Curved Back (Fig. 581).—Due to the lumbar curvature, this section is actually frontal. The _spinal cord_ is cut lengthwise. It is flanked by _spinal ganglia_, except midway on the left side where a slightly deeper plane includes several *spinal nerves*. The somites show spindle-shaped *myotomes* and more laterally located *'dermatomes.'* The medial side of each somite is a *sclerotome;* this shows subdivision into a caudal denser and a cranial less dense half.

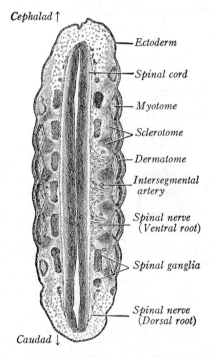

FIG. 581.—Transverse section through the curved back of a 10 mm. embryo. × 23.

Recombination of the dense half of one somite with the sparser half of the somite next caudad will produce a definitive *vertebra* (*cf*. Fig. 338). *Intersegmental arteries* appear between some of the somites on the left side.

(C) THE ANATOMY OF AN EIGHTEEN MM. PIG EMBRYO

Most of the important organs are laid down in 10 mm. embryos. Older stages are chiefly instructive, therefore, to demonstrate the growth and differentiation of parts already present, rather than the introduction of new ones. Dissections show perfectly the form and relations of organs, their relative rates of growth and changes of position. Since the illustrations indicate better than descriptions the several structures and their states of development, only certain selected features will be mentioned.

External Form.—The neck and back are much straighter than before, but the ventral body is still highly convex. The head is relatively larger, the umbilical cord smaller. The sense organs are prominent, and the face, with snout and jaws, is plain. The branchial grooves and cervical sinus have disappeared from the neck. The limbs show indications of proximal and distal divisions, and the hand and foot are paddle-like. Several mammary gland primordia occur along the mammary ridges, now located more ventrally. The genital tubercle has become a distinct phallus.

Lateral Dissection (Fig. 582).—The cerebral hemispheres are larger and the cerebellum is appearing. Beneath the cerebellum is the prominent pontine flexure of the brain, pointing ventrad. Nerves and ganglia show clearly; the brachial and lumbo-sacral plexuses, opposite the limbs, are noteworthy. The liver and lungs are relatively larger and more plainly lobed than before; the heart and mesonephroi are smaller.

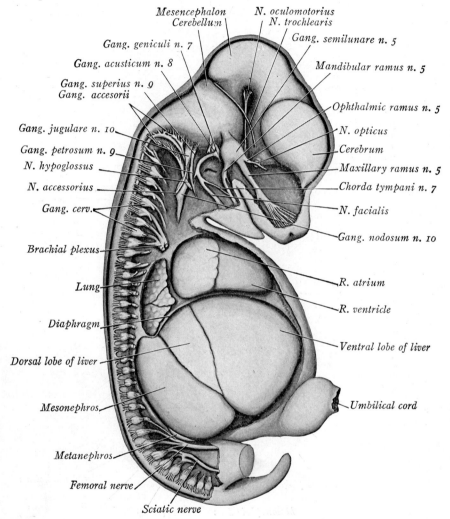

FIG. 582.—Lateral dissection of an 18 mm. pig embryo, viewed from the right side.   × 8.

Midsagittal Dissection (Fig. 583).—The corpus striatum has developed in the floor of the cerebral hemisphere, a chorioid plexus invades the fourth ventricle, and the neural (posterior) lobe of the hypophysis is growing into association with the detached Rathke's pouch. Sclerotomic primordia of vertebræ condense about the notochord. The viscera show only quantitative changes from the 10 mm. stage, but the urogenital sinus and rectum are now separate, as are the aorta and

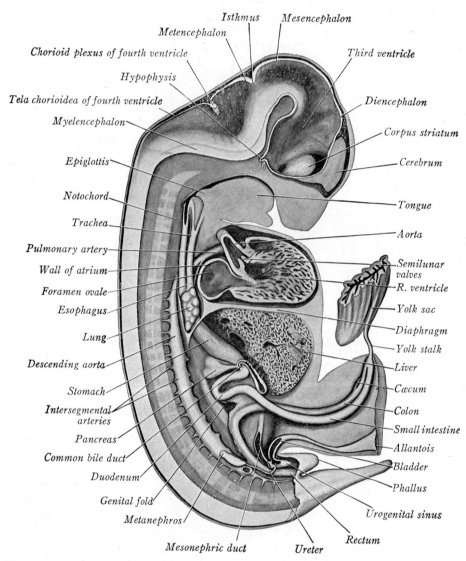

Isthmus   Mesencephalon

Metencephalon

Chorioid plexus of fourth ventricle

Hypophysis

Third ventricle

Tela chorioidea of fourth ventricle

Diencephalon

Myelencephalon

Corpus striatum

Cerebrum

Epiglottis

Notochord

Tongue

Trachea

Aorta

Pulmonary artery

Semilunar valves

Wall of atrium

R. ventricle

Foramen ovale

Yolk sac

Esophagus

Diaphragm

Lung

Yolk stalk

Descending aorta

Liver

Stomach

Cæcum

Intersegmental arteries

Colon

Pancreas

Small intestine

Common bile duct

Allantois

Duodenum

Bladder

Genital fold

Phallus

Metanephros

Urogenital sinus

Mesonephric duct   Ureter   Rectum

FIG. 583.—Median dissection of an 18 mm. pig embryo, after removal of the right half.   × 8.

pulmonary artery. The intestinal loop has rotated until the cranial and caudal limbs lie right and left, respectively. The cæcum is conspicuous and a urinary bladder has developed between the allantois and urogenital sinus.

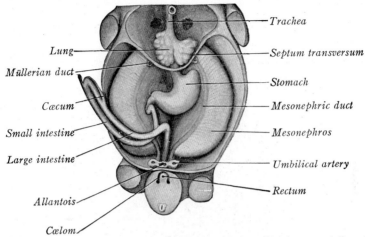

FIG. 584.—Ventral dissection of a 15 mm. pig embryo. × 6. The heart and liver have been removed and the lungs are viewed through the transparent pericardium.

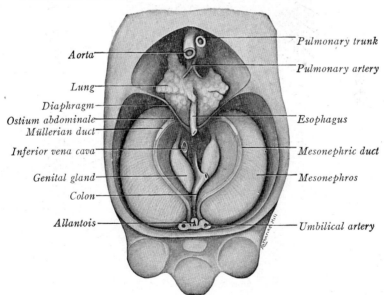

FIG. 585.—Ventral dissection of an 18 mm. pig embryo. × 7. The heart, liver, stomach and small intestine have been removed.

Ventral Dissections.—The lungs, septum transversum, stomach, intestine and mesonephroi are the chief organs seen in the 15 mm. embryo shown as Fig. 584. Of special interest are the beginnings of the Müllerian ducts.

Fig. 585 is a dissection of a slightly larger embryo (18 mm.). From it the stomach and small intestine have been removed to display the genital glands.

These organs have advanced rapidly since the 10 mm. stage. They are now definitely established and localized as recognizable gonads. Each Müllerian duct opens cranially by a funnel-shaped ostium; the duct proper is growing caudad as a blind tube.

(D) THE ANATOMY OF A THIRTY-FIVE MM. PIG EMBRYO

External Form.—The embryo is straighter, slenderer and its ventral surface less protuberant. The head, with its prominent snout, is shaping like that of a

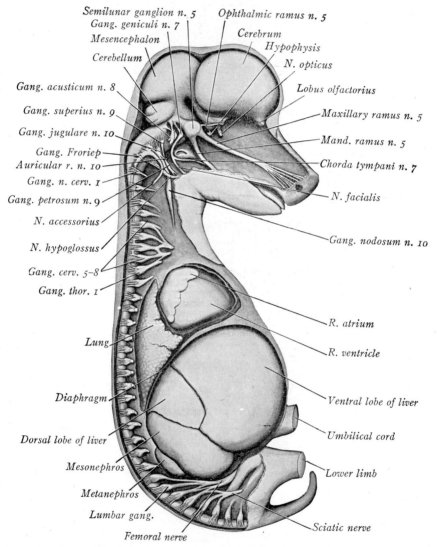

Semilunar ganglion n. 5
Gang. geniculi n. 7
Mesencephalon
Cerebellum
Gang. acusticum n. 8
Gang. superius n. 9
Gang. jugulare n. 10
Gang. Froriep
Auricular r. n. 10
Gang. n. cerv. 1
Gang. petrosum n. 9
N. accessorius
N. hypoglossus
Gang. cerv. 5–8
Gang. thor. 1
Lung
Diaphragm
Dorsal lobe of liver
Mesonephros
Metanephros
Lumbar gang.
Femoral nerve

Ophthalmic ramus n. 5
Cerebrum
Hypophysis
N. opticus
Lobus olfactorius
Maxillary ramus n. 5
Mand. ramus n. 5
Chorda tympani n. 7
N. facialis
Gang. nodosum n. 10
R. atrium
R. ventricle
Ventral lobe of liver
Umbilical cord
Lower limb
Sciatic nerve

FIG. 586.—Lateral dissection of a 35 mm. pig embryo, viewed from the right side. × 4.

lower mammal, and the neck becomes distinct. Digits have appeared on the elongate extremities. The umbilical cord and tail are losing rapidly in relative size.

Lateral Dissection (Fig. 586).—The spinal cord and brain are relatively smaller, but the latter is becoming highly specialized and folded. The cerebral hemispheres are large, and olfactory lobes extend forward from the rhinencephalon. The body of the embryo elongates faster than the spinal cord, so that the spinal nerves, at first directed at right angles, course obliquely in the lumbo-sacral

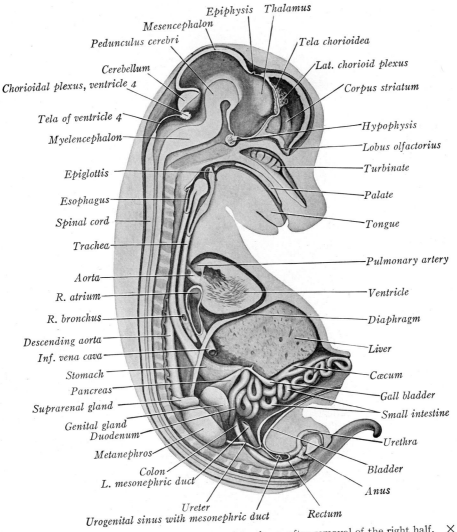

FIG. 587.—Median dissection of a 35 mm. pig embryo, after removal of the right half.   × 4.

region. Note especially how the viscera have receded caudad (*cf.* Figs. 545 and 549), and how the liver dominates the abdomen as the mesonephros loses prominence. The kidney is exceptional in that it shifts cephalad.

Midsagittal Section (Fig. 587).—New features of the brain are the olfactory lobes, the chorioid plexus of the third and lateral ventricles, the thalami, the epiphysis, and the consolidated hypophysis. The primitive mouth cavity is now divided by the palatine folds into upper nasal passages and lower oral cavity. Of the viscera, the distinct genital and suprarenal glands and the enlarged metanephros command attention, as does the coiling of the intestine. The ureters have acquired separate openings at the base of the bladder, and the urethra extends to the tip of the phallus.

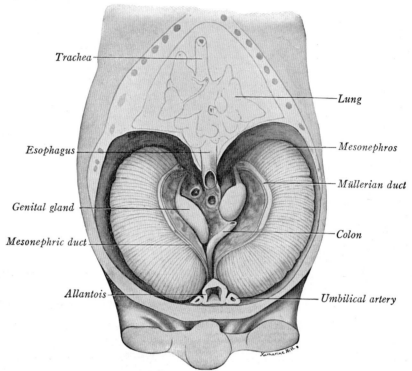

Trachea

Lung

Esophagus

Mesonephros

Müllerian duct

Genital gland

Mesonephric duct

Colon

Allantois

Umbilical artery

FIG. 588.—Ventral dissection of the abdomen of a 24 mm. pig embryo. × 6.

Ventral Dissection (Fig. 588).—The chief new features are the markedly lobate lungs and the longer Müllerian ducts with expanded upper ends. The mesonephros is nearing its maximum absolute size.

RECOMMENDED COLLATERAL READING

Patten, B. M.   The Embryology of the Pig.   Blakiston.

INDEX

27